ADVANCED
CALCULUS

ADVANCED
CALCULUS

Stephen Hoffman

Professor of Mathematics
Bates College

PRENTICE-HALL, INC., ENGLEWOOD CLIFFS, N.J.

PRENTICE-HALL INTERNATIONAL, INC. *London*
PRENTICE-HALL OF AUSTRALIA, PTY. LTD. *Sydney*
PRENTICE-HALL OF CANADA, LTD. *Toronto*
PRENTICE-HALL OF INDIA PRIVATE LTD. *New Delhi*
PRENTICE-HALL OF JAPAN, INC. *Tokyo*

Library of Congress Catalog Card Number 74-84037

Printed in the United States of America

13-010272-5

Current Printing (last digit):

10 9 8 7 6 5 4 3 2 1

To my parents

PREFACE

The many generalizations of Stokes' Theorem which have been developed have shown that theorems of this type play an important role in several branches of mathematics. It occurred to me that a detailed examination of the tools and techniques used in treating the classical Divergence Theorem and Stokes' Theorem concerning vectors, curves, and surfaces might be revealing. It was.

What such a study revealed is the body of material usually classified as "Advanced Calculus." The topics seemed to follow in a natural order and to be related to each other in a reasonable manner. The result is this book, designed for a two-semester course.

The basic assumption is that the student has completed elementary calculus and is ready for a course in which he not only learns mathematics new to him, but also takes a closer look at the calculus he has already learned. The intent throughout is twofold: to illustrate how one might go about searching for theorems and to be as careful as possible in the statement of those theorems. There are essentially no applications to disciplines other than mathematics included.

In certain portions of the book it is assumed that the student is familiar with some abstract algebra. A brief appendix on elementary linear algebra is included for use when such is not the case.

The first three chapters are intended to provide the machinery used in Chapter 4 to treat the Divergence Theorem and Stokes' Theorem. Chapters 5 through 7 look more closely at the concepts used in these proofs: integration, convergence, and differentiability. Chapter 8 considers the pathology introduced by improper integrals, and Chapter 9 considers infinite series by analogy with improper integrals. Chapter 10 then examines various methods of representing functions by using such tools. The final chapter re-examines the classical vector theorems of Chapter 4 in the light of basic definitions and ϵ-δ-N proofs.

Three appendices, on linear algebra, ordinary, and partial differential equations, are included as supplementary material.

STEPHEN HOFFMAN

Lewiston, Maine

CONTENTS

ADVANCED
CALCULUS

VECTORS 1

1-1 Vector Spaces

The word *vector* is frequently used by scientists to denote a physical quantity which has both magnitude and direction. Although the words quantity, magnitude, and direction may seem familiar and comforting, they are somewhat vague for mathematical usage. The mathematical definition of the mathematical entity known as a vector is a result of abstracting characteristics shared by many mathematical systems. The particular abstraction we use here is that of a *vector space*.

Definition 1-1-1. The set **V** is a *vector space* provided

(i) There exists a binary operation + between pairs of elements of **V** such that

V-1: For all **u** and **v** in **V**, **u** + **v** = **v** + **u**.

V-2: For all **u**, **v**, and **w** in **V**, **u** + (**v** + **w**) = (**u** + **v**) + **w**.

V-3: There exists an element **0** of **V** such that for all **u** in **V**, **u** + **0** = **u**.

V-4: For every **u** in **V** there exists an element −**u** in **V** such that **u** + (−**u**) = **0**.

(ii) There exists an operation combining any element **u** of **V** with any real number a to produce the element a**u** of **V** such that

S-1: For every **u** in **V**, 1**u** = **u** and 0**u** = **0**.

S-2: For every **u** and **v** in **V** and every real number a, a(**u** + **v**) = a**u** + a**v**.

S-3: For every **u** in **V** and all real numbers a and b, $(a + b)$**u** = a**u** + b**u** and (ab)**u** = a(b**u**).

The elements of a vector space are called *vectors*. The binary operation + in a vector space is called *vector addition*. The operation of combining a vector **u** with a real number a to produce the vector a**u** is called *scalar multiplication*.

1

If we are also using ordinary addition and multiplication of real numbers, we must be careful to distinguish between the sum of two real numbers $a + b$ and the vector sum of two elements of our vector space $\mathbf{u} + \mathbf{v}$; we must also distinguish between the multiplication of two real numbers ab and the scalar multiplication of the vector $\mathbf{u}$ by the real number a resulting in $a\mathbf{u}$. The use of boldface type for vectors and vector addition should help to make this distinction clear.

EXAMPLE. We let $\mathbf{V}_2$ be the set of all ordered pairs of real numbers—objects of the form (p, q) where p and q are real numbers. In order to make this set of ordered pairs into a vector space, we must specify the procedure for finding the vector sum of two elements of the space and the procedure for finding the result of scalar multiplying an element of the space by a real number. Although there might conceivably be many ways in which one might do this, we must be careful that the operations in fact do result in the definition's being satisfied. We will elect to impose the vector addition in $\mathbf{V}_2$ by

$$(p, q) + (r, s) = (p + r, q + s)$$

(Note that the symbol $+$ on the left refers to the vector addition of two vectors and the symbol $+$ occurring in both components is the ordinary addition of real numbers.)

We further specify a scalar multiplication in $\mathbf{V}_2$ by

$$a(p, q) = (ap, aq)$$

(Note that the juxtaposition of the real number a with the vector (p, q) indicates scalar multiplication, whereas the products ap and aq in the components of the vector on the right are ordinary products of two real numbers.)

We now proceed to verify that the set $\mathbf{V}_2$ with the operations of vector addition and scalar multiplication which we have imposed does form a vector space. To do this, we will use the appropriate properties of the ordinary addition and multiplication of real numbers.

V-1:	$(p, q) + (r, s) = (p + r, q + s)$	by the definition of vector addition imposed on $\mathbf{V}_2$
	$= (r + p, s + q)$	since addition of real numbers is commutative
	$= (r, s) + (p, q)$	by the definition of vector addition imposed on $\mathbf{V}_2$
V-2:	$(p, q) + [(r, s) + (t, u)]$	
	$= (p, q) + (r + t, s + u)$	by the definition of vector addition imposed on $\mathbf{V}_2$
	$= (p + [r + t], q + [s + u])$	by the definition of vector addition imposed on $\mathbf{V}_2$

$$= ([p + r] + t, [q + s] + u)$$ since addition of real numbers is associative

$$= (p + r, q + s) + (t, u)$$ by the definition of vector addition imposed on $\mathbf{V_2}$

$$= [(p, q) + (r, s)] + (t, u)$$ by the definition of vector addition imposed on $\mathbf{V_2}$

V-3:   We let the zero vector **0** be given by

$$\mathbf{0} = (0, 0)$$

Then, for all (p, q) in $\mathbf{V_2}$, we have

$$(p, q) + (0, 0) = (p + 0, q + 0)$$ by the definition of vector addition imposed on $\mathbf{V_2}$

$$= (p, q)$$ by the addition property of the real number 0

V-4:   We let $-(p, q)$ be $(-p, -q)$. (Note that the symbol $-$ on the left refers to the vector opposite, whereas the symbols $-$ on the right refer to the opposites of real numbers.) We have then

$$(p, q) + [-(p, q)] = (p, q) + (-p, -q)$$
$$= (p + [-p], q + [-q])$$ by the definition of vector addition imposed on $\mathbf{V_2}$

$$= (0, 0)$$ by the addition of opposites of real numbers

$$= \mathbf{0}$$

S-1: $(1)(p, q) = ([1]p, [1]q)$ by the definition of scalar multiplication imposed on $\mathbf{V_2}$

$$= (p, q)$$ by the multiplication property of the real number 1

$(0)(p, q) = ([0]p, [0]q)$ by the definition of scalar multiplication imposed on $\mathbf{V_2}$

$$= (0, 0)$$ by the multiplication property of the real number 0

$$= \mathbf{0}$$

S-2: $a[(p, q) + (r, s)]$
$$= a(p + r, q + s)$$ by the definition of vector addition imposed on $\mathbf{V_2}$

$$= (a[p + r], a[q + s])$$ by the definition of scalar multiplication imposed on $\mathbf{V_2}$

$$= (ap + ar, aq + as) \quad \text{by the distributive law for real numbers}$$

$$= (ap, aq) + (ar, as) \quad \text{by the definition of vector addition imposed on } \mathbf{V_2}$$

$$= a(p, q) + a(r, s) \quad \text{by the definition of scalar multiplication imposed on } \mathbf{V_2}$$

S-3: $[a + b](p, q)$

$$= ([a + b]p, [a + b]q) \quad \text{by the definition of scalar multiplication imposed on } \mathbf{V_2}$$

$$= (ap + bp, aq + bq) \quad \text{by the distributive law for real numbers}$$

$$= (ap, aq) + (bp, bq) \quad \text{by the definition of vector addition imposed on } \mathbf{V_2}$$

$$= a(p, q) + b(p, q) \quad \text{by the definition of scalar multiplication imposed on } \mathbf{V_2}$$

$$[ab](p, q) = ([ab]p, [ab]q) \quad \text{by the definition of scalar multiplication imposed on } \mathbf{V_2}$$

$$= (a[bp], a[bq]) \quad \text{by the associativity of multiplication of real numbers}$$

$$= a(bp, bq) \quad \text{by the definition of scalar multiplication imposed on } \mathbf{V_2}$$

$$= a[b(p, q)] \quad \text{by the definition of scalar multiplication imposed on } \mathbf{V_2}$$

For convenience in writing we will adopt the following shorthand: Whenever we are describing a set by using the words "the set of all . . . such that . . . ," we replace the words *the set of all* by a brace, {, the words *such that* by a vertical line, |, and we indicate the end of the phrase by another brace,}. Under this system

"the set of all *r* such that *r* is a real number"

becomes

$$\{r \mid r \text{ is a real number}\}$$

In addition, we will adopt the customary symbol $\in$ as an abbreviation of the words "is an element of" or "is in" so that

"*a* is an element of *A*"

becomes

$$a \in A$$

Finally, we will use $\notin$ to denote "is not an element of."

We use these notations to introduce a symbolism for intervals of real numbers.

Definition 1-1-2. If a and b are real numbers for which $a < b$,

$$[a, b] = \{x \mid a \leq x \leq b\}$$
$$]a, b[= \{x \mid a < x < b\}$$
$$[a, b[= \{x \mid a \leq x < b\}$$
$$]a, b] = \{x \mid a < x \leq b\}$$

If c is any real number,

$$[c, +\infty[= \{x \mid x \geq c\}$$
$$]c, +\infty[= \{x \mid x > c\}$$
$$]-\infty, c] = \{x \mid x \leq c\}$$
$$]-\infty, c[= \{x \mid x < c\}$$

All these sets are called *intervals*. The intervals $]a, b[$, $]c, +\infty[$, and $]-\infty, c[$ are called *open*. The intervals $[a, b]$, $[c, +\infty[$, and $]-\infty, c]$ are called *closed*.

Definition 1-1-3. The set A is a *subset* of the set B, written $A \subseteq B$, provided that $x \in A$ implies $x \in B$.

EXAMPLE. $[-3, 1[\subseteq]-4, 1]$ since $-3 \leq x < 1$ implies $-4 < x \leq 1$.

We also concern ourselves with the following ways of combining sets:

Definition 1-1-4. If A and B are sets,

$$A \cap B = \{x \mid x \in A \text{ and } x \in B\}$$
$$A \cup B = \{x \mid x \in A \text{ or } x \in B \text{ or both}\}$$
$$A - B = \{x \mid x \in A \text{ but } x \notin B\}$$

EXAMPLES.

$$[0, 3] \cap [1, 4] = [1, 3]$$
$$]-2, 1] \cap [0, 3[= [0, 1]$$
$$]-1, 2[\cup]1, 4[=]-1, 4[$$
$$[0, 4[\cup]0, 2[= [0, 4[$$
$$[0, 5] - [0, 3] =]3, 5]$$
$$]0, 10[- [1, 5[=]0, 1[\cup [5, 10[$$

The concept of an ordered pair includes the idea that two ordered pairs (a, b) and (p, q) are equal if, and only if, both $a = p$ and $b = q$. Thus the ordered pairs $(2, 3)$ and $(3, 2)$ are unequal. This concept is readily extended to that of an ordered *n-tuple* where we have $(a_1, a_2, \ldots, a_n)$ and $(b_1, b_2, \ldots, b_n)$ equal if, and only if, $a_1 = b_1, a_2 = b_2, \ldots,$ and $a_n = b_n$. We will use the following two definitions to formalize these extensions of the concept of ordered pair.

Definition 1-1-5. If A and B are sets,

$$A \times B = \{(a, b) \mid a \in A \text{ and } b \in B\}$$

Definition 1-1-6. If n is a positive integer,

$$\mathbf{V}_n = \{(x_1, x_2, \ldots, x_n) \mid x_1, x_2, \ldots, \text{ and } x_n \text{ are real numbers}\}$$

Finally, we establish the definition we will use for that mathematical entity known as a *function*.

Definition 1-1-7. D and T are sets. f is a *function on D into T* provided that

(i) $f \subseteq D \times T$.
(ii) For every $x \in D$, there exists $y \in T$ such that $(x, y) \in f$.
(iii) If $(x, y) \in f$ and $(x, z) \in f$, then $y = z$.
D is called the *domain* of f.

$$\{y \mid \text{there exists } x \in D \text{ such that } (x, y) \in f\}$$

is called the *range* of f.

This definition is often connected with the concept of a *mapping* whereby to each element x of the domain D there corresponds exactly one element y of the range. In this concept, we will write $f(x)$ as a symbol for that element of the range which corresponds to x. In the terminology of the definition given, we use $f(x)$ as a symbol for the second element of that ordered pair of f whose first element is x.

EXERCISES

1. Under what conditions will $A \times B = B \times A$?

2. If f is a function on a set of real numbers into the real numbers, the graph of f is defined to be the set of points in a plane with a rectangular coordinate system whose coordinates constitute the function. Give a geometric characterization of the graph of a function in terms of vertical lines in the plane.

3. In $\mathbf{V}_3$ we construct a vector addition and scalar multiplication by

$$(a, b, c) + (p, q, r) = (a + p, b + q, c + r)$$

and

$$a(p, q, r) = (ap, aq, ar)$$

Show that $\mathbf{V}_3$ is a vector space.

4. Generalize the result of Exercise 3 to $\mathbf{V_n}$, where n is any positive integer.

5. If f and g are functions into the real numbers, give a definition for the sum $f + g$.

6. Let

$$F = \{f \mid f \text{ is a function on } [0, 1] \text{ into the real numbers}\}$$

We define vector addition as the addition of functions, and we define scalar multiplication of the function f by the real number a as the function given by $af(x)$. Show that F is a vector space.

7. If $A \subseteq B$ but $A \neq B$ and f is a function on B into any set, the function g, on A into the same set, given by

$$g(x) = f(x) \qquad \text{for } x \in A$$

is called the *restriction of f to A*. Show that $g \subseteq f$.

1-2   Norms in a Vector Space

In the definition of a vector space given in the preceding section there is no mention of the "magnitude" or "length" of a vector. For at least some vector spaces there is a fairly natural way of assigning a length to each vector. For example, in $\mathbf{V_2}$, we may take the length of a vector (a, b) to be the (non-negative) number $\sqrt{a^2 + b^2}$. In other vector spaces we may suffer from an embarrassment of riches: there are several ways of assigning a length to each vector, none of which seems particularly preferable over the others. We use ideas suggested by the properties of the absolute value of a real number to construct

> **Definition 1-2-1.** The vector space $\mathbf{V}$ is a *normed* vector space pro-
> vided that to each vector $\mathbf{v} \in \mathbf{V}$ there corresponds a real number $\|\mathbf{v}\|$
> with the following properties:
>
> (i) For all $\mathbf{v} \in \mathbf{V}$, $\|\mathbf{v}\| \geq 0$.
> (ii) For all $\mathbf{v} \in \mathbf{V}$, $\|\mathbf{v}\| = 0$ if, and only if, $\mathbf{v} = \mathbf{0}$.
> (iii) For all $\mathbf{u}$ and $\mathbf{v}$ in $\mathbf{V}$, $\|\mathbf{u} + \mathbf{v}\| \leq \|\mathbf{u}\| + \|\mathbf{v}\|$.
> (iv) For all $\mathbf{u} \in \mathbf{V}$ and all real numbers a, $\|a\mathbf{u}\| = |a|\,\|\mathbf{u}\|$.

The verification that, in $\mathbf{V_2}$, $\|(a, b)\| = \sqrt{a^2 + b^2}$ actually has the properties called for in the definition is left to the exercises.

As a somewhat less obvious introduction of a norm into a vector space, let us consider F, the set of all continuous functions on $[0, 1]$ into the real numbers. This set becomes a vector space if vector addition is taken to be the addition of functions

$$f + g = \{(x, f(x) + g(x)) \mid x \in [0, 1]\}$$

and the scalar multiplication of the vector f by the real number a is given by

$$af = \{(x, af(x)) \mid x \in [0, 1]\}$$

One way of giving a norm to the vectors of this space is

$$\|f\| = \max \{|f(x)| \mid 0 \le x \le 1\}$$

We will show that property (iii) above (the "triangle inequality") is satisfied.

Any continuous function whose domain is a closed bounded interval and whose range is a set of real numbers actually assumes its maximum value at some number in the domain. Further, if f and g are two continuous functions on $[0, 1]$ into the real numbers, then the functions $|f|$, $|g|$, and $|f + g|$ are also continuous. Thus there exist numbers a, b, and c in $[0, 1]$ such that

$$\|f\| = \max \{|f(x)| \mid 0 \le x \le 1\} = |f(a)|$$
$$\|g\| = \max \{|g(x)| \mid 0 \le x \le 1\} = |g(b)|$$

and

$$\|f + g\| = \max \{|f(x) + g(x)| \mid 0 \le x \le 1\} = |f(c) + g(c)|$$

For any $t \in [0, 1]$,

$$|f(t) + g(t)| \le |f(t)| + |g(t)| \le |f(a)| + |g(b)|$$

Then, in particular, for $t = c$,

$$|f(c) + g(c)| \le |f(a)| + |g(b)|$$

But this inequality says

$$\|f + g\| \le \|f\| + \|g\|$$

We note, finally, certain relations between the norm in a normed vector space and the operation of vector subtraction.

For all $\mathbf{u}$ and $\mathbf{v} \in \mathbf{V}$,

$$\|\mathbf{u} - \mathbf{v}\| \ge 0$$
$$\|\mathbf{u} - \mathbf{v}\| = \|\mathbf{v} - \mathbf{u}\|$$
$$\|\mathbf{u} - \mathbf{v}\| = 0 \quad \text{if, and only if, } \mathbf{u} = \mathbf{v}$$

and for all $\mathbf{u}$, $\mathbf{v}$, and $\mathbf{w} \in \mathbf{V}$,

$$\|\mathbf{u} - \mathbf{v}\| = \|(\mathbf{u} - \mathbf{w}) + (\mathbf{w} - \mathbf{v})\| \le \|\mathbf{u} - \mathbf{w}\| + \|\mathbf{w} - \mathbf{v}\|$$

In $\mathbf{V}_2$ with the norm given above, these properties are exactly those possessed by the distance between points in the plane whose rectangular coordinates are the ordered pairs **u** and **v**. We may view this situation in the reverse order by realizing that if we consider the vector space $\mathbf{V_n}$ as the n-dimensional Euclidean space with the distance between points given by

$$\sqrt{(x_1 - y_1)^2 + (x_2 - y_2)^2 + \cdots + (x_n - y_n)^2}$$

then the norm of a vector can be taken as the distance between the point with that n-tuple as its rectangular coordinates and the origin. Thus in $\mathbf{V_n}$ we have

$$\|(x_1, x_2, \ldots, x_n)\| = \sqrt{x_1^2 + x_2^2 + \cdots + x_n^2}$$

One use we can make of the norm in a vector space is to give meaning to the concept of continuity for a function on that vector space into the real numbers. While we reserve a more complete discussion for a later chapter, it is useful here to exhibit such a definition to illustrate the form to be taken. We consider a vector space **V** in which there is a norm $\|\mathbf{v}\|$ for every vector **v**. Given a specific vector $\mathbf{p} \in \mathbf{V}$, we say that a function f on **V** into the real numbers is continuous at **p** provided that for every $\epsilon > 0$ there exists $\delta > 0$ such that if $\|\mathbf{v} - \mathbf{p}\| < \delta$, then $|f(\mathbf{v}) - f(\mathbf{p})| < \epsilon$.

EXERCISES

1. Verify that, in $\mathbf{V_2}$, $\|(a, b)\| = \sqrt{a^2 + b^2}$ has the properties required of a norm.

2. Verify that, in $\mathbf{V_3}$, $\|(a, b, c)\| = \sqrt{a^2 + b^2 + c^2}$ has the properties required of a norm.

3. Show that, in $\mathbf{V_2}$, $\|(a, b)\| = |a| + |b|$ also gives a norm.

4. In the vector space of all continuous functions on $[0, 1]$ into the real numbers, show that

$$\|f\| = \int_0^1 |f|$$

gives a norm.

5. Consider the vector space of all functions on $[0, 1]$ into the real numbers which have only a finite number of points of discontinuity. Why does

$$\|f\| = \max \{|f(x)| \mid 0 \le x \le 1\}$$

not give a norm for this space? Does

$$\|f\| = \int_0 |f|$$

give a norm for this space?

In the following exercises, K is a three-dimensional cube with center (a, b, c) and length of side 2. F is a function on K into the real numbers. g is a function on an appropriate two-dimensional square into the real numbers given by $g(x, y) = F(x, y, c)$. φ is a function on an appropriate interval into the real numbers given by $\varphi(x) = g(x, b)$.

6. Give explicitly the domains of F, g, and φ.

7. Prove that if F is continuous at (a, b, c), then g is continuous at (a, b).

8. Show that the converse of the proposition in Exercise 7 is false.

9. Prove that if g is continuous at (a, b), then φ is continuous at a.

10. Show that the converse of the proposition in Exercise 9 is false.

1-3   Geometric Aspects

We have a particular interest in the two vector spaces

$$\mathbf{V_2} = \{(x, y) \mid x \text{ and } y \text{ are real numbers}\}$$

and

$$\mathbf{V_3} = \{(x, y, z) \mid x, y, \text{ and } z \text{ are real numbers}\}$$

For these spaces, vector addition, scalar multiplication, norm, and distance are given by

$$(a, b) + (p, q) = (a + p, b + q)$$
$$a(p, q) = (ap, aq)$$
$$\|(a, b)\| = \sqrt{a^2 + b^2}$$
$$d_2(\mathbf{u}, \mathbf{v}) = \|\mathbf{u} - \mathbf{v}\|$$

and

$$(a, b, c) + (p, q, r) = (a + p, b + q, c + r)$$
$$a(p, q, r) = (ap, aq, ar)$$
$$\|(a, b, c)\| = \sqrt{a^2 + b^2 + c^2}$$
$$d_3(\mathbf{u}, \mathbf{v}) = \|\mathbf{u} - \mathbf{v}\|$$

In this section we will be concerned with the possible relation between the vectors in these spaces and such purely geometric things as points, lines, and planes. Since every vector of $\mathbf{V_2}$ is an ordered pair of real numbers, we may, if we like, consider the vector as the rectangular coordinate label of a point in a plane. In the same way we may consider a vector of $\mathbf{V_3}$ as the rectangular coordinate label of a point in space. It is somewhat more convenient, however, to consider vectors as somehow being represented by line segments and, moreover, by line segments which have a direction or sense. More specifically, and more formally, we have

Definition 1-3-1. For two points P and Q of a plane or of space, the *directed line segment* $\overrightarrow{PQ}$ will be the ordered pair of points (P, Q). P is called the *initial point* of the oriented line segment $\overrightarrow{PQ}$. Q is called the *terminal point* of the oriented line segment $\overrightarrow{PQ}$.

Because of the terminology established in this definition, two distinct points P and Q will determine two different directed line segments: $\overrightarrow{PQ}$ and $\overrightarrow{QP}$. Thus the role of initial and terminal point is interchanged for the directed line segment $\overrightarrow{PQ}$ whose direction is opposite to that of $\overrightarrow{QP}$. When we also have a rectangular coordinate system in a plane or in space, then we may consider directed line segments as representing vectors of $\mathbf{V_2}$ or $\mathbf{V_3}$. The manner in which this is done is given in

Definition 1-3-2. In a plane with a rectangular coordinate system, if the point P has coordinates (p_1, p_2) and the point Q has coordinates (q_1, q_2), then the directed line segment $\overrightarrow{PQ}$ is called a *representation* of the vector $\mathbf{v} \in \mathbf{V_2}$ provided that

$$\mathbf{v} = (q_1 - p_1, q_2 - p_2)$$

Conversely, given a vector $\mathbf{v} = (v_1, v_2) \in \mathbf{V_2}$, any directed line segment $\overrightarrow{AB}$ where A has coordinates (a_1, a_2) and B has coordinates (b_1, b_2) will be a representation of the vector $\mathbf{v}$ whenever

$$b_1 - a_1 = v_1 \quad \text{and} \quad b_2 - a_2 = v_2$$

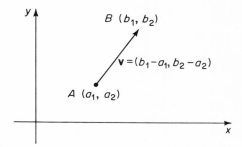

Figure 1-1

Definition 1-3-3. In (three-dimensional) space with a rectangular coordinate system, if the point P has coordinates (p_1, p_2, p_3) and the point Q has coordinates (q_1, q_2, q_3), then the directed line segment $\overrightarrow{PQ}$ is called a *representation* of the vector $\mathbf{v} \in \mathbf{V}_3$ provided that

$$\mathbf{v} = (q_1 - p_1, q_2 - p_2, q_3 - p_3)$$

Conversely, given a vector $\mathbf{v} = (v_1, v_2, v_3) \in \mathbf{V}_3$, any directed line segment $\overrightarrow{AB}$ where A has coordinates (a_1, a_2, a_3) and B has coordinates (b_1, b_2, b_3) will be a representation of the vector $\mathbf{v}$ whenever

$$b_1 - a_1 = v_1, \qquad b_2 - a_2 = v_2, \quad \text{and} \quad b_3 - a_3 = v_3$$

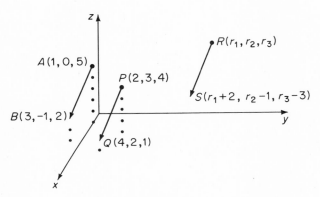

Figure 1-2

For example, in $\mathbf{V}_3$, if A has coordinates $(1, 0, 5)$ and B has coordinates $(3, -1, 2)$, then the directed line segment $\overrightarrow{AB}$ is a representation of the vector $(2, -1, -3) \in \mathbf{V}_3$. If P has coordinates $(2, 3, 4)$ and Q has coordinates $(4, 2, 1)$, then $\overrightarrow{PQ}$ is also a representation of the vector $(2, -1, -3)$. In fact, given any point R with coordinates (r_1, r_2, r_3), if the point S has coordinates $(r_1 + 2, r_2 - 1, r_3 - 3)$, then $\overrightarrow{RS}$ will be a representation of the vector $(2, -1, -3)$. We note further that all the directed line segments which represent the vector $(2, -1, -3)$ have length $\sqrt{14}$; this number is precisely the norm of the vector $(2, -1, -3)$. Another property common to all representations of a nonzero vector is given in

Theorem 1-3-1. If, in a plane with a rectangular coordinate system, the directed line segments $\overrightarrow{PQ}$ and $\overrightarrow{RS}$ are both representations of the vector $\mathbf{v} \in \mathbf{V}_2$, then

    (i) The line segments PQ and RS are parallel.
    (ii) The line segments PR and QS are parallel.
    (iii) (Length of PQ) = (Length of RS) = $\|\mathbf{v}\|$.

Proof. Let P, Q, R, and S have coordinates (p_1, p_2), (q_1, q_2), (r_1, r_2), and (s_1, s_2), respectively. From the definition of a representation of a vector, we have

$$\mathbf{v} = (q_1 - p_1, q_2 - p_2) = (s_1 - r_1, s_2 - r_2)$$

This means that

$$q_1 - p_1 = s_1 - r_1 \quad \text{and} \quad q_2 - p_2 = s_2 - r_2$$

But then

$$q_1 + r_1 = s_1 + p_1 \quad \text{and} \quad q_2 + r_2 = s_2 + p_2$$

so that

$$\left(\frac{q_1 + r_1}{2}, \frac{q_2 + r_2}{2} \right) = \left(\frac{s_1 + p_1}{2}, \frac{s_2 + p_2}{2} \right)$$

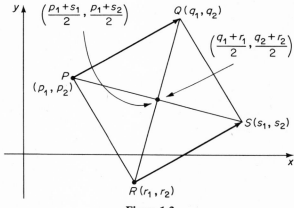

Figure 1-3

The ordered pair on the left is the rectangular coordinate label of the midpoint of the line segment QR. The ordered pair on the right is the rectangular coordinate label of the midpoint of the line segment SP. Thus the line segments QR and SP bisect each other. Consequently the quadrilateral $PRSQ$ must be a parallelogram with PQ parallel to RS and PR parallel to QS.

Finally,

$$\begin{aligned}
(\text{Length of } PQ) &= \sqrt{(q_1 - p_1)^2 + (q_2 - p_2)^2} \\
&= \|\mathbf{v}\| \\
&= \sqrt{(s_1 - r_1)^2 + (s_2 - r_2)^2} \\
&= (\text{Length of } RS)
\end{aligned}$$
          ∎

We have, of course, a similar theorem concerning representations of vectors in $\mathbf{V}_3$:

Theorem 1-3-2. If, in (three-dimensional) space with a rectangular coordinate system, the directed line segments $\overrightarrow{PQ}$ and $\overrightarrow{RS}$ are both representations of the vector $\mathbf{v} \in \mathbf{V_3}$, then

(i) The line segment PQ is parallel to the line segment RS.
(ii) (Length of PQ) = (Length of RS) = $\|\mathbf{v}\|$.
(iii) The line segment PR is parallel to the line segment QS.

The proof is left to the exercises.

So far we have only allowed representations of nonzero vectors. For the sake of completeness we introduce

Definition 1-3-4. In a plane with a rectangular coordinate system, any point will be considered a representation of the vector $\mathbf{0} \in \mathbf{V_2}$. In (three-dimensional) space with a rectangular coordinate system, any point will be considered a representation of the vector $\mathbf{0} \in \mathbf{V_3}$.

The way in which we treat directed line segments as representations of vectors allows us to give a direct geometric interpretation to the operations of vector addition and scalar multiplication. It should be noted that we have arranged things so that the vector spaces $\mathbf{V_2}$ and $\mathbf{V_3}$ have been constructed in a purely algebraic way so that, in this manner of doing things, the geometry follows the algebra. It would have been possible to reverse this order.

For the geometric interpretation of vector addition in $\mathbf{V_2}$, we have

Theorem 1-3-3. Let $\overrightarrow{PQ}$ be a representation of the nonzero vector $\mathbf{u} \in \mathbf{V_2}$. If $\overrightarrow{QT}$ is that representation of the nonzero vector $\mathbf{v} \in \mathbf{V_2}$ with initial point Q, then $\overrightarrow{PT}$ is a representation of $\mathbf{u} + \mathbf{v}$.

Proof. We let P and Q have coordinates (p_1, p_2) and (q_1, q_2), respectively. Since $\overrightarrow{PQ}$ is a representation of $\mathbf{u}$, we must have

$$\mathbf{u} = (q_1 - p_1, q_2 - p_2)$$

Let $\mathbf{v} = (v_1, v_2)$ and T have coordinates (t_1, t_2). Since $\overrightarrow{QT}$ is a representation of $\mathbf{v}$, we must have

$$t_1 - q_1 = v_1 \quad \text{and} \quad t_2 - q_2 = v_2$$

or

$$t_1 = q_1 + v_1 \quad \text{and} \quad t_2 = q_2 + v_2$$

Thus to say that $\overrightarrow{QT}$ is that representation of $\mathbf{v}$ with initial point Q means that

T has coordinates $(q_1 + v_1, q_2 + v_2)$. But

$$\mathbf{u} + \mathbf{v} = ((q_1 - p_1) + v_1, (q_2 - p_2) + v_2)$$
$$= ((q_1 + v_1) - p_1, (q_2 + v_2) - p_2)$$

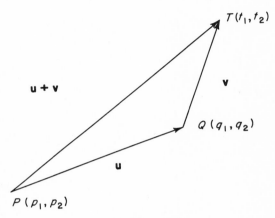

Figure 1-4

This last equation is exactly what is meant by saying that the directed line segment $\overrightarrow{PT}$ is a representation of the vector $\mathbf{u} + \mathbf{v}$.   ∎

In like manner we can prove the analogous theorem for $\mathbf{V}_3$:

Theorem 1-3-4. Let $\overrightarrow{PQ}$ be a representation of the nonzero vector $\mathbf{u} \in \mathbf{V}_3$. If $\overrightarrow{QT}$ is that representation of the nonzero vector $\mathbf{v} \in \mathbf{V}_3$ with initial point Q, then $\overrightarrow{PT}$ is a representation of $\mathbf{u} + \mathbf{v}$.

The proof is left to the exercises.

Another geometric interpretation of addition of vectors is given in the following manner: We consider two nonzero vectors $\mathbf{u}$ and $\mathbf{v}$ and a fixed point A. We let $\overrightarrow{AP}$ and $\overrightarrow{AQ}$ be the representations of $\mathbf{u}$ and $\mathbf{v}$, respectively, which have initial point A. If the line segments AP and AQ are not segments of one straight line (that is, if AP and AQ are not collinear), we let $\overrightarrow{QR}$ be that representation of $\mathbf{u}$ with initial point Q. Theorems 1-3-1 and 1-3-2 tell us that $\overrightarrow{PR}$ must then be a representation of $\mathbf{v}$. But then Theorem 1-3-4 tells us that $\overrightarrow{AR}$ is a representation of $\mathbf{u} + \mathbf{v}$. Theorem 1-3-2 also tells us that $AQRP$ is a parallelogram.

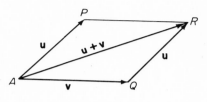

Figure 1-5

Our interpretation of a directed line segment as a representation of a vector allows us a geometric view of the operation of scalar multiplication of a nonzero vector $\mathbf{v}$ by a nonzero real number a:

Theorem 1-3-5. Let $\overrightarrow{PQ}$ be a representation of the nonzero vector $\mathbf{u} \in V_2$. If $a > 0$ and $\overrightarrow{PR}$ is a representation of $a\mathbf{u}$, then P, Q, and R are on one line,

$$\text{(Length of } PR) = a(\text{Length of } PQ)$$

and P is not between Q and R. If $a < 0$ and $\overrightarrow{PS}$ is a representation of $a\mathbf{u}$, then P, Q, and S are on one line,

$$\text{(Length of } PS) = |a| \ (\text{Length of } PQ)$$

and P is between Q and S.

Proof. Let P have coordinates (p_1, p_2).

Part 1: $a > 0$. Let Q have coordinates (q_1, q_2). Then

$$\mathbf{u} = (q_1 - p_1, q_2 - p_2)$$
$$a\mathbf{u} = (a(q_1 - p_1), a(q_2 - p_2))$$
$$\begin{aligned}
\text{Length of } PR &= \|a\mathbf{u}\| \\
&= \sqrt{[a(q_1 - p_1)]^2 + [a(q_2 - p_2)]^2} \\
&= \sqrt{a^2(q_1 - p_1)^2 + a^2(q_2 - p_2)^2} \\
&= \sqrt{a^2} \sqrt{(q_1 - p_1)^2 + (q_2 - p_2)^2} \\
&= a \|\mathbf{u}\|
\end{aligned}$$

Since $\overrightarrow{PR}$ is a representation of $a\mathbf{u}$, R must have coordinates

$$(p_1 + a(q_1 - p_1), p_2 + a(q_2 - p_2))$$

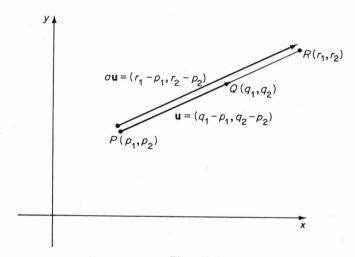

Figure 1-6

For convenience we let

$$r_1 = p_1 + a(q_1 - p_1) \quad \text{and} \quad r_2 = p_2 + a(q_2 - p_2)$$

If $q_1 - p_1 = 0$, then $r_1 - p_1 = a(q_1 - p_1) = 0$ and PQ and PR are both vertical lines. On the other hand, if $q_1 - p_1 \neq 0$, then

$$\begin{aligned}
\text{Slope of } PR &= \frac{r_2 - p_2}{r_1 - p_1} \\
&= \frac{a(q_2 - p_2)}{a(q_1 - p_1)} \\
&= \frac{q_2 - p_2}{q_1 - p_1} \\
&= \text{slope of } PQ
\end{aligned}$$

so that PR and PQ are parallel. Thus in either case, P, Q, and R are on one line.

If P is between Q and R, then $q_1 - p_1$ and $p_1 - r_1$ have the same sign and $q_2 - p_2$ and $p_2 - r_2$ have the same sign. In other words, if P is between Q and R, then $(q_1 - p_1)(p_1 - r_1) > 0$ and $(q_2 - p_2)(p_2 - r_2) > 0$. But

$$(q_1 - p_1)(p_1 - r_1) = -a(q_1 - p_1)^2 < 0$$

and

$$(q_2 - p_2)(p_2 - r_2) = -a(q_2 - p_2)^2 < 0$$

so that P cannot be between Q and R.

Part 2: $a < 0$. The proof is left to the exercises.   ∎

We have, for V_3, the analogous theorem:

Theorem 1-3-6. Let $\overrightarrow{PQ}$ be a representation of the nonzero vector $\mathbf{u} \in V_3$. If $a > 0$ and $\overrightarrow{PR}$ is a representation of $a\mathbf{u}$, then P, Q, and R are on one line,

$$(\text{Length of } PR) = a(\text{Length of } PQ)$$

and P is not between Q and R. If $a < 0$ and $\overrightarrow{PS}$ is a representation of $a\mathbf{u}$, then P, Q, and S are on one line,

$$(\text{Length of } PS) = |a| \, (\text{Length of } PQ)$$

and P is between Q and S.

The proof is left to the exercises.

EXERCISES

1. Prove Theorem 1-3-2.

2. Prove Theorem 1-3-4.

3. Complete the proof of Theorem 1-3-5.

4. Prove Theorem 1-3-6.

5. In the plane, the points O, A, B, C, and D have rectangular coordinates given by O, $(0, 0)$; A, $(1, 2)$; B, $(-2, 4)$; C, $(-3, 1)$; and D, $(3, 5)$. Let $\overrightarrow{OA}$, $\overrightarrow{OB}$, $\overrightarrow{OC}$, and $\overrightarrow{OD}$ be representations of the vectors $\mathbf{a}$, $\mathbf{b}$, $\mathbf{c}$, and $\mathbf{d}$, respectively. Sketch representations of the vectors $\mathbf{a} + \mathbf{b}$, $\mathbf{a} - \mathbf{b}$, $\mathbf{a} + \mathbf{b} + \mathbf{c}$, and $(\mathbf{a} + \mathbf{b}) - (\mathbf{c} + \mathbf{d})$.

6. In the plane, P, Q, and R are not on a line. Show that if $\overrightarrow{PQ}$ is a representation of $\mathbf{a}$, $\overrightarrow{QR}$ is a representation of $\mathbf{b}$, and $\overrightarrow{RP}$ is a representation of $\mathbf{c}$, then $\mathbf{a} + \mathbf{b} + \mathbf{c} = \mathbf{0}$. Does the result change if P, Q, and R are on one line?

7. Generalize Exercise 6 to V_3.

8. In a plane, the points P, Q, and R are not on a line. $\overrightarrow{PQ}$ is a representation of $\mathbf{a}$ and $\overrightarrow{PR}$ is a representation of $\mathbf{b}$. Show that for any vector $\mathbf{v} \in V_2$ there exist unique numbers x and y such that $\mathbf{v} = x\mathbf{a} + y\mathbf{b}$. Does the result change if P, Q, and R are on a line?

9. Generalize the result of Exercise 8 to V_3.

10. Use vector methods in V_2 to show that the diagonals of a parallelogram bisect each other. Hint: Consider the directed sides of the parallelogram as representations of vectors 2a and 2b and show that the midpoint of one diagonal must also be the midpoint of the other.

1-4 Linear Independence and Dependence

In any vector space, given the vectors $v_1, v_2, \ldots, v_n$ and the real numbers $c_1, c_2, \ldots, c_n$, the vector

$$c_1 v_1 + c_2 v_2 + \cdots + c_n v_n$$

is called a *linear combination* of the vectors $v_1, v_2, \ldots, v_n$. We have seen (Exercise 8 of Section 1-3) that in a plane if the nonzero vectors **a** and **b** of V_2 do not have representations parallel to each other, then any vector **v** of V_2 can be expressed as a linear combination of **a** and **b**.

From the geometric point of view this means that if $\overrightarrow{PQ}$, $\overrightarrow{PR}$, and $\overrightarrow{PS}$ are representations of **a**, **b**, and **v**, respectively, then PS is the diagonal of a parallelogram with PQ lying along one side and PR lying along another. In this case, expressing **v** as the particular linear combination $x\mathbf{a} + y\mathbf{b}$ of the vectors **a** and **b**, we see that the representation of $x\mathbf{a}$ with initial point P will be one side of this parallelogram and the representation of $y\mathbf{b}$ with initial point P will be the other. From the vector-algebraic point of view, one conclusion which can be drawn is that if **v** were the vector **0**, then this parallelogram would have to collapse to one point—that is—the numbers x and y would have to be 0.

Now let us examine the situation in V_2 in which we have a set of three nonzero vectors **a**, **b**, and **c**, with no two of them having parallel representations. We want to know if we can find numbers x, y, and z for any vector **v** of V_2 such that

$$\mathbf{v} = x\mathbf{a} + y\mathbf{b} + z\mathbf{c}$$

Geometrically this gets a bit messy so that it will be easier to consider this as an algebraic problem. If $\mathbf{v} = (v_1, v_2)$, $\mathbf{a} = (a_1, a_2)$, $\mathbf{b} = (b_1, b_2)$, and $\mathbf{c} = (c_1, c_2)$, then the vector equation above is equivalent to the numerical equations

$$v_1 = xa_1 + yb_1 + zc_1$$
$$v_2 = xa_2 + yb_2 + zc_2$$

We will make things still easier by restricting ourselves to the question of finding numbers x, y, and z so that $\mathbf{v} = \mathbf{0}$ or

$$a_1 x + b_1 y + c_1 z = 0$$
$$a_2 x + b_2 y + c_2 z = 0$$

We know that **a** and **b** do not have parallel representations. If $\overrightarrow{OA}$ is a representation of **a**, then A has coordinates (a_1, a_2); and if $a_1 \neq 0$, OA will have slope a_2/a_1. Similarly, if $\overrightarrow{OB}$ is a representation of **b**, then OB will have slope b_2/b_1, provided $b_1 \neq 0$. Since OA and OB are not parallel, we must have $a_1 b_2 - a_2 b_1 \neq 0$. But if $a_1 = 0$, OA is a vertical line so that OB is not a vertical line and $b_1 \neq 0$. In this case, if $a_1 b_2 - a_2 b_1 = 0$, then $a_2 b_1 = 0$ (since $a_1 = 0$) and $a_2 = 0$ (since $b_1 \neq 0$) so that **a** is the zero vector. This violates our assumption that **a**, **b**, and **c** were nonzero vectors, so whether or not OA is vertical, we must have $a_1 b_2 - a_2 b_1 \neq 0$. Turning now to our numerical equations, we have, multiplying the first by a_2 and the second by a_1,

$$a_1 a_2 x + a_2 b_1 y + a_2 c_1 z = 0$$
$$a_1 a_2 x + a_1 b_2 y + a_1 c_2 z = 0$$

which yields

$$(a_1 b_2 - a_2 b_1)y + (a_1 c_2 - a_2 c_1)z = 0$$

or

$$y = \frac{a_2 c_1 - a_1 c_2}{a_1 b_2 - a_2 b_1} z$$

Similar manipulations will yield

$$x = \frac{b_1 c_2 - b_2 c_1}{a_1 b_2 - a_2 b_1} z$$

We are now confronted with an embarrassment of riches. Not only can we find numbers x, y, and z such that $x\mathbf{a} + y\mathbf{b} + z\mathbf{c} = \mathbf{0}$, but we can find infinitely many sets of such numbers. In particular, if x and y are related to z by the two "solutions" of this system of two equations in three variables, then we may let z be any number we please.

For the vector space $\mathbf{V}_2$, then there is something rather special about a set consisting of two vectors **a** and **b**, both nonzero and having no representations which are parallel: If a linear combination $x\mathbf{a} + y\mathbf{b} = \mathbf{0}$, then $x = y = 0$. This property is not shared by a set consisting of three (or indeed more than three) vectors, all nonzero, with no two having parallel representations. We can give a name to this property for any set in any vector space by

Definition 1-4-1. $\mathbf{V}$ is a vector space. The set $\mathbf{v}_1, \mathbf{v}_2, \ldots, \mathbf{v}_n$ of vectors of $\mathbf{V}$ is called *linearly independent* provided that if $c_1, c_2, \ldots, c_n$ are real numbers such that the linear combination

$$c_1\mathbf{v}_1 + c_2\mathbf{v}_2 + \cdots + c_n\mathbf{v}_n = 0$$

then we must have $c_1 = c_2 = \cdots = c_n = 0$. A set of vectors of $\mathbf{V}$ is called *linearly dependent* when that set is not linearly independent.

EXAMPLES. In V_3 we consider the set $\{(0, 2, 1), (3, 0, 2), (1, 1, 0)\}$. The vector equation

$$x(0, 2, 1) + y(3, 0, 2) + z(1, 1, 0) = (0, 0, 0)$$

yields the three numerical equations

$$3y + z = 0$$
$$2x + z = 0$$
$$x + 2y = 0$$

The first two equations yield $y = \frac{2}{3}x$ which together with the third equation yield $\frac{7}{3}x = 0$, or $x = 0$. But then the second equation gives $x = 0$ so that we also have $y = 0$. Thus the given set of three vectors in V_3 is a linearly independent set.

In V_3 we consider the set $\{(1, 2, 4), (3, 1, 0), (1, -3, -8)\}$. The vector equation

$$x(1, 2, 4) + y(3, 1, 0) + z(1, -3, -8) = (0, 0, 0)$$

yields the numerical equations

$$x + 3y + z = 0$$
$$2x + y - 3z = 0$$
$$4x - 8z = 0$$

The third equation gives $x = 2z$. Substitution of this in the first equation gives $y = -z$. Thus if $z = c$, $x = 2c$, $y = -c$, we have all three equations satisfied and it is not necessarily true that $x = y = z = 0$. That is, there exist three numbers, not all of which are zero; in particular, $x = 2$, $y = -1$, $z = 1$, such that

$$2(1, 2, 4) + (-1)(3, 1, 0) + (1)(1, -3, -8) = (0, 0, 0)$$

and so the given set of vectors is linearly dependent.

Finally we give a definition of the dimension of a vector space:

> **Definition 1-4-2.** **V** is a vector space. The positive integer n is the *dimension* of **V** provided that there exists a linearly independent set of n nonzero vectors of **V** and any set containing more than n nonzero vectors of **V** is linearly dependent.

Under this definition, V_2 has dimension 2, V_3 has dimension 3, etc. We can extend the definition by saying

> **Definition 1-4-3.** The *dimension* of a vector space **V** is *infinite* provided that for every positive integer n there exists a set of n nonzero vectors of **V** which is linearly independent.

EXERCISES

1. In the vector space of all continuous functions on $[0, 1]$ into the real numbers,

$$f_1 = \{(t, 1) \mid 0 \leq t \leq 1\}$$
$$f_2 = \{(t, t) \mid 0 \leq t \leq 1\}$$
$$f_3 = \{(t, t^2) \mid 0 \leq t \leq 1\}$$
$$f_4 = \{(t, 4t^2 - 3t + 5) \mid 0 \leq t \leq 1\}$$

Show that the sets $\{f_1, f_2, f_3\}$ and $\{f_1, f_2, f_4\}$ are linearly independent and that the set $\{f_1, f_2, f_3, f_4\}$ is linearly dependent.

In Exercises 2–7, determine whether the following sets of vectors of $\mathbf{V_2}$ are linearly independent or linearly dependent.

2. $\{(1, 0), (0, 1)\}$

3. $\{(1, 1), (2, 0)\}$

4. $\{(1, 3), (2, 6)\}$

5. $\{(1, 1), (1, 2)\}$

6. $\{(1, 0), (0, 1), (3, 4)\}$

7. $\{(1, 2), (3, 4), (5, 7)\}$

8. g is the polynomial function given by

$$g(x) = c_0 + c_1 x + c_2 x^2 + \cdots + c_n x^n, \qquad 0 \leq x \leq 1$$

Show that $g = \{(x, 0) \mid 0 \leq x \leq 1\}$ if, and only if, $c_0 = c_1 = \cdots = c_n = 0$. (Consider the first n derivatives of g.)

9. Show that, in $\mathbf{V_3}$, any set of four nonzero vectors is linearly dependent.

10. Prove that a set of linearly independent vectors in any vector space must consist only of nonzero vectors.

11. Prove that the dimension of $\mathbf{V_n}$ is n.

12. If $\mathbf{V}$ is a vector space of dimension n and $\mathbf{e_1}, \mathbf{e_2}, \ldots, \mathbf{e_n}$ is a linearly independent set of vectors of $\mathbf{V}$, prove that for any vector $\mathbf{v}$ of $\mathbf{V}$ there exists a unique set of real numbers $v_1, v_2, \ldots, v_n$ such that

$$\mathbf{v} = v_1 \mathbf{e_1} + v_2 \mathbf{e_2} + \cdots + v_n \mathbf{e_n}$$

1-5 Inner Products and Orthogonality

Since $\mathbf{V_3}$ is a collection of ordered triples of real numbers, there is no a priori geometric structure to this space. If we choose to consider that directed line segments are representations of vectors in V_3, however, then we may use geometric ideas in forming definitions for V_3. In particular, if **a** and **b** are two nonzero vectors of V_3 and $\overrightarrow{OA}$ and $\overrightarrow{OB}$ are representations of **a** and **b**, respectively, with O being the origin of a rectangular coordinate system, then the coordinates of A and B are precisely the ordered triples which are the vectors **a** and **b**. Now if $\mathbf{a} = (a_1, a_2, a_3)$ and $\mathbf{b} = (b_1, b_2, b_3)$, the angle between the line segments OA and OB can be determined as follows:

The direction cosines of the line segment OA are

$$\frac{a_1}{\sqrt{a_1^2 + a_2^2 + a_3^2}}, \qquad \frac{a_2}{\sqrt{a_1^2 + a_2^2 + a_3^2}}, \qquad \frac{a_3}{\sqrt{a_1^2 + a_2^2 + a_3^2}}$$

with similar direction cosines for the line segment OB. If we denote the angle between these line segments as θ, with the restriction that $0 \leq \theta \leq \pi$, then we have

$$\cos \theta = \frac{a_1 b_1 + a_2 b_2 + a_3 b_3}{\sqrt{a_1^2 + a_2^2 + a_3^2} \sqrt{b_1^2 + b_2^2 + b_3^2}}$$

This equation is equivalent to

$$a_1 b_1 + a_2 b_2 + a_3 b_3 = \|\mathbf{a}\| \, \|\mathbf{b}\| \cos \theta$$

We call the number $a_1 b_1 + a_2 b_2 + a_3 b_3$ the *inner product* or *dot product* of the vectors **a** and **b** of V_3 and denote it by $\mathbf{a} \cdot \mathbf{b}$. This process of combining two vectors of V_3 to produce a real number has the following properties:

(i) For all **a** and $\mathbf{b} \in V_3$, $\mathbf{a} \cdot \mathbf{b} = \mathbf{b} \cdot \mathbf{a}$.

(ii) For any **a**, **b**, and $\mathbf{c} \in V_3$, $\mathbf{a} \cdot (\mathbf{b} + \mathbf{c}) = \mathbf{a} \cdot \mathbf{b} + \mathbf{a} \cdot \mathbf{c}$.

(iii) For any **a** and $\mathbf{b} \in V_3$ and any real number c, $\mathbf{a} \cdot (c\mathbf{b}) = (c\mathbf{a}) \cdot \mathbf{b} = c\,\mathbf{a} \cdot \mathbf{b}$.

(iv) For every vector $\mathbf{a} \in V_3$, $\mathbf{a} \cdot \mathbf{a} = \|\mathbf{a}\|^2$.

We use the properties of the inner product in V_3 to construct a general definition for all normed vector spaces.

> **Definition 1-5-1.** The normed vector space **V** is an *inner product space* provided that for every pair of vectors **a** and **b** in **V** there exists a real number $\mathbf{a} \cdot \mathbf{b}$ (called the inner product of **a** and **b**) with properties (i)–(iv) listed above.

EXAMPLES. In V_n, we can define an inner product by

$$(a_1, a_2, \ldots, a_n) \cdot (b_1, b_2, \ldots, b_n) = a_1 b_1 + a_2 b_2 + \cdots + a_n b_n$$

It can easily be seen that this operation has properties (i)–(iv) mentioned in the definition of an inner product space.

The vector space of all continuous functions on $[0, 1]$ into the real numbers can become a normed vector space in several ways. One of them assigns to each function (vector) the norm given by

$$\|f\| = \left[\int_0^1 f^2\right]^{1/2}$$

For this normed vector space we may construct an inner product by

$$f \cdot g = \int_0^1 fg$$

Again it can be easily seen that the operation of inner product in this space satisfies the definition.

Returning to V_3, if $\mathbf{a} = (a_1, a_2, a_3)$ and $\mathbf{b} = (b_1, b_2, b_3)$ are two nonzero vectors with representations $\overrightarrow{OA}$ and $\overrightarrow{OB}$, the line segments OA and OB will be perpendicular to each other whenever θ, the angle between them, is $\pi/2$. In this case, $\cos \theta = 0$ so that $\mathbf{a} \cdot \mathbf{b} = a_1b_1 + a_2b_2 + a_3b_3 = 0$. Thus if the representations $\overrightarrow{OA}$ and $\overrightarrow{OB}$ of the nonzero vectors $\mathbf{a}$ and $\mathbf{b}$ are perpendicular, then $\mathbf{a} \cdot \mathbf{b} = 0$. It is also true that if $\mathbf{a}$ and $\mathbf{b}$ are nonzero vectors and $\mathbf{a} \cdot \mathbf{b} = 0$, then any representations of $\mathbf{a}$ and $\mathbf{b}$ with the same initial point will be perpendicular. It will also be true, however, that if either or both of the vectors $\mathbf{a}$ and $\mathbf{b}$ is $\mathbf{0}$, then we will have $\mathbf{a} \cdot \mathbf{b} = 0$. Thus we will not use the word "perpendicular" in the case of vectors, but we will say that in an inner product space two vectors are *orthogonal* if their inner product is 0. With this terminology, the vector $\mathbf{0}$ is orthogonal to every vector.

In V_3 we see that the vectors $(1, 0, 0)$, $(0, 1, 0)$, and $(0, 0, 1)$ are pairwise orthogonal. In the vector space of all continuous functions on $[0, 1]$ into the real numbers with the norm and inner product given above, any two functions of the form

$$\{(x, \cos 2n\pi x) \mid 0 \le x \le 1\}$$

and

$$\{(x, \cos 2m\pi x) \mid 0 \le x \le 1\}$$

where m and n are two different positive integers will be orthogonal.

In V_3 the set of vectors $(1, 0, 0)$, $(0, 1, 0)$, $(0, 0, 1)$ is clearly a linearly independent set since

$$c_1(1, 0, 0) + c_2(0, 1, 0) + c_3(0, 0, 1) = (0, 0, 0)$$

if, and only if, $(c_1, c_2, c_3) = (0, 0, 0)$; that is, $c_1 = c_2 = c_3 = 0$.

The relation between orthogonality and linear independence for an inner product space is given in

Theorem 1-5-1. $\mathbf{V}$ is a vector space with an inner product. If the k nonzero vectors $\mathbf{v_1}, \mathbf{v_2}, \ldots, \mathbf{v_k}$ are mutually orthogonal, then they form a linearly independent set.

Proof. If there exist k numbers $c_1, c_2, \ldots, c_k$ with the property that

$$c_1 \mathbf{v}_1 + c_2 \mathbf{v}_2 + \cdots + c_k \mathbf{v}_k = \mathbf{0}$$

then, for $i = 1, 2, \ldots, k$, we have

$$\mathbf{v}_i \cdot (c_1 \mathbf{v}_1 + c_2 \mathbf{v}_2 + \cdots + c_k \mathbf{v}_k) = 0$$

and

$$c_i \mathbf{v}_i \cdot \mathbf{v}_i = 0$$

since, for $i \neq j$, $\mathbf{v}_i \cdot \mathbf{v}_j = 0$. Thus, for $i = 1, 2, \ldots, k$,

$$c_i \, \|\mathbf{v}_i\|^2 = 0$$

and

$$c_i = 0$$

since $\mathbf{v}_i \neq \mathbf{0}$.   ∎

We know that in space we cannot have more than three mutually perpendicular lines passing through a given point. This means that in $\mathbf{V}_3$ we cannot have more than three mutually orthogonal nonzero vectors. But the dimension of $\mathbf{V}_3$ is three since we cannot have in $\mathbf{V}_3$ a linearly independent set containing more than three vectors. (Recall that in a linearly independent set all the vectors must be nonzero vectors.) In the general case we have

Theorem 1-5-2. $\mathbf{V}$ is a vector space with an inner product. If $\mathbf{V}$ has dimension n, then at most n nonzero vectors of $\mathbf{V}$ can be mutually orthogonal.

The proof is obvious and will be omitted.

Again returning to $\mathbf{V}_3$, we saw that if θ is the angle between representations $\overrightarrow{OA}$ and $\overrightarrow{OB}$ of the nonzero vectors $\mathbf{a}$ and $\mathbf{b}$, then

$$\mathbf{a} \cdot \mathbf{b} = \|\mathbf{a}\| \, \|\mathbf{b}\| \cos \theta$$

Since $|\cos \theta| \leq 1$, we must then have

$$|\mathbf{a} \cdot \mathbf{b}| \leq \|\mathbf{a}\| \, \|\mathbf{b}\|$$

In terms of the numbers which are the components of the vectors $\mathbf{a}$ and $\mathbf{b}$, this statement is equivalent to

$$|a_1 b_1 + a_2 b_2 + a_3 b_3| \leq \sqrt{a_1^2 + a_2^2 + a_3^2} \, \sqrt{b_1^2 + b_2^2 + b_3^2}$$

or, in more compact notation,

$$\left| \sum_{i=1}^{3} a_i b_i \right| \leq \left[\sum_{i=1}^{3} a_i^2 \right]^{1/2} \left[\sum_{i=1}^{3} b_i^2 \right]^{1/2}$$

A simple exercise in mathematical induction (see Exercise 13) shows that for any two sets of numbers $\{a_1, a_2, \ldots, a_n\}$ and $\{b_1, b_2, \ldots, b_n\}$ we will have

$$\left| \sum_{i=1}^{n} a_i b_i \right| \le \left[\sum_{i=1}^{n} a_i^2 \right]^{1/2} \left[\sum_{i=1}^{n} b_i^2 \right]^{1/2}$$

In particular then, if f and g are two continuous functions on $[0, 1]$ into the real numbers, then applying this last inequality to $\{f(1/n), f(2/n), \ldots, f(n/n)\}$ and $\{g(1/n), g(2/n), \ldots, g(n/n)\}$ yields

$$\left| \sum_{i=1}^{n} f\left(\frac{i}{n}\right) g\left(\frac{i}{n}\right) \right| \le \left[\sum_{i=1}^{n} \left\{ f\left(\frac{i}{n}\right) \right\}^2 \right]^{1/2} \left[\sum_{i=1}^{n} \left\{ g\left(\frac{i}{n}\right) \right\}^2 \right]^{1/2}$$

Multiplying both sides by $1/n$ yields

$$\left| \sum_{i=1}^{n} f\left(\frac{i}{n}\right) g\left(\frac{i}{n}\right) \frac{1}{n} \right| \le \left[\sum_{i=1}^{n} \left[f\left(\frac{i}{n}\right) \right]^2 \frac{1}{n} \right]^{1/2} \left[\sum_{i=1}^{n} \left[g\left(\frac{i}{n}\right) \right]^2 \frac{1}{n} \right]^{1/2}$$

Each of the sums above is a typical element of a sequence which converges to the integral of an appropriate function. Taking limit then gives the inequality

$$\left| \int_0^1 fg \right| \le \left[\int_0^1 f^2 \right]^{1/2} \left[\int_0^1 g^2 \right]^{1/2}$$

We then see that the relation $|\mathbf{a} \cdot \mathbf{b}| \le \|\mathbf{a}\| \, \|\mathbf{b}\|$ also holds in the vector space of continuous functions on $[0, 1]$ into the real numbers with inner product and norm as given earlier. This inequality for integrals is often called the Cauchy inequality, sometimes the Cauchy-Schwarz inequality, and occasionally the Cauchy-Schwarz-Bunyakovski inequality.

For our convenience in further dealings with the three-dimensional vector space $\mathbf{V}_3$ we establish the following:

Definition 1-5-2. In $\mathbf{V}_3$,

$$\mathbf{i} = (1, 0, 0)$$
$$\mathbf{j} = (0, 1, 0)$$
$$\mathbf{k} = (0, 0, 1)$$

We will hereafter find it convenient to exhibit any vector of $\mathbf{V}_3$ as a linear combination of the vectors $\mathbf{i}$, $\mathbf{j}$, and $\mathbf{k}$. For example, the vector $(3, 5, 7)$ will be given as $3\mathbf{i} + 5\mathbf{j} + 7\mathbf{k}$.

EXERCISES

1. Show that the vectors $\mathbf{i}$, $\mathbf{j}$, and $\mathbf{k}$ are mutually orthogonal.

2. Find the length of the vector $3\mathbf{i} - 4\mathbf{j} + 12\mathbf{k}$.

3. Find the length of the vector $4\mathbf{i} + 12\mathbf{j} - 3\mathbf{k}$.

4. Find the angle between intersecting representations of the vectors $3\mathbf{i} - 4\mathbf{j} + 12\mathbf{k}$ and $4\mathbf{i} + 12\mathbf{j} - 3\mathbf{k}$.

5. The directed line segments $\overrightarrow{OA}$ and $\overrightarrow{OB}$ are representations of the nonzero vectors $\mathbf{a}$ and $\mathbf{b}$ in $\mathbf{V_3}$. The line through A, perpendicular to OB, intersects OB at the point P. Find a relation between the length of OP and $\mathbf{a} \cdot \mathbf{b}$.

6. $\overrightarrow{BC}$ and $\overrightarrow{BA}$ are representations of the nonzero vectors $\mathbf{c}$ and $\mathbf{a}$ of $\mathbf{V_3}$. Find the distance between the point A and the line BC in terms of the vectors $\mathbf{c}$ and $\mathbf{a}$.

7. Prove that the inner product given for $\mathbf{V_3}$ actually satisfies requirements (i)–(iv) in the definition of an inner product space.

8. Use the inner product in $\mathbf{V_3}$ to find an equation of the plane which contains the point with rectangular coordinates $(1, 2, 3)$ which is perpendicular to the line joining the points with rectangular coordinates $(-1, 0, 4)$ and $(2, -1, 0)$. (A line perpendicular to a plane must be perpendicular to every line in that plane which passes through the point of intersection.)

9. Generalize Exercise 8 to find an equation for the plane passing through any given point, perpendicular to any given line.

10. Show that if m and n are distinct positive integers, then

$$\int_0^1 \cos 2n\pi x \cos 2m\pi x \; dx = 0$$

11. Expand the proof of Theorem 1-5-1 to exhibit exactly which properties of the inner product were used to show that

$$\mathbf{v}_i \cdot (c_1\mathbf{v}_1 + c_2\mathbf{v}_2 + \cdots + c_k\mathbf{v}_k) = c_i\mathbf{v}_i \cdot \mathbf{v}_i$$

12. Complete the details in the proof of Theorem 1-5-2.

13. Show that

$$\left(\sum_{i=1}^n a_i^2\right)\left(\sum_{i=1}^n b_i^2\right) - \left(\sum_{i=1}^n a_i b_i\right)^2 \geq 0$$

implies that

$$\left(\sum_{i=1}^{n+1} a_i^2\right)\left(\sum_{i=1}^{n+1} b_i^2\right) - \left(\sum_{i=1}^{n+1} a_i b_i\right)^2 \geq 0$$

That is, give the induction argument referred to in the development leading to the Cauchy inequality.

1-6   The Cross Product in $\mathbf{V_3}$

In any vector space we always have the operations of vector addition and scalar multiplication. In an inner product vector space we also have the "dot product" multiplication of two vectors to produce a real number. In particular, for all the vector spaces V_n, $n = 1, 2, \ldots$, we have these three operations. We now introduce an operation peculiar to V_3 which will be a "multiplication" of a vector by a vector to produce a vector.

Definition 1-6-1. In V_3, the *cross product* $\mathbf{a} \times \mathbf{b}$ of the vector $\mathbf{a}$ by the vector $\mathbf{b}$ is defined as follows: If $\mathbf{a} = 0$ or $\mathbf{b} = 0$, then $\mathbf{a} \times \mathbf{b} = 0$. If $\mathbf{a} \neq 0$ and $\mathbf{b} \neq 0$, then $\mathbf{a} \times \mathbf{b}$ is that vector of V_3 such that

(i) If θ is the angle between $\mathbf{a}$ and $\mathbf{b}$, then $\|\mathbf{a} \times \mathbf{b}\| = \|\mathbf{a}\| \, \|\mathbf{b}\| \sin \theta$.

(ii) $(\mathbf{a} \times \mathbf{b}) \cdot \mathbf{a} = (\mathbf{a} \times \mathbf{b}) \cdot \mathbf{b} = 0$.

(iii) If $\mathbf{a} = (a_1, a_2, a_3)$, $\mathbf{b} = (b_1, b_2, b_3)$, and $\mathbf{a} \times \mathbf{b} = (c_1, c_2, c_3)$, then

$$\begin{vmatrix} a_1 & a_2 & a_3 \\ b_1 & b_2 & b_3 \\ c_1 & c_2 & c_3 \end{vmatrix} \geq 0$$

Geometrically, this definition says that if $\overrightarrow{OA}$, $\overrightarrow{OB}$, and $\overrightarrow{OC}$ are representations of $\mathbf{a}$, $\mathbf{b}$, and $\mathbf{a} \times \mathbf{b}$, respectively, then

1. The length of OC is the area of the parallelogram with sides OA and OB.

2. OA, OB, and OC are mutually perpendicular.

3. The line segments OA, OB, and OC, in that order, are oriented with respect to each other as are the x axis, y axis, and z axis, in that order. (See Figure 1-7.)

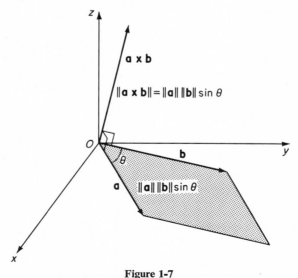

Figure 1-7

EXAMPLE. Let $\mathbf{a} = (3, 4, 0)$ and $\mathbf{b} = (0, 0, 2)$. Then $\|\mathbf{a}\| = 5$ and $\|\mathbf{b}\| = 2$. $\mathbf{a} \cdot \mathbf{b} = 0$ so $\cos \theta = 0$ and $\sin \theta = 1$. Then $\|\mathbf{a} \times \mathbf{b}\| = 10$. Let $\mathbf{a} \times \mathbf{b} = (c_1, c_2, c_3)$. $(\mathbf{a} \times \mathbf{b}) \cdot \mathbf{a} = 0$ implies that $3c_1 + 4c_2 = 0$. $(\mathbf{a} \times \mathbf{b}) \cdot \mathbf{b} = 0$ implies $2c_3 = 0$. Thus $c_3 = 0$ and there is some number d such that $c_1 = 4d$ and $c_2 = -3d$. We now have $\mathbf{a} \times \mathbf{b} = d(4, -3, 0)$. Further, $\|\mathbf{a} \times \mathbf{b}\| = 5|d| = 10$ so that $d = 2$ or $d = -2$. If $d = -2$, the determinant in the definition is -100. If $d = 2$, this determinant is 100. Since the definition requires the determinant to be non-negative, we must have $d = 2$ and

$$(3, 4, 0) \times (0, 0, 2) = (8, -6, 0)$$

In terms of the unit vectors $\mathbf{i}$, $\mathbf{j}$, and $\mathbf{k}$, this equation says

$$(3\mathbf{i} + 4\mathbf{j}) \times (2\mathbf{k}) = 8\mathbf{i} - 6\mathbf{j}$$

We make use of the following chain of theorems to compute the cross product of two vectors in $\mathbf{V}_3$:

Theorem 1-6-1. For any two vectors $\mathbf{a}$ and $\mathbf{b}$ of $\mathbf{V}_3$,

$$\mathbf{a} \times \mathbf{b} = -(\mathbf{b} \times \mathbf{a})$$

Proof. Reversing the position of two rows in a determinant is equivalent to a multiplication by -1. ∎

Theorem 1-6-2. For any vector $\mathbf{a}$ of $\mathbf{V}_3$,

$$\mathbf{a} \times \mathbf{a} = 0$$

Proof

$$\sin \theta = 0$$ ∎

Theorem 1-6-3. For any vector $\mathbf{a}$ of $\mathbf{V}_3$, and any real number c,

$$\mathbf{a} \times (c\mathbf{a}) = 0$$

Proof

$$\sin \theta = 0$$ ∎

Theorem 1-6-4. In $\mathbf{V}_3$,

$$\mathbf{i} \times \mathbf{i} = \mathbf{j} \times \mathbf{j} = \mathbf{k} \times \mathbf{k} = 0$$

Proof. Theorem 1-6-2. ∎

Theorem 1-6-5. In $\mathbf{V}_3$,

$$\mathbf{i} \times \mathbf{j} = \mathbf{k}$$

Proof

$$\|\mathbf{i}\| = \|\mathbf{j}\| = 1; \qquad \sin\theta = 1$$

$$\begin{vmatrix} 1 & 0 & 0 \\ 0 & 1 & 0 \\ 0 & 0 & 1 \end{vmatrix} = 1 > 0$$

∎

Corollary 1-6-5-1. In V_3,

$$\mathbf{j} \times \mathbf{i} = -\mathbf{k}$$

Proof. Theorems 1-6-1 and 1-6-5.   ∎

Theorem 1-6-6. In V_3,

$$\mathbf{j} \times \mathbf{k} = \mathbf{i}$$

Corollary 1-6-6-1. In V_3,

$$\mathbf{k} \times \mathbf{j} = -\mathbf{i}$$

Theorem 1-6-7. In V_3,

$$\mathbf{k} \times \mathbf{i} = \mathbf{j}$$

Corollary 1-6-7-1. In V_3,

$$\mathbf{i} \times \mathbf{k} = -\mathbf{j}$$

Theorem 1-6-8. If **a** and **b** are any two vectors of V_3 and c is any real number, then

$$\mathbf{a} \times (c\mathbf{b}) = (c\mathbf{a}) \times \mathbf{b} = c(\mathbf{a} \times \mathbf{b})$$

Theorem 1-6-9. If **a**, **b**, and **c** are any vectors of V_3, then

$$\mathbf{a} \times (\mathbf{b} + \mathbf{c}) = (\mathbf{a} \times \mathbf{b}) + (\mathbf{a} \times \mathbf{c})$$

The proofs of these last two theorems are left to the exercises.

The most frequently used technique in the actual evaluation of the cross product of two vectors of V_3 is given in

Theorem 1-6-10. In V_3, if $\mathbf{a} = a_1\mathbf{i} + a_2\mathbf{j} + a_3\mathbf{k}$ and $\mathbf{b} = b_1\mathbf{i} + b_2\mathbf{j} + b_3\mathbf{k}$, then

$$\mathbf{a} \times \mathbf{b} = (a_2b_3 - a_3b_2)\mathbf{i} + (a_3b_1 - a_1b_3)\mathbf{j} + (a_1b_2 - a_2b_1)\mathbf{k}$$

Proof

$$\mathbf{a} \times \mathbf{b} = (a_1\mathbf{i} + a_2\mathbf{j} + a_3\mathbf{k}) \times (b_1\mathbf{i} + b_2\mathbf{j} + c_3\mathbf{k})$$
$$= (a_1\mathbf{i}) \times (b_1\mathbf{i} + b_2\mathbf{j} + b_3\mathbf{k}) + (a_2\mathbf{j}) \times (b_1\mathbf{i} + b_2\mathbf{j} + b_3\mathbf{k})$$
$$+ (a_3\mathbf{k}) \times (b_1\mathbf{i} + b_2\mathbf{j} + c_3\mathbf{k})$$
$$= (a_1b_1)(\mathbf{i} \times \mathbf{i}) + (a_1b_2)(\mathbf{i} \times \mathbf{j}) + (a_1b_3)(\mathbf{i} \times \mathbf{k})$$
$$+ (a_2b_1)(\mathbf{j} \times \mathbf{i}) + (a_2b_2)(\mathbf{j} \times \mathbf{j}) + (a_2b_3)(\mathbf{j} \times \mathbf{k})$$
$$+ (a_3b_1)(\mathbf{k} \times \mathbf{i}) + (a_3b_2)(\mathbf{k} \times \mathbf{j}) + (a_3b_3)(\mathbf{k} \times \mathbf{k})$$
$$= a_1b_2\mathbf{k} - a_1b_3\mathbf{j} - a_2b_1\mathbf{k} + a_2b_3\mathbf{i} + a_3b_1\mathbf{j} - a_3b_2\mathbf{i}$$
$$= (a_2b_3 - a_3b_2)\mathbf{i} + (a_3b_1 - a_1b_3)\mathbf{j} + (a_1b_2 - a_2b_1)\mathbf{k} \qquad \blacksquare$$

A convenient device in remembering this last theorem is to consider $\mathbf{a} \times \mathbf{b}$ as the value of the "determinant"

$$\begin{vmatrix} \mathbf{i} & \mathbf{j} & \mathbf{k} \\ a_1 & a_2 & a_3 \\ b_1 & b_2 & b_3 \end{vmatrix}$$

Many theorems can be found relating the operations of vector addition, scalar multiplication, and cross product multiplication. Among the more prominent ones is

Theorem 1-6-11. If $\mathbf{a}$, $\mathbf{b}$, and $\mathbf{c}$ are any three vectors of $\mathbf{V_3}$, then

$$\mathbf{a} \times (\mathbf{b} \times \mathbf{c}) = (\mathbf{a} \cdot \mathbf{c})\mathbf{b} - (\mathbf{a} \cdot \mathbf{b})\mathbf{c}$$

Proof. If $\mathbf{a} \cdot \mathbf{b} = 0$ or $\mathbf{a} \cdot \mathbf{c} = 0$, the theorem is trivially true. If $\mathbf{a} \cdot \mathbf{b} \neq 0$ and $\mathbf{a} \cdot \mathbf{c} \neq 0$, then taking representations of $\mathbf{b} \times \mathbf{c}$ and $\mathbf{a} \times (\mathbf{b} \times \mathbf{c})$ with the same initial point will give a representation of $\mathbf{b} \times \mathbf{c}$ perpendicular to a representation of $\mathbf{a} \times (\mathbf{b} \times \mathbf{c})$. Then the representation of $\mathbf{a} \times (\mathbf{b} \times \mathbf{c})$ must lie in the plane formed by the representations of $\mathbf{b}$ and $\mathbf{c}$. Thus there are real numbers x and y such that

$$\mathbf{a} \times (\mathbf{b} \times \mathbf{c}) = x\mathbf{b} + y\mathbf{c}$$

Taking dot product of both sides of this equation with $\mathbf{a}$ yields

$$0 = x(\mathbf{a} \cdot \mathbf{b}) + y(\mathbf{a} \cdot \mathbf{c})$$

Since neither of the dot products on the right is 0, there is some real number r such that

$$\frac{x}{\mathbf{a} \cdot \mathbf{c}} = \frac{-y}{\mathbf{a} \cdot \mathbf{b}} = r$$

The number r depends on the vectors $\mathbf{a}$, $\mathbf{b}$, and $\mathbf{c}$, and we emphasize this dependence by writing $r = r(\mathbf{a}, \mathbf{b}, \mathbf{c})$. We then have

$$\mathbf{a} \times (\mathbf{b} \times \mathbf{c}) = x\mathbf{b} + y\mathbf{c}$$
$$= r(\mathbf{a}, \mathbf{b}, \mathbf{c})[(\mathbf{a} \cdot \mathbf{c})\mathbf{b} - (\mathbf{a} \cdot \mathbf{b})\mathbf{c}]$$

and our goal is to prove that, for all $\mathbf{a}$, $\mathbf{b}$, and $\mathbf{c}$, $r(\mathbf{a}, \mathbf{b}, \mathbf{c}) = 1$.

For the particular case in which $\mathbf{a} = \mathbf{b}$, we have

$$\mathbf{a} \times (\mathbf{a} \times \mathbf{c}) = r(\mathbf{a}, \mathbf{a}, \mathbf{c})[(\mathbf{a} \cdot \mathbf{c})\mathbf{a} - (\mathbf{a} \cdot \mathbf{a})\mathbf{c}]$$

Taking dot product of each side with $\mathbf{c}$ yields

$$\mathbf{c} \cdot [\mathbf{a} \times (\mathbf{a} \times \mathbf{c})] = r(\mathbf{a}, \mathbf{a}, \mathbf{c})[(\mathbf{a} \cdot \mathbf{c})(\mathbf{a} \cdot \mathbf{c}) - (\mathbf{a} \cdot \mathbf{a})(\mathbf{c} \cdot \mathbf{c})]$$

Now, for any three vectors $\mathbf{u}$, $\mathbf{v}$, and $\mathbf{w}$ of V_3, we have

$$\mathbf{u} \cdot (\mathbf{v} \times \mathbf{w}) = \mathbf{v} \cdot (\mathbf{w} \times \mathbf{u}) = \mathbf{w} \cdot (\mathbf{u} \times \mathbf{v})$$

(See Exercise 4.) Applying this with $\mathbf{u} = \mathbf{c}$, $\mathbf{v} = \mathbf{a}$, and $\mathbf{w} = \mathbf{a} \times \mathbf{c}$ gives

$$(\mathbf{a} \times \mathbf{c}) \cdot (\mathbf{c} \times \mathbf{a}) = r(\mathbf{a}, \mathbf{a}, \mathbf{c})[(\mathbf{a} \cdot \mathbf{c})^2 - (\mathbf{a} \cdot \mathbf{a})(\mathbf{c} \cdot \mathbf{c})]$$
$$- \|\mathbf{a} \times \mathbf{c}\|^2 = r(\mathbf{a}, \mathbf{a}, \mathbf{c})[\|\mathbf{a}\|^2 \|\mathbf{c}\|^2 \cos^2 \theta - \|\mathbf{a}\|^2 \|\mathbf{c}\|^2]$$
$$- \|\mathbf{a}\|^2 \|\mathbf{c}\|^2 \sin^2 \theta = r(\mathbf{a}, \mathbf{a}, \mathbf{c}) \|\mathbf{a}\|^2 \|\mathbf{c}\|^2 (\cos^2 \theta - 1)$$
$$r(\mathbf{a}, \mathbf{a}, \mathbf{c}) = 1$$

We then have

$$\mathbf{a} \times (\mathbf{a} \times \mathbf{c}) = (\mathbf{a} \cdot \mathbf{c})\mathbf{a} - (\mathbf{a} \cdot \mathbf{a})\mathbf{c}$$

Similarly,

$$(\mathbf{a} \times \mathbf{b}) \times \mathbf{b} = -\mathbf{b} \times (\mathbf{b} \times \mathbf{a}) = (\mathbf{a} \cdot \mathbf{b})\mathbf{b} - (\mathbf{b} \cdot \mathbf{b})\mathbf{a}$$

Returning to the equation

$$r(\mathbf{a}, \mathbf{b}, \mathbf{c})[(\mathbf{a} \cdot \mathbf{c})\mathbf{b} - (\mathbf{a} \cdot \mathbf{b})\mathbf{c}] = \mathbf{a} \times (\mathbf{b} \times \mathbf{c})$$

taking dot product of both sides with $\mathbf{b}$ leads to

$$r(\mathbf{a}, \mathbf{b}, \mathbf{c})[(\mathbf{a} \cdot \mathbf{c})(\mathbf{b} \cdot \mathbf{b}) - (\mathbf{a} \cdot \mathbf{b})(\mathbf{b} \cdot \mathbf{c})] = \mathbf{b} \cdot [\mathbf{a} \times (\mathbf{b} \times \mathbf{c})]$$
$$= (\mathbf{b} \times \mathbf{c}) \cdot (\mathbf{b} \times \mathbf{a})$$
$$= -(\mathbf{a} \times \mathbf{b}) \cdot (\mathbf{b} \times \mathbf{c})$$
$$= -\mathbf{c} \cdot [(\mathbf{a} \times \mathbf{b}) \times \mathbf{b}]$$
$$= -\mathbf{c} \cdot [(\mathbf{a} \cdot \mathbf{b})\mathbf{b} - (\mathbf{b} \cdot \mathbf{b})\mathbf{a}]$$
$$= (\mathbf{a} \cdot \mathbf{c})(\mathbf{b} \cdot \mathbf{b}) - (\mathbf{a} \cdot \mathbf{b})(\mathbf{b} \cdot \mathbf{c})$$

Thus $r(\mathbf{a}, \mathbf{b}, \mathbf{c}) = 1$ and the theorem is proved.   ∎

EXERCISES

1. Prove Theorem 1-6-8.

2. Prove Theorem 1-6-9.

3. $a = (1, 2, 3)$, $b = (-1, -1, 0)$, $c = (0, -2, 3)$. Find $a \times b$, $c \times a$, $b \times c$, $a \cdot (b \times c)$, $b \cdot (c \times a)$, and $c \cdot (a \times b)$.

4. Prove that, for all a, b, and c in V_3,

$$a \cdot (b \times c) = b \cdot (c \times a) = c \cdot (a \times b)$$

5. If a and b are given, discuss the representations of a vector r with the property that $r \times a = b$.

6. If a and b are given vectors, and d is a given real number, discuss the representations of a vector r with the properties that $r \times a = b$ and $r \cdot a = d$.

7. Use the cross product to find an equation of the plane through $(2, 3, -1)$ which is perpendicular to the line passing through $(-3, 0, 5)$ and $(2, 1, 0)$.

8. Generalize Exercise 7 to find an equation of the plane through any given point perpendicular to any given line.

9. Use vector methods to find the volume of a tetrahedron.

10. Use vector methods to find the distance from a point to a plane.

11. Prove that $(a \times b) \times (c \times d) = (a \cdot (b \times c))c - (a \cdot (b \times c))d$.

12. Prove that $(a \times b) \cdot (c \times d) = (a \cdot c)(b \cdot d) - (b \cdot c)(a \cdot d)$.

13. r is the function on $[0, 2\pi]$ into V_3 given by $r(t) = (\cos t, \sin t, 0)$. Sketch the set of points whose coordinates are the range of r.

14. Assuming that component-wise differentiation is valid, find r'. On the diagram of Exercise 13, draw representations of $r'(t)$ with initial point $r(t)$, for $t = 0$, $\pi/2$, π.

15. Find r''. On the diagram of Exercise 13, draw a representation of $r''(t)$ with initial point $r(t)$ for $t = 0$, $\pi/2$, π.

1-7   Applications to Geometry

It is often convenient to use methods of vector algebra in handling geometric problems in a plane or in space. In this section we will consider the use of the algebra of V_2 in proving theorems of elementary plane geometry and the use of the algebra of V_3 in solving geometric problems. To illustrate the methods, we consider two specific situations.

Case 1: A theorem of elementary plane geometry states the medians of a triangle meet at a point which is a point of trisection of each median. We will prove this theorem by using the algebra of V_2.

We begin with the points A, B, and C as the vertices of a triangle. Let $\overrightarrow{CA}$ be a representation of the vector $6\mathbf{a}$ and $\overrightarrow{CB}$ be a representation of the vector $6\mathbf{b}$. Then $\overrightarrow{AB}$ must be a representation of the vector $6\mathbf{b} - 6\mathbf{a}$.

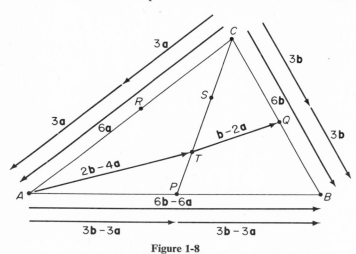

Figure 1-8

Let P, Q, and R be the respective midpoints of the line segments AB, BC, and CA. We have

$\overrightarrow{CR}$ and $\overrightarrow{RA}$ are representations of $3\mathbf{a}$.
$\overrightarrow{CQ}$ and $\overrightarrow{QB}$ are representations of $3\mathbf{b}$.
$\overrightarrow{AP}$ and $\overrightarrow{PB}$ are representations of $3\mathbf{b} - 3\mathbf{a}$.

Draw the median CP. Let S and T be the two trisection points of CP. Since P can be reached from C by the path CAP,

$\overrightarrow{CP}$ is a representation of $6\mathbf{a} + (3\mathbf{b} - 3\mathbf{a}) = 3\mathbf{a} + 3\mathbf{b}$.
$\overrightarrow{CS}$, $\overrightarrow{ST}$, and $\overrightarrow{TP}$ are representations of $\mathbf{a} + \mathbf{b}$.
$\overrightarrow{CT}$ and $\overrightarrow{SP}$ are representations of $2\mathbf{a} + 2\mathbf{b}$.

At this stage one would hope that either S or T would lie on the other medians, AQ and BR. If we consider the line segments AS and SQ, we see (via the path ACS) that

$\overrightarrow{AS}$ is a representation of $-6\mathbf{a} + (\mathbf{a} + \mathbf{b}) = -5\mathbf{a} + \mathbf{b}$

and (via the path SCQ) that

$$\overrightarrow{SQ} \text{ is a representation of } -(a + b) + 3b = -a + 2b.$$

Thus the line segments AS and SQ are not parts of one straight line and we have guessed wrong.

On the other hand, if we examine the line segments AT and TQ, we find (via the path APT) that

$$\overrightarrow{AT} \text{ is a representation of } (3b - 3a) - (a + b) = 2b - 4a$$

and that (via the path TCQ)

$$\overrightarrow{TQ} \text{ is a representation of } -(2a + 2b) + 3b = b - 2a.$$

Since $2b - 4a = 2(b - 2a)$, the line segments AT and TQ are part of one straight line, they do indeed form the median AQ, and T is a trisection point of this median.

Turning now to the third median BR, we find, for the line segment BT (via the path BQT), that

$$\overrightarrow{BT} \text{ is a representation of } -3b - (b - 2a) = 2a - 4b$$

and, for the line segment TR (via the path TAR), that

$$\overrightarrow{TR} \text{ is a representation of } -(2b - 4a) - 3a = a - 2b$$

so that the line segments BT and TR are part of one straight line, they do form the median BR, and also T is a trisection point of this median.

We have thus proved that all three medians of the triangle ABC meet at the point T and that this point T is a trisection point of each median.

Case 2: A theorem of solid geometry says that any two skew lines (lines which neither intersect nor are parallel) have a common perpendicular. We will use vector methods in V_3 to find the length of such a common perpendicular—that is, to find the distance between two skew lines.

We consider the line passing through the points A, with rectangular coordinates $(1, 0, 3)$, and B, with rectangular coordinates $(4, 12, 7)$. If $\overrightarrow{AB}$ is a representation of the vector a, then $a = 3i + 12j + 4k$ and $\|a\| = 13$. We consider also the line through the points C with coordinates $(-3, 1, -1)$ and D with coordinates $(9, 5, 1)$. If $\overrightarrow{CD}$ is a representation of the vector b, then $b = 12i + 4j + 3k$ and $\|b\| = 13$.

Let P be the terminal point of that representation of b which has initial point A. Then P must have coordinates $(13, 4, 6)$. If Q is the terminal point of that representation of a which has initial point P, then Q must have coordinates $(0, 13, 2)$.

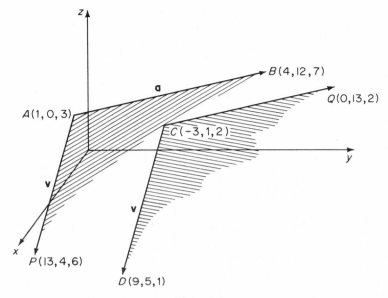

Figure 1-9

The planes ABP and CDQ are parallel to each other. The plane ABP contains the line AB. The plane CDQ contains the line CD. The distance between these planes must then be the length of the common perpendicular between these two skew lines.

Any representation of $\mathbf{a} \times \mathbf{b}$ will be perpendicular to both the planes ABP and CDQ. Thus any directed line segment which joins these two planes and is perpendicular to them must be some scalar multiple of $\mathbf{a} \times \mathbf{b}$. We have

$$\mathbf{a} \times \mathbf{b} = 20\mathbf{i} + 39\mathbf{j} - 132\mathbf{k}; \qquad \|\mathbf{a} \times \mathbf{b}\| = \sqrt{19{,}345}$$

A line segment of length 1, perpendicular to the two planes here, must then be a representation of one of the vectors

$$\pm \frac{1}{\|\mathbf{a} + \mathbf{b}\|} \mathbf{a} \times \mathbf{b} = \pm \frac{1}{\sqrt{19{,}345}} (20\mathbf{i} + 39\mathbf{j} - 132\mathbf{k})$$

The line segment AC joins the two planes but is not perpendicular to them. If $\overrightarrow{AC}$ is a representation of the vector $\mathbf{c}$, then $\mathbf{c} = -3\mathbf{i} + \mathbf{j} - 5\mathbf{k}$; $\|\mathbf{c}\| = \sqrt{35}$.

If θ is the angle between a line through A, perpendicular to the plane CDQ and the line segment AC, then θ is also the angle between the vector $\mathbf{c}$ and one of the vectors $\pm(1/\|\mathbf{a} \times \mathbf{b}\|)\mathbf{a} \times \mathbf{b}$. Thus the distance between these two planes, which is the length of the line segment drawn from A to the plane CDQ, must be

$$(\text{Length of } AC) \cos\theta = \|\mathbf{c}\| \, |\cos\theta|$$

$$= (1) \, \|\mathbf{c}\| \, |\cos\theta|$$

$$= \left| \mathbf{c} \cdot \frac{1}{\|\mathbf{a} \times \mathbf{b}\|} \, \mathbf{a} \times \mathbf{b} \right|$$

$$= \frac{1}{\sqrt{19{,}345}} \, |(20\mathbf{i} + 39\mathbf{j} - 132\mathbf{k}) \cdot (-3\mathbf{i} + \mathbf{j} - 5\mathbf{k})|$$

$$= \frac{639}{\sqrt{19{,}345}}$$

EXERCISES

Use vector methods in V_2 to prove the following theorems of plane geometry.

1. The diagonals of a parallelogram bisect each other.

2. The midpoint of the line joining the midpoints of two opposite sides of a quadrilateral is also the midpoint of the line segment joining the midpoints of the two sides.

3. The lines perpendicular to the midpoints of each side of a triangle meet in a point.

4. The side AB of a triangle ABC is extended to the point P. A line through P intersects BC at Q and AC at R. Then

$$\left(\frac{\text{length } AR}{\text{length } AC}\right)\left(\frac{\text{length } BQ}{\text{length } BC}\right)\left(\frac{\text{length } AP}{\text{length } AB}\right) = 1$$

5. The lines from each vertex of a triangle, perpendicular to the opposite side, meet in a point.

6. The sum of the squares of the lengths of the diagonals of a parallelogram is equal to the sum of the squares of the lengths of the sides.

Use vector methods in V_3 for the following:

7. Find the distance from the point with coordinates $(0, 1, 2)$ to the line passing through the points with coordinates $(-2, 1, 4)$ and $(3, 0, 0)$.

8. Generalize the result of Exercise 7 to find the distance from any point to any line.

9. Find the distance between the point with coordinates $(2, -1, 0)$ and the plane determined by the points with coordinates $(3, 0, 1)$, $(0, 0, 0)$, and $(0, -1, 3)$.

10. Generalize the result of Exercise 9 to find the distance from any point to any plane.

11. Find the distance between the line passing through the points with coordinates $(1, 2, 3)$ and $(-1, -1, 0)$ and the line passing through the points with coordinates $(0, 0, 0)$ and $(2, 0, 1)$.

12. Generalize the result of Exercise 11 to find the distance between any two skew lines.

CURVES AND SURFACES 2

2-1 Continuous Functions

Although we defer a thorough discussion of continuity to Chapter 6, we will consider here those particular aspects of the subject which are needed in treating curves and surfaces. We begin with a consideration of functions on intervals of real numbers into the vector space $\mathbf{V_n}$.

Definition 2-1-1. $\mathbf{F}$ is a function on the closed interval $[a, b]$ into $\mathbf{V_n}$. $c \in \,]a, b[$. $\lim_{t \to c} \mathbf{F}(t) = \mathbf{v}$ means that for every $\epsilon > 0$ there exists $\delta > 0$ such that if $0 < |t - c| < \delta$, then $\|\mathbf{F}(t) - \mathbf{v}\| < \epsilon$.

Definition 2-1-2. $\mathbf{F}$ is a function on the closed interval $[a, b]$ into $\mathbf{V_n}$. $\lim_{t \to a+} \mathbf{F}(t) = \mathbf{u}$ means that for every $\epsilon > 0$ there exists $\delta > 0$ such that if $a < t < a + \delta$, then $\|\mathbf{F}(t) - \mathbf{u}\| < \epsilon$.

Definition 2-1-3. $\mathbf{F}$ is a function on the closed interval $[a, b]$ into $\mathbf{V_n}$. $\lim_{t \to b-} \mathbf{F}(t) = \mathbf{w}$ means that for every $\epsilon > 0$ there exists $\delta > 0$ such that if $b - \delta < t < b$, then $\|\mathbf{F}(t) - \mathbf{w}\| < \epsilon$.

We combine these concepts of limit and one-sided limit to form

Definition 2-1-4. $\mathbf{F}$ is a function on the closed interval $[a, b]$ into $\mathbf{V_n}$. $\mathbf{F}$ is *continuous* provided that

(i) For all $c \in \,]a, b[$, $\lim_{t \to c} \mathbf{F}(t) = \mathbf{F}(c)$.

(ii) $\lim_{t \to a+} \mathbf{F}(t) = \mathbf{F}(a)$.

(iii) $\lim_{t \to b-} \mathbf{F}(t) = \mathbf{F}(b)$.

Dropping requirement (ii) above gives a definition for a continuous function on $]a, b]$. Dropping (iii) gives a definition for a continuous function on $[a, b[$. Dropping both (ii) and (iii) provides us with a definition for a continuous function on $]a, b[$. We now give

> **Definition 2-1-5.** A *curve* in $\mathbf{V_n}$ is a continuous function on an interval of real numbers into $\mathbf{V_n}$. The range of such a function is called the *path* of the curve.

EXAMPLE. The helix which spirals along a circular cylinder of unit radius whose axis is the z axis is the function given by the equation

$$\mathbf{r}(t) = \cos t\mathbf{i} + \sin t\mathbf{j} + t\mathbf{k}$$

The path of this helix then consists of those points whose rectangular coordinates have the form $(\cos t, \sin t, t)$.

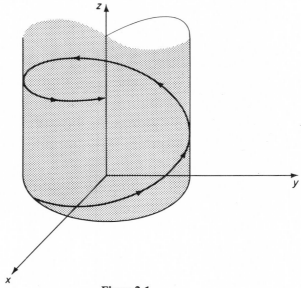

Figure 2-1

In order to discuss surfaces, we need the following concept about sets in the plane:

> **Definition 2-1-6.** A set in the plane is called *connected* provided every pair of points in this set can be joined by the path of a curve and this path lies entirely within the set.

EXAMPLE. The portion of the plane inside any circle is connected. The set consisting of the union of two nonintersecting discs is not connected.

For any set in the plane, connected or not, we have

Definition 2-1-7. D is a subset of the plane. $\mathbf{F}$ is a function on D into $\mathbf{V_n}$. $\mathbf{L} \in \mathbf{V_n}$. $\mathbf{a} \in D$.

$$\lim_{\substack{\mathbf{v} \to \mathbf{a} \\ \mathbf{v} \in D}} \mathbf{F}(\mathbf{v}) = \mathbf{L}$$

means that for every $\epsilon > 0$ there exists $\delta > 0$ such that if $0 < \|\mathbf{v} - \mathbf{a}\| < \delta$ and $\mathbf{v} \in D$, then $\|\mathbf{F}(\mathbf{v}) - \mathbf{L}\| < \epsilon$.

This definition of a restricted form of limit allows us to construct

Definition 2-1-8. D is a subset of the plane. $\mathbf{F}$ is a function on D into $\mathbf{V_n}$. $\mathbf{F}$ is *continuous* provided that, for all $\mathbf{a} \in D$,

$$\lim_{\substack{\mathbf{v} \to \mathbf{a} \\ \mathbf{v} \in D}} \mathbf{F}(\mathbf{v}) = \mathbf{F}(\mathbf{a})$$

We may now combine this kind of continuity with the concept of connectedness to produce

Definition 2-1-9. A *surface* in $\mathbf{V_3}$ is a continuous function on a connected set in the plane into $\mathbf{V_3}$. The range of such a function is called the *trace* of the surface.

EXAMPLE. The top half of a sphere of unit radius, centered at the origin, is the surface given by

$$\mathbf{r}(x, y) = x\mathbf{i} + y\mathbf{j} + \sqrt{1 - x^2 - y^2}\,\mathbf{k}$$

the domain being $\{(x, y) \mid x^2 + y^2 \leq 1\}$.

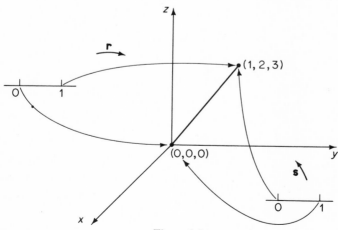

Figure 2-2

It should be noted that curves and surfaces are functions and thus are not completely determined if we know only the set of points which is the range of the function. It may well happen that many different curves will have the same path or that many different surfaces will have the same trace. For example, the line segment in V_3 joining the points with coordinates $(0, 0, 0)$ and $(1, 2, 3)$ is the path of the curve given by

$$\mathbf{r}(t) = t\mathbf{i} + 2t\mathbf{j} + 3t\mathbf{k}, \qquad 0 \le t \le 1$$

and is also the path of the curve given by

$$\mathbf{s}(t) = (1 - t)\mathbf{i} + (2 - 2t)\mathbf{j} + (3 - 3t)\mathbf{k}, \qquad 0 \le t \le 1$$

The example given of a surface, the surface whose trace is the "top" half of the unit sphere, is merely one surface whose trace is this set of points. Another would be the surface given by

$$\mathbf{s}(\theta, \varphi) = \cos \theta \sin \varphi \mathbf{i} + \sin \theta \sin \varphi \mathbf{j} + \cos \varphi \mathbf{k}$$

with domain

$$\left\{ (\theta, \varphi) \,\middle|\, 0 \le \theta \le 2\pi, 0 \le \varphi \le \frac{\pi}{2} \right\}$$

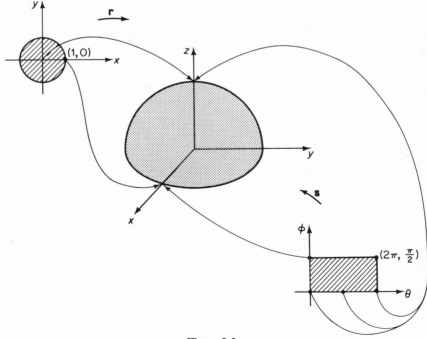

Figure 2-3

EXERCISES

1. Show that if **F** is a function on the connected set D in the plane into V_2, then the range of **F** is also connected.

2. Find a curve whose path is a circle in V_3 which lies in a plane parallel to the x-y coordinate plane.

3. Generalize Exercise 2 to find a curve whose path is any given circle in V_3.

4. Find a curve whose path is the line segment joining the points $(2, 0, 1)$ and $(0, 1, 3)$.

5. Generalize Exercise 4 to find a curve whose path is the line segment joining any two given points. Find a second curve with the same path.

6. Find a surface whose trace is the top face of a rectangular parallelepiped with edges parallel to the coordinate axes, one corner at $(0, 0, 0)$ and the opposite corner at (a, b, c).

7. Generalize Exercise 6 to find a surface whose trace is a given rectangular parallelepiped with edges parallel to the coordinate axes.

8. Find a surface whose trace is the sphere centered at the origin of unit radius.

9. Generalize Exercise 8 to find a surface whose trace is any given sphere.

10. Show that a rectangle in the plane is connected.

11. What is needed to show that, given the trace of any surface, there is another surface with the same trace whose domain is a rectangle?

2-2 Differentiable Curves

In this section we examine the relation between the derivatives of a function and certain geometric aspects of a curve. Since a curve is a continuous function on an interval into V_3, we need a definition for the derivative of such a function:

Definition 2-2-1. **r** is a function on $[a, b]$ into V_3. $c \in]a, b[$. **r** is *differentiable* at c provided that

$$\lim_{h \to 0} \frac{1}{h} [\mathbf{r}(c + h) - \mathbf{r}(c)]$$

exists. The *derivative* of **r**, denoted by **r**′, is the function given by this limit.

EXAMPLE. If **r** is the function on [0, 1] into V_3 given by

$$\mathbf{r}(t) = \cos t\mathbf{i} + \sin t\mathbf{j} + t\mathbf{k}$$

then **r′** is given by

$$\mathbf{r}'(t) = \lim_{h \to 0} \frac{1}{h} [\cos (t + h)\mathbf{i} + \sin (t + h)\mathbf{j} + (t + h)\mathbf{k}$$
$$- \cos t\mathbf{i} - \sin t\mathbf{j} - t\mathbf{k}]$$

$$= \left[\lim_{h \to 0} \frac{\cos (t + h) - \cos t}{h}\right]\mathbf{i}$$

$$+ \left[\lim_{h \to 0} \frac{\sin (t + h) - \sin t}{h}\right]\mathbf{j}$$

$$+ \left[\lim_{h \to 0} \frac{t + h - t}{h}\right]\mathbf{k}$$

But each of the limits in this last expression is exactly that limit of the difference quotient which occurs in the definition of derivative for the elementary functions, so that

$$\mathbf{r}'(t) = (-\sin t)\mathbf{i} + \cos t\mathbf{j} + (1)\mathbf{k}$$

We will use the usual notation for successive derivatives of curves, writing **r′**, **r″**, **r‴**, etc.

In this section we consider a "nice" function **r** on the interval [a, b] into V_3—that is, a curve. By "nice" we mean that the function **r** has whatever properties of differentiability we need.

For every number t in the interval [a, b], there will be a representation of the vector **r**(t) whose initial point is the origin and whose terminal point has coordinates **r**(t). This terminal point will be a point on the path of the curve **r**. Let us now fix a number $c \in]a, b[$.

The representations of **r**(c + h) and **r**(c) with the origin as initial point will have terminal points on the path of **r**. Suppose we denote these terminal points by $P(c + h)$ and $P(c)$, respectively. (We assume that h is sufficiently small so that $c + h \in]a, b[$.) The directed line segment $\overrightarrow{P(c)P(c + h)}$ is then a representation of the vector **r**(c + h) − **r**(c). If $h \neq 0$, any representation of the vector

$$\frac{1}{h} [\mathbf{r}(c + h) - \mathbf{r}(c)]$$

with initial point $P(c)$ will lie on the line through $P(c)$ and $P(c + h)$.

The tangent line to the path of the curve **r**, at the point $P(c)$, is defined to be that line through $P(c)$ which contains a representation of the vector **r′**(c), provided that **r′**(c) ≠ **0**.

We make the assumption that, for all $c \in]a, b[$, **r′**(c) ≠ **0** and we construct two new functions. We first define the function ℓ, on $]a, b[$ into the

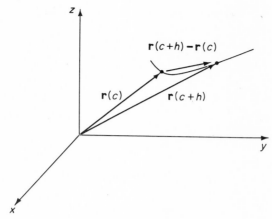

Figure 2-4

real numbers, by specifying that the derivative ℓ' is given by

$$\ell'(t) = \|\mathbf{r}'(t)\|, \quad a < t < b$$

We then have

$$\ell(t) = \int_a^t \|\mathbf{r}'\|, \quad a < t < b$$

It is a simple matter to extend the domain of the function ℓ to include the number a merely by taking $\ell(a) = 0$. As part of the "niceness" of $\mathbf{r}$, we assume that

$$L = \ell(b) = \int_a^b \|\mathbf{r}'\|$$

exists. Then ℓ is a function on $[a, b]$ onto $[0, L]$. The number L is defined to be the *length* of the curve $\mathbf{r}$ and, in this case, the curve is called *rectifiable*.

Now, since $\ell'(t) = \|\mathbf{r}'(t)\| > 0$, ℓ is a strictly increasing function. Thus there exists a function ℓ^{-1}, on $[0, L]$ onto $[a, b]$, which is the inverse of ℓ. We construct a new curve $\mathbf{R}$ by $\mathbf{R} = \mathbf{r}(\ell^{-1})$. Then $\mathbf{R}$ is a function on $[0, L]$ into $\mathbf{V}_3$ whose path is exactly the path of $\mathbf{r}$.

We note that

$$\mathbf{R}'(s) = \mathbf{r}'(\ell^{-1}(s))\{\ell^{-1}\}'(s)$$

$$= \mathbf{r}'(\ell^{-1}(s))\frac{1}{\ell'(\ell^{-1}(s))}$$

$$= \mathbf{r}'(\ell^{-1}(s))\frac{1}{\|\mathbf{r}'(\ell^{-1}(s))\|}, \quad \text{since } \ell' = \|\mathbf{r}'\|$$

This means that, for $0 < s < L$,

$$\|\mathbf{R}'(s)\| = 1$$

EXAMPLE

$$\mathbf{r}(t) = \cos t\mathbf{i} + \sin t\mathbf{j} + t\mathbf{k}, \qquad 0 < t < 1$$

$$\mathbf{r}'(t) = -\sin t\mathbf{i} + \cos t\mathbf{j} + \mathbf{k}, \qquad 0 < t < 1$$

$$\ell'(t) = \sqrt{2}, \qquad 0 < t < 1$$

$$\ell(t) = \sqrt{2}\, t, \qquad 0 < t < 1$$

$$\ell^{-1}(s) = \frac{1}{\sqrt{2}}\, s, \qquad 0 < s < \sqrt{2}$$

$$\mathbf{R}(s) = \cos\frac{s}{\sqrt{2}}\mathbf{i} + \sin\frac{s}{\sqrt{2}}\mathbf{j} + \frac{s}{\sqrt{2}}\mathbf{k}, \qquad 0 < s < \sqrt{2}$$

$$\mathbf{R}'(s) = \frac{1}{\sqrt{2}}\left[-\sin\frac{s}{\sqrt{2}}\mathbf{i} + \cos\frac{s}{\sqrt{2}}\mathbf{j} + \mathbf{k}\right], \qquad 0 < s < \sqrt{2}$$

$$\|\mathbf{R}'(s)\| = 1, \qquad 0 < s < \sqrt{2}$$

In order to differentiate specific curves (that is, functions into $\mathbf{V}_3$), we need theorems concerning the derivatives of vector-algebraic combinations of such functions. The theorems are analogous to the theorems for elementary functions and their proofs are similar. We state these results in

Theorem 2-2-1. $\mathbf{u}$ and $\mathbf{v}$ are functions on a set of real numbers into $\mathbf{V}_3$. f is a function on the same set of real numbers into the real numbers. If $\mathbf{u}$, $\mathbf{v}$, and f are differentiable at c, then

  (i) $\mathbf{u} + \mathbf{v}$ is differentiable at c and $\{\mathbf{u} + \mathbf{v}\}'(c) = \mathbf{u}'(c) + \mathbf{v}'(c)$.
 (ii) $f\mathbf{u}$ is differentiable at c and $\{f\mathbf{u}\}'(c) = f'(c)\mathbf{u}(c) + f(c)\mathbf{u}'(c)$.
(iii) $\mathbf{u} \cdot \mathbf{v}$ is differentiable at c and $\{\mathbf{u} \cdot \mathbf{v}\}'(c) = \mathbf{u}'(c) \cdot \mathbf{v}'(c) + \mathbf{u}(c) \cdot \mathbf{v}'(c)$.
 (iv) $\mathbf{u} \times \mathbf{v}$ is differentiable at c and $\{\mathbf{u} \times \mathbf{v}\}'(c) = \mathbf{u}'(c) \times \mathbf{v}(c)$
      $+ \mathbf{u}(c) \times \mathbf{v}'(c)$.

One theorem of immediate use for our function $\mathbf{R}$ is

Theorem 2-2-2. If $\mathbf{u}$ is a differentiable function on $]a, b[$ such that, for $a < t < b$, $\|\mathbf{u}(t)\| = 1$, then, for $a < t < b$, $\mathbf{u}(t) \cdot \mathbf{u}'(t) = 0$.

Proof. If $a < t < b$, then $\|\mathbf{u}(t)\|^2 = \mathbf{u}(t) \cdot \mathbf{u}(t) = 1$. Thus by property (iii) of Theorem 2-2-1,

$$\mathbf{u}'(t) \cdot \mathbf{u}(t) + \mathbf{u}(t) \cdot \mathbf{u}'(t) = 0$$

$$2\mathbf{u}(t) \cdot \mathbf{u}'(t) = 0$$

$$\mathbf{u}(t) \cdot \mathbf{u}'(t) = 0 \qquad\qquad \blacksquare$$

Applying this theorem to the curve $\mathbf{R}$ yields the result that

$$\mathbf{R}''(s) \cdot \mathbf{R}'(s) = 0 \qquad \text{for } 0 < s < L$$

Since $\mathbf{R}'(s)$ never has the value $\mathbf{0}$, if we assume that $\mathbf{R}''(s)$ never has the value $\mathbf{0}$, we may conclude

1. The representation of $\mathbf{R}'(s)$ with initial point $P(\ell^{-1}(s))$ is tangent to the path of $\mathbf{R}$.

2. The representation of $\mathbf{R}''(s)$ with initial point $P(\ell^{-1}(s))$ is perpendicular to that tangent.

We introduce the notation $\mathbf{T} = \mathbf{R}'$ and call the function $\mathbf{T}$ the unit tangent vector function of the curve $\mathbf{r}$. Then $\mathbf{R}'' = \mathbf{T}'$.

Although $\|\mathbf{T}\|$ is a constant function, $\|\mathbf{T}'\|$ need not be a constant function. We have assumed that $\mathbf{T}'$ is never $\mathbf{0}$. We can now construct two new functions. First we let κ be the function on $]0, L[$ into the non-negative real numbers given by

$$\kappa(s) = \|\mathbf{T}'(s)\|, \qquad 0 < s < L$$

and then, under the assumption that κ never has the value 0, we let $\mathbf{N}$ be the function on $]0, L[$ into $\mathbf{V}_3$ given by

$$\mathbf{N}(s) = \frac{1}{\kappa(s)} \mathbf{T}'(s), \qquad 0 < s < L$$

The function κ is called the curvature function of the curve $\mathbf{r}$, and the function $\mathbf{N}$ is called the unit principal normal vector function of the curve $\mathbf{r}$.

For the example above we have

$$\mathbf{T}(s) = \frac{1}{\sqrt{2}} \left[-\sin \frac{s}{\sqrt{2}} \mathbf{i} + \cos \frac{s}{\sqrt{2}} \mathbf{j} + \mathbf{k} \right], \qquad 0 < s < \sqrt{2}$$

$$\mathbf{T}'(s) = \frac{1}{2} \left[-\cos \frac{s}{\sqrt{2}} \mathbf{i} - \sin \frac{s}{\sqrt{2}} \mathbf{j} \right], \qquad 0 < s < \sqrt{2}$$

$$\kappa(s) = \frac{1}{2}, \qquad 0 < s < \sqrt{2}$$

$$\mathbf{N}(s) = -\cos \frac{s}{\sqrt{2}} \mathbf{i} - \sin \frac{s}{\sqrt{2}} \mathbf{j}, \qquad 0 < s < \sqrt{2}$$

We note that, given the tangent to the path of $\mathbf{r}$ at a particular point $P(\ell^{-1}(s))$, there are many lines in space which are perpendicular to this tangent line at this point. We have singled out that particular one which contains a representation of $\mathbf{N}(s)$ and called it the principal normal to the path of $\mathbf{r}$. We now proceed to single out another of those normal lines for particular attention.

We have, for $0 < s < L$,

$$\mathbf{N}(s) \cdot \mathbf{T}(s) = 0$$

Differentiation yields

$$\mathbf{N}'(s) \cdot \mathbf{T}(s) + \mathbf{N}(s) \cdot \mathbf{T}'(s) = 0$$

But $\mathbf{T}'(s) = \kappa(s)\mathbf{N}(s)$ so that

$$\mathbf{N}'(s) \cdot \mathbf{T}(s) + \mathbf{N}(s) \cdot [\kappa(s)\mathbf{N}(s)] = 0$$
$$\mathbf{N}'(s) \cdot \mathbf{T}(s) + \kappa(s) = 0 \qquad \text{since } \|\mathbf{N}(s)\| = 1$$
$$\mathbf{N}'(s) \cdot \mathbf{T}(s) + \kappa(s)[\mathbf{T}(s) \cdot \mathbf{T}(s)] = 0 \qquad \text{since } \|\mathbf{T}(s)\| = 1$$
$$[\mathbf{N}'(s) + \kappa(s)\mathbf{T}(s)] \cdot \mathbf{T}(s) = 0$$

We now make the assumption that $\kappa(s)\mathbf{T}(s) + \mathbf{N}'(s)$ is never $\mathbf{0}$ and we construct two new functions. First we let τ be that function on $]0, L[$ into the non-negative real numbers given by

$$\tau(s) = \|\kappa(s)\mathbf{T}(s) + \mathbf{N}'(s)\|, \qquad 0 < s < L$$

and then let $\mathbf{B}$ be that function on $]0, L[$ into $\mathbf{V}_3$ given by

$$\mathbf{B}(s) = \frac{1}{\tau(s)} [\kappa(s)\mathbf{T}(s) + \mathbf{N}'(s)], \qquad 0 < s < L$$

The function τ is called the *torsion* function for the curve $\mathbf{r}$ and the function $\mathbf{B}$ is called the unit binormal vector function for the curve $\mathbf{r}$. Since the representation of $\mathbf{B}(s)$ with initial point $P(\ell^{-1}(s))$ is perpendicular to the tangent to the path of $\mathbf{r}$, we have thus singled out this particular normal line and called it the binormal. We then have immediately that $\mathbf{N}' = -\kappa\mathbf{T} + \tau\mathbf{B}$ and $\mathbf{B} \cdot \mathbf{T}$ is the constant zero function.

We note further that, for $0 < s < L$,

$$\mathbf{B}(s) \cdot \mathbf{N}(s) = \frac{1}{\tau(s)} [\kappa(s)\mathbf{T}(s) + \mathbf{N}'(s)] \cdot \mathbf{N}(s)$$
$$= 0, \qquad \text{since } \mathbf{T} \cdot \mathbf{N} = 0 \quad \text{and} \quad \mathbf{N}' \cdot \mathbf{N} = 0$$

Thus the vectors $\mathbf{T}(s)$, $\mathbf{N}(s)$, and $\mathbf{B}(s)$ are mutually orthogonal and each has length 1. Since the dimension of $\mathbf{V}_3$ is three, any nonzero vector which is orthogonal to two of these must be a scalar multiple of the third.

We know, since $\|\mathbf{B}\|$ is a constant function, that $\mathbf{B}'(s) \cdot \mathbf{B}(s) = 0$. We also have

$$\mathbf{B}(s) \cdot \mathbf{T}(s) = 0$$

Differentiation yields

$$\mathbf{B}'(s) \cdot \mathbf{T}(s) + \mathbf{B}(s) \cdot \mathbf{T}'(s) = 0$$
$$\mathbf{B}'(s) \cdot \mathbf{T}(s) + \mathbf{B}(s) \cdot [\kappa(s)\mathbf{N}(s)] = 0$$
$$\mathbf{B}'(s) \cdot \mathbf{T}(s) = 0 \qquad \text{since} \quad \mathbf{B}(s) \cdot \mathbf{N}(s) = 0$$

The assumption that $\mathbf{B}'(s)$ is never $\mathbf{0}$ then yields $\mathbf{B}'(s)$ as orthogonal to both $\mathbf{B}(s)$ and $\mathbf{T}(s)$. There must then be a number $f(s)$ such that

$$\mathbf{B}'(s) = f(s)\mathbf{N}(s)$$

We also know that, for $0 < s < L$,

$$\mathbf{B}(s) \cdot \mathbf{N}(s) = 0$$

Differentiation yields

$$\mathbf{B}'(s) \cdot \mathbf{N}(s) + \mathbf{B}(s) \cdot \mathbf{N}'(s) = 0$$
$$[f(s)\mathbf{N}(s)] \cdot \mathbf{N}(s) + \mathbf{B}(s) \cdot [\tau(s)\mathbf{B}(s) - \kappa(s)\mathbf{T}(s)] = 0$$
$$f(s) + \tau(s) = 0, \quad \text{since} \quad \mathbf{N}(s) \cdot \mathbf{N}(s) = \mathbf{B}(s) \cdot \mathbf{B}(s) = 1$$
$$\text{and} \quad \mathbf{B}(s) \cdot \mathbf{T}(s) = 0$$

We can then conclude that, for $0 < s < L$,

$$\mathbf{B}'(s) = -\tau(s)\mathbf{N}(s)$$

The relations we have found between these vector functions,

$$\mathbf{T}' = \kappa\mathbf{N}$$
$$\mathbf{N}' = -\kappa\mathbf{T} + \tau\mathbf{B}$$
$$\mathbf{B}' = -\tau\mathbf{N}$$

are known as the Frenet-Serret formulas.

Finally we note that since

$$\|\mathbf{B}(s)\| = \|\mathbf{N}(s)\| = \|\mathbf{T}(s)\| = 1$$

and

$$\mathbf{B}(s) \cdot \mathbf{T}(s) = \mathbf{B}(s) \cdot \mathbf{N}(s) = \mathbf{N}(s) \cdot \mathbf{T}(s) = 0$$

we must have

$$\mathbf{B} = \pm\mathbf{T} \times \mathbf{N}$$

Either choice of sign is consistent with the Frenet-Serret formulas and we can find examples for which either holds.

EXERCISES

1. If $\mathbf{u}$ is a function on $]a, b[$ into V_3 and $c \in]a, b[$, give a definition for $\lim_{t \to c} \mathbf{u}(t) = \mathbf{L}$.

2. Prove that if $\lim_{t \to c} \mathbf{u}(t) = \mathbf{L}$ and $\lim_{t \to c} \mathbf{v}(t) = \mathbf{M}$, then $\lim_{t \to c} \{\mathbf{u} \times \mathbf{v}\}(t) = \mathbf{L} \times \mathbf{M}$.

3. Assuming the appropriate limit theorems, prove that if $\mathbf{u}$ and $\mathbf{v}$ are functions on $]a, b[$ into V_3, then $\mathbf{u}' \times \mathbf{v} + \mathbf{u} \times \mathbf{v}' \subseteq \{\mathbf{u} \times \mathbf{v}\}'$.

4. If $\mathbf{u}$ and $\mathbf{v}$ are functions on an interval into V_3 and $\mathbf{a} \in V_3$ such that $\mathbf{u}' = \mathbf{a} \times \mathbf{u}$ and $\mathbf{v}' = \mathbf{a} \times \mathbf{v}$, prove that $\{\mathbf{u} \times \mathbf{v}\}' = \mathbf{a} \times (\mathbf{u} \times \mathbf{v})$.

5. If $\mathbf{a}$ and $\mathbf{b}$ are vectors of V_3, find a general solution to the differential equation $\mathbf{u}''(t) = \mathbf{a}t \times \mathbf{b}$.

6. If **u** is a function on $]a, b[$ into $\mathbf{V_3}$ which never has the value **0** and if $\mathbf{v} = (1/\|\mathbf{u}\|)\mathbf{u}$, find $\mathbf{v}'$ in terms of **u** and $\mathbf{u}'$ (note that $\|\mathbf{u}\|^2 = \mathbf{u} \cdot \mathbf{u}$).

7. The plane curve **r** is the function on $]a, b[$ into $\mathbf{V_3}$ given by $\mathbf{r}(t) = x(t)\mathbf{i} + y(t)\mathbf{j}$. Find the curvature in terms of the functions x and y.

8. The curve **r** is given by

$$\mathbf{r}(t) = a \cos t\mathbf{i} + a \sin t\mathbf{j} + bt\mathbf{k}.$$

Find the functions **T**, **N**, **B**, κ, and τ for **r**.

9. Show that if the curve **r** is given by

$$\mathbf{r}(t) = x(t)\mathbf{i} + y(t)\mathbf{j}$$

then $\tau(t) = 0$.

10. For a curve **r**, prove that

$$\mathbf{r}' \cdot (\mathbf{r}'' \times \mathbf{r}''') = \pm\kappa^2\tau, \quad \text{where } r' \text{ indicates } \left(\frac{d}{ds}\right)\mathbf{r}$$

11. Generalize Theorem 2-2-2 to $\mathbf{V_n}$.

12. Generalize the Frenet-Serret formulas to $\mathbf{V_n}$ by using $n - 1$ "curvatures" $\kappa_1, \kappa_2, \ldots, \kappa_{n-1}$.

2-3 Differentiability

We know that a surface is a continuous function whose domain is a connected two-dimensional set and whose range is a subset of $\mathbf{V_3}$. In order to examine various surfaces by using the ideas of differentiation, we need a preliminary look at the concept of differentiation for such functions. This section is devoted to such an examination.

We first consider the familiar situation of an elementary function and allow the concept of the derivative of such a function to lead us to a definition of differentiability for functions whose domains are sets of dimension exceeding unity.

Let us examine two functions f and g on the interval $[-1, 1]$ into the real numbers. We suppose that

$$f(x) = x^{1/3} + x, \quad -1 \leq x \leq 1$$

and

$$g(x) = x^{5/3} + x, \quad -1 \leq x \leq 1$$

From elementary calculus we see that the derivatives are given by

$$f'(x) = \tfrac{1}{3}x^{-2/3} + 1, \quad -1 < x < 0 \quad \text{and} \quad 0 < x < 1$$
$$g'(x) = \tfrac{5}{3}x^{2/3} + 1, \quad -1 < x < 1$$

We note particularly that g is differentiable at 0, whereas f is not differentiable at 0. Using the definition of derivative, we have

and

$$f'(x) = \lim_{h \to 0} \frac{f(x+h) - f(x)}{h}$$

$$g'(x) = \lim_{h \to 0} \frac{g(x+h) - g(x)}{h}$$

An examination of the numerators in each of these difference quotients will reveal to us exactly how the behavior of each function at 0 occurs. We have

$$f(0+h) - f(0) = h^{1/3} + h = (1)h + h(h^{-2/3})$$
$$g(0+h) - g(0) = h^{5/3} + h = (1)h + h(h^{2/3})$$

Thus

$$\frac{f(0+h) - f(0)}{h} = 1 + h^{-2/3}$$

$$\frac{g(0+h) - g(0)}{h} = 1 + h^{2/3}$$

We see that f is not differentiable at 0 because $\lim_{h \to 0} h^{-2/3}$ does not exist and g is differentiable at 0 because $\lim_{h \to 0} h^{2/3}$ does exist.

We may rewrite the two numerators by giving

$$f(0+h) - f(0) = (1)h + h\eta_f(h)$$
$$g(0+h) - g(0) = (1)h + h\eta_g(h)$$

where

$$\eta_f(h) = h^{-2/3} \quad \text{and} \quad \eta_g(h) = h^{2/3}$$

We have noted that g is differentiable at 0 and $\lim_{h \to 0} \eta_g(h) = 0$ and that f is not differentiable at 0 and $\lim_{h \to 0} \eta_f(h)$ does not exist.

In each of these cases we have expressed the difference of values of the function as the sum of two numbers: The first is the value of a linear function without constant term and the second is the product of the values of the identity function with the value of a function we have denoted by η. We use this form of the numerator of the difference quotient to suggest a definition of differentiability for a function whose domain is a subset of $\mathbf{V}_n$ where $n \geq 2$.

Definition 2-3-1. $D \subseteq \mathbf{V}_n$. f is a function on D into the real numbers. $\mathbf{a} \in D$. f is *differentiable at* $\mathbf{a}$ provided there exists $\mathbf{A} \in \mathbf{V}_n$, there exists $\delta > 0$, and there exists a function η_f on $\{\mathbf{h} \mid \|\mathbf{h}\| < \delta\}$ into the real numbers such that

(i) If $\|\mathbf{h}\| < \delta$, then $f(\mathbf{a} + \mathbf{h}) - f(\mathbf{a}) = \mathbf{h} \cdot \mathbf{A} + \|\mathbf{h}\|\, \eta_f(\mathbf{h})$.
(ii) $\lim_{\mathbf{h} \to 0} \eta_f(\mathbf{h}) = 0$.

In the particular case $n = 2$, we would then have the function f differentiable at $\mathbf{a} = (a_1, a_2)$ provided there exists $\mathbf{A} = (A_1, A_2) \in \mathbf{V_n}$ and there exists $\delta > 0$ and a function η on $\{\mathbf{h} \mid \|\mathbf{h}\| < \delta\}$ into the real numbers such that whenever $\|\mathbf{h}\| < \delta$,

$$f(\mathbf{a} + \mathbf{h}) - f(\mathbf{a}) = f(a_1 + h_1, a_2 + h_2) - f(a_1, a_2)$$
$$= \mathbf{h} \cdot \mathbf{A} + \|\mathbf{h}\| \, \eta(\mathbf{h})$$
$$= h_1 A_1 + h_2 A_2 + \sqrt{h_1^2 + h_2^2} \, \eta(h_1, h_2)$$

We note also that in this case when $h_2 = 0$ but $h_1 \neq 0$, we have

$$f(a_1 + h_1, a_2) - f(a_1, a_2) = h_1 A_1 + |h_1| \, \eta(h_1, 0)$$
$$\frac{f(a_1 + h_1, a_2) - f(a_1, a_2)}{h_1} = A_1 + \frac{|h_1|}{h_1} \eta(h_1, 0)$$

On the other hand, when $h_1 = 0$ but $h_2 \neq 0$, we have

$$f(a_1, a_2 + h_2) - f(a_1, a_2) = h_2 A_2 + |h_2| \, \eta(0, h_2)$$
$$\frac{f(a_1, a_2 + h_2) - f(a_1, a_2)}{h_2} = A_2 + \frac{|h_2|}{h_2} \eta(0, h_2)$$

If f is differentiable at $\mathbf{a} = (a_1, a_2)$, then we see that

$$\lim_{h_1 \to 0} \frac{f(a_1 + h_1, a_2) - f(a_1, a_2)}{h_1}$$

exists and is A_1 and also that

$$\lim_{h_2 \to 0} \frac{f(a_1, a_2 + h_2) - f(a_1, a_2)}{h_2}$$

exists and is A_2.

The two limits are used to define the partial derivatives of the function f. For the general case we have

Definition 2-3-2. $D \subseteq \mathbf{V_n}$. f is a function on D into the real numbers. For $k = 1, 2, \ldots, n$, f_k, the *partial derivative of f with respect to the kth component*, is defined to be the function given by

$$f_k(a_1, a_2, \ldots, a_n) = \lim_{h \to 0} \frac{f(\mathbf{a} + h\mathbf{e}_k) - f(\mathbf{a})}{h}$$

where $\mathbf{e}_k$ is that particular unit vector of $\mathbf{V_n}$ whose kth component is 1 and whose remaining components are 0.

EXAMPLE. Let f be the function on $\mathbf{V_3}$ given by

$$f(x, y, z) = x^3 y + 2yz - z^2 x$$

Then

$$f_1(x, y, z) = \lim_{h \to 0} \frac{f(x + h, y, z) - f(x, y, z)}{h}$$

$$= y \lim_{h \to 0} \frac{(x + h)^3 - x^3}{h} - z^2 \lim_{h \to 0} \frac{(x + h) - x}{h}$$

$$= 3x^2 y - z^2$$

$$f_2(x, y, z) = x^3 + 2z$$

$$f_3(x, y, z) = 2y - 2xz$$

With these definitions of differentiability and of the partial derivatives it is easy to prove

Theorem 2-3-1. $D \subseteq \mathbf{V}_n$. f is a function on D into the real numbers. $\mathbf{a} \in D$. If f is differentiable at $\mathbf{a}$, then, for $k = 1, 2, \ldots, n, f_k(\mathbf{a})$ exists.

We will use a notation of multiple subscripts to denote partial derivatives of higher order. In this manner of writing, the order of the subscripts is of significance. If f is a function on $\mathbf{V}_2$, then f_1 is the partial derivative of f with respect to the first component. $f_{1,2}$ is the partial derivative of f_1 with respect to the second component. $f_{2,1}$ is the partial derivative of f_2 with respect to the first component. A theorem which relates these two second-order partial derivatives is

Theorem 2-3-2. $D \subseteq \mathbf{V}_2$. f is a function on D into the real numbers. $\mathbf{a} = (p, q)$ is an interior point of D. If $f, f_1, f_2, f_{1,2}$, and $f_{2,1}$ are continuous at $\mathbf{a}$ and in some neighborhood of $\mathbf{a}$, then $f_{1,2}(\mathbf{a}) = f_{2,1}(\mathbf{a})$.

Proof. Since $\mathbf{a}$ is an interior point of D, there exists $\eta > 0$ such that if $|h| < \eta$, then $(p + h, q + h) \in D$. Thus $\{(p + h, q + h) \,|\, |h| < \eta\}$ is a square neighborhood of $\mathbf{a}$ which lies entirely within D. We consider the function given by

$$g(h) = \frac{1}{h^2} [f(p + h, q + h) - f(p, q + h) - f(p + h, q) + f(p, q)]$$

with $0 < h < \eta$. We may also assume η sufficiently small so that $f, f_1, f_2, f_{1,2}$, and $f_{2,1}$ are continuous at every point of this square neighborhood of (p, q).

We note that the Fundamental Theorem of Calculus tells us that

$$g(h) = \frac{1}{h^2} \left[\int_p^{p+h} f_1(x, q + h) \, dx - \int_p^{p+h} f_1(x, q) \, dx \right]$$

$$= \frac{1}{h^2} \int_p^{p+h} [f_1(x, q + h) - f_1(x, q)] \, dx$$

$$= \frac{1}{h^2} \int_p^{p+h} \left[\int_q^{q+h} f_{1,2}(x, y) \, dy \right] dx$$

Rewriting $g(h)$ yields

$$g(h) = \frac{1}{h^2}\left[f(p+h, q+h) - f(p+h, q) - f(p, q+h) + f(p, q)\right]$$

$$= \frac{1}{h^2}\left[\int_q^{q+h} f_2(p+h, y)\, dy - \int_q^{q+h} f_2(p, y)\, dy\right]$$

$$= \frac{1}{h^2}\int_q^{q+h}\left[f_2(p+h, y) - f_2(p, y)\right] dy$$

$$= \frac{1}{h^2}\int_q^{q+h}\left[\int_p^{p+h} f_{2,1}(x, y)\, dx\right] dy$$

Since $f_{1,2}$ is continuous at (p, q), given $\epsilon > 0$, there exists $\delta > 0$ such that if $|h| < \delta$ and $p < x < p + h$ and $q < y < q + h$, then

$$f_{1,2}(p, q) - \epsilon < f_{1,2}(x, y) < f_{1,2}(p, q) + \epsilon$$

Then, for $0 < h < \delta$, $p < x < p + h$, and $q < y < q + h$, we have

$$h[f_{1,2}(p, q) - \epsilon] < \int_q^{q+h} f_{1,2}(x, y)\, dy < h[f_{1,2}(p, q) + \epsilon]$$

$$h^2[f_{1,2}(p, q) - \epsilon] < \int_p^{p+h}\left[\int_q^{q+h} f_{1,2}(x, y)\, dy\right] dx < h^2[f_{1,2}(p, q) + \epsilon]$$

This means that $|h| < \delta$ implies $|g(h) - f_{1,2}(p, q)| < \epsilon$. Consequently,

$$\lim_{h \to 0} g(h) = f_{1,2}(p, q)$$

In like manner we can show that

$$\lim_{h \to 0} g(h) = f_{2,1}(p, q)$$

∎

We postpone a further discussion of differentiability and partial derivatives until Chapter 7. For the purposes of dealing with surfaces we need only add definitions of differentiability and partial derivatives for functions into $\mathbf{V}_3$. As it happens, it is a simple matter to construct such definitions for functions into $\mathbf{V}_n$ where $n \geq 2$.

Definition 2-3-3. $D \subset \mathbf{V}_m$. $\mathbf{f}$ is a function on D into $\mathbf{V}_n$. For $k = 1, 2, \ldots, n$, $f^{(k)}$, the *kth component function* of $\mathbf{f}$, is that function on D into the real numbers such that, for all $\mathbf{v} \in D$,

$$\mathbf{f}(\mathbf{v}) = (f^{(1)}(\mathbf{v}), f^{(2)}(\mathbf{v}), \ldots, f^{(n)}(\mathbf{v}))$$

EXAMPLE. If $\mathbf{f}$ is that function on $\mathbf{V_2}$ into $\mathbf{V_3}$ given by

$$\mathbf{f}(x, y) = (x, y, x^2 + y^2)$$

then

$$f^{(1)}(x, y) = x$$
$$f^{(2)}(x, y) = y$$
$$f^{(3)}(x, y) = x^2 + y^2$$

In this case the trace of the surface is the paraboloid of revolution attained by revolving the graph of $z = x^2$, $y = 0$ about the z axis.

Definition 2-3-4. $D \subseteq \mathbf{V_m}$. $\mathbf{f}$ is a function on D into $\mathbf{V_n}$. For $k = 1, 2, \ldots, m$, $\mathbf{f}_k$, the partial derivative of $\mathbf{f}$ with respect to the kth component, is the function with component functions given by

$$\mathbf{f}_k = (f_k^{(1)}, f_k^{(2)}, \ldots, f_k^{(n)})$$

We emphasize that, in the scheme of notation being used, superscripts are used to denote component functions and subscripts are used to denote partial derivatives of a function. For the example given above,

$$\mathbf{f}(x, y) = (x, y, x^2 + y^2)$$

we have

$$f_1^{(1)}(x, y) = 1, \qquad f_2^{(1)}(x, y) = 0$$
$$f_1^{(2)}(x, y) = 0, \qquad f_2^{(2)}(x, y) = 1$$
$$f_1^{(3)}(x, y) = 2x, \qquad f_2^{(3)}(x, y) = 2y$$

EXERCISES

1. Prove Theorem 2-3-1.

2. f is the function given by $f(x, y) - \sqrt{x^2 + y^2}$. Find $f_1, f_2, f_{1,1}, f_{1,2}$, and $f_{2,2}$.

3. Repeat Exercise 2 for f given by $f(x, y) = \log(x + y)$.

4. Examine $f_{1,2}(0, 0)$ and $f_{2,1}(0, 0)$ for the function given by

$$f(x, y) = \begin{cases} \dfrac{xy(x^2 - y^2)}{x^2 + y^2} & \text{for} \quad (x, y) \neq (0, 0) \\ 0 & \text{for} \quad (x, y) = (0, 0) \end{cases}$$

In Exercises 5–10, f is a function on $\{(x, y) \mid (x - a)^2 + (y - b)^2 < r^2\}$ into the real numbers with the property that $f_1, f_2, f_{1,1}, f_{1,2}, f_{2,1}$, and $f_{2,2}$ are continuous. p and q are fixed numbers with the property that $p^2 + q^2 < r^2$. φ is the function on $[-1, 1]$ into the real numbers given by

$$\varphi(t) = f(a + tp, b + tq)$$

5. Show that φ is differentiable and that

$$\varphi'(t) = pf_1(a + tp, b + tq) + qf_2(a + tp, b + tq)$$

6. Show that

$$\varphi''(t) = p^2 f_{1,1}(a + tp, b + tq) + 2pq f_{1,2}(a + tp, b + tq) + q^2 f_{2,2}(a + tp, b + tq)$$

7. Prove that if $[f_{1,2}(a, b)]^2 - f_{1,1}(a, b)f_{2,2}(a, b) < 0$, then $\varphi''(0)f_{1,1}(a, b) > 0$. *Suggestion:* Complete the square.

8. Use the mean value theorem to show there exists θ_1, θ_2 with $0 < \theta_1 < 1$, $0 < \theta_2 < 1$ such that

$$\varphi(t) = \varphi(0) + t\varphi'(\theta_1 t) + \theta_1 t \varphi''(\theta_2 t)$$

9. Prove that if $D \subseteq V_2$, (a, b) is an interior point of D; $f, f_1, f_2, f_{1,1}$, $f_{1,2}$, and $f_{2,2}$ are continuous at (a, b); $f_1(a, b) = f_2(a, b) = 0$; $[f_{1,2}(a, b)]^2 - f_{1,1}(a, b)f_{2,2}(a, b) < 0$; and $f_{1,1}(a, b) < 0$; then $f(a, b)$ is a relative maximum value for f.

10. State and prove a theorem analogous to that in Exercise 9 for a relative minimum value of f.

In Exercises 11–14, find all relative extreme values for the functions given by

11. $f(x, y) = x^2 - xy + y^2$

12. $f(x, y) = x^2 - 4xy + y^2$

13. $f(x, y) = \cos x \sinh y$

14. $f(x, y) = \dfrac{y}{x^2 + y^2}$

2-4 Differentiable Surfaces

The definition of the word "surface" requires that a surface be a continuous function on a connected subset of the plane into V_3. In this section we will follow the procedure used in treating curves and consider only "nice" surfaces—those which have whatever properties we need whenever we need them. Our object is to examine relations between geometric properties of the trace of a surface and the behavior of the partial derivatives of that surface.

To simplify matters, initially we suppose that we are dealing with a surface **r** whose domain is a rectangle

$$R = \{(u, v) \mid a < u < b \quad \text{and} \quad c < v < d\}$$

Thus if (p, q) is a fixed point of R, the point with rectangular coordinates $(r^{(1)}(u, v), r^{(2)}(u, v), r^{(3)}(u, v))$ will lie on the trace of the surface **r**.

We now fix a number p in the open interval $]a, b[$ and consider the function $\mathbf{w}_p$ on $]c, d[$ into V_3 given by

$$\mathbf{w}_p(v) = \mathbf{r}(p, v), \qquad c < v < d$$

Since $\mathbf{r}$ is continuous, $\mathbf{w}_p$ must be continuous. This means that $\mathbf{w}_p$ is a curve and clearly the path of the curve $\mathbf{w}_p$ lies on the trace of the surface $\mathbf{r}$. We saw in the preceding section that if $\mathbf{r}$ is differentiable at (p, q), then (p, q) is in the domain of both partial derivatives $\mathbf{r}_1$ and $\mathbf{r}_2$. This means that the curve $\mathbf{w}_p$ is differentiable at q and

$$\mathbf{w}_p'(q) = \mathbf{r}_2(p, q)$$

From our treatment of differentiable curves, we know that if $\mathbf{w}_p(q) \neq \mathbf{0}$, then the representation of this vector with initial point $\mathbf{r}(p, q)$ will be tangent to the path of the curve $\mathbf{w}_q$. In terms of the surface $\mathbf{r}$, if $\mathbf{r}_2(p, q) \neq \mathbf{0}$, then the representation of this vector with initial point $\mathbf{r}(p, q)$ will be tangent to the trace of $\mathbf{r}$.

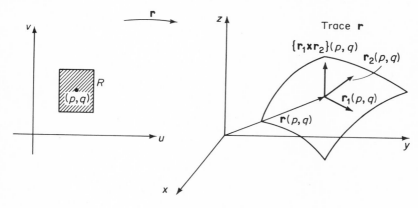

Figure 2-5

In like manner, if $\mathbf{r}_1(p, q) \neq \mathbf{0}$, then the representation of this vector with initial point $\mathbf{r}(p, q)$ will be another tangent to the trace of $\mathbf{r}$. It is possible, of course, that these ostensibly different tangent lines are the same. In order to avoid this possibility, we will take as part of the "niceness" of the function $\mathbf{r}$ that for all points (p, q) of the rectangle R the representations of $\mathbf{r}_1(p, q)$ and $\mathbf{r}_2(p, q)$ with initial point $\mathbf{r}(p, q)$ actually determine a tangent plane to the trace of $\mathbf{r}$. In terms of vector algebra this means that

$$\mathbf{r}_1(p, q) \times \mathbf{r}_2(p, q) \neq \mathbf{0} \qquad \text{for} \quad (p, q) \in R$$

Under this assumption we may now define, for any surface $\mathbf{r}$, a new function on R into V_3, given by

$$\mathbf{n}(u, v) = \frac{1}{\|\mathbf{r}_1(u, v) \times \mathbf{r}_2(u, v)\|} \, \mathbf{r}_1(u, v) \times \mathbf{r}_2(u, v)$$

Since, for all $(u, v) \in R$, $\|\mathbf{n}(u, v)\| = 1$, and the representation of $\mathbf{n}(u, v)$ with initial point $\mathbf{r}(u, v)$ is perpendicular to the tangent plane to the trace of $\mathbf{r}$, we call n the *unit normal vector function* for the surface $\mathbf{r}$.

EXAMPLE. We consider a surface whose trace is the top half of the sphere centered at the origin, with radius 1. This trace is the graph of the rectangular coordinate equation

$$z = \sqrt{1 - x^2 - y^2}, \qquad x^2 + y^2 \leq 1$$

Since we find it convenient to have a rectangular connected subset of the plane, we will consider the trace to be the graph of the cylindrical coordinate equation

$$z = \sqrt{1 - \rho^2}, \qquad 0 \leq \rho \leq 1, \qquad 0 \leq \theta \leq 2\pi$$

We recall the relation between rectangular coordinates (x, y, z) and cylindrical coordinates (ρ, θ, z) is given by

$$x = \rho \cos \theta, \qquad y = \rho \sin \theta$$

We now consider the surface $\mathbf{r}$, given by

$$\mathbf{r}(\rho, \theta) = \rho \cos \theta \mathbf{i} + \rho \sin \theta \mathbf{j} + \sqrt{1 - \rho^2} \, \mathbf{k}$$

where

$$(\rho, \theta) \in R = \{(\rho, \theta) \,|\, 0 \leq \rho \leq 1, 0 \leq \theta \leq 2\pi\}$$

Taking partial derivatives, we have

$$\mathbf{r}_1(\rho, \theta) = \cos \theta \mathbf{i} + \sin \theta \mathbf{j} - \frac{\rho}{\sqrt{1 - \rho^2}} \mathbf{k}$$

$$\mathbf{r}_2(\rho, \theta) = -\rho \sin \theta \mathbf{i} + \rho \cos \theta \mathbf{j}$$

$$\mathbf{r}_1(\rho, \theta) \times \mathbf{r}_2(\rho, \theta) = \frac{\rho}{\sqrt{1 - \rho^2}} \cos \theta \mathbf{i} + \frac{\rho}{\sqrt{1 - \rho^2}} \sin \theta \mathbf{j} + \rho \mathbf{k}$$

$$\|\mathbf{r}_1(\rho, \theta) \times \mathbf{r}_2(\rho, \theta)\| = \frac{\rho}{\sqrt{1 - \rho^2}}$$

$$\mathbf{n}(\rho, \theta) = \rho \cos \theta \mathbf{i} + \rho \sin \theta \mathbf{j} + \sqrt{1 - \rho^2} \, \mathbf{k}$$

For a particular point $(\frac{3}{5}, 0)$ in the domain of these functions, we have

$$\mathbf{r}(\tfrac{3}{5}, 0) = \tfrac{3}{5}\mathbf{i} + \tfrac{4}{5}\mathbf{k}$$
$$\mathbf{n}(\tfrac{3}{5}, 0) = \tfrac{3}{5}\mathbf{i} + \tfrac{4}{5}\mathbf{k}$$

The representation of $\mathbf{n}(\frac{3}{5}, 0)$ with initial point $\mathbf{r}(\frac{3}{5}, 0)$ is then directed away from the interior of the hemisphere.

One of the problems encountered in treating nice surfaces which are closed—that is, whose traces divide space into a bounded and unbounded part—is to be able to decide which of the vector functions $\mathbf{r}_1 \times \mathbf{r}_2$ or $\mathbf{r}_2 \times \mathbf{r}_1$ will have representations which "point outward." For any specific surface with a continuous unit normal vector function, one can decide between these two directions by examining one specific value of $\mathbf{n}$. Since $\|\mathbf{n}\|$ is identically 1, we cannot have a unit normal directed outward at one point and inward at a second without having the function $\mathbf{n}$ discontinuous at some point. Thus we will restrict our attention to surfaces for which $\mathbf{r}_1$ and $\mathbf{r}_2$ are continuous and for which $\mathbf{r}_1$, $\mathbf{r}_2$, and $\mathbf{r}_1 \times \mathbf{r}_2$ never take the value $\mathbf{0}$.

For such surfaces we define the surface area by

Definition 2-4-1. If the surface $\mathbf{r}$ is a continuously differentiable function on the connected subset D of the plane, into V_3, for which $\mathbf{r}_1$, $\mathbf{r}_2$, and $\mathbf{r}_1 \times \mathbf{r}_2$ never take the value $\mathbf{0}$, the *area* $A(\mathbf{r})$ of the surface $\mathbf{r}$ is defined to be the number

$$\iint\limits_{D} \|\mathbf{r}_1 \times \mathbf{r}_2\|$$

EXERCISES

In Exercises 1–4, find outward directed unit normal vector functions for each of the following surfaces.

1. $\mathbf{r}(u, v) = \cos v \cos u\mathbf{i} + \cos v \sin u\mathbf{j} + \sin v\mathbf{k}; \qquad 0 \leq u \leq 2\pi, 0 \leq v \leq \pi$

2. $\mathbf{r}(u, v) = u \cos v\mathbf{i} + u \sin v\mathbf{j} + u^2\mathbf{k}; \qquad 0 \leq u \leq 1, 0 \leq v \leq 2\pi$

3. $\mathbf{r}(u, v) = u\mathbf{i} + v\mathbf{j} + \sqrt{u^2 + v^2}\,\mathbf{k}; \qquad u^2 + v^2 \leq 1$

4. $\mathbf{r}(u, v) = (5 - \cos u) \cos v\mathbf{i} + (5 - \cos u) \sin v\mathbf{j} + \sin v\mathbf{k}; \qquad 0 \leq u \leq 2\pi,$ $0 \leq v \leq \pi$

5. For a, b, and c positive numbers, find a function $\mathbf{r}$ which is a surface whose trace is the rectangular parallelepiped with sides parallel to the coordinate axes and the origin and the point (a, b, c) as opposite vertices.

6. Find a unit normal vector function $\mathbf{n}$ for the surface in Exercise 5 which has representations directed away from the region enclosed by the parallelepiped.

7. Show that the area of a nice surface $\mathbf{r}$ is given by

$$A(\mathbf{r}) = \iint\limits_{D} \sqrt{\|\mathbf{r}_1\|^2 \|\mathbf{r}_2\|^2 - (\mathbf{r}_1 \cdot \mathbf{r}_2)^2}$$

8. Find the areas of the surfaces in Exercises 1, 2, 3, and 5.

9. The boundaries of the state of Wyoming form a "rectangle" on the surface of a sphere. These boundaries are the parallels of latitude 41°N and 45°N and the meridians of longitude 104°W and 111°W. Find the area of Wyoming. (Consider the radius of the earth as 4000 miles.)

10. If the trace of the surface **r** is the graph of the rectangular coordinate equation $z = f(x, y)$, find a unit normal vector function for S. Find an integral giving the area of **r**.

11. Repeat Exercise 10 when the trace is the graph of the rectangular coordinate equation $F(x, y, z) = 0$.

12. Repeat Exercise 10 when the trace is the result of revolving the graph (in the plane) of $y = f(x)$ about the x axis.

LINE AND SURFACE INTEGRALS 3

3-1 Surface Integrals

In this section we will consider various integrals associated with a continuously differentiable surface. We assume a knowledge of the technique of multiple integration but we will defer a detailed examination of the concept of integration to Chapter 5. We consider a surface $\mathbf{r}$ which is a continuous function on the connected plane set D into V_3. Thus for every $(u, v) \in D$ the representation of $\mathbf{r}(u, v)$ with initial point the origin has its terminal point on the trace of the surface $\mathbf{r}$. We further assume the existence of a continuous function $\mathbf{n}$ on D into V_3 such that, for all $(u, v) \in D$,

$$\|\mathbf{n}(u, v)\| = 1$$

and the representation of $\mathbf{n}(u, v)$ with initial point $\mathbf{r}(u, v)$ will be normal to the trace of $\mathbf{r}$. For our purposes the fact that $\mathbf{n}$ is a continuous function will be taken to be equivalent to the statement that, for all $(u, v) \in D$,

$$\{\mathbf{r}_1 \times \mathbf{r}_2\}(u, v) \neq 0$$

At this stage we will not treat the fine points involved in the case of surfaces for which the domain of the unit normal vector function $\mathbf{n}$ does not include all the domain of $\mathbf{r}$.

We consider now various kinds of functions whose domain is the range of a surface, and we form definitions of certain "surface integrals" for those functions.

Definition 3-1-1. S is the trace of the continuously differentiable surface $\mathbf{r}$. $\mathbf{r}$ is a function on the connected plane set D into V_3. There exists a continuous unit normal vector function for $\mathbf{r}$. If f is a function on S into the real numbers, the *surface integral of f over S* is the real number given by

$$\iint_S f = \iint_D f(\mathbf{r}) \, \|\mathbf{r}_1 \times \mathbf{r}_2\|$$

EXAMPLE. Let S be the sphere centered at the origin of radius 1 and let the unit normal vector function have representations directed away from the origin. Then S can be the trace of the surface $\mathbf{r}$, where

$$\mathbf{r}(u, v) = \sin u \cos v \mathbf{i} + \sin u \sin v \mathbf{j} + \cos u \mathbf{k}, \qquad 0 \leq u \leq \pi, 0 \leq v \leq 2\pi$$

The unit normal vector function specified is then simply given by

$$\mathbf{n}(u, v) = \mathbf{r}(u, v)$$

and the domains of these functions are the rectangle

$$D = \{(u, v) \mid 0 \leq u \leq \pi, 0 \leq v \leq 2\pi\}$$

Differentiation yields

$$\{\mathbf{r}_1 \times \mathbf{r}_2\}(u, v) = \sin^2 u \cos v \mathbf{i} + \sin^2 u \sin v \mathbf{j} + \sin u \cos v \mathbf{k}$$

$$\|\mathbf{r}_1 \times \mathbf{r}_2\|(u, v) = \sin u$$

For any function f on S into the real numbers, we have

$$\iint_S f = \iint_R f(\mathbf{r}) \, \|\mathbf{r}_1 \times \mathbf{r}_2\|$$

$$= \int_0^{2\pi} \int_0^{\pi} f(\sin u \cos v, \sin u \sin v, \cos u) \sin u \, du \, dv$$

In particular, if f is a constant function, say one given by $f(x, y, z) = a$, we would have

$$\iint_S f = 4\pi a$$

In the special case in which $a = 1$, we see that we have precisely the area of S.

Obviously we can weaken the requirements of the definition by insisting only that the functions f and $\mathbf{r}$ have properties which insure the existence of the integral.

Definition 3-1-2. S is the trace of the continuously differentiable surface $\mathbf{r}$. $\mathbf{r}$ is a function on the connected plane set D into $\mathbf{V}_3$. There exists a continuous unit normal vector function for $\mathbf{r}$. If $\mathbf{F}$ is a function on S into $\mathbf{V}_3$, the *surface integral of* $\mathbf{F}$ *over* S is the vector given by

$$\iint_S \mathbf{F} = \left[\iint_S F^{(1)} \right] \mathbf{i} + \left[\iint_S F^{(2)} \right] \mathbf{j} + \left[\iint_S F^{(3)} \right] \mathbf{k}$$

In this manner the surface integral of a function $\mathbf{F}$, into $\mathbf{V}_3$, is the vector whose components are the numbers which are the surface integrals of the components of $\mathbf{F}$. In terms of multiple integrals we have immediately from the definition of surface integral:

Theorem 3-1-1. If S is the trace of the continuously differentiable surface $\mathbf{r}$, where $\mathbf{r}$ is a function on the connected plane set D into $\mathbf{V_3}$ for which there exists a continuous unit normal vector function, then, for $\mathbf{F}$ a function on S into $\mathbf{V_3}$,

$$\iint_S \mathbf{F} = \iint_D \mathbf{F(r)} \, \|\mathbf{r}_1 \times \mathbf{r}_2\|$$

EXAMPLE. Let S be the top half of the unit sphere, as above, and let $\mathbf{F}$ be the function given by

$$\mathbf{F}(x, y, z) = x\mathbf{i} + y\mathbf{j} + z\mathbf{k}$$

Then $\mathbf{F(r)} = \mathbf{r}$ so that

$$\iint_S \mathbf{F} = \iint_D \mathbf{F(r)} \, \|\mathbf{r}_1 \times \mathbf{r}_2\|$$

$$= \int_0^{2\pi} \int_0^{\pi} [\sin u \cos v \mathbf{i} + \sin u \sin v \mathbf{j} + \cos u \mathbf{k}] \sin u \, du \, dv$$

$$= \left[\int_0^{2\pi} \int_0^{\pi} \sin^2 u \cos v \, du \, dv \right] \mathbf{i}$$

$$+ \left[\int_0^{2\pi} \int_0^{\pi} \sin^2 u \sin v \, du \, dv \right] \mathbf{j}$$

$$+ \left[\int_0^{2\pi} \int_0^{\pi} \sin u \cos u \, du \, dv \right] \mathbf{k}$$

$$= 0\mathbf{i} + 0\mathbf{j} + 0\mathbf{k}$$

$$= \mathbf{0}$$

We are now in a position to use these two definitions to create new kinds of surface integrals:

Definition 3-1-3. S is the trace of the continuously differentiable surface $\mathbf{r}$. $\mathbf{r}$ is a function on the connected plane set D into $\mathbf{V_3}$. There exists a continuous unit normal vector function $\mathbf{n}$ for the surface $\mathbf{r}$. If f is a function on S into the real numbers or $\mathbf{F}$ is a function on S into $\mathbf{V_3}$,

$$\iint_S f\mathbf{n} \quad \text{is the vector} \quad \iint_D f(\mathbf{r})\,\mathbf{r}_1 \times \mathbf{r}_2$$

$$\iint_S \mathbf{F} \cdot \mathbf{n} \quad \text{is the number} \quad \iint_D [\mathbf{F(r)}] \cdot [\mathbf{r}_1 \times \mathbf{r}_2]$$

$$\iint_S \mathbf{n} \times \mathbf{F} \quad \text{is the vector} \quad \iint_D [\mathbf{r}_1 \times \mathbf{r}_2] \times [\mathbf{F(r)}]$$

EXERCISES

Evaluate $\iint\limits_S \mathbf{F} \cdot \mathbf{n}$ for Exercises 1–4.

1. $\mathbf{F}(x, y, z) = x\mathbf{i} + y\mathbf{j} + z\mathbf{k}$. S is the rectangular parallelepiped with sides parallel to the coordinate axes and whose opposite vertices are the origin and the point with coordinates (a, b, c), where $a > 0$, $b > 0$, and $c > 0$. $\mathbf{n}$ has representations directed away from the region enclosed by S.

2. $\mathbf{F}(x, y, z) = x^2\mathbf{i} + y^2\mathbf{j} + z^2\mathbf{k}$. S is the sphere centered at the origin with radius 1. $\mathbf{n}$ has representations directed away from the origin.

3. $\mathbf{F}(x, y, z) = xz\mathbf{i} + yz\mathbf{j} + z^2\mathbf{k}$. S and $\mathbf{n}$ are the same as in Exercise 2.

4. $\mathbf{F}$ is the same as in Exercise 3. S is the sphere of radius 1 centered at $(0, 0, c)$. $\mathbf{n}$ has representations directed away from the center of the sphere.

5. S is the trace of the surface $\mathbf{r}$, given by

$$\mathbf{r}(x, y) = x\mathbf{i} + y\mathbf{j} + f(x, y)\mathbf{k}$$

where f is a differentiable function on the connected plane set D into the real numbers. The unit normal vector function is chosen so that, for all $(x, y) \in D$,

$$\mathbf{k} \cdot \mathbf{n}(x, y) > 0$$

$\mathbf{F} = L\mathbf{i} + M\mathbf{j} + N\mathbf{k}$ is a continuous function on S into $\mathbf{V}_3$. Show that

$$\iint\limits_S \mathbf{F} \cdot \mathbf{n} = \iint\limits_D [-L(\mathbf{r})f_1 - M(\mathbf{r})f_2 + N(\mathbf{r})]$$

6. Find an integral representation of the surface integral of $\mathbf{F} = L\mathbf{i} + M\mathbf{j} + N\mathbf{k}$ over the graph of the equation $x = g(x, z)$ where $\mathbf{n}$ has a positive second component.

7. Find an integral representation of the surface integral of $\mathbf{F} = L\mathbf{i} + M\mathbf{j} + N\mathbf{k}$ over the graph of the equation $x = h(y, z)$ where $\mathbf{n}$ has a positive third component.

8. For $\mathbf{F}$ and $\mathbf{r}$ in Exercise 5, find an integral representation of $\iint\limits_S \mathbf{n} \times \mathbf{F}$.

9. Repeat Exercise 8 for the surface given in Exercise 6.

10. Repeat Exercise 8 for the surface given in Exercise 7.

11–14. Evaluate $\iint\limits_S \mathbf{n} \times \mathbf{F}$ for the functions and surfaces given in Exercises 1–4.

15. S is the trace of the surface $\mathbf{r}$, given by

$$\mathbf{r}(u, v) = f(u, v)\mathbf{i} + g(u, v)\mathbf{j} + h(u, v)\mathbf{k}, \qquad (u, v) \in D$$

If $\mathbf{F} = L\mathbf{i} + M\mathbf{j} + N\mathbf{k}$ is a continuous function on S into $\mathbf{V_3}$, show that

$$\iint\limits_{S} \mathbf{F} \cdot \mathbf{n} = \pm \iint\limits_{D} \begin{vmatrix} L(\mathbf{r}) & M(\mathbf{r}) & N(\mathbf{r}) \\ f_1 & g_1 & h_1 \\ f_2 & g_2 & h_2 \end{vmatrix}$$

3-2   The Gradient

In this section, and in the two which follow, we establish analogues of the derivative of an elementary function. In this section we consider functions whose domains are subsets of $\mathbf{V_3}$ and whose ranges are sets of real numbers.

Definition 3-2-1. $D \subseteq \mathbf{V_3}$. f is a function on D into the real numbers. For $\mathbf{a} \in D$, we consider a collection $\{B_k \mid k = 1, 2, \ldots\}$ of subsets of $\mathbf{V_3}$ such that

(i) For $k = 1, 2, \ldots, \mathbf{a} \in B_k$.

(ii) For $k = 1, 2, \ldots, B_{k+1} \subseteq B_k$.

(iii) For every $\epsilon > 0$ there exists N such that B_N is entirely contained in the sphere, centered at $\mathbf{a}$, of radius ϵ.

(iv) For $k = 1, 2, \ldots, B_k$ is bounded by S_k, the trace of a continuously differentiable surface $\mathbf{r}_k$ for which there exists a continuous unit normal vector function $\mathbf{n}_k$ with representations directed away from B_k.

(v) For $k = 1, 2, \ldots$, the volume of $B_k = V_k > 0$. If

$$\lim_{k} \frac{1}{V_k} \iint\limits_{S_k} f\mathbf{n_k}$$

exists and is independent of the choice of $\{B_k\}$ satisfying requirements (i)–(v), then the function given by this limit is grad f, where

$$\{\operatorname{grad} f\}(\mathbf{a}) = \lim_{k} \frac{1}{V_k} \iint\limits_{S_k} f\mathbf{n_k}$$

where the domain of grad f is the set of all $\mathbf{a} \in D$ for which the limit exists.

In this definition we are considering a collection of shrinking "blobs"—the B_k—which shrink to a single point $\mathbf{a}$, and we require that the vector which is the limit, at a fixed point $\mathbf{a}$, for one collection be equal to the vector which is the limit given above for the second collection. Obviously the existence or nonexistence of this limit will be determined by the properties of the function f and the set D. For a nice function, we have

Theorem 3-2-1. If $D \subseteq V_3$, f is a function on D into the real numbers, and (a, b, c) is a point of D such that f, f_1, f_2, and f_3 are continuous in a neighborhood of (a, b, c), then $\{\text{grad} f\}(a, b, c)$ exists and is the vector

$$f_1(a, b, c)\mathbf{i} + f_2(a, b, c)\mathbf{j} + f_3(a, b, c)\mathbf{k}$$

Proof

Part 1: Since f, f_1, f_2, and f_3 are continuous in some neighborhood of (a, b, c), this point must be an interior point of D. Thus given any collection $\{B_t \mid t > 0\}$ of sets in V_3 satisfying requirements (i)–(v) in the definition of gradient, there must exist, for at least each sufficiently small t, a $\delta > 0$ such that if $0 < h < \delta$, $0 < k < \delta$, and $0 < \ell < \delta$, then the rectangular box with sides parallel to the coordinate axes and opposing corners (a, b, c) and $(a + h, b + k, c + \ell)$ will be contained in B_t. In this case $\lim\limits_{t \to 0+}$ will be equivalent to $\lim\limits_{(h,k,\ell) \to (0,0,0)+}$ —that is, limit in V_3 where we restrict the limit process to the "first octant."

Part 2: We let

$$B_{h,k,\ell} = \{(x, y, z) \mid a \leq x \leq a + h, b \leq y \leq b + k, c \leq z \leq c + \ell\}$$

and let $S_{h,k,\ell}$ be the boundary of $B_{h,k,\ell}$. If $\mathbf{r}_{h,k,\ell}$ is a surface with trace $S_{h,k,\ell}$, then an appropriately directed unit normal vector function $\mathbf{n}_{h,k,\ell}$ will have values $\mathbf{i}, -\mathbf{i}, \mathbf{j}, -\mathbf{j}, \mathbf{k}$, and $-\mathbf{k}$, depending on the part of $S_{h,k,\ell}$ on which the evaluation is done. For the purposes of the surface integral, we may ignore the discontinuities which occur on the edges of $S_{h,k,\ell}$ and we see that

$$\iint\limits_{S_{h,k,\ell}} f\mathbf{n}_{h,k,\ell} = \left[\int_b^{b+k} \int_a^{a+h} f(x, y, c + \ell) \, dx \, dy \right] \mathbf{k}$$

$$+ \left[\int_b^{b+k} \int_a^{a+h} f(x, y, c) \, dx \, dy \right] (-\mathbf{k})$$

$$+ \left[\int_a^{a+h} \int_c^{c+\ell} f(x, b + k, z) \, dz \, dx \right] \mathbf{j}$$

$$+ \left[\int_a^{a+h} \int_c^{c+\ell} f(x, b, z) \, dz \, dx \right] (-\mathbf{j})$$

$$+ \left[\int_c^{c+\ell} \int_b^{b+k} f(a + h, y, z) \, dy \, dz \right] \mathbf{i}$$

$$+ \left[\int_c^{c+\ell} \int_b^{b+k} f(a, y, z) \, dy \, dz \right] (-\mathbf{i})$$

The six integrals above are, respectively, the integrals over the top, bottom, right side, left side, front, and rear of the box $B_{h,k,\ell}$. Collecting terms, we see

$$\frac{1}{V_{h,k,\ell}} \iint\limits_{S_{h,k,\ell}} f\mathbf{n}_{h,k,\ell} = \frac{1}{k}\int_b^{b+k} \frac{1}{h}\int_a^{a+h} \frac{f(x,y,c+\ell)-f(x,y,c)}{\ell}\, dx\, dy\, \mathbf{k}$$

$$+ \frac{1}{h}\int_a^{a+h}\frac{1}{\ell}\int_c^{c+\ell}\frac{f(x,b+k,z)-f(x,b,z)}{k}\, dz\, dx\, \mathbf{j}$$

$$+ \frac{1}{\ell}\int_c^{c+\ell}\frac{1}{k}\int_b^{b+k}\frac{f(a+h,y,z)-f(a,y,z)}{h}\, dy\, dz\, \mathbf{i}$$

Since f_1, f_2, and f_3 are continuous in some neighborhood of (a,b,c), given $\epsilon > 0$, there exists $\delta > 0$ such that if

$$\|(x,y,z) - (a,b,c)\| < \delta \quad \text{and} \quad \|(h,k,\ell)\| < \delta$$

then

$$f_3(x,y,c) - \frac{\epsilon}{3} < \frac{f(x,y,c+\ell)-f(x,y,c)}{\ell} < f_3(x,y,c) + \frac{\epsilon}{3}$$

$$f_2(x,b,z) - \frac{\epsilon}{3} < \frac{f(x,b+k,z)-f(x,b,z)}{k} < f_2(x,b,z) + \frac{\epsilon}{3}$$

and

$$f_1(a,y,z) - \frac{\epsilon}{3} < \frac{f(a+h,y,z)-f(a,y,z)}{h} < f_1(a,y,z) + \frac{\epsilon}{3}$$

Integration in the first string of inequalities yields

$$\frac{1}{k}\int_b^{b+k}\frac{1}{h}\int_a^{a+h} f_3(x,y,c)\, dx\, dy - \frac{\epsilon}{3}$$

$$< \frac{1}{k}\int_b^{b+k}\frac{1}{h}\int_a^{a+h}\frac{f(x,y,c+\ell)-f(x,y,c)}{\ell}\, dx\, dy$$

$$< \frac{1}{k}\int_b^{b+k}\frac{1}{h}\int_a^{a+h} f_3(x,y,c)\, dx\, dy + \frac{\epsilon}{3}$$

Since f_3 is continuous at every point of $B_{h,k,\ell}$, the intermediate value theorem for integrals applies and we have, for $b \leq y \leq b+k$, the existence of θ_y, $0 < \theta_y < 1$ such that

$$\int_a^{a+h} f_3(x,y,c)\, dx = hf_3(x+\theta_y h, y, c)$$

This tells us that

$$\frac{1}{k}\int_b^{b+k}\frac{1}{h}\int_a^{a+h} f_3(x,y,c)\, dx\, dy = \frac{1}{k}\int_b^{b+k} f_3(a+\theta_y h, y, c)\, dy$$

Once again, applying the intermediate value theorem, we see that there exists θ, $0 < \theta < 1$, such that

$$\int_b^{b+k} f_3(a + \theta_y h, y, c) = k f_3(a + \theta_{\theta y} h, b + \theta k, c)$$

and

$$\frac{1}{k}\int_b^{b+k}\frac{1}{h}\int_a^{a+h} f_3(x, y, c)\,dx\,dy = f_3(a + \theta_{\theta y} h, b + \theta k, c)$$

Since f_3 is continuous at (a, b, c), we see that

$$\lim_{(h,k,\ell)\to(0,0,0)+}\frac{1}{k}\int_b^{b+k}\frac{1}{h}\int_a^{a+h}\frac{f(x, y, c + \ell) - f(x, y, c)}{\ell}\,dx\,dy$$

must exist and be the number $f_3(a, b, c)$.

Applying similar reasoning to the remaining two components shows us that $\{\text{grad}\,f\}(a, b, c)$ must exist and be the vector

$$f_1(a, b, c)\mathbf{i} + f_2(a, b, c)\mathbf{j} + f_3(a, b, c)\mathbf{k} \qquad\blacksquare$$

If we use the customary notation for partial derivatives, the theorem may be summarized by saying that when $w = f(x, y, z)$, then

$$\text{grad}\,w = \frac{\partial w}{\partial x}\mathbf{i} + \frac{\partial w}{\partial y}\mathbf{j} + \frac{\partial w}{\partial z}\mathbf{k}$$

A convenient notational device often used is to introduce the "vector operator"

$$\nabla = \frac{\partial}{\partial x}\mathbf{i} + \frac{\partial}{\partial y}\mathbf{j} + \frac{\partial}{\partial z}\mathbf{k}$$

Although ∇ is not actually a vector of $\mathbf{V}_3$ (since its apparent components are not numbers), it is treated in manipulation as if it were a vector for which no vector operations are commutative. Thus if w is a dependent variable of a function on a subset of $\mathbf{V}_3$ into the real numbers, ∇w is a dependent (vector) variable of the gradient of this function, but $w\nabla$ is merely another "operator."

Following the pattern set in the investigation of the derivative of elementary functions, we now turn to the relations between the gradient and algebraic combinations of functions.

Theorem 3-2-2. $D \subseteq \mathbf{V}_3$. f and g are functions on D into the real numbers.

(i) $\{\text{grad}\,f + \text{grad}\,g\} \subseteq \text{grad}\,(f + g)$

(ii) $\{\text{grad}\,f - \text{grad}\,g\} \subseteq \text{grad}\,(f - g)$

(iii) $\{f\,\text{grad}\,g + g\,\text{grad}\,f\} \subseteq \text{grad}\,(fg)$

(iv) $\left\{\dfrac{1}{g^2}\,[g\,\text{grad}\,f - f\,\text{grad}\,g]\right\} \subseteq \text{grad}\,(f/g)$

This theorem may be proved either by direct appeal to the definition of gradient or by using the theorem expressing gradient in terms of partial derivatives.

EXERCISES

In Exercises 1–3, find grad f when

1. $f(x, y, z) = xyz$

2. $f(x, y, z) = x^2 + y^2 + z^2$

3. $f(x, y, z) = \sqrt{x^2 + y^2 + z^2}$

4. Use the definition of gradient to prove requirement (i) of Theorem 3-2-2.

5. Use Theorem 3-2-1 to prove requirement (iii) of Theorem 3-2-2.

6. Find all functions f such that

$$\{\text{grad } f\}(x, y, z) = x\mathbf{i} + y\mathbf{j} + z\mathbf{k}$$

In Exercises 7–9, the set $S \subseteq V_3$ is the trace of the surface $\mathbf{r}$. D is the plane set which is the domain of $\mathbf{r}$. F is a differentiable function on S into the real numbers. S is the graph of $F(x, y, z) = 0$.

7. Describe the composite function $F(\mathbf{r})$.

8. Show that, for all $(u, v) \in D$,

$$\{[\{\text{grad } F\}(\mathbf{r})] \cdot \mathbf{r}_1\}(u, v) = \{[\{\text{grad } F\}(\mathbf{r})] \cdot \mathbf{r}_2\}(u, v) = 0$$

9. Show that for all points P, of S, the representation of $\{\text{grad } F\}(P)$ with initial point P is perpendicular to S.

10. Use the concept of gradient to show that the radii of a sphere are normal to it.

11. Find an equation of the plane through $(3, 4, 5)$ which is tangent to the graph of $z = \sqrt{x^2 + y^2}$.

12. Find an equation of the plane tangent to the graph of $z = f(x, y)$ at the point $(a, b, f(a, b))$.

13. The graphs of $x^2 + y^2 + z^2 = 4$ and $z = \sqrt{x^2 + y^2}$ intersect in the path of a curve. Find an equation of the plane perpendicular to this path at the point $(1, 1, \sqrt{2})$.

14. Find an equation of the plane perpendicular to the path of a curve which is the intersection of the graphs of $F(x, y, z) = 0$ and $G(x, y, z) = 0$, at the point (a, b, c).

3-3   Divergence and Curl

In the preceding section we formed a definition for the gradient of a function on a three-dimensional set into the real numbers. Using the same notation—$\{B_k \mid k = 1, 2, \ldots\}$—as in Definition 3-2-1 for a collection of "shrinking" sets whose "limit" is the single point $\mathbf{a}$, we have

> **Definition 3-3-1.** If $\mathbf{v}$ is a function on the three-dimensional set D into $\mathbf{V}_3$, then for every $\mathbf{a} \in D$, for which the limit exists and is independent of the choice of $\{Bt\}$ satisfying (i)–(v),
>
> $$\{\operatorname{div} \mathbf{v}\}(\mathbf{a}) = \lim_{t \to 0} \frac{1}{V_t} \iint\limits_{S_t} \mathbf{v} \cdot \mathbf{n}_t$$
>
> div $\mathbf{v}$ is called the *divergence* of $\mathbf{v}$.

> **Definition 3-3-2.** If $\mathbf{v}$ is a function on the three-dimensional set D into $\mathbf{V}_3$, then for every $\mathbf{a} \in D$, for which the limit exists and is independent of the choice of $\{Bt\}$ satisfying (i)–(v),
>
> $$\{\operatorname{curl} \mathbf{v}\}(\mathbf{a}) = \lim_{t \to 0} \frac{1}{V_t} \iint\limits_{S_t} \mathbf{n}_t \times \mathbf{v}$$

We examine the case in which the function $\mathbf{v}$ has components given by

$$\mathbf{v} = F\mathbf{i} + G\mathbf{j} + H\mathbf{k}$$

and we consider a point (a, b, c) in the domain of $\mathbf{v}$ with the rectangular boxes

$$B_{h,k,\ell} = \{(x, y, z) \mid a \le x \le a + h, b \le y \le b + k, c \le z \le c + \ell\}$$

We then have

$$\frac{1}{V_{h,k,\ell}} \iint\limits_{S_{h,k,\ell}} \mathbf{v} \cdot \mathbf{n}_{h,k,\ell} = \frac{1}{k} \int_b^{b+k} \frac{1}{h} \int_a^{a+h} \frac{H(x, y, c + \ell) - H(x, y, c)}{\ell} \, dx \, dy$$

$$+ \frac{1}{h} \int_a^{a+h} \frac{1}{\ell} \int_c^{c+\ell} \frac{G(x, b + k, z) - G(x, b, z)}{k} \, dz \, dx$$

$$+ \frac{1}{\ell} \int_c^{c+\ell} \frac{1}{k} \int_b^{b+k} \frac{F(a + h, y, z) - F(a, y, z)}{h} \, dy \, dz$$

A limit argument similar to that used in the proof of Theorem 3-2-1 gives, as a result,

Theorem 3-3-1. $\mathbf{v} = F\mathbf{i} + G\mathbf{j} + H\mathbf{k}$ is a function on a three-dimensional set into $\mathbf{V}_3$. If $\mathbf{v}$ has continuous partial derivatives at every point in some neighborhood of the point P, then $\{\text{div }\mathbf{v}\}(P)$ exists and is the number

$$F_1(P) + G_2(P) + H_3(P)$$

For the curl of a function into $\mathbf{V}_3$, the development is longer, but essentially the same, and gives

Theorem 3-3-2. $\mathbf{v} = F\mathbf{i} + G\mathbf{j} + H\mathbf{k}$ is a function on a three-dimensional set into $\mathbf{V}_3$. If $\mathbf{v}$ has continuous partial derivatives at every point in a neighborhood of the point P, then $\{\text{curl }\mathbf{v}\}(P)$ exists and is the vector

$$\{(H_2 - G_3)\mathbf{i} + (F_3 - H_1)\mathbf{j} + (G_1 - F_2)\mathbf{k}\}(P)$$

The details of the proofs of these theorems are left to the exercises.

In terms of the "operator" ∇ for $\mathbf{v} = (v^1, v^2, v^3)$, these results become

$$\nabla \cdot \mathbf{v} = v_1^1 + v_2^2 + v_3^3$$
$$\nabla \times \mathbf{v} = (v_2^3 - v_3^2)\mathbf{i} + (v_3^1 - v_1^3)\mathbf{j} + (v_1^2 - v_2^1)\mathbf{k}$$

We now examine some of the relations between divergence and curl—which are vector analogues of the derivative—and vector algebraic combinations of functions.

Theorem 3-3-3. If $\mathbf{u}$ and $\mathbf{v}$ are two functions on a three-dimensional set into $\mathbf{V}_3$ and P is a point for which $\{\text{div }\mathbf{u}\}(P)$ and $\{\text{div }\mathbf{v}\}(P)$ exist, then $\{\text{div}\}\,(\mathbf{u} + \mathbf{v})(P)$ exists and is the number

$$\{\text{div }\mathbf{u} + \text{div }\mathbf{v}\}(P)$$

This theorem may be restated by the relation

$$\text{div }\mathbf{u} + \text{div }\mathbf{v} \subseteq \text{div }(\mathbf{u} + \mathbf{v})$$

or, in terms of the "operator" ∇,

$$\nabla \cdot \mathbf{u} + \nabla \cdot \mathbf{v} \subseteq \nabla \cdot (\mathbf{u} + \mathbf{v})$$

The theorem may be proved by direct appeal to the definition of divergence and the use of the theorem concerning the limit of the sum of two functions.

In dealing with vector algebra, we have three different kinds of multiplications: the scalar product of a real number and a vector, the inner product of two vectors, and the cross product of two vectors. For functions we have the following situation: If f is a function on a three-dimensional set into the real numbers and $\mathbf{u}$ and $\mathbf{v}$ are functions on that same set into $\mathbf{V}_3$, then $f\mathbf{u}$ will be a function into $\mathbf{V}_3$, $\mathbf{u} \cdot \mathbf{v}$ will be a function into the real numbers, and $\mathbf{u} \times \mathbf{v}$ will be a function into $\mathbf{V_3}$. We would expect some relations among div $f\mathbf{u}$, curl $f\mathbf{u}$, grad $\mathbf{u} \cdot \mathbf{v}$, div $(\mathbf{u} \times \mathbf{v})$, and curl $(\mathbf{u} \times \mathbf{v})$ and the functions grad f, div $\mathbf{u}$, div $\mathbf{v}$, curl $\mathbf{u}$, and curl $\mathbf{v}$. It is to be hoped that, at least in some cases, we would arrive at an analogue of the theorem on the derivative of the product of elementary functions. One such analogy does occur in

Theorem 3-3-4. If f is a function on a three-dimensional set into the real numbers, $\mathbf{v}$ is a function on the same set into $\mathbf{V_3}$, and both f and $\mathbf{v}$ have continuous partial derivatives, then

$$\text{div } (f\mathbf{v}) \supseteq [\text{grad } f] \cdot \mathbf{v} + f \text{ div } \mathbf{v}$$

Proof

Let $\mathbf{v} = L\mathbf{i} + M\mathbf{j} + N\mathbf{k}$

Then

$$f\mathbf{v} = (fL)\mathbf{i} + (fM)\mathbf{j} + (fN)\mathbf{k}$$

$$\text{div } (f\mathbf{v}) = (fL)_1 + (fM)_2 + (fN)_3$$

$$\supseteq f_1 L + f L_1 + f_2 M + f M_2 + f_3 N + f N_3$$

$$= (f_1 L + f_2 M + f_3 N) + f(L_1 + M_2 + N_3)$$

$$= [\text{grad } f] \cdot \mathbf{v} + f \text{ div } \mathbf{v} \qquad \blacksquare$$

Unfortunately the analogy to the theorem about the derivative of the product of elementary functions does not always hold. One example of this occurs in

Theorem 3-3-5. If $\mathbf{u}$ and $\mathbf{v}$ are functions on a three-dimensional set into $\mathbf{V_3}$ and both $\mathbf{u}$ and $\mathbf{v}$ have continuous partial derivatives, then

$$\text{div } (\mathbf{u} \times \mathbf{v}) \supseteq (\text{curl } \mathbf{u}) \cdot \mathbf{v} - (\text{curl } \mathbf{v}) \cdot \mathbf{u}$$

Proof

$$\mathbf{u} \times \mathbf{v} = (u^2 v^3 - u^3 v^2)\mathbf{i} + (u^3 v^1 - u^1 v^3)\mathbf{j} + (u^1 v^2 - u^2 v^1)\mathbf{k}$$

$$\text{div } (\mathbf{u} \times \mathbf{v}) = (u^2 v^3 - u^3 v^2)_1 + (u^3 v^1 - u^1 v^3)_2 + (u^1 v^2 - u^2 v^1)_3$$

$$\supseteq u_1^2 v^3 + u^2 v_1^3 - u_1^3 v^2 - u^2 v_1^3$$

$$+ u_2^3 v^1 + u^3 v_2^1 - u_2^1 v^3 - u^1 v_2^3$$

$$+ u_3^1 v^2 + u^1 v_3^2 - u_3^2 v^1 - u^2 v_3^1$$

$$= (u_2^3 - u_3^2)v^1 + (u_3^1 - u_1^3)v^2 + (u_1^2 - u_2^1)v^3$$

$$- u^1(v_2^3 - v_3^2) - u^2(v_3^1 - v_1^3) - u^3(v_1^2 - v_2^1)$$

$$= (\text{curl } \mathbf{u}) \cdot \mathbf{v} - \mathbf{u} \cdot (\text{curl } \mathbf{v}) \qquad \blacksquare$$

The analogy does hold, however, in

Theorem 3-3-6. If f is a function on a three-dimensional set into the real numbers, $\mathbf{v}$ is a function on the same set into $\mathbf{V}_3$, and f and $\mathbf{v}$ have continuous partial derivatives, then

$$\operatorname{curl}(f\mathbf{v}) \supseteq f\operatorname{curl}\mathbf{v} + (\operatorname{grad} f) \times \mathbf{v}$$

Proof

$$f\mathbf{v} = (fv^1)\mathbf{i} + (fv^2)\mathbf{j} + (fv^3)\mathbf{k}$$

$$\begin{aligned}
\operatorname{curl}(f\mathbf{v}) &= [(fv^3)_2 - (fv^2)_3]\mathbf{i} + [(fv^1)_3 - (fv^3)_1]\mathbf{j} + [(fv^2)_1 - (fv^1)_2]\mathbf{k} \\
&\supseteq (f_2 v^3 + fv_2^3 - f_3 v^2 - fv_3^2)\mathbf{i} + (f_3 v^1 + fv_3^1 - f_1 v^3 - fv_1^3)\mathbf{j} \\
&\quad + (f_1 v^2 + fv_1^2 - f_2 v^1 - fv_2^1)\mathbf{k} \\
&= f[(v_2^3 - v_3^2)\mathbf{i} + (v_3^1 - v_1^3)\mathbf{j} + (v_1^2 - v_2^1)\mathbf{k}] \\
&\quad + (f_2 v^3 - f_3 v^2)\mathbf{i} + (f_3 v^1 - f_1 v^3)\mathbf{j} + (f_1 v^2 - f_2 v^1)\mathbf{k} \\
&= f\operatorname{curl}\mathbf{v} + (\operatorname{grad} f) \times \mathbf{v}
\end{aligned}$$
∎

The following two theorems are of particular interest.

Theorem 3-3-7. If f is a function on a three-dimensional set into the real numbers and f, all its first partial derivatives, and all its second partial derivatives are continuous in some neighborhood of the point P, then

$$\{\operatorname{curl}(\operatorname{grad} f)\}(P) = 0$$

Proof

$$\operatorname{grad} f = f_1\mathbf{i} + f_2\mathbf{j} + f_3\mathbf{k}$$
$$\begin{aligned}
\operatorname{curl}(\operatorname{grad} f) &= (f_{32} - f_{23})\mathbf{i} + (f_{13} - f_{31})\mathbf{j} + (f_{21} - f_{12})\mathbf{k} \\
&= 0
\end{aligned}$$
∎

Theorem 3-3-8. If $\mathbf{v}$ is a function on a three-dimensional set into $\mathbf{V}_3$ and $\mathbf{v}$, all its first partial derivatives, and all its second partial derivatives are continuous in some neighborhood of the point P, then

$$\operatorname{div}(\operatorname{curl}\mathbf{v})(P) = 0$$

Proof

$$\operatorname{curl}\mathbf{v} = (v_3^2 - v_2^3)\mathbf{i} + (v_1^3 - v_3^1)\mathbf{j} + (v_2^1 - v_1^2)\mathbf{k}$$
$$\begin{aligned}
\operatorname{div}(\operatorname{curl}\mathbf{v}) &= (v_3^2 - v_2^3)_1 + (v_1^3 - v_3^1)_2 + (v_2^1 - v_1^2)_3 \\
&\supseteq v_{31}^2 - v_{21}^3 + v_{12}^3 - v_{32}^1 + v_{23}^1 - v_{13}^2
\end{aligned}$$
∎

EXERCISES

In Exercises 1–4, find div v and curl v for the functions given by

   1. $v(x, y, z) = xi + yj + zk$

   2. $v(x, y, z) = x^2i + y^2j + z^2k$

   3. $v(x, y, z) = (x^2 + y^2 + z^2)^{-1/2} (xi + yj + zk)$

   4. $v(x, y, z) = x^2yi + xy^2j$

In Exercises 5–9, find appropriate "expansions" of

   5. curl (curl v)

   6. curl (u × v)

   7. grad [u · (v × w)]

   8. div [u × (v × w)]

   9. div ([grad f] × [grad g])

In Exercises 10–13, $r(x, y, z) = xi + yj + zk$. f is a differentiable function on $[0, +\infty[$ into the real numbers. $a \in V_3$. Show that

   10. For all P, curl $(f(\|r\|)r)(P) = 0$.

   11. div $[f(\|r\|)r] = \|r\| f'(\|r\|) + 3f(\|r\|)$

   12. curl $[\|r\|^n a \times r] = (n + 2)\|r\|^n a - n\|r\|^{n-2}(a \cdot r)r$

   13. grad $[\|r\|^{-3}a \cdot r] = -$curl $[\|r\|^{-3}a \times r]$

   14. Give the details of the proof of Theorem 3-3-1.

   15. Give the details of the proof of Theorem 3-3-2.

3-4   Line Integrals

In this section we will be concerned with an integral which arises from considering a function whose domain is a three-dimensional set, which set includes within it the path of at least one oriented curve—a continuous function on an interval of real numbers in which the points of the trace are ordered linearly. Thus any path gives rise to two oriented curves and we will consider the orientation given by the linear ordering of the real numbers in the defining interval.

   For example, for the line segment joining the origin to the point $(1, 2, 3)$, oriented from the origin to the point $(1, 2, 3)$, we give the function

$$r(t) = ti + 2tj + 3tk, \qquad 0 \le t \le 1$$

and the opposite orientation—from the point $(1, 2, 3)$ to the origin—will be indicated by giving the function

$$\mathbf{r}(t) = t\mathbf{i} + 2t\mathbf{j} + 3t\mathbf{k}, \qquad 1 \geq t \geq 0$$

We will consider integrals for functions into the real numbers and also for functions into $\mathbf{V}_3$.

Definition 3-4-1. If γ is the oriented curve given by the differentiable function $\mathbf{r}$ on the closed interval $[a, b]$ into $\mathbf{V}_3$, and $\mathbf{v}$ is a function on a three-dimensional set which includes the path of the curve γ, into $\mathbf{V}_3$, then the line integral of $\mathbf{v}$ over the oriented curve γ,

$$\int_{\gamma} \mathbf{v} \cdot \mathbf{T} \text{ is the number } \int_a^b [\mathbf{v}(\mathbf{r}) \cdot \mathbf{r}']$$

Definition 3-4-2. If γ is the oriented curve given by the differentiable function $\mathbf{r}$ on the closed interval $[a, b]$ into $\mathbf{V}_3$, and f is a function of a three-dimensional set which includes the path of the curve γ, into the real numbers, then the line integral of f over the oriented curve γ,

$$\int_{\gamma} f\mathbf{T}, \text{ is the vector } \int_a^b [f(\mathbf{r})\mathbf{r}']$$

EXAMPLES. Let γ be the helix given by

$$\mathbf{r}(t) = \cos t\mathbf{i} + \sin t\mathbf{j} + t\mathbf{k}, \qquad 0 \leq t \leq 2\pi$$

The orientation given makes $\mathbf{r}(0) = (1, 0, 0)$ the coordinates of the initial point of γ and $\mathbf{r}(2\pi) = (1, 0, 2\pi)$ the coordinates of the terminal point of γ.

For the function into $\mathbf{V}_3$ given by

$$\mathbf{v}(x, y, z) = x^2\mathbf{i} + y^2\mathbf{j} + z^2\mathbf{k}$$

we have

$$\int_{\gamma} \mathbf{v} \cdot \mathbf{T} = \int_0^{2\pi} [\mathbf{v}(\mathbf{r}(t)) \cdot \mathbf{r}'(t)] \, dt$$

$$= \int_0^{2\pi} (\cos^2 t\mathbf{i} + \sin^2 t\mathbf{j} + t^2\mathbf{k}) \cdot (-\sin t\mathbf{i} + \cos t\mathbf{j} + \mathbf{k}) \, dt$$

$$= \int_0^{2\pi} [-\cos^2 t \sin t + \sin^2 t \cos t + t^2] \, dt$$

$$= \tfrac{8}{3}\pi^3$$

For the function into the real numbers given by $f(x, y, z) = x + y + z$, we have

$$\int_{\gamma} f\mathbf{T} = \int_0^{2\pi} [f(\mathbf{r}(t))\mathbf{r}'(t)] \, dt$$

$$= \int_0^{2\pi} (\cos t + \sin t + t)(-\sin t\mathbf{i} + \cos t\mathbf{j} + \mathbf{k}) \, dt$$

$$= \pi\mathbf{i} + \pi\mathbf{j} + 2\pi^2\mathbf{k}$$

In order that the number $\int_\gamma \mathbf{v} \cdot \mathbf{T}$ exist, it is necessary that the inner product of the composite function $\mathbf{v(r)}$ and the function $\mathbf{r}'$ be integrable on $[a, b]$. Similarly, the vector $\int_\gamma f\mathbf{T}$ will exist if the scalar multiplication of the composite $f(\mathbf{r})$ and the function $\mathbf{r}'$ produces a function integrable on $[a, b]$.

The relation between the line integrals over oppositely oriented curves is treated in the exercises.

One of the items of particular interest concerning line integrals of functions whose domains are a given portion of three-dimensional space is whether or not the integral over different paths joining two fixed points depends on the path chosen. The independence of path of the line integral—when it occurs—is one of the more interesting ways of describing the behavior of the function being integrated. One interesting result is given in

> **Theorem 3-4-1.** f is a continuously differentiable function on the connected three-dimensional set D into the real numbers. If A and B are any two points of D, γ_1 and γ_2 are continuously differentiable oriented curves, with paths lying entirely in D, joining A and B, and oriented from A to B, then
>
> $$\int_{\gamma_1} (\operatorname{grad} f) \cdot \mathbf{T} = \int_{\gamma_2} (\operatorname{grad} f) \cdot \mathbf{T}$$

Proof. The fact that f is continuously differentiable assures that $\operatorname{grad} f$ is continuous. If the curves γ_1 and γ_2 are given by the functions $\mathbf{u}$ and $\mathbf{v}$, then the hypothesis says that $\mathbf{u}'$ and $\mathbf{v}'$ are continuous so that both line integrals exist.

Let γ_1 be given by the function $\mathbf{u}$ on $[a, b]$ into $\mathbf{V}_3$ and γ_2 be given by the function $\mathbf{v}$ on $[p, q]$ into $\mathbf{V}_3$. Then, by hypothesis, $\mathbf{u}(a) = \mathbf{v}(p)$ gives the coordinates of A and $\mathbf{u}(b) = \mathbf{v}(q)$ gives the coordinates of B.

We have

$$\operatorname{grad} f = f_1\mathbf{i} + f_2\mathbf{j} + f_3\mathbf{k}$$
$$\{\operatorname{grad} f\}(\mathbf{u}) = f_1(\mathbf{u})\mathbf{i} + f_2(\mathbf{u})\mathbf{j} + f_3(\mathbf{u})\mathbf{k}$$
$$[\{\operatorname{grad} f\}(\mathbf{u})] \cdot \mathbf{u}' = f_1(\mathbf{u})(u^1)' + f_2(\mathbf{u})(u^2)' + f_3(\mathbf{u})(u^3)'$$
$$= [f(\mathbf{u})]'$$

Similarly,

$$[\{\operatorname{grad} f\}(\mathbf{v})] \cdot \mathbf{v}' = [f(\mathbf{v})]'$$

Integrating, we find

$$\int_\gamma (\operatorname{grad} f) \cdot \mathbf{T} = \int_a^b [f(\mathbf{u})]'$$
$$= f(\mathbf{u}(b)) - f(\mathbf{u}(a))$$
$$= f(B) - f(A)$$

and

$$\int_{\gamma} (\text{grad } f) \cdot \mathbf{T} = \int_{p}^{q} [f(\mathbf{v})]'$$

$$= f(\mathbf{v}(q)) - f(\mathbf{v}(p))$$

$$= f(B) - f(A)$$

Thus the line integral over an oriented curve of the gradient of a numerically valued function is determined only by the values of this function at the end points of the curve and is independent of the path chosen within the region of continuity of the gradient. ∎

The converse of the theorem is provided by

Theorem 3-4-2. $\mathbf{v}$ is a function on the connected three-dimensional set D into $\mathbf{V}_3$. If, for any two points A and B of D, and every pair of continuously differentiable curves γ_1 and γ_2 with paths joining A and B, lying entirely within D, and oriented from A to B,

$$\int_{\gamma_1} \mathbf{v} \cdot \mathbf{T} = \int_{\gamma_2} \mathbf{v} \cdot \mathbf{T}$$

then there exists a function f on D into the real numbers such that $\mathbf{v} = \text{grad } f$.

Proof. We pick one specific point A of D. The hypothesis implies that the line integral over every oriented curve with path lying within D and with initial point A must exist. We form the function f on D into the real numbers by saying that, for every point P of D, $f(P)$ is that one number which results from finding $\int_{\gamma} \mathbf{v} \cdot \mathbf{T}$ for all continuously differentiable curves γ with paths lying in D, joining A and P, and oriented from A to P.

We now examine a point P of D with coordinates (a, b, c). If $h > 0$ and $\{(a + th, b, c) \mid 0 \leq t \leq 1\} \subseteq D$, then

$$f(a + h, b, c) = \int_{\gamma_1} \mathbf{v} \cdot \mathbf{T}$$

$$f(a, b, c) = \int_{\gamma_2} \mathbf{v} \cdot \mathbf{T}$$

$$f(a + h, b, c) - f(a, b, c) = \int_{\gamma_3} \mathbf{v} \cdot \mathbf{T}$$

in which γ_1 is the "direct sum" of γ_2 and γ_3. That is, γ_2 is some continuously differentiable curve, with path lying within D, and oriented from A to P; γ_3 is the oriented line segment from (a, b, c) to $(a + h, b, c)$; and γ_1 is the oriented curve which is formed by adjoining γ_3 to γ_2. We now have

$$f(a + h, b, c) - f(a, b, c) = \int_0^h [\mathbf{v}(\mathbf{r}(a + t)) \cdot \mathbf{r}'(a + t)]\, dt$$

But on the oriented line segment we have

$$\mathbf{r}(t) = (a + t)\mathbf{i} + b\mathbf{j} + c\mathbf{k}, \qquad 0 \le t \le h$$
$$\mathbf{r}'(t) = \mathbf{i}, \qquad 0 \le t \le h$$
$$\mathbf{v}(\mathbf{r}(t)) \cdot \mathbf{r}'(t) = v^1(\mathbf{r}(t)), \qquad 0 \le t \le h$$

The difference quotient leading to the partial derivative f_1 then becomes

$$\frac{f(a + h, b, c) - f(a, b, c)}{h} = \frac{1}{h}\int_0^h v^1(\mathbf{r}(t))\, dt$$

Since $\mathbf{v}$ is continuous, the component function v^1 is also continuous and the Fundamental Theorem of Calculus tells us that $\lim_{h \to 0}$ exists for the function given by the right side of this last equation and that this limit will be the number $v^1(\mathbf{r}(0)) = v^1(a, b, c)$. Thus $f_1(a, b, c)$ exists and is $v^1(a, b, c)$.

Similar arguments show that $f_2(a, b, c) = v^2(a, b, c)$ and $f_3(a, b, c) = v^3(a, b, c)$, so that $\{\mathrm{grad}\, f\}(a, b, c)$ exists and is the vector $\mathbf{v}(a, b, c)$. ∎

We have now seen that performing the operation of taking the gradient of a sufficiently nice function on a three-dimensional set into the real numbers will produce a function into $\mathbf{V}_3$, taking the divergence of a function into $\mathbf{V}_3$ will produce a function into the real numbers, and taking the curl of a function in $\mathbf{V}_3$ will produce a function into $\mathbf{V}_3$. Given a curve whose path is included in the domain of any of these functions, we can form the line integral for an orientation of that curve, and this line integral will be either a vector or a number. For a surface whose trace is in the domain of any of these functions, we can form the surface integral for a unit normal vector function, and this surface integral will be either a vector or a number. If a connected three-dimensional set with positive volume is included in the domain of any of these functions, we can form the integral of the function over this set, and this integral will be either a vector or a number.

Our next task will be to examine possible relationships among line integral, surface integral, and integral over a three-dimensional set and the operations of forming gradient, divergence, and curl. We will examine particularly two classic theorems: *Gauss's Theorem* (also known as *the divergence theorem*), which relates three-dimensional integrals, surface integrals, and the divergence; and *Stokes' Theorem*, which relates surface integrals, line integrals, and the curl.

EXERCISES

1. If the curve γ is given by the function $\mathbf{r}$ on $[a, b]$ into $\mathbf{V}_3$, with orientation from $\mathbf{r}(a)$ to $\mathbf{r}(b)$, discuss the curve given by $\mathbf{u}$ on $[b, 2b - a]$ given by $\mathbf{u}(t) = \mathbf{r}(2b - t)$ with orientation from $\mathbf{u}(b)$ to $\mathbf{u}(2b - a)$.

2. If γ is the oriented curve given by the continuous function $\mathbf{r}$ on $[a, b]$ into $\mathbf{V}_3$ with orientation from $\mathbf{r}(a)$ to $\mathbf{r}(b)$ and γ^* is the oriented curve given by the same function with orientation from $\mathbf{r}(b)$ to $\mathbf{r}(a)$, show that

$$\int_\gamma \mathbf{v} \cdot \mathbf{T} = - \int_{\gamma^*} \mathbf{v} \cdot \mathbf{T}$$

Find $\int_\gamma \mathbf{v} \cdot \mathbf{T}$ for the following curves and functions.

3. $\mathbf{v}(x, y, z) = x^2\mathbf{i} + y^2\mathbf{j} + z^2\mathbf{k}$. The parabola $y = x^2, z = 0$ oriented from $(0, 0, 0)$ to $(1, 1, 0)$.

4. $\mathbf{v}(x, y, z) = (x^2 - y^2)\mathbf{i} + 2xy\mathbf{j}$. The unit circle of the x-y plane, oriented counterclockwise.

5. $\mathbf{v}$ is the same as in Exercise 3. The oriented line segment from $(0, 0, 0)$ to $(1, 2, 3)$.

6. $\mathbf{v}$ is the same as in Exercise 4. The broken line joining $(0, 0, 0)$, $(1, 0, 0)$, $(1, 2, 0)$, and $(1, 2, 3)$, with the points oriented in that order.

7. Show that if the curve γ is the "direct sum" of the curves γ_1 and γ_2, that is, γ_1 is oriented from A to B, γ_2 is oriented from B to C, and γ consists of the points of both γ_1 and γ_2 with orientation from A to C, then

$$\int_\gamma \mathbf{v} \cdot \mathbf{T} = \int_{\gamma_1} \mathbf{v} \cdot \mathbf{T} + \int_{\gamma_2} \mathbf{v} \cdot \mathbf{T}$$

8. Complete the proof of Theorem 3-4-2 by showing that $f_2(a, b, c) = v^2(a, b, c)$ and $f_3(a, b, c) = v^3(a, b, c)$.

9. The oriented curve γ is the rectangle with vertices $(0, 0, 0)$, $(a, 0, 0)$, $(a, b, 0)$, and $(0, b, 0)$ (where $a > 0$ and $b > 0$), oriented so the points appear in that order. R is the rectangular region enclosed by the path of $\gamma \cdot \mathbf{v} = P\mathbf{i} + Q\mathbf{j}$ is a continuously differentiable function on R into $\mathbf{V}_3$. Show that

$$\int_\gamma \mathbf{v} \cdot \mathbf{T} = \iint_R (Q_1 - P_2)$$

Note that

$$\iint_R f = \int_0^a \int_0^b f(x, y) \, dy \, dx = \int_0^b \int_0^a f(x, y) \, dx \, dy$$

10. Repeat Exercise 8 with γ the triangle with vertices $(0, 0, 0)$, $(a, 0, 0)$, and $(a, b, 0)$ and R the region enclosed.

11. Prove that if D is a connected three-dimensional set and γ is any closed continuously differentiable oriented curve with path in D, then for any continuous differentiable function f on D into the real numbers,

$$\int_{\gamma} (\operatorname{grad} f) \cdot \mathbf{T} = 0$$

12. Show that for the function and region in Exercise 11, if C_1 and C_2 are two coplanar concentric circles with the property that the circles and the annular region enclosed by them are inside D and with the same orientation relative to a line perpendicular to their plane, then

$$\int_{C_1} (\operatorname{grad} f) \cdot \mathbf{T} = \int_{C_2} (\operatorname{grad} f) \cdot \mathbf{T}$$

CLASSICAL VECTOR THEOREMS 4

4-1 The Fundamental Theorem of Calculus

The preceding chapters have developed the concepts of differential and integral calculus for functions whose domains and ranges may be vector spaces other than the set of real numbers. The particular vector spaces which have interested mathematicians for some time are the real numbers V_2 and V_3. For a function on a three-dimensional set into the real numbers or into V_3, we have three types of integrals: line integral, surface integral, and (the elementary Riemann) three-dimensional integral. We also have, for such functions, three analogues of the derivative: gradient of a function into the real numbers and divergence and curl of a function into V_3.

Elementary calculus, which is concerned with functions on a set of numbers into the real numbers, has, as a central theorem,

> **Theorem 4-1-1 (the Fundamental Theorem of Calculus).** If f is a continuous function on $[a, b]$ into the real numbers, then f has antiderivatives; and if F is any antiderivative of f, then
>
> $$\int_a^b f = F(b) - F(a)$$

Proofs of this theorem, or of equivalent theorems, can be found in most elementary calculus texts. As stated here, the continuity of the function f on the closed interval $[a, b]$ raises the question of the behavior of this function at each end point. If the definition of continuity used only requires that

$$\lim_{t \to a+} f(t) = f(a) \quad \text{and} \quad \lim_{t \to b-} f(t) = f(b)$$

then we must consider a function F such that, for any t in the open interval $]a, b[$, $F'(t) = f(t)$ and also such that the one-sided derivatives at the end points have the property

$$\{D_+ F\}(a) = f(a) \quad \text{and} \quad \{D_- F\}(b) = f(b)$$

The major purpose of this chapter is to examine analogues of this fundamental theorem which apply to functions whose domains and ranges are not sets of real numbers. We will examine theorems which relate integrals of one sort to certain analogues of the derivative.

In order to emphasize the major ideas in these theorems, we will content ourselves with slightly weaker theorems than are possible. That is, we will include enough hypotheses so that the proofs are straightforward and require no special consideration of awkward spots in the behavior of the functions. We illustrate this by beginning with a version of the Fundamental Theorem of Calculus in which the hypotheses are sufficiently strong so that there is no need for special consideration of the end points of an interval nor for consideration of one-sided limits or one-sided derivatives.

> **Theorem 4-1-2.** If f is a continuous function on $[p, q]$ into the real numbers and $[a, b] \subseteq \,]p, q[$, then the restriction of f to $[a, b]$ has antiderivatives; if F is any such antiderivative, we have
>
> $$\int_a^b f = F(b) - F(a)$$

Proof. By hypothesis, f is continuous on the closed interval $[p, q]$. Thus, for every t in the open interval $]p, q[$, we have $[a, t] \subseteq \,]p, q[$ or $[t, a] \subseteq \,]p, q[$ and the restriction of f to $[a, t]$ or $[t, a]$ is a continuous function. By definition, $\int_a^a f$ is the number 0 so that, for every $t \in \,]p, q[$, $\int_a^t f$ exists. We construct a new function G on $]p, q[$ into the real numbers by the rule

$$G(t) = \int_a^t f$$

We now fix the number $x \in [a, b]$ and choose $\epsilon > 0$. By hypothesis, f is continuous at x. Thus there exists $\delta_{\epsilon,x} > 0$ such that $|t - x| < \delta_{\epsilon,x}$ implies that t is in the domain of f and that $|f(t) - f(x)| < \epsilon$.

Since $|h| < \delta_{\epsilon,x}$ implies that the number $x + h$ is in the domain of f, and since f is a continuous function, then for $|h| < \delta_{\epsilon,x}$ the restriction of f to the interval $[x, x + h]$ or $[x + h, x]$ is also continuous. This means that if $|h| < \delta_{\epsilon,x}$, then $\int_x^{x+h} f$ must exist.

Now $0 < h < \delta_{\epsilon,x}$ implies

$$h[f(x) - \epsilon] < \int_x^{x+h} f < h[f(x) + \epsilon]$$

and $-\delta_{\epsilon,x} < h < 0$ implies

$$(-h)[f(x) - \epsilon] < \int_x^{x+h} f < (-h)[f(x) + \epsilon]$$

Combining these inequalities shows that $0 < |h| < \delta_{\epsilon,x}$ implies

$$f(x) - \epsilon < \frac{1}{h} \int_x^{x+h} f < f(x) + \epsilon$$

We have thus shown that for a fixed number $x \in [a, b]$ and for any $\epsilon > 0$ there exists $\delta_{\epsilon,x} > 0$ such that if $0 < |h| < \delta_{\epsilon,x}$, then $\dfrac{1}{h}\displaystyle\int_{x}^{x+h} f$ exists and is a number within ϵ units of the fixed number $f(x)$. That is, for each fixed $x \in [a, b]$,

$$\lim_{h \to 0} \frac{1}{h} \int_{x}^{x+h} f = f(x)$$

Since, for each $x \in [a, b]$,

$$\int_{x}^{x+h} f = G(x + h) - G(x)$$

we have also shown that, for every $x \in [a, b]$, $G'(x) = f(x)$. Thus the restriction of f to $[a, b]$ has an antiderivative, namely the restriction of G to $[a, b]$. Any function which differs from G by a constant function also has the property that its restriction to $[a, b]$ is an antiderivative of f on $[a, b]$.

If F is any antiderivative of the restriction of f to $[a, b]$, then F must differ from the restriction of G to $[a, b]$ by a constant and we must have

$$F(b) - F(a) = G(b) - G(a)$$
$$= \int_{a}^{b} f - \int_{a}^{a} f$$
$$= \int_{a}^{b} f$$

In the next two sections we examine theorems which are analogous to Theorem 4-1-2; in these theorems the hypotheses are made sufficiently strong so that the proofs are easy, although perhaps lengthy.

EXERCISES

f is the function given by $f(x) = 2x + 3, 0 \le x \le 3$.

1. Find $\delta_{\epsilon,x}$ such that, for each $x \in [1, 2]$, $|t - x| < \delta_{\epsilon,x}$ implies

$$|f(t) - f(x)| < \epsilon$$

2. For $x \in [1, 2]$ and $0 < h < \delta_{\epsilon,x}$, evaluate $\dfrac{1}{h}\displaystyle\int_{x}^{x+h} f$.

3. Repeat Exercise 2 for $-\delta_{\epsilon,x} < h < 0$.

4. Find $\delta_{\epsilon,x}$ such that, for all $x \in [1, 2]$, $0 < |h| < \delta_{\epsilon,x}$ implies

$$\left| f(x) = \frac{1}{h} \int_{x}^{x+h} f \right| < \epsilon$$

5. The function G is constructed from the rule $G(t) = \displaystyle\int_{1}^{t} f, 0 \le t \le 3$. Find an explicit algebraic rule for G.

6. Find G'. For which values of x is $G'(x) = f(x)$?

7–12. Repeat Exercises 1–6 for the function f given by $f(x) = x^2$, $0 \le x \le 3$. The function f is given by

$$f(x) = \begin{cases} x, & 0 \le x < 1 \\ 2x + 1, & 1 \le x < 2 \\ 3x + 2, & 2 \le x \le 3 \end{cases}$$

13. Draw the graph of f.

14. Find $\displaystyle\int_1^2 f$.

15. The function G is given by

$$G(t) = \int_1^t f, \qquad 0 \le t \le 3$$

Find an explicit algebraic rule for G.

16. Compare $\{D_-G\}(1)$ and $\{D_+G\}(1)$ with $f(1)$. Compare $\{D_-G\}(2)$ and $\{D_+G\}(2)$ with $f(2)$.
The function f is given by

$$f(x) = \begin{cases} 1, & x \text{ rational}, & 0 \le x < 1, \, 2 < x \le 3 \\ 2, & x \text{ irrational}, & 0 < x < 1, \qquad 2 < x < 3 \\ x^2, & & 1 \le x \le 2 \end{cases}$$

17. Describe the graph of f.

18. Find $\displaystyle\int_1^2 f$.

19. G is the function given by $G(t) = \displaystyle\int_1^t f$. Find an explicit algebraic rule for G and find the domain of G.

20. Find G'.

21. If H is the function given by $H(t) = \displaystyle\overline{\int_1^t} f$ (the upper integral), find an explicit algebraic rule for H and find the domain of H.

22. Find H'.

23. Compare $\{D_-H\}(1)$ and $\{D_+H\}(1)$ with $f(1)$. Compare $\{D_-H\}(2)$ and $\{D_+H\}(2)$ with $f(2)$.

4-2   The Classical Divergence Theorem

In this section we will examine the weakest theorem concerning the relation between the surface integral of a function into V_3 and the three-dimensional integral of the divergence of that function. The word "weakest" is used here to indicate that the theorem has the strongest hypotheses—that is, more is required of the surfaces, three-dimensional sets, and function than is really necessary to reach the same conclusion.

Throughout we will be discussing a specific three-dimensional set W which has the property that it has a nonzero volume and the property that it is enclosed by S, the trace of a surface. In fact, it will be S which determines the three-dimensional set W. Basically, we require that S have the property that any line which is parallel to one of the three rectangular coordinate axes intersects S at most twice. Thus S is divisible into a top and bottom which are mutually bounded by the path of a curve. S can also be divided into a left side and a right side which are bounded by the path of another curve. Finally, S can also be separated into a front side and a rear side which are separated by the path of still another curve.

We further require that each one of these six possible subdivisions of S be the graph of an equation which expresses one of the variables x, y, or z as a dependent variable of a function whose domain is a two-dimensional set, which set is described by the remaining two variables.

More specifically, we require the existence of a two-dimensional set $R_{x,y}$ (which we think of as the projection of S onto the x-y coordinate plane) which is the domain of two functions φ_B and φ_T such that

$$W = \{(x, y, z) \mid \varphi_B(x, y) \leq z \leq \varphi_T(x, y) \quad \text{and} \quad (x, y) \in R_{x,y}\}$$

In this way we require the top of S to be the graph of the equation $z = \varphi_T(x, y)$ and the bottom of S to be the graph of the equation $z = \varphi_B(x, y)$.

We also require the existence of a two-dimensional set $R_{y,z}$ (which we think of as the projection of S onto the y-z coordinate plane) which is the domain of two functions φ_R and φ_F such that

$$W = \{(x, y, z) \mid \varphi_R(y, z) \leq x \leq \varphi_F(y, z) \quad \text{and} \quad (y, z) \in R_{y,z}\}$$

We are thus requiring here that the rear of S be the graph of the equation $x = \varphi_R(y, z)$ and that the front of S be the graph of the equation $x = \varphi_F(y, z)$.

Finally we require the existence of a two-dimensional set $R_{x,z}$ (which we think of as the projection of S onto the x-z coordinate plane) which is the domain of two functions φ_G and φ_F such that

$$W = \{(x, y, z) \mid \varphi_G(x, z) \leq y \leq \varphi_D(x, z) \quad \text{and} \quad (x, z) \in R_{x,z}\}$$

This means that the left side of S is the graph of the equation $y = \varphi_G(x, z)$ and the right side of S is the graph of the equation $y = \varphi_D(x, z)$.

We now turn our attention to the closed plane paths which bound these two-dimensional sets. These paths are thought of as the projections of the space paths which separate the "halves" of S. The projections of these plane paths onto the appropriate coordinate axes are line segments and the end points of those line segments are determined by the largest and smallest of the coordinates of the points of the three-dimensional set W. For definiteness we will adopt the following notation:

The projection of $R_{x,y}$ on the x axis will be the line segment $\{(x, 0, 0) \mid a \leq x \leq b\}$. What we have thus far imposed on the set W means that there exist two functions f_{BG} and f_{BD} on $[a, b]$ into the real numbers such that

$$R_{x,y} = \{(x, y) \mid f_{BG}(x) \leq y \leq f_{BD}(x) \quad \text{and} \quad a \leq x \leq b\}$$

Since the top and bottom of S meet in a path whose projection onto the x-y plane is the boundary of $R_{x,y}$, we must have, for all $x \in [a, b]$,

$$\varphi_B(x, f_{BG}(x)) = \varphi_T(x, f_{BG}(x))$$

and

$$\varphi_B(x, f_{BD}(x)) = \varphi_T(x, f_{BD}(x))$$

The projection of $R_{x,y}$ on the y axis will be the line segment $\{(0, y, 0) \mid c \leq y \leq d\}$. What we have thus far imposed on the set W means that there exist two functions f_{BR} and f_{BF} on $[c, d]$ into the real numbers such that

$$R_{x,y} = \{(x, y) \mid f_{BR}(y) \leq x \leq f_{BF}(y) \quad \text{and} \quad c \leq y \leq d\}$$

Since the top and bottom of S meet in a path whose projection onto the x-y plane is the boundary of $R_{x,y}$, we must have, for all $y \in [c, d]$,

$$\varphi_B(f_{BR}(y), y) = \varphi_T(f_{BR}(y), y)$$

and

$$\varphi_B(f_{BF}(y), y) = \varphi_T(f_{BF}(y), y)$$

Turning now to the two-dimensional set $R_{y,z}$, the projection of this set onto the y axis is necessarily $\{(y, 0) \mid c \leq y \leq d\}$. Thus there are two functions f_{RB} and f_{RT} on $[c, d]$ into the real numbers such that

$$R_{y,z} = \{(y, z) \mid f_{RB}(y) \leq z \leq f_{RT}(y) \quad \text{and} \quad c \leq y \leq d\}$$

Since the front and rear of S meet in a path whose projection onto the y-z plane is the boundary of $R_{y,z}$, we must have, for all $y \in [c, d]$,

$$\varphi_F(y, f_{RB}(y)) = \varphi_R(y, f_{RB}(y))$$

and

$$\varphi_F(y, f_{RT}(y)) = \varphi_R(y, f_{RT}(y))$$

We let the projection of $R_{y,z}$ onto the z axis be $\{(0, z) \mid p \leq z \leq q\}$. Then there exist two functions f_{RG} and f_{RD} on $[p, q]$ into the real numbers

such that

$$R_{y,z} = \{(y, z) \mid f_{RG}(z) \leq y \leq f_{RD}(z) \quad \text{and} \quad p \leq z \leq q\}$$

Since the front and rear of S meet in a path whose projection onto the y-z plane is the boundary of $R_{y,z}$, we must have, for all $z \in [p, q]$,

$$\varphi_F(f_{RG}(z), z) = \varphi_R(f_{RG}(z), z)$$

and

$$\varphi_F(f_{RD}(z), z) = \varphi_R(f_{RD}(z), z)$$

The projection of $R_{x,z}$ onto the x axis is now necessarily $\{(x, 0) \mid a \leq x \leq b\}$ and there are two functions f_{GB} and f_{GT} on $[a, b]$ into the real numbers such that

$$R_{x,z} = \{(x, z) \mid f_{GB}(x) \leq z \leq f_{GT}(x) \quad \text{and} \quad a \leq x \leq b\}$$

Further, we must have, for all $x \in [a, b]$,

$$\varphi_G(x, f_{GB}(x)) = \varphi_D(x, f_{GB}(x))$$

and

$$\varphi_G(x, f_{GT}(x)) = \varphi_D(x, f_{GT}(x))$$

Finally, the projection of $R_{x,z}$ onto the z axis must be $\{(0, z) \mid p \leq z \leq q\}$ and there are two functions f_{GR} and f_{GF} on $[p, q]$ into the real numbers such that

$$R_{x,z} = \{(x, z) \mid f_{GR}(z) \leq x \leq f_{GT}(z) \quad \text{and} \quad p \leq z \leq q\}$$

Further, we must have, for all $z \in [p, q]$,

$$\varphi_G(f_{GR}(z), z) = \varphi_D(f_{GR}(z), z)$$

and

$$\varphi_G(f_{GF}(z), z) = \varphi_D(f_{GF}(z), z)$$

We now consider the function $\mathbf{v}$, on W into $\mathbf{V}_3$, given by

$$\mathbf{v} = L\mathbf{i} + M\mathbf{j} + N\mathbf{k}$$

Assuming that the three component functions of $\mathbf{v}$ have partial derivatives which are continuous on W, div $\mathbf{v} = L_1 + M_2 + N_3$ will be integrable on W and

$$\iiint_W \text{div } \mathbf{v} = \iiint_W L_1 + \iiint_W M_2 + \iiint_W N_3$$

We may use iterated integration to begin the evaluation of the three integrals on the right:

$$\iiint_W L_1 = \iint_{R_{y,z}} \left[\int_{x=\varphi_R(y,z)}^{x=\varphi_F(y,z)} L_1(x, y, z)\, dx \right] dy\, dz$$

$$= \iint_{R_{y,z}} [L(\varphi_F(y, z), y, z) - L(\varphi_R(y, z), y, z)]\, dy\, dz$$

$$\iiint_W M_2 = \iint_{R_{x,z}} \left[\int_{y=\varphi_G(x,z)}^{y=\varphi_D(x,z)} M_2(x, y, z)\, dy \right] dx\, dz$$

$$= \iint_{R_{x,z}} [M(x, \varphi_D(x, z), z) - M(x, \varphi_G(x, z), z)]\, dx\, dz$$

$$\iiint_W N_3 = \iint_{R_{x,y}} \left[\int_{z=\varphi_B(x,y)}^{z=\varphi_T(x,y)} N_3(x, y, z)\, dz \right] dx\, dy$$

$$= \iint_{R_{x,y}} [N(x, y, \varphi_T(x, y)) - N(x, y, \varphi_B(x, y))]\, dx\, dy$$

Next we turn our attention to the surface integral of the function **v** over the surface with trace S, which bounds the three-dimensional set W. If **n** is a unit normal vector function for S, then we have

$$\iint_S \mathbf{v} \cdot \mathbf{n} = \iint_S (L\mathbf{n} \cdot \mathbf{i} + M\mathbf{n} \cdot \mathbf{j} + N\mathbf{n} \cdot \mathbf{k})$$

For definiteness (and also to make things come out right) we will take that unit normal vector function for S whose representations are oriented away from W.

We divide the surface S into two parts: the front, S_F, which is the graph of $x = \varphi_F(y, z)$ and the rear, S_R, which is the graph of $x = \varphi_R(y, z)$. An outward-directed normal vector function for S_F is then given by

$$\{\mathbf{r}_1 \times \mathbf{r}_2\}(\varphi_F(y, z), y, z) = \mathbf{i} - \{\varphi_F\}_1(y, z)\mathbf{j} - \{\varphi_F\}_2(y, z)\mathbf{k}$$

since, in order to be directed away from W, the first component must be positive. We then have

$$\iint_{S_F} L\mathbf{n} \cdot \mathbf{i} = \iint_{R_{y,z}} [L(\varphi_F(y, z), y, z)]\, dy\, dz$$

In like manner, an outward-directed normal vector function for S_R is given by

$$\{\mathbf{r}_1 \times \mathbf{r}_2\}(\varphi_R(y, z), y, z) = -\mathbf{i} + \{\varphi_R\}_1(y, z)\mathbf{j} + \{\varphi_R\}_2(y, z)\mathbf{k}$$

and

$$\iint_{S_R} L\mathbf{n} \cdot \mathbf{i} = -\iint_{R_{y,z}} L(\varphi_R(y, z), y, z)\, dy\, dz$$

S_D is the graph of $y = \varphi_D(x, z)$. Here we have an outward-directed normal vector function given by

$$\{\mathbf{r}_1 \times \mathbf{r}_2\}(x, \varphi_D(x, z), z) = -\{\varphi_D\}_1(x, z)\mathbf{i} + \mathbf{j} - \{\varphi_D\}_2(x, z)\mathbf{k}$$

and

$$\iint_{S_D} M\mathbf{n} \cdot \mathbf{j} = \iint_{R_{x,z}} M(x, \varphi_D(x, z), z) \, dx \, dz$$

S_G is the graph of $y = \varphi_G(x, z)$ and we have

$$\{\mathbf{r}_1 \times \mathbf{r}_2\}(x, \varphi_G(x, z), z) = \{\varphi_G\}_1(x, z)\mathbf{i} - \mathbf{j} + \{\varphi_G\}_2(x, z)\mathbf{k}$$

and

$$\iint_{S_G} M\mathbf{n} \cdot \mathbf{j} = -\iint_{R_{x,z}} M(x, \varphi_G(x, z), z) \, dx \, dz$$

Finally, for the division of S into top and bottom "halves," we have, for S_T,

$$\{\mathbf{r}_1 \times \mathbf{r}_2\}(x, y, \varphi_T(x, y)) = -\{\varphi_T\}_1(x, y)\mathbf{i} - \{\varphi_T\}_2(x, y)\mathbf{j} + \mathbf{k}$$

$$\iint_{S_T} N\mathbf{n} \cdot \mathbf{k} = \iint_{R_{x,y}} N(x, y, \varphi_T(x, y)) \, dx \, dy$$

and, for S_B,

$$\{\mathbf{r}_1 \times \mathbf{r}_2\}(x, y, \varphi_B(x, y)) = \{\varphi_B\}_1(x, y)\mathbf{i} + \{\varphi_B\}_2(x, y)\mathbf{j} - \mathbf{k}$$

$$\iint_{S_B} N\mathbf{n} \cdot \mathbf{k} = -\iint_{R_{x,y}} N(x, y, \varphi_B(x, y)) \, dx \, dy$$

Combining these results gives

$$\iint_{S} L\mathbf{n} \cdot \mathbf{i} = \left\{ \iint_{S_F} + \iint_{S_R} \right\} L\mathbf{n} \cdot \mathbf{i}$$

$$= \iint_{R_{y,z}} [L(\varphi_F(y, z), y, z) - L(\varphi_R(y, z), y, z)] \, dy \, dz$$

$$\iint_{S} M\mathbf{n} \cdot \mathbf{j} = \left\{ \iint_{S_G} + \iint_{S_D} \right\} M\mathbf{n} \cdot \mathbf{j}$$

$$= \iint_{R_{x,z}} [M(x, \varphi_D(x, z), z) - M(x, \varphi_G(x, z), z)] \, dx \, dz$$

$$\iint_{S} N\mathbf{n} \cdot \mathbf{k} = \left\{ \iint_{S_T} + \iint_{S_B} \right\} N\mathbf{n} \cdot \mathbf{k}$$

$$= \iint_{R_{x,\cdot}} [N(x, y, \varphi_T(x, y)) - N(x, y, \varphi_B(x, y))] \, dx \, dy$$

So that

$$\iint_S \mathbf{v} \cdot \mathbf{n} = \iiint_W \mathrm{div}\ \mathbf{v}$$

The classical theorem which we have now proved is known as the divergence theorem, or Gauss's Theorem. The hypotheses required that the function $\mathbf{v}$ have a divergence which must have sufficiently nice behavior at sufficiently many points of W so that the integral will exist and our partial evaluation of it will be valid. The function $\mathbf{v}$ must have sufficiently nice behavior at sufficiently many points of S so that the surface integral will exist. The surface with trace S is required to have the geometric property that lines parallel to the coordinate axes intersect the trace in at most two points. This, in turn, will imply that the six subdivisions of S be the graphs of six functions, each on a two-dimensional set into the real numbers. These functions must have partial derivatives with behavior sufficiently nice on S so that a unit vector function exists for S—that is, so that the surface integral will exist. All this being given, the theorem then results from six applications of the fundamental theorem of calculus and of theorems concerning the evaluation of a three-dimensional integral in terms of iterated integration.

One purpose of this book is to examine the possibility of strengthening this version of the divergence theorem, that is, how the hypotheses can be weakened without changing the conclusion. This will be done in Chapter 11. Another purpose of the book is to examine closely the major tools used in the proof given here. This examination begins in the next chapter.

EXERCISES

1. Show that the divergence theorem also applies to a function

$$\mathbf{v} = L\mathbf{i} + M\mathbf{j} + N\mathbf{k}$$

on the rectangular box with opposing corners $(0, 0, 0)$ and (a, b, c) (where $a > 0$, $b > 0$, and $c > 0$) and sides parallel to the coordinate planes.

Consider the tetrahedron W with vertices $(0, 0, 0)$, $(2, 4, 6)$, $(4, 2, 2)$, and $(6, 6, 4)$.

2. Find linear equations whose graphs are the planes containing the faces of W.

3. Find the projection of each face of W onto the x-y plane. Give the vertices of these triangles and equations for each side.

4. Give the functions whose graphs are the faces of W.

5. Find the functions f_{BR} and f_{BF} whose graphs bound $R_{x,y}$.

6. The projections of the four faces of W onto the x-y plane divide $R_{x,y}$ into four triangles. For each of these triangles, determine which face of W forms part of the top face S_T and which forms part of the bottom face S_B.

7. Find the functions φ_B and φ_T whose graphs are S_B and S_T.

8. Find a normal vector function $\mathbf{r}_1 \times \mathbf{r}_2$ for S, the surface of W.

9. Write $\displaystyle\iint_S \mathbf{v} \cdot \mathbf{n}$ as an iterated integral.

10. Write $\displaystyle\iiint_W \text{div } \mathbf{v}$ as an iterated integral.

11. If $\mathbf{v}$ is a constant function into V_3, the divergence theorem shows that $\displaystyle\iint_S \mathbf{v} \cdot \mathbf{n} = 0$. How could this result be determined without the use of this theorem?

12. Give a full statement of the version of the divergence theorem proved in this section.

4-3   Stokes' Theorem

In this section we examine a classical vector theorem which considers a surface with trace S bounded by the path of a curve γ, and gives a relation between the line integral along the curve—with an orientation imposed on the curve—and the surface integral with one of the unit normal vector functions specified. We assume, for definiteness, that the rearmost and most forward points of the trace of S have x coordinates a and b, respectively, that the leftmost and rightmost points have y coordinates c and d, respectively, and that the lowest and highest points have z coordinates p and q, respectively. We finally assume that any line parallel to a coordinate axis intersects S at most once and that the projections onto the three coordinate planes are two-dimensional sets bounded by the graphs of functions. We are thus considering a two-dimensional set $R_{x,y}$ and assuming that there exists a continuously differentiable function F on $R_{x,y}$ into the real numbers such that

$$S = \{(x, y, F(x, y)) \mid (x, y) \in R_{x,y}\}$$

We fix one of the (two possible) normal vector functions for S by taking

$$\{\mathbf{r}_1 \times \mathbf{r}_2\}(x, y, F(x, y)) = -F_1(x, y)\mathbf{i} - F_2(x, y)\mathbf{j} + \mathbf{k}$$

The closed plane path which bounds $R_{x,y}$ will be assumed to be the union of the graphs of two functions f_D and f_G on $[a, b]$ into the real numbers such that

$$R_{x,y} = \{(x, y) \mid f_G(x) \leq y \leq f_D(x) \text{ and } a \leq x \leq b\}$$

We now fix an orientation on the space curve γ whose path bounds the surface S by orienting its projection in the x-y plane in a counterclockwise manner. This projection is assumed to be given by the graphs of two continuously differentiable functions f_G and f_D on $[a, b]$ into $[c, d]$ such that

$$R_{x,y} = \{(x, y) \mid f_G(x) \leq y \leq f_D(x) \text{ and } a \leq x \leq b\}$$

With the orientation given to γ, this curve will then be given by

$$\mathbf{r}(x) = \begin{cases} x\mathbf{i} + f_G(x)\mathbf{j} + F(x, f_G(x))\mathbf{k}, & a \leq x \leq b \\ (2b - x)\mathbf{i} + f_D(2b - x)\mathbf{j} \\ \quad + F(2b - x, f_D(2b - x))\mathbf{k}, & b \leq x \leq 2b - a \end{cases}$$

A tangent vector function for the curve γ will then be given by

$$\mathbf{r}'(x) = \begin{cases} \mathbf{i} + f_G'(x)\mathbf{j} + [F_1(x, f_G(x)) + F_2(x, f_G(x))f_G'(x)]\mathbf{k}, & a < x < b \\ -\mathbf{i} - f_D'(2b - x)\mathbf{j} - [F_1(2b - x, f_D(2b - x)) \\ \quad + F_2(2b - x, f_D(2b - x))f_D'(2b - x)]\mathbf{k}, & b < x < 2b - a \end{cases}$$

We now give the surface S a definite position by requiring that every vector in the range of the unit normal vector function have positive numbers for all three components. This positioning then requires that the projection of the path of γ onto the z-x plane (with the z axis horizontal) be oriented in a counterclockwise manner. We use $R_{z,x}$ to denote the projection of the trace onto this plane and assume the existence of a continuously differentiable function G on $R_{z,x}$ into the real numbers such that $\{(x, G(z, x), z) \mid (z, x) \in R_{z,x}\}$ is the trace of S. Our assumption about the positioning then implies that a normal vector function for S is given by

$$\{\mathbf{r}_1 \times \mathbf{r}_2\}(x, G(z, x), z) = -G_2(z, x)\mathbf{i} + \mathbf{j} - G_1(z, x)\mathbf{k}$$

The set $R_{z,x}$ is bounded by the projection of the path of γ onto the z-x plane and this projection is the graph of two continuously differentiable functions g_R and g_F on $[p, q]$ into $[a, b]$ such that

$$R_{z,x} = \{(z, x) \mid g_R(z) \leq x \leq g_F(z) \text{ and } p \leq z \leq q\}$$

The orientation given to γ and the position of S now require that γ be given by

$$\mathbf{r}(z) = \begin{cases} g_R(z)\mathbf{i} + G(z, g_R(z))\mathbf{j} + z\mathbf{k}, & p \leq z \leq q \\ g_F(2q - z)\mathbf{i} + G(2q - z, g_F(2q - z))\mathbf{j} \\ \qquad + (2q - z)\mathbf{k}, & q \leq z \leq 2q - p \end{cases}$$

A tangent vector function for γ is thus given by

$$\mathbf{r}'(z) = \begin{cases} g_R'(z)\mathbf{i} + [G_1(z, g_R(z)) + G_2(z, g_R(z))g_R'(z)]\mathbf{j} + \mathbf{k}, & p < z < q \\ -g_F'(2q - z)\mathbf{i} - [G_1(2q - z, g_F(2q - z)) \\ \qquad + G_2(2q - z, g_F(2q - z))g_F'(2q - z)]\mathbf{j} - \mathbf{k}, & q < z < 2q - p \end{cases}$$

Finally the position of S requires that the projection of the path of γ onto the y-z plane be oriented in a counterclockwise manner. We use $R_{y,z}$ to denote the projection of S onto this plane and assume the existence of two continuously differentiable functions h_B and h_T on $[c, d]$ into $[p, q]$ such that

$$R_{y,z} = \{(y, z) \mid h_B(y) \leq z \leq h_T(y) \text{ and } c \leq y \leq d\}$$

There then will exist a continuously differentiable function H on $R_{y,z}$ into the real numbers such that S is

$$\{(H(y, z), y, z) \mid (y, z) \in R_{y,z}\}$$

A properly oriented normal vector function for S is thus given by

$$\{\mathbf{r}_1 \times \mathbf{r}_2\}(H(y, z), y, z) = \mathbf{i} - H_1(y, z)\mathbf{j} - H_2(y, z)\mathbf{k}$$

The orientation given to γ requires that this curve also be given by

$$\mathbf{r}(y) = \begin{cases} H(y, h_B(y))\mathbf{i} + y\mathbf{j} + h_B(y)\mathbf{k}, & c \leq y \leq d \\ H(2d - y, h_T(2d - y))\mathbf{i} + (2d - y)\mathbf{j} \\ \qquad + h_T(2d - y)\mathbf{k}, & d \leq y \leq 2d - c \end{cases}$$

From this, a tangent vector function is given by

$$\mathbf{r}'(y) = \begin{cases} [H_1(y, h_B(y)) + H_2(y, h_B(y))h_B'(y)]\mathbf{i} + \mathbf{j} + h_B'(y)\mathbf{k}, & c < y < d \\ -[H_1(2d - y, h_T(2d - y)) + H_2(2d - y, h_T(2d - y))h_T'(2d - y])\mathbf{i} \\ \qquad - \mathbf{j} - h_T'(2d - y)\mathbf{k}, & d < y < 2d - c \end{cases}$$

We are now ready to consider the continuously differentiable function on S into $\mathbf{V}_3$ given by

$$\mathbf{v} = L\mathbf{i} + M\mathbf{j} + N\mathbf{k}$$

We have

$$\int_\gamma \mathbf{v} \cdot \mathbf{T} = \int_\gamma [L\mathbf{i} \cdot \mathbf{T} + M\mathbf{j} \cdot \mathbf{T} + N\mathbf{k} \cdot \mathbf{T}]$$

$$= \int_a^b L(x, f_G(x), F(x, f_G(x)))\, dx - \int_a^b L(x, f_D(x), F(x, f_D(x)))\, dx$$

$$+ \int_c^d M(H(y, h_B(y)), y, h_B(y))\, dy - \int_c^d M(H(y, h_T(y)), y, h_T(y))\, dy$$

$$+ \int_p^q N(g_R(z), G(z, g_R(z)), z)\, dz - \int_p^q N(g_F(z), G(z, g_F(z)), z)\, dz$$

$$= \int_a^b \int_{f_D(x)}^{f_G(x)} \frac{\partial}{\partial y} [L(x, y, F(x, y))]\, dy\, dx$$

$$+ \int_c^d \int_{h_T(x)}^{h_B(x)} \frac{\partial}{\partial z} [M(H(y, z), y, z)]\, dz\, dy$$

$$+ \int_p^q \int_{g_F(z)}^{g_R(z)} \frac{\partial}{\partial x} [N(x, G(z, x), z)]\, dx\, dz$$

$$= - \iint_{R_{x,y}} [L_2(x, y, F(x, y)) + L_3(x, y, F(x, y))F_2(x, y)]\, dy\, dx$$

$$- \iint_{R_{y,z}} [M_1(H(y, z), y, z)H_1(y, z) + M_3(H(y, z), y, z)]\, dz\, dy$$

$$- \iint_{R_{z,x}} [N_1(x, G(z, x), z) + N_2(x, G(z, x), z)G_2(z, x)]\, dz\, dx$$

$$= \iint_{R_{x,y}} [L_3(x, y, F(x, y))\mathbf{j} - L_2(x, y, F(x,y))\mathbf{k}]$$

$$\cdot [-F_1(x, y)\mathbf{i} - F_2(x, y)\mathbf{j} + \mathbf{k}]\, dy\, dx$$

$$+ \iint_{R_{y,z}} [-M_3(H(y, z), y, z)\mathbf{i} + M_1(H(y, z), y, z)\mathbf{k}]$$

$$\cdot [\mathbf{i} - H_1(y, z)\mathbf{j} - H_2(y, z)\mathbf{k}]\, dz\, dy$$

$$+ \iint_{R_{z,x}} [N_2(x, G(z, x), z)\mathbf{i} - N_1(x, G(z, x), z)\mathbf{j}]$$

$$\cdot [-G_2(z, x)\mathbf{i} + \mathbf{j} - G_1(z, x)\mathbf{k}]\, dz\, dx$$

$$= \iint_S (L_3\mathbf{j} - L_2\mathbf{k}) \cdot \mathbf{n} + \iint_S (-M_3\mathbf{j} + M_1\mathbf{k}) \cdot \mathbf{n} + \iint_S (N_2\mathbf{i} - N_1\mathbf{j}) \cdot \mathbf{n}$$

$$= \iint_S [(N_2 - M_3)\mathbf{i} + (L_3 - N_1)\mathbf{j} + (M_1 - L_2)\mathbf{k}] \cdot \mathbf{n}$$

$$= \iint_S (\text{curl } \mathbf{v}) \cdot \mathbf{n}$$

We have thus arrived at a relation between the line integral of $\mathbf{v}$ and the surface integral of curl $\mathbf{v}$. One striking result of this conclusion—known as Stokes' Theorem—is that if we are given a closed path in three-dimensional space which bounds the trace of many different surfaces, then the surface integral of the curl of a function into $\mathbf{V_3}$ must be the same number for every one of these surfaces. This, of course, occurs only under hypotheses which guarantee the steps taken.

These hypotheses required that the function $\mathbf{v}$ have a curl with sufficiently nice behavior at sufficiently many points of S so that curl $\mathbf{v}$ is integrable on S. The trace S must have a unit normal vector function whose representations are consistently directed with respect to S. The version of the theorem which we have proved here requires that any line parallel to one of the coordinate axes intersects S in at most one point. The functions involved in giving S must have sufficient properties so that all the integrals used exist. The path γ which bounds S must be given by functions with sufficient properties so that the line integral exists. Finally the relative orientation of the curve to the unit normal vector function for S must be chosen so that we have the two integrals being equal to, rather than opposites of, each other.

A shorter proof, which does not depend on the projectability of S is given by

Theorem 4-3-1. $R = [a, b] \times [c, d]$. $\mathbf{r}$ is a one-to-one continuously differentiable function on R into $\mathbf{V_3}$ such that $\mathbf{r_1} \times \mathbf{r_2}$ does not vanish on R. Neither $\mathbf{r_1}$ nor $\mathbf{r_2}$ vanishes on the boundary of R. The set S is the trace of $\mathbf{r}$ and the curve γ is given by the restriction of $\mathbf{r}$ to the boundary of R. If $\mathbf{v}$ is continuously differentiable and γ is oriented by a counterclockwise orientation of the boundary of R and a unit normal vector function for S is given by $\mathbf{r_1} \times \mathbf{r_2}$, then

$$\iint_S (\text{curl } \mathbf{v}) \cdot \mathbf{n} = \int_\gamma \mathbf{v} \cdot \mathbf{T}$$

Proof

$$
\iint_S (\text{curl } \mathbf{v}) \cdot \mathbf{n} = \iint_R \{ [v_2^3(\mathbf{r}) - v_3^2(\mathbf{r})](r_1^2 r_2^3 - r_1^3 r_2^2)
$$
$$
+ [v_3^1(\mathbf{r}) - v_1^3(\mathbf{r})](r_1^3 r_2^1 - r_1^1 r_2^3)
$$
$$
+ [v_1^2(\mathbf{r}) - v_2^1(\mathbf{r})](r_1^1 r_2^2 - r_1^2 r_2^1) \}
$$
$$
= \iint_R \{ [v_1^1(\mathbf{r})r_1^1 + v_2^1(\mathbf{r})r_1^2 + v_3^1(\mathbf{r})r_1^3]r_2^1 + v^1(\mathbf{r})r_{21}^1
$$
$$
+ [v_1^2(\mathbf{r})r_1^1 + v_2^2(\mathbf{r})r_1^2 + v_3^2(\mathbf{r})r_1^3]r_2^2 + v^2(\mathbf{r})r_{21}^2
$$
$$
+ [v_1^3(\mathbf{r})r_1^1 + v_2^3(\mathbf{r})r_1^2 + v_3^3(\mathbf{r})r_1^3]r_2^3 + v^3(\mathbf{r})r_{21}^3
$$
$$
- [v_1^1(\mathbf{r})r_2^1 + v_2^1(\mathbf{r})r_2^2 + v_3^1(\mathbf{r})r_2^3]r_1^1 - v^1(\mathbf{r})r_{12}^1
$$
$$
- [v_1^2(\mathbf{r})r_2^1 + v_2^2(\mathbf{r})r_2^2 + v_3^2(\mathbf{r})r_2^3]r_1^2 - v^2(\mathbf{r})r_{12}^2
$$
$$
- [v_1^3(\mathbf{r})r_2^1 + v_2^3(\mathbf{r})r_2^2 + v_3^3(\mathbf{r})r_2^3]r_1^3 - v^3(\mathbf{r})r_{12}^3 \}
$$
$$
= \iint_R \{ [v^1(\mathbf{r})r_2^1]_1 + [v^2(\mathbf{r})r_2^2]_1 + [v^3(\mathbf{r})r_2^3]_1
$$
$$
- [v^1(\mathbf{r})r_1^1]_2 - [v^2(\mathbf{r})r_1^2]_2 - [v^3(\mathbf{r})r_1^3]_2 \}
$$
$$
= \iint_R \{ [\mathbf{v}(\mathbf{r}) \cdot \mathbf{r}_2]_1 - [\mathbf{v}(\mathbf{r}) \cdot \mathbf{r}_1]_2 \}
$$
$$
= \int_c^d \int_a^b [\mathbf{v}(\mathbf{r}) \cdot \mathbf{r}_2]_1(u, v)\, du\, dv - \int_a^b \int_c^d [\mathbf{v}(\mathbf{r}) \cdot \mathbf{r}_1]_2(u, v)\, dv\, du
$$
$$
= \int_a^b [\mathbf{v}(\mathbf{r}) \cdot \mathbf{r}_1](u, c)\, du + \int_c^d [\mathbf{v}(\mathbf{r}) \cdot \mathbf{r}_2](b, v)\, dv
$$
$$
+ \int_b^a [\mathbf{v}(\mathbf{r}) \cdot \mathbf{r}_1](u, d)\, du + \int_d^c [\mathbf{v}(\mathbf{r}) \cdot \mathbf{r}_2](a, v)\, dv
$$
$$
= \int_\gamma \mathbf{v} \cdot \mathbf{T} \qquad\blacksquare
$$

EXERCISES

1. Prove that Stokes' Theorem holds in the case of a surface with trace perpendicular to one of the coordinate axes, in particular the rectangle with vertices $(0, 0, 0)$, $(0, a, 0)$, $(0, b, 0)$ and $(a, b, 0)$. (Take $a > 0$ and $b > 0$.)

2. Prove that Stokes' Theorem holds in the case of a surface with trace parallel to one of the coordinate axes, in particular the rectangle with vertices $(0, 0, 0)$, $(0, a, b)$, (a, b, c), and $(0, 0, c)$—where $a > 0$, $b > 0$, and $c > 0$.

Consider the triangle with vertices $(2, 5, 0)$, $(4, 1, 2)$, and $(5, 1, 4)$.

3. Find a linear equation whose graph is the plane containing this triangle.

4. Find a vector function whose representations are normals to the given triangle, directed away from the origin.

5. Find $R_{x,y}$, the projection onto the *x-y* plane.

6. Find the function F, on $R_{x,y}$ into the real numbers, whose graph is this triangle.

7. Find the function giving normals with the orientation away from the origin.

8. Orient the boundary so that the three given points occur in the order mentioned. Find a function giving this oriented curve.

9. Find a tangent vector function for this oriented curve.

10. Give rules for the functions f_D and f_G whose graphs bound $R_{x,y}$.

11. Find $R_{z,x}$, the projection of S onto the *z-x* plane.

12. Find the function G, on $R_{z,x}$ into the real numbers, whose graph is the triangle.

13. Find a normal vector function in terms of G.

14. With the orientation given to the boundary, find a function $\mathbf{r}(z)$ giving this curve.

15. Find $\mathbf{r}'(z)$.

16. Find the functions g_R and g_F whose graphs bound $R_{z,x}$.

17. Find $R_{y,z}$, the projection onto the *y-z* plane.

18. Find the function H on $R_{y,z}$ into the real numbers whose graph is the triangle.

19. Use H to find a normal vector function.

20. Find $\mathbf{r}(y)$ which gives the boundary.

21. Find $\mathbf{r}'(y)$.

22. Find the functions h_B and h_T whose graphs bound $R_{y,z}$.

In the following exercises, $\mathbf{v}(x, y, z) = z\mathbf{i} + x\mathbf{j} + y\mathbf{k}$.

23. Find curl $\mathbf{v}$.

24. Evaluate $\displaystyle\iint_S (\text{curl } \mathbf{v}) \cdot \mathbf{n}$.

25. Evaluate $\displaystyle\int_\gamma \mathbf{v} \cdot \mathbf{T}$.

26. Give an exact statement of the first version of Stokes' Theorem.

4-4 Plan for Further Investigation

The first three chapters of this book developed the concepts of vector, curve and surface, and surface and line integral. The present chapter has brought together these concepts in two classical vector theorems. These theorems are, in effect, vector analogues of the fundamental theorem of calculus.

The theorems themselves involve integration. It then seems reasonable that we examine closely what is meant by an integral. That being done, it is worthwhile to examine the methods used to evaluate integrals or, failing that, to approximate the values by means which control the order of accuracy. This is done in Chapter 5.

The manipulations used in the derivation of formulas for expressing gradient, divergence, and curl in terms of rectangular coordinates require the interchange in the order of taking multiple limits. In Chapter 6 we examine the general notion of limit and of continuity, paying particular attention to conditions which are sufficient to allow such interchange.

Since we have dealt with analogues of the derivative for functions involving vectors, we will next turn, in Chapter 7, to an examination of the idea of differentiation itself. In particular, we will examine functions whose domains and ranges are general n-dimensional sets.

Up to that point, although we will be dealing with sets in spaces of arbitrary (finite positive integer) dimension, those sets have been bounded. In Chapter 8 we consider integration for functions whose domains or ranges are not bounded sets. This leads into the more general notion of how misbehavior of a function may still not prevent the existence of an integral.

Examining the idea of misbehavior of a function naturally leads to the question of how such misbehavior might be found. This brings up the search for a method or methods of representing functions which allow the determination of their behaviors by the use of general tools. Chapter 9 discusses how infinite series are used to give some results along this line, and Chapter 10 examines other methods of representing functions.

Since Chapters 5 through 10 are an investigation into the concepts and methods used in the proofs of the Divergence Theorem and Stokes' Theorem, which we have used in this present chapter, we will conclude in Chapter 11, by giving more general proofs of these two classic theorems, which proofs use nothing more than the definitions of divergence, curl, line integral, surface integral, and integral. Thus the next six chapters will try to show why that which we have done in this present chapter is actually a valid procedure, and the final chapter will show how we could have proved these two classical theorems without this machinery.

INTEGRATION 5

5-1 Quadrable Sets

Any attempt to investigate the methods of proof of the classical vector theorems, or of any of their generalizations, necessarily must involve an investigation of the integral. In order that we may simultaneously discuss line integrals, surface integrals, and three-dimensional integrals, it is useful to introduce a general concept of an integral over an n-dimensional set. For the existence of such an integral we must require certain properties of the function being integrated—the integrand—and also require certain properties of the set on which the integration is taking place. For the latter we develop the following chain of definitions.

Definition 5-1-1. The n-dimensional set R is a *rectangle* provided that R is the Cartesian product of n intervals of real numbers

$$R = \mathop{X}_{k=1}^{n} I_k$$

where, for $k = 1, 2, \ldots, n$, I_k is an interval.

If all the intervals I_k are closed, then the rectangle R is said to be closed. If all the intervals I_k are open, then the rectangle R is said to be open. If at least one of the intervals I_k is neither closed nor open, or if at least one interval I_k is closed and another interval I_j is open, then no particular name is given to the rectangle R.

Definition 5-1-2. The n-dimensional rectangle $R = \mathop{X}_{k=1}^{n} I_k$. For $k = 1, 2, \ldots, n$, the interval I_k has end points a_k and b_k, where $a_k \leq b_k$. The *n-dimensional volume $V_n(R)$* is the number given by

$$V_n(R) = \prod_{k=1}^{n} (b_k - a_k)$$

99

We will be concerned with arbitrary sets in an n-dimensional space and we are looking for a method of relating these sets to n-dimensional rectangles with edges parallel to the coordinate axes. Our hope is that we will arrive at a reasonable definition for what might be called the n-dimensional volume of such a set. We continue the chain of definitions by

Definition 5-1-3. M is an n-dimensional set. *C is a covering of M* means that C is a collection of a finite number of n-dimensional rectangles $C = \{R_j \mid j = 1, 2, \ldots, m\}$ such that all the rectangles R_j are mutually disjoint except for boundary points and

$$M \subseteq \bigcup_{j=1}^{m} R_j$$

Definition 5-1-4. M is an n-dimensional set.

$$C = \{R_j \mid j = 1, 2, \ldots, m\}$$

is a covering of M. The *outer content approximation given by C to M*, $V_{C,n,e}(M)$, is the number given by

$$V_{C,n,e}(M) = \sum_{j=1}^{m} V_n(R_j)$$

We can now define an "outer volume" by

Definition 5-1-5. M is an n-dimensional set. The n-dimensional *outer content* $V_{n,e}(M)$ is the number

$$V_{n,e}(M) = \inf \{V_{C,n,e}(M) \mid C \text{ is a covering of } M\}$$

Every n-dimensional set which is bounded necessarily has many possible coverings and each of these coverings produces a non-negative number for an outer content approximation. Since this set of non-negative numbers is bounded below, we may conclude

Theorem 5-1-1. If M is a bounded n-dimensional set, then $V_{n,e}(M)$ exists.

EXAMPLE. For $n = 2$ we let

$$M = \{(x, y) \mid 0 \leq y \leq x^2, 0 \leq x \leq 1\}$$

Thus M is the portion of the plane bounded by the x axis, the vertical line with equation $x = 1$ and that portion of the parabola which is the graph of $y = x^2$ lying between the points with coordinates $(0, 0)$ and $(1, 1)$. For any covering C of

M, one expects there will exist (see the exercises) a particular covering C_m consisting of rectangles of the form

$$R_k = \left\{ (x,y) \,\Big|\, 0 \le y \le \frac{k^2}{m^2}, \quad \frac{(k-1)}{m} \le x \le \frac{k}{m} \right\}$$

where $k = 1, 2, \ldots, m$, with the property that

$$M \subseteq \bigcup_{k=1}^{m} R_k \subseteq \bigcup_{I \in C} I$$

For these special coverings we have

$$V_{C,2,e}(M) \ge V_{C_m,2,e}(M)$$
$$= \sum_{k=1}^{m} \frac{k^2}{m^2} \frac{1}{m}$$
$$= \frac{1}{m^3} \sum_{k=1}^{m} k^2$$
$$= \frac{1}{3} + \frac{1}{2m} + \frac{1}{6m^2}$$

Thus
$$V_{2,e}(M) = \inf \{ V_{C,2,e}(M) \mid C \text{ is a covering of } M \}$$
$$= \lim_{m \to \infty} V_{C_m,2,e}(M)$$
$$= \tfrac{1}{3}$$

The concept of n-dimensional outer content will be matched by the following chain of definitions.

Definition 5-1-6. M is an n-dimensional set. *P is a packing of M* means that P is a collection of a finite number of n-dimensional rectangles $P = \{R_j \mid j = 1, 2, \ldots, m\}$ such that all the rectangles R_j are mutually disjoint except for boundary points and

$$\bigcup_{k=1}^{m} R_j \subseteq M$$

We define now the analogue of the outer content approximation.

Definition 5-1-7. M is an n-dimensional set.
$$P = \{R, \mid j = 1, 2, \ldots, m\}$$
is a packing of M. The *inner content approximation given by P to M*, $V_{P,n,i}(M)$, is the number

$$V_{P,n,i}(M) = \sum_{j=1}^{m} V_n(R_j)$$

Since we have taken the inner content approximation as the sum of the n-dimensional volumes of the rectangles making up the packing, it is natural to have

***Definition* 5-1-8.** M is an n-dimensional set. The n-dimensional *inner content* $V_{n,i}(M)$ is the number

$$V_{n,i}(M) = \sup \{V_{P,n,i}(M) \,|\, P \text{ is a packing of } M\}$$

It is certainly possible to have an n-dimensional set for which there are only trivial packings—that is, those with zero inner content approximation. For example, if we consider a plane as a subset of three-dimensional space and take any subset of that plane as the set M, then there exists no three-dimensional rectangle with positive volume which is a subset of this plane set. If we allow rectangles in an n-dimensional space to be Cartesian products of intervals, one of which has zero length, then the n-dimensional volume of such rectangles must be zero. If we have a three-dimensional set which is in fact a subset of some plane, then every possible packing must have zero three-dimensional inner content approximation, so that the three-dimensional inner content must be zero.

Further, any bounded n-dimensional set which does contain an n-dimensional rectangle with positive volume will be contained in some (large) n-dimensional rectangle. Thus the collection of inner content approximations will be bounded above by the volume of this encompassing rectangle so that the supremum of this collection of numbers must exist. In other words,

***Theorem* 5-1-2.** If M is a bounded n-dimensional set, then $V_{n,i}(M)$ exists.

For the example given above, with the two-dimensional set bounded by the line joining the origin to the point with coordinates $(1, 0)$, the line joining the points with coordinates $(1, 0)$ and $(1, 1)$, and that portion of the graph of $y = x^2$ which joins the origin to the point with coordinates $(1, 1)$, we can hope that for any packing P there exists a packing P_m, made up of two-dimensional rectangles of the form

$$R_k = \left\{(x, y) \,\Big|\, 0 \le y \le \frac{(k-1)^2}{m^2}, \quad \frac{k-1}{m} \le x \le \frac{k}{m}\right\}$$

where $k = 2, 3, \ldots, m$ such that

$$\bigcup_{R \in P} R \subseteq \bigcup_{k=2}^{m} R_k \subseteq M$$

Thus

$$V_{P,2,i}(M) \le V_{P_m,2,i}(M)$$
$$= \sum_{k=2}^{m} \frac{(k-1)^2}{m^2} \frac{1}{m}$$
$$= \frac{1}{m^3} \sum_{j=1}^{m-1} j^2$$
$$= \frac{1}{3} - \frac{1}{2m} + \frac{1}{6m^2}$$

and

$$V_{2,i}(M) = \sup \{V_{P,2,i}(M) \mid P \text{ is a packing of } M\}$$
$$= \lim_{m \to \infty} V_{P_m,2,i}(M)$$
$$= \tfrac{1}{3}$$

It is worthy of note that the two-dimensional inner content of this particular set is exactly the same number as the two-dimensional outer content. This highly desirable situation is formalized in

Definition 5-1-9. M is an n-dimensional set. M *is quadrable* means that $V_{n,i}(M) = V_{n,e}(M)$. The number which is the common value of the inner and outer content is called the n-*dimensional content* of M, $V_n(M)$.

The first thing to be noticed in the investigation of integrals of functions on n-dimensional sets is that such integrals are only meaningful when the n-dimensional set is quadrable. As for what sets are quadrable, we have at the moment only two immediate theorems.

Theorem 5-1-3. An interval is a quadrable set of real numbers.

Theorem 5-1-4. Any n-dimensional rectangle is a quadrable n-dimensional set.

EXERCISES

1. In two-dimensional space the rectangle R is the union of two rectangles R_1 and R_2 and these two rectangles have only boundary points in common. Prove that $V_2(R) = V_2(R_1) + V_2(R_2)$.

2. In two-dimensional space the rectangle R is decomposed into n rectangles $R_1, R_2, \ldots, R_n$ which are mutually disjoint except for boundary points. Prove that

$$V_2(R) = \sum_{k=1}^{n} V_2(R_k)$$

M is the two-dimensional triangular set given by

$$M = \{(x, y) \mid b \leq y \leq mx + b, 0 \leq x \leq c\}$$

where $m > 0$ and $b > 0$ are fixed. Let n be a fixed positive integer.

3. The line segment joining $(0, b)$ to $(c, mc + b)$ is divided into n segments of equal length. Find the coordinates of the division points.

4. In Exercise 3, calling the division points $P_1, P_2, \ldots, P_{n-1}$, and taking P_0 to be $(0, b)$ and P_n to be $(c, mc + b)$, we may form a covering C_n of M by rectangles $\bar{R}_1, \bar{R}_2, \ldots, \bar{R}_n$ by taking, for $k = 1, 2, \ldots, n$, $\bar{R}_k$ to be the rectangle with vertical sides the lines through P_{k-1} and P_k and horizontal sides through P_0 and P_k. Find $V_2(\bar{R}_k)$.

5. For the covering in Exercise 4, find $V_{C_n,2,e}(M)$.

6. Find $\lim\limits_{n\to\infty} V_{C_n,2,e}(M)$.

The problem now is to show that for any covering C of M there will exist a positive integer n and a covering C_n of the form given in Exercise 4, such that $V_{C_n,2,e}(M) \leq V_{C,2,e}(M)$.

7. Prove that for any covering C of M which has the property that one or more of the rectangles of C has an upper edge entirely above the line with equation $y = mx + b$, lower edge below the line with equation $y = b$, left side to the left of the line with equation $x = 0$, or right side to the right of the line with equation $y = c$, there will exist a covering C^* such that every rectangle of C^* is either entirely within M or has its upper right-hand corner on the line with equation $y = mx + b$ and such that $V_{C^*,2,e}(M) \leq V_{C,2,e}(M)$.

8. Prove that for any covering C^* of M of the form given in Exercise 7 there will exist a covering C^{**} of M in which every rectangle has its base on the line with equation $y = b$ and its upper right-hand corner on the line with equation $y = mx + b$ such that $V_{C^{**},2,e}(M) \leq V_{C^*,2,e}(M)$.

9. Prove that for every covering C^{***} of M of the form given in Exercise 8 and with the additional property that the width of each rectangle is a rational number multiple of c there will exist a positive integer n and a covering C_n of the form given in Exercise 4 for which $V_{C_n,2,e}(M) \leq V_{C^{***},2,e}(M)$.

We now have to show that any covering of the type given in Exercise 8 may be replaced by one of the type given in Exercise 9.

10. On the line with equation $y = mx + b$ the points $P_0, P_1, \ldots, P_q$ are those with x coordinates

$$0 = x_0 < x_1 < x_2 < \cdots < x_q = c$$

The positive numbers $g_1, g_2, \ldots, g_{q-1}$ and $d_1, d_2, \ldots, d_{q-1}$ are chosen so that, for $k = 1, 2, \ldots, q - 1$, $x_{k-1} < x_k - g_k$ and $x_k + d_k < x_{k+1}$ and also that $x_k - g_k$ and $x_k + d_k$ are rational number multiples of c. C^{**} is the covering of M of the form in Exercise 8 given by the points $P_0, P_1, \ldots, P_q$. C^{***} is the covering of M given by the points P_0, P_q and the $2q - 2$ points with x coordinates $x_k - g_k$ and $x_k + d_k$. Show that the numbers g_k and d_k can be chosen so that

$$V_{C^{***},2,e}(M) \leq V_{C^{**},2,e}(M)$$

11. Prove that $V_{2,e}(M) = \lim\limits_{n\to\infty} V_{C_n,2,e}(M)$.

12. Let P_n be the packing of M consisting of the rectangles $\underline{R}_1, \underline{R}_2, \ldots, \underline{R}_{n-1}$ such that, for $k = 1, 2, \ldots, n - 1$, $\underline{R}_k$ has vertical sides through P_k and P_{k+1} and horizontal sides through P_0 and P_k. Find $V_2(\underline{R}_k)$.

13. Find $V_{P_n,2,i}(M)$.

14. Find $\lim\limits_{n\to\infty} V_{P_n,2,i}(M)$.

15. Sketch the proof that $\lim\limits_{n\to\infty} V_{P_n,2,i}(M) = V_{2,i}(M)$.

5-2 Integration on Quadrable Sets

We will be concerned here with functions whose domains include some quadrable n-dimensional set and whose ranges are sets of real numbers. Various definitions will be set up in such a manner that the primary attention is focused on the set's being quadrable, while the consideration of possible properties of the functions will be left to the theorems. We begin with

> **Definition 5-2-1.** A is a quadrable n-dimensional set; f is a function on A into the real numbers. $P = \{B_k \mid k = 1, 2, \ldots, m\}$ is a packing of A. The *lower sum for f given by P* is the number
>
> $$\underline{S}_P(f; A) = \sum_{k=1}^{m} [\inf f(B_k)] V_n(B_k)\dagger$$

The definition of a packing does not require that the set A actually be the union of the n-dimensional rectangles in the packing so that in the particular case $n = 1$—that is, when A is a set of real numbers—we are not quite in agreement with the concept of the lower Riemann sum. Since we do not require that the rectangles of a packing entirely fill up the set being "packed," we must be careful, in determining a definition for the n-dimensional integral, that we have an analogue of the situation in which one partition of an interval is a refinement of another. We then establish

> **Definition 5-2-2.**
>
> $$P_1 = \{B_{1,k} \mid k = 1, 2, \ldots, m_1\} \quad \text{and} \quad P_2 = \{B_{2,k} \mid k = 1, 2, \ldots, m_2\}$$
>
> are two packings of the n-dimensional set A. P_2 *is denser than* P_1 means
>
> $$\bigcup_{k=1}^{m_1} B_{1,k} \subseteq \bigcup_{k=1}^{m_2} B_{2,k}$$
>
> and if, for any j or k, $B_{1,k}$ and $B_{2,j}$ have interior points in common, then $B_{2,j} \subseteq B_{1,k}$.

This definition means that every rectangle of the packing P_1 is the union of a finite number (perhaps only one) of the rectangles of the packing P_2 and there may also be some rectangles of the packing P_2 whose interiors are

† Recall that if B is a set in the domain of the function f, then $f(B) = \{f(x) \mid x \in B\}$.

entirely outside all the rectangles of the packing P_1. With this concept we have

> **Theorem 5-2-1.** If f is a function on the quadrable n-dimensional set A into the non-negative real numbers—that is, $x \in A$, $f(x) \geq 0$, and P_1 and P_2 are packings of A with P_2 denser than P_1, then
>
> $$\underline{S}_{P_2}(f; A) \geq \underline{S}_{P_1}(f; A)$$

Proof. Since P_2 is denser than P_1, we may index the rectangles of P_2 in such a manner that we segregate those which form each individual rectangle of the packing P_1. That is,

There exists an integer j_1 such that, for $j = 1, 2, \ldots, j_1$, $B_{2,j} \subseteq B_{1,1}$;

There exists an integer $j_2 > j_1$ such that, for $j = j_1 + 1, j_1 + 2, \ldots, j_2$, $B_{2,j} \subseteq B_{1,2} \ldots$;

$\ldots$;

There exists an integer j_{m_1} such that, for $j = j_{m_1-1} + 1, j_{m_1-1} + 2, \ldots, j_{m_1}$, $B_{2,j} \subseteq B_{1,m_1}$; and,

For $j = j_{m_1} + 1, j_{m_1} + 2, \ldots, m_2$, the interior of $B_{2,j}$ does not intersect any of the rectangles of P_1

Considering those rectangles of P_2 whose union is the first rectangle of P_1, we have, for $j = 1, 2, \ldots, j_1$,

$$\inf f(B_{2,j}) \geq \inf f(B_{1,1})$$
$$[\inf f(B_{2,j})]V_n(B_{2,j}) \geq [\inf f(B_{1,1})]V_n(B_{2,j})$$

So

$$\sum_{j=1}^{j_1} [\inf f(B_{2,j})]V_n(B_{2,j}) \geq [\inf f(B_{1,1})]V_n(B_{1,1})$$

In like manner, for $j = j_1 + 1, j_1 + 2, \ldots, j_2$,

$$\inf f(B_{2,j}) \geq \inf f(B_{1,2})$$
$$[\inf f(B_{2,j})]V_n(B_{2,j}) \geq [\inf f(B_{1,2})]V_n(B_{2,j})$$

So

$$\sum_{j=j_1+1}^{j_2} [\inf f(B_{2,j})]V_n(B_{2,j}) \geq [\inf f(B_{1,2})]V_n(B_{1,2})$$

Continuing, we wind up by having, for $j = j_{m_1-1} + 1, j_{m_1-1} + 2, \ldots, j_{m_1}$,

$$\inf f(B_{2,j}) \geq \inf f(B_{1,m_1})$$
$$[\inf f(B_{2,j})]V_n(B_{2,j}) \geq [\inf f(B_{1,m_1})]V_n(B_{2,j})$$

So

$$\sum_{j=j_{m_1-1}+1}^{j_{m_1}} [\inf f(B_{2,j})]V_n(B_{2,j}) \geq [\inf f(B_{1,m_1})]V_n(B_{1,m_1})$$

Adding the terms in these m_1 inequalities gives

$$\sum_{j=1}^{j_{m_1}} \inf f(B_{2,j}) V_n(B_{2,j}) \geq \underline{S}_{P_1}(f; A)$$

Since the remaining rectangles of the packing P_2 have non-negative content and since the range of f consists of non-negative numbers, we conclude that

$$\underline{S}_{P_2}(f; A) \geq \underline{S}_{P_1}(f; A) \qquad\qquad ∎$$

Our geometric instinct tells us that we will more closely approximate the n-dimensional set A if we take successively denser packings. Since we are dealing with non-negative numbers and since, as we have just proved, denser packings give larger "lower sums," we are led to

Definition 5-2-3. A is a quadrable n-dimensional set and f is a function on A into the non-negative real numbers. The *lower integral of f on A* is the number

$$\underline{\int}_A f = \sup \{\underline{S}_P(f; A) \mid P \text{ is a packing of } A\}$$

Thus far we have a definition only for quadrable sets and for functions whose ranges consist only of non-negative numbers. It may happen, of course, that the lower sums for a given function on a given quadrable set are not bounded above so that the lower integral will not exist. We begin the investigation of what properties of the function are enough to insure that the lower integral exists with

Theorem 5-2-2. If f is a bounded function on the quadrable n-dimensional set A into the non-negative real numbers, then $\underline{\int}_A f$ exists.

Proof. The hypothesis that f is bounded implies the existence of a positive number M such that $f(A) \subseteq [0, M]$. For any packing $P = \{B_j \mid j = 1, 2, \ldots, r\}$ of A, we have, for $j = 1, 2, \ldots, r$,

$$0 \leq \inf f(B_j) \leq M$$

Then, for $j = 1, 2, \ldots, r$,

$$0 \leq [\inf f(B_j)] V_n(B_j) \leq M V_n(B_j)$$

Thus

$$0 \leq \underline{S}_P(f; A) \leq M \sum_{j=1}^{r} V_n(B_j) \leq M V_{P,n,i}(A)$$

Since A is quadrable, we then have

$$0 \leq \underline{S}_P(f; A) \leq M V_{n,i}(A) = M V_n(A)$$

The set of all lower sums is thus bounded above by the fixed number $MV_n(A)$ so that its supremum—which is the lower integral—must exist.   ∎

The lower integral, when it exists, can be determined by taking successively denser packings. We now turn to similar estimates from above.

> *Definition 5-2-4.* A is a quadrable n-dimensional set; f is a function on A into the real numbers. $C = \{C_k \mid k = 1, 2, \ldots, m\}$ is a covering of A. The *upper sum for f given by* C is the number
>
> $$\bar{S}_C(f; A) = \sum_{k=1}^{m} [\sup f(C_k \cap A)] V_n(C_k)$$

For our purposes it is only necessary that the quadrable set A be entirely in the domain of the function (actually, even this requirement may be relaxed somewhat). For this reason we make certain that we consider only those parts of the rectangles of the covering which are actually in the domain. Analogous to the definition of one packing's being denser than another, we have

> *Definition 5-2-5*
>
> $$C_1 = \{B_{1,k} \mid k = 1, 2, \ldots, m_1\} \quad \text{and} \quad C_2 = \{B_{2,k} \mid k = 1, 2, \ldots, m_2\}$$
>
> are two coverings of the n-dimensional set A. C_2 *is finer than* C_1 means
>
> $$\bigcup_{k=1}^{m_2} B_{1,k} \subseteq \bigcup_{k=1}^{m_1} B_{2,k}$$
>
> and if, for any j or k, $B_{1,k}$ and $B_{2,j}$ have interior points in common, then $B_{2,j} \subseteq B_{1,k}$.

This definition means that any rectangle in the covering C_1 is made up of a finite number of rectangles of the covering C_2 and that C_1 may possibly have other rectangles which do not themselves intersect A. The relation between upper sums for two coverings, one of which is finer than the other, is given in

> *Theorem 5-2-3.* If f is a function on the quadrable n-dimensional set A into the non-negative real numbers and C_1 and C_2 are coverings of A with C_2 finer than C_1, then
>
> $$\bar{S}_{C_2}(f; A) \leq \bar{S}_{C_1}(f; A)$$

The proof of this theorem is similar to that of the analogous theorem for lower sums and is left to the exercises. Since finer partitions give smaller "upper sums," we are led to

Definition 5-2-6. A is a quadrable n-dimensional set and f is a function on A into the non-negative real numbers. The *upper integral of f on A* is the number

$$\overline{\int_A} f = \inf \{ \bar{S}_P(f; A) \mid C \text{ is a covering of } A \}$$

We then have, almost immediately,

Theorem 5-2-4. If f is a bounded function on the n-dimensional quadrable set A into the non-negative real numbers, then $\overline{\int_A} f$ exists.

The proof of this theorem is left to the exercises. Of more interest is the following theorem which relates these two kinds of integrals:

Theorem 5-2-5. If f is a function on the quadrable n-dimensional set A into the non-negative real numbers and if both $\underline{\int_A} f$ and $\overline{\int_A} f$ exist, then

$$\underline{\int_A} f \le \overline{\int_A} f$$

Proof. Pick $\epsilon > 0$. From the definition of lower integral there exists a packing $P_1 = \{ B_{1,j} \mid j = 1, 2, \ldots, m_1 \}$ of A with the property that

$$\underline{\int_A} f - \frac{\epsilon}{2} < \underline{S}_{P_1}(f; A) \le \underline{\int_A} f$$

From the definition of upper integral there exists a covering $C_1 = \{ R_{1,k} \mid k = 1, 2, \ldots, m_2 \}$ of A with the property that

$$\overline{\int_A} f \le \bar{S}_{C_1}(f; A) < \overline{\int_A} f + \frac{\epsilon}{2}$$

Let $C_2 = \{ R_{2,k} \mid k = 1, 2, \ldots, m_3 \}$ be the covering of A which consists of all rectangles of the form $R_{1,k} \cap B_{1,j}$ and also all rectangles which result from decomposing the sets of the form $R_{1,k} - B_{1,j}$ into n-dimensional rectangles. By this construction the covering C_2 is finer than C_1 so that

$$\overline{\int_A} f \le \bar{S}_{C_2}(f; A) \le \bar{S}_{C_1}(f; A) < \overline{\int_A} f + \frac{\epsilon}{2}$$

Let P_2 be that packing of A which consists of those rectangles of the covering C_2 whose interiors are subsets of A and let $P_2 = \{ B_{2,j} \mid j = 1, 2, \ldots, m_4 \}$. From the construction of the covering C_2, the packing P_2 must be denser than the packing P_1 and since P_2 consists of rectangles of C_2, we must have

$m_4 \leq m_3$. Thus

$$\int_A f - \frac{\epsilon}{2} < \underline{S}_{P_1}(f; A) \leq \underline{S}_{P_2}(f; A) \leq \int_A f$$

Further, for $k = 1, 2, \ldots, m_4$,

$$\inf f(B_{2,k}) \leq \sup f(B_{2,k})$$
$$[\inf f(B_{2,k})]V_n(B_{2,k}) \leq [\sup f(B_{2,k})]V_n(B_{2,k})$$

Thus

$$\underline{S}_{P_2}(f; A) = \sum_{k=1}^{m_4} [\inf f(B_{2,k})]V_n(B_{2,k})$$
$$\leq \sum_{k=1}^{m_4} [\sup f(B_{2,k})]V_n(B_{2,k})$$
$$= \sum_{k=1}^{m_4} [\sup f(R_{2,k})]V_n(R_{2,k})$$
$$\leq \sum_{k=1}^{m_3} [\sup f(R_{2,k})]V_n(R_{2,k})$$
$$= \bar{S}_{C_2}(f; A)$$

Combining the inequalities established yields

$$\int_A f - \frac{\epsilon}{2} < \underline{S}_{P_2}(f; A) \leq \bar{S}_{C_2}(f; A) < \overline{\int_A} f + \frac{\epsilon}{2}$$

so that

$$-\frac{\epsilon}{2} < \overline{\int_A} f - \int_A f$$

Since ϵ is an arbitrary positive number, $\displaystyle\overline{\int_A} f - \int_A f$ must be greater than every negative number; that is, it must be non-negative. ∎

Up to now we have given definitions for upper and lower integral only for functions whose ranges consist of non-negative numbers. We complete the definitions by

Definition 5-2-7. f is a function on the quadrable n-dimensional set A into the real numbers such that $f^{-1}([0, +\infty[)$ and $f^{-1}(]-\infty, 0])$ are quadrable sets.† The *lower integral of f on A* is the number

$$\int_A f = -\overline{\int_{f^{-1}(]-\infty,0])}} (-f) + \int_{f^{-1}([0,+\infty[)} f$$

† Recall that if B is a set and f a function, $f^{-1}(B) = \{x \mid f(x) \in B\}$.

The *upper integral of f on A* is the number

$$\overline{\int_A} f = -\overline{\int_{f^{-1}(]-\infty,0])} (-f)} + \overline{\int_{f^{-1}([0,+\infty[)} f}$$

EXERCISES

1. Prove Theorem 5-2-3.

2. Prove Theorem 5-2-4.

3. If A is a quadrable n-dimensional set and f is the constant function on A into the real numbers whose range consists of the single number 1, show that

$$\underline{\int_A} f = \overline{\int_A} f = V_n(A)$$

The function f on $D = [0, 1] \times [0, 2]$ into the real numbers is given by $f(x, y) = y$.

4. Describe the graph of f.

5. The collection of $2n^2$ squares, each of side $1/n$,

$$\left\{ R_{i,j} = \left[\frac{i-1}{n}, \frac{i}{n}\right] \times \left[\frac{j-1}{n}, \frac{j}{n}\right] \,\middle|\, i = 1, 2, \ldots, n; j = 1, 2, \ldots, 2n \right\}$$

is simultaneously a packing P_n and a covering C_n of D. Find $\inf f(R_{i,j})$ and $\sup f(R_{i,j})$.

6. Find $\underline{S}_{P_n}(f; D)$ and $\bar{S}_{C_n}(f; D)$.

7. Find $\underline{\int_D} f$ and $\overline{\int_D} f$ and justify the method used.

8–11. Repeat Exercises 4–7 for f given by $f(x, y) = 2 - y$.

12–14. Repeat Exercises 4–7 for f given by

$$f(x, y) = \begin{cases} y, & x \text{ rational} \\ 2 - y, & x \text{ irrational} \end{cases}$$

5-3 Integrable Functions

If we have a particularly well-behaved function whose domain includes a quadrable set, then it may well happen that the upper and lower integrals of this function on this set are the same number. We formalize this situation in

Definition 5-3-1. f is a function on the n-dimensional set D into the real numbers. A is a quadrable subset of D. f *is integrable on* A means

$$\underline{\int_A} f = \overline{\int_A} f$$

In this case the number which is the common value of the upper and lower integral is *the integral of* f *on* A, denoted by $\int_A f$.

Before attempting to discover methods of evaluation of integrals of such functions on such sets, it might be well to look at a simple example for which we can actually determine the upper and lower integrals. We will consider the function f whose domain is the entire two-dimensional plane, given by

$$f(x, y) = 1 - x - y$$

In three-dimensional space with a rectangular coordinate system, the graph of f is that plane which passes through the points with coordinates $(1, 0, 0)$, $(0, 1, 0)$, and $(0, 0, 1)$. We consider the triangle in the two-dimensional plane A with vertices having rectangular coordinates $(0, 0)$, $(1, 0)$, and $(0, 1)$. In considering the integral of f on A, we are interested in that part of the graph of f which is above the corresponding triangle in the x-y coordinate plane whose vertices have coordinates $(0, 0, 0)$, $(1, 0, 0)$, and $(0, 1, 0)$.

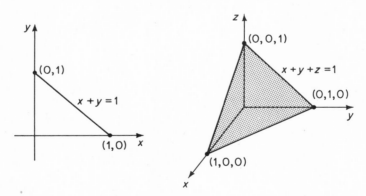

Figure 5-1

This portion of the graph of f is a plane triangle lying in the first octant of the space whose vertices are the points of intersection of the plane which is the graph of $x + y + z = 1$ with the three coordinate axes.

We will find packings and coverings of the triangle A by considering a decomposition of the unit square into n^2 smaller squares, each of which has side $1/n$. Then, for $i = 1, 2, \ldots, n$ and $j = 1, 2, \ldots, n$, these squares will have vertices with coordinates $((i-1)/n, (j-1)/n)$, $(i/n, (j-1)/n)$, $(i/n, j/n)$, and $((i-1)/n, j/n)$.

In order to have a packing or a covering of the triangle A, we need only take some of these squares. The determination of which ones we take for a packing will be done by examining those squares whose upper right-hand corners are on the hypotenuse.

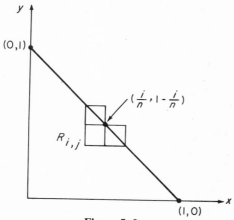

Figure 5- 2

Denoting the square with indices i and j by $R_{i,j}$, if the upper right-hand corner of this square lies on the hypotenuse of A, then the point with coordinates $(i/n, j/n)$ must be on the graph of $x + y = 1$. We then must have

$$\frac{j}{n} = 1 - \frac{i}{n}$$

or $j = n - i$. Then, for $j = 1, 2, \ldots, n - i$ and $i = 1, 2, \ldots, n - 1$, the square $R_{i,j}$ will lie inside the triangle A.

Similarly we have a covering of the triangle A by considering those squares for which the hypotenuse of A is a diagonal. For this we want the lower right-hand corner to be on the graph of $x + y = 1$. This point has coordinates $(i/n, (j-1)/n)$ so we must have

$$\frac{j-1}{n} = 1 - \frac{i}{n}$$

or $j = n - i + 1$. Then, for $j = 1, 2, \ldots, n - i + 1$ and $i = 1, 2, \ldots, n$, the square $R_{i,j}$ will be part of a covering of A.

We use P_n and C_n to denote the packing and covering, respectively, of A given by the appropriate squares of side $1/n$. For either the packing or the covering, the fact that the graph of f is a plane with direction numbers $1, 1, 1$ indicates that the maximum value of f on any of the squares will be attained at that vertex nearest the origin and the minimum value will be attained at that vertex farthest from the origin. Then we have

$$\inf f(R_{i,j}) = f\left(\frac{i}{n}, \frac{j}{n}\right)$$

$$= 1 - \frac{i}{n} - \frac{j}{n}$$

and

$$\sup f(R_{i,j}) = f\left(\frac{i-1}{n}, \frac{j-1}{n}\right)$$

$$= 1 - \frac{i-1}{n} - \frac{j-1}{n}$$

For the packing P_n we find

$$\underline{S}_{P_n}(f; A) = \sum_{i=1}^{n-1}\sum_{j=1}^{n-i}[\inf f(R_{i,j})]\frac{1}{n^2}$$

$$= \sum_{i=1}^{n-1}\sum_{j=1}^{n-i}\left[1 - \frac{i}{n} - \frac{j}{n}\right]\frac{1}{n^2}$$

$$= \frac{1}{n^3}\sum_{i=1}^{n-1}\sum_{j=1}^{n-i}[(n-i) - j]$$

$$= \frac{1}{n^3}\sum_{i=1}^{n-1}\left[(n-i)^2 - \frac{1}{2}(n-i)(n-i+1)\right]$$

(In the first term we are merely adding $n-i$ terms, each of which is $n-i$; and in the second we are adding the first $n-i$ positive integers.)

$$= \frac{1}{2n^3}\sum_{i=1}^{n-1}[(n-i)^2 - (n-i)]$$

$$= \frac{1}{2n^3}\sum_{k=1}^{n-1}(k^2 - k)$$

$$= \frac{1}{2n^3}\left[\frac{1}{6}(n-1)n(2n-1) - \frac{1}{2}(n-1)n\right]$$

$$= \frac{1}{6} - \frac{3}{4n} + \frac{5}{12n^2}$$

It is clear that any packing of A by rectangles whose sides have rational number length will have a denser packing made of sides having length $1/n$ (namely by taking n to be a common denominator of all the rational number lengths). An arbitrary packing of A, of course, need not have such rectangles, but the limit process of approximating any irrational number by a sequence of rational numbers suggests that in order to determine the lower integral of f on

A it is sufficient to consider packings of the form P_n. Since larger values of *n* give denser packings, we will have

$$\underline{\int_A} f = \lim_{n \to \infty} \underline{S}_{P_n}(f; A) = \frac{1}{6}$$

This result should not be surprising since we would expect the integral to be the volume of the tetrahedron bounded by the graph of *f* and the three coordinate planes.

For the covering C_n, we have

$$\bar{S}_{C_n}(f; A) = \sum_{i=1}^{n} \sum_{j=1}^{n-i+1} [\sup f(R_{i,j})] \frac{1}{n^2}$$

$$= \sum_{i=1}^{n} \sum_{j=1}^{n-i+1} \left(1 - \frac{i-1}{n} - \frac{j-1}{n}\right) \frac{1}{n^2}$$

$$= \sum_{i=0}^{n-1} \sum_{j=0}^{n-i} \left(1 - \frac{i}{n} - \frac{j}{n}\right) \frac{1}{n^2}$$

$$= \frac{1}{n^3} \sum_{i=0}^{n-1} \sum_{j=0}^{n-i} [(n - i) - j]$$

$$= \underline{S}_{P_n}(f; A) + \frac{1}{n^3} \sum_{j=0}^{n} (n - j)$$

$$= \underline{S}_{P_n}(f; A) + \frac{1}{n^3} \left[\frac{1}{2} n(n + 1)\right]$$

$$= \frac{1}{6} - \frac{1}{4n} + \frac{11}{12n^2}$$

Thus

$$\overline{\int_A} f = \lim_{n \to \infty} \bar{S}_{C_n}(f; A) = \frac{1}{6}$$

and the function *f*, given by $f(x, y) = 1 - x - y$, is integrable on the quadrable set $A = \{(x, y) \mid 0 \leq y \leq 1 - x, 0 \leq x \leq 1\}$ and the integral of *f* on *A* is $\frac{1}{6}$.

In order to determine whether any function is integrable on a given quadrable set, it will be convenient to use the following immediate consequence of the definitions:

Theorem 5-3-1. *f* is a function on the quadrable *n*-dimensional set *A* into the non-negative real numbers. *f* is integrable on *A* if, and only if, for every $\epsilon > 0$ there exists a packing P_ϵ of *A* and a covering C_ϵ of *A* such that

$$\bar{S}_{C_\epsilon}(f; A) - \underline{S}_{P_\epsilon}(f; A) < \epsilon$$

The proof of this theorem is not difficult but somewhat lengthy and will be omitted.

In order to have a supply of integrable functions, we have

Theorem 5-3-2. If f is a continuous non-negative function on the closed, quadrable n-dimensional set A, then f is integrable on A. (*Remark:* The theorem can be strengthened somewhat by dropping the requirement that A be closed and adding the requirement that f be uniformly continuous.)

Proof. Since f is non-negative, A is quadrable and consequently bounded. Since f is continuous and A is a closed, bounded set, then f is bounded. Thus there exists a positive number M such that $f(A) \subseteq [-M, M]$. Consequently both

$$\underline{\int}_A f \quad \text{and} \quad \overline{\int}_A f$$

will exist. ∎

We choose $\epsilon > 0$ and let B be a positive number to be specified later. From the definition of lower integer, there exists a packing P_ϵ of A such that

$$\underline{\int}_A f - \frac{\epsilon}{B} < \underline{S}_{P_\epsilon}(f; A) \le \underline{\int}_A f$$

From the definition of upper integral, there exists a covering C_ϵ of A such that

$$\overline{\int}_A f \le \overline{S}_{C_\epsilon}(f; A) < \overline{\int}_A f + \frac{\epsilon}{B}$$

Without loss of generality we may assume that the packing P_ϵ is a subcollection of the covering C_ϵ, since if this were not the case, we could merely take the denser packing and finer covering which result from considering all intersections of the rectangles in the two collections.

Since f is continuous on the closed bounded set A, f is uniformly continuous on A. There then will exist $\delta > 0$ such that if r and s are any two points of A such that $d_n(r, s) < \delta$, then

$$|f(r) - f(s)| < \frac{\epsilon}{B}$$

The packing and covering which gave lower and upper sums approximately equal to the lower and upper integrals may not have consisted of rectangles small enough so that within any one of them the requirement called for by uniform continuity is met. There exists a packing P_ϵ^*, however, which is denser than P_ϵ such that for all rectangles R in P_ϵ^* the diameter of

R is less than the δ given above. Since P_ϵ^* is denser than P_ϵ, we have

$$\underline{\int}_A f - \frac{\epsilon}{B} < \underline{S}_{P_\epsilon}(f; A) \leq \underline{S}_{P_\epsilon^*}(f; A) \leq \underline{\int}_A f$$

In addition there exists a covering C_ϵ^* of A which is finer than C_ϵ such that for every rectangle R of C_ϵ^* the diameter of R is less than δ. Since C_ϵ^* is finer than C_ϵ,

$$\overline{\int}_A f \leq \bar{S}_{C_\epsilon^*}(f; A) \leq \bar{S}_{C_\epsilon^*}(f; A) < \overline{\int}_A f + \frac{\epsilon}{B}$$

Again, without loss of generality, we may assume that the packing P_ϵ^* is a subcollection of the covering C_ϵ^* for the same reason as before.

The fact that A is a quadrable n-dimensional set implies that

$$V_{n,e}(A) = V_{n,i}(A) = V_n(A)$$

The definition of inner and outer content of a set means that corresponding to the given ϵ there exists a packing P_ϵ^{**} of A such that

$$V_{n,i}(A) - \frac{\epsilon}{B} < V_{P_\epsilon^{**},n,i}(A) \leq V_{n,i}(A) = V_n(A)$$

In addition, there exists a covering C_ϵ^{**} of A such that

$$V_n(A) = V_{n,e}(A) \leq V_{C_\epsilon^{**},n,e}(A) < V_{n,e}(A) + \frac{\epsilon}{B}$$

Again, without loss of generality we may assume that the packing P_ϵ^{**} is a subcollection of the covering C_ϵ^{**}.

The packing and covering P_ϵ^* and C_ϵ^* consist of rectangles which are sufficiently small so that within each one of them any two values of f differ by at most ϵ/B. The packing and covering P_ϵ^{**} and C_ϵ^{**} are those which approximate the n-dimensional content of A to within ϵ/B. Clearly any packing which is denser than both P_ϵ^* and P_ϵ^{**} will inherit the properties of these packings in regard to content of A and variation of f, and the same will be true for any covering which is finer than both C_ϵ^* and C_ϵ^{**}.

We let P_ϵ^{***} be a packing of A which is denser than P_ϵ^* and P_ϵ^{**}. Then, for every R in P_ϵ^{***}, the diameter of R is less than δ

$$\underline{\int}_A f - \frac{\epsilon}{B} < \underline{S}_{P_\epsilon^{***}}(f; A) \leq \underline{\int}_A f$$

and

$$V_n(A) - \frac{\epsilon}{B} < V_{P_\epsilon^{***},n,i}(A) \leq V_n(A)$$

We let C_ϵ^{***} be a covering of A which is finer than C_ϵ^* and C_ϵ^{**}. Then, for every R in C_ϵ^{***}, the diameter of R is less than δ

$$\overline{\int_A} f \le \overline{S}_{C_\epsilon^{***}}(f; A) < \overline{\int_A} f + \frac{\epsilon}{B}$$

and

$$V_n(A) \le V_{C_\epsilon^{***}, n, e}(A) < V_n(A) + \frac{\epsilon}{B}$$

Again, without loss of generality we may assume that the packing P_ϵ^{***} is a subcollection of the covering C_ϵ^{***}. But this means that we may index the rectangles of C_ϵ^{***} in such a manner that

$$P_\epsilon^{***} = \{R_j \mid j = 1, 2, \ldots, p\}$$

and

$$C_\epsilon^{***} = \{R_j \mid j = 1, 2, \ldots, p + m\}$$

We then have

$$\overline{S}_{C_\epsilon^{***}}(f; A) - \underline{S}_{P_\epsilon^{***}}(f; A) = \sum_{j=1}^{p+m} [\sup f(R_j)]V_n(R_j) - \sum_{j=1}^{p} [\inf f(R_j)]V_n(R_j)$$

$$= \sum_{j=p+1}^{p+m} [\sup f(R_j)]V_n(R_j)$$

$$+ \sum_{j=1}^{p} [\sup f(R_j) - \inf f(R_j)]V_n(R_j)$$

But since the diameter of all these rectangles is less than δ, then, for $j = 1, 2, \ldots, p$, we have

$$\sup f(R_j) - \inf f(R_j) < \frac{2\epsilon}{B}$$

The function f is bounded on A so that, for $j = 1, 2, \ldots, p + m$, we have

$$\sup f(R_j) < M$$

As a result, we conclude that

$$\overline{S}_{C_\epsilon^{***}}(f; A) - \underline{S}_{P_\epsilon^{***}}(f; A) \le M \sum_{j=p+1}^{p+m} V_n(R_j) + \frac{2\epsilon}{B} \sum_{j=1}^{p} V_n(R_j)$$

$$= M\left[\sum_{j=1}^{p+m} V_n(R_j) - \sum_{j=1}^{p} V_n(R_j) \right] + \frac{2\epsilon}{B} \sum_{j=1}^{p} V_n(R_j)$$

$$= M[V_{C_\epsilon^{***}, n, e}(A) - V_{P_\epsilon^{***}, n, i}(A)] + \frac{2\epsilon}{B} V_{P_\epsilon^{***}, n, i}(A)$$

$$< M\left[V_n(A) + \frac{\epsilon}{B} - V_n(A) + \frac{\epsilon}{B} \right] + \frac{2\epsilon}{B} V_n(A)$$

$$= \frac{2}{B} [M + V_n(A)]\epsilon$$

We now need only pick the positive number $B = 2[M + V_n(A)]$ in order to complete the proof.

We are thus assured that any continuous function whose domain includes a closed quadrable n-dimensional set is necessarily integrable over such a set. In the next section we will examine one of the standard methods of evaluating such integrals. ∎

EXERCISES

Let g be the function given by

$$g(x, y) = 1 - x - y, \qquad (x, y) \in A = \{(x, y) \mid 0 \leq y \leq 1 - x, \, 0 \leq x \leq 1\}$$

For every positive integer n, let P_n and C_n be the packings and coverings of D given in this section. Let $\epsilon > 0$ and $B > 0$ be given.

1. Find N_1 such that $n \geq N_1$ implies

$$\int_A g - \frac{\epsilon}{B} < \underline{S}_{P_n}(g; D) \leq \int_A g$$

2. Find N_2 such that $n \geq N_2$ implies

$$\int_A g \leq \overline{S}_{C_n}(g; D) < \int_A g + \frac{\epsilon}{B}$$

3. Find $\delta > 0$ such that for all (p, q) and (r, s) in D if $d_2((p, q), (r, s)) < \delta$, then $|f(p, q) - f(r, s)| < \epsilon/B$. *Hint:* The graph of $|x - a| + |y - b| = c$ is a square.

4. Find N_3 such that $n \geq N_3$ implies $1/n < \delta$, where δ is the one found in Exercise 3.

5. Find N_4 such that $n \geq N_4$ implies $1/n < \delta$ and the inequalities in Exercises 1 and 2 are satisfied.

6. Find N_5 such that $n \geq N_5$ implies

$$V_2(D) - \frac{\epsilon}{B} < V_{P_n, 2, i}(D) \leq V_2(D)$$

7. Find N_6 such that $n \geq N_6$ implies

$$V_2(D) \leq V_{C_n, 2, e}(D) < V_2(D) + \frac{\epsilon}{B}$$

8. Find N_7 such that $n \geq N_7$ implies $1/n < \delta$ and the inequalities in Exercises 1, 2, 6, and 7 are satisfied.

9. Why does $n \geq N_7$ imply that, for each R in C_n, $\sup g(R) - \inf g(R) < \epsilon/B$?

10. Which rectangles of C_n are not in P_n?

11. Find an upper bound for the range of g.

12. Find $V_{C_n,2,e}(D) - V_{P_n,2,i}(D)$.

13. Why does $n \geq N_7$ imply that $V_{C_n,2,e}(D) - V_{P_n,2,i}(D) < 2\epsilon/B$?

14. For $\epsilon = 0.1$, find N such that $n \geq N$ implies that $\bar{S}_{C_n}(f; D) - S_{P_n}(f; D) < 0.1$.

15. h is the function on D into the real numbers given by

$$h(x, y) = \begin{cases} 1 - x - y, & 0 \leq y \leq 1 - x, 0 < x \leq 1 \\ 3, & 0 \leq y \leq 1, x = 0 \end{cases}$$

Show that h is integrable on D and that

$$\int_D h = \int_D g$$

5-4 Iterated Integrals

We are concerned here with the form of the quadrable set on which the integration is being performed more than with any specific properties of the function being integrated. Our basic form of two-dimensional region is one which is bounded above and below by paths which are the graphs of continuous functions. Given a function whose domain includes such a two-dimensional set, we will construct infinitely many functions whose domains are intervals of numbers, and from these functions we will construct a single function whose domain is an interval. Our theorems will relate the integral of the original function on the given two-dimensional set to the integrals of these various functions with number domains. We have

Theorem 5-4-1. φ_T is a continuous function on the closed interval $[a, b]$ into the real numbers. φ_B is a continuous function on $[a, b]$ into the real numbers. For all $x \in [a, b]$, $\varphi_B(x) \leq \varphi_T(x)$. $A = \{(x, y) \mid \varphi_B(x) \leq y \leq \varphi_T(x) \text{ and } a \leq x \leq b\}$. f is a continuous function on A into the real numbers.

If, for each fixed $x \in [a, b]$, the function g_x on the closed interval $[\varphi_B(x), \varphi_T(x)]$ into the real numbers is given by $g_x(y) = f(x, y)$, then g_x is integrable on $[\varphi_B(x), \varphi_T(x)]$.

If the function ψ on the interval $[a, b]$ into the real numbers is given by then

$$\psi(x) = \int_{\varphi_B(x)}^{\varphi_T(x)} g_x$$

ψ is integrable on $[a, b]$ and

$$\int_a^b \psi = \int_A f$$

Proof. Since f is continuous on A, then, for each x in $[a, b]$, g_x is continuous and thus integrable on $[\varphi_B(x), \varphi_T(x)]$.

For a given $\epsilon > 0$ there exists a packing, P_ϵ of A and a covering C_ϵ of A such that

$$\int_A f - \epsilon < \underline{S}_{P_\epsilon}(f; A) \leq \bar{S}_{C_\epsilon}(f; A) < \int_A f + \epsilon$$

and also such that

$$\bar{S}_{C_\epsilon}(f; A) - \underline{S}_{P_\epsilon}(f; A) < \epsilon$$

Without loss of generality we may assume that the packing P_ϵ is a subcollection of the covering C_ϵ so that the rectangles in these collections may be indexed by

$$P_\epsilon = \{R_i \mid i = 1, 2, \ldots, p\}$$

and

$$C_\epsilon = \{R_i \mid i = 1, 2, \ldots, p + m\}$$

For $i = 1, 2, \ldots, p + m$, we let $R_i = [x_{i-1}, x_i] \times [y_{i-1}, y_i]$. We may further assume that

$$\bigcup_{i=1}^{p+m} [x_{i-1}, x_i] = [a, b]$$

since we may discard any rectangles lying entirely outside A.

For each fixed index i, certain of the rectangles of the covering C_ϵ will lie in the vertical strip between the graphs of $x = x_{i-1}$ and $x = x_i$. We let $J_i = \{j \mid x_j = x_i\}$—that is, J_i is the set of indices j such that the rectangles with these indices form a vertical strip. We further order the indices in J_i, $J_i = \{j_k \mid k = 1, 2, \ldots, k_i\}$, so that

$$y_{j_1} < y_{j_2} < \cdots < y_{j_{k_i}}$$

Then for ξ_i any number in the interval $[x_{i-1}, x_i]$,

$$\psi(\xi_i) = \int_{\varphi_B(\xi_i)}^{\varphi_T(\xi_i)} g_{\xi_i}$$

$$= \left\{ \int_{\varphi_B(\xi_i)}^{y_{j_1}} + \sum_{k=2}^{k_i-1} \int_{y_{j_{k-1}}}^{y_{j_k}} + \int_{y_{j_{k_i}}}^{\varphi_T(\xi_i)} \right\} g_{\xi_i}$$

$$\leq \sum_{k=1}^{k_i} [\sup g_{\xi_i}([y_{j_{k-1}}, y_{j_k}])](y_{j_k} - y_{j_{k-1}})$$

$$\leq \sum_{k=1}^{k_i} [\sup f(R_{j_k})](y_{j_k} - y_{j_{k-1}})$$

Thus

$$\psi(\xi_i)(x_i - x_{i-1}) \leq \sum_{k=1}^{k_i} [\sup f(R_{j_k})]V_2(R_{j_k})$$

Now we let I be the set of indices $\{i_r \mid r = 0, 1, \ldots, q\}$ such that the intervals $\{[x_{i_{r-1}}, x_{i_r}] \mid r = 1, 2, \ldots, q\}$ form a partition of $[a, b]$. (We are thus considering successive columns of rectangles of the covering.) We have

$$\sum_{r=1}^{q} \psi(\xi_{i_r})(x_{i_r} - x_{i_{r-1}}) \leq \sum_{r=1}^{q} \sum_{k=1}^{k_{i_r}} [\sup f(R_{j_k})]V_2(R_{j_k})$$
$$= \bar{S}_{C_\epsilon}(f; A)$$

Since the numbers ξ_i were arbitrarily chosen in each interval $[x_{i-1}, x_i]$, we then must have

$$\sum_{r=1}^{q} [\sup \psi([x_{i_{r-1}}, x_{i_r}])](x_{i_r} - x_{i_{r-1}}) \leq \bar{S}_{C_\epsilon}(f; A)$$

which implies that

$$\overline{\int_a^b} \psi \leq \bar{S}_{C_\epsilon}(f; A)$$

In like manner we can also show that

$$\underline{\int_a^b} \psi \geq \underline{S}_{P_\epsilon}(f; A)$$

so that

$$\overline{\int_a^b} \psi - \underline{\int_a^b} \psi \leq \bar{S}_{C_\epsilon}(f; A) - \underline{S}_{P_\epsilon}(f; A) < \epsilon$$

and ψ is integrable on $[a, b]$.

Further

$$\int_a^b \psi = \overline{\int_a^b} \psi \leq \bar{S}_{C_\epsilon}(f; A) < \int_A f + \epsilon$$

and

$$\int_a^b \psi = \underline{\int_a^b} \psi \geq \underline{S}_{P_\epsilon}(f; A) > \int_A f - \epsilon$$

implies that

$$\left| \int_a^b \psi - \int_A f \right| < \epsilon$$

so that

$$\int_a^b \psi = \int_A f$$

and the proof is complete. ∎

The obvious companion to this theorem is

Theorem 5-4-2. φ_G and φ_D are two continuous functions on $[c, d]$ with the property that, for all $y \in [c, d]$, $\varphi_G(y) \leq \varphi_D(y)$. $A = \{(x, y) \mid \varphi_G(y) \leq x \leq \varphi_D(y) \text{ and } c \leq y \leq d\}$. f is a continuous function on A into the real numbers.

If, for each $y \in [c, d]$, the function h_y on $[\varphi_G(y), \varphi_D(y)]$ is given by $h_y(x) = f(x, y)$, then h_t is integrable on $[\varphi_G(y), \varphi_D(y)]$.

If the function χ on $[c, d]$ into the real numbers is given by

$$\chi(y) = \int_{\varphi_G(y)}^{\varphi_D(y)} h_y$$

then χ is integrable on $[c, d]$ and

$$\int_c^d \chi = \int_A f$$

It should be noted that it is possible to have a function whose domain includes a quadrable set for which the functions g_x, mentioned in Theorem 5-4-1, are all integrable and the function ψ of the theorem is also integrable, but for which $\int_A^b \psi$ and $\int_A f$ are not the same number; in fact, the latter integral does not exist. An interesting example is given by the function f, specified for $(x, y) \in [0, 1] \times [0, 1]$ by

$$f(x, y) = \begin{cases} 1, & \text{if } x \text{ is rational} \\ 2y, & \text{if } x \text{ is irrational} \end{cases}$$

The graph of f lies above the unit square of the x-y plane and consists of some points on the horizontal plane with equation $z = 1$ (whose x coordinates are rational numbers) and of some points on the slanted plane with equation $z = 2y$ (whose x coordinates are irrational numbers).

To find $\underline{\int_A} f$ and $\overline{\int_A} f$, it is convenient to divide the unit square into the two rectangles $A_1 = [0, 1] \times [0, \frac{1}{2}]$ and $A_2 = [0, 1] \times [\frac{1}{2}, 1]$. If R_k is any rectangle in a decomposition of A_1 (which decomposition is simultaneously a packing and a covering), then $\sup f(R_k)$ will be the z coordinate of a point in the horizontal plane—that is, $\sup f(R_k) = 1$. Thus

$$\overline{\int_{A_1}} f = \int_{A_1} 1 = \frac{1}{2}$$

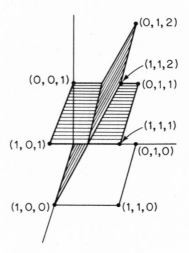

Figure 5-3

Further, $\inf f(R_k)$ will be the z coordinate of a point on the slanted plane with equation $z = 2y$. Thus

$$\int_{\underline{A_1}} f = \int_{A_1} g, \qquad \text{where } g(x, y) = 2y$$

Since g is continuous,

$$\int_{\underline{A_1}} f = \int_0^{1/2} 2t\, dt = \frac{1}{4}$$

In like manner, $\overline{\int_{A_2}} f$ will be determined by z coordinates of points on the slanted plane, so that

$$\overline{\int_{A_2}} f = \int_{A_2} g = \int_{1/2}^1 2t\, dt = \frac{3}{4}$$

and $\int_{\underline{A_2}} f$ will be determined by z coordinates of points on the horizontal plane so that

$$\int_{\underline{A_2}} f = \int_{A_2} 1 = \frac{1}{2}$$

We conclude that

$$\overline{\int_A} f = \overline{\int_{A_1}} f + \overline{\int_{A_2}} f = \frac{1}{2} + \frac{3}{4} = \frac{5}{4}$$

$$\int_{\underline{A}} f = \int_{\underline{A_1}} f + \int_{\underline{A_2}} f = \frac{1}{4} + \frac{1}{2} = \frac{3}{4}$$

Since the lower integral is actually less than the upper integral, f is not integrable on A.

The function g_x of Theorem 5-4-1 is given by the following: If x is a rational number, for all $y \in [0, 1]$, $g_x(y) = 1$. If x is an irrational number, then for all $y \in [0, 1]$, $g_x(y) = 2y$. Then the function ψ of the theorem is given by

$$\text{If } x \text{ is rational, } \psi(x) = \int_0^1 g_x = 1$$

$$\text{If } x \text{ is irrational, } \psi(x) = \int_0^1 g_x = \int_0^1 2t \, dt = 1$$

Since ψ is a constant function, ψ is integrable on $[0, 1]$ and $\int_0^1 \psi = 1$.

For this example, examining the functions given in Theorem 5-4-2 yields, for any fixed $y \in [0, 1]$,

$$h_y(x) = \begin{cases} 1, & \text{if } x \text{ is rational} \\ 2y, & \text{if } x \text{ is irrational} \end{cases}$$

Since y is fixed, the range of h_y consists of the two numbers 1 and $2y$. In particular, if $0 \le y < \frac{1}{2}$, then $2y < 1$ so that

$$\overline{\int_0^1} h_y = 1 \quad \text{and} \quad \underline{\int_0^1} h_y = 2y$$

which means that h_y is not integrable. For $\frac{1}{2} < y \le 1$, one can also see that h_y is not integrable.

The results given in the two theorems relating the two-dimensional integral to the two iterated integrals are perhaps more impressive by writing

$$\int_A f = \int_{x=a}^{x=b} \left\{ \int_{y=\varphi_B(x)}^{y=\varphi_T(x)} f(x, y) \, dy \right\} dx$$

$$= \int_{y=c}^{y=d} \left\{ \int_{x=\varphi_G(y)}^{x=\varphi_D(y)} f(x, y) \, dx \right\} dy$$

EXAMPLE. We consider f, given by $f(x, y) = 1 - x - y$, and, as in the preceding section, we take

$$A = \{(x, y) \mid 0 \le 1 - x \le y \text{ and } 0 \le x \le 1\}$$
$$= \{(x, y) \mid 0 \le x \le 1 - y \text{ and } 0 \le y \le 1\}$$

From the consideration of upper and lower integrals in the preceding sections, we found

$$\int_A f = \frac{1}{6}$$

The bottom boundary of A is the graph of

$$y = \varphi_B(x) = 0, \qquad 0 \le x \le 1$$

The top boundary of A is the graph of

$$y = \varphi_T(x) = 1 - x, \qquad 0 \le x \le 1$$

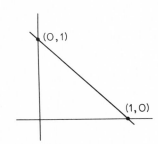

Figure 5-4

The left edge of A is the graph of

$$x = \varphi_G(y) = 0, \qquad 0 \le y \le 1$$

The right edge of A is the graph of

$$x = \varphi_D(y) = 1 - y, \qquad 0 \le y \le 1$$

Then our two theorems yield

$$\int_{x=0}^{x=1} \int_{y=\varphi_B(x)}^{y=\varphi_T(x)} f(x,y)\, dy\, dx = \int_{x=0}^{x=1} \int_{y=0}^{y=1-x} (1 - x - y)\, dy\, dx$$

$$= \int_0^1 \frac{(1-x)^2}{2}\, dx$$

$$= \frac{1}{6}$$

and

$$\int_{y=0}^{y=1} \int_{x=\varphi_G(y)}^{x=\varphi_D(y)} f(x,y)\, dx\, dy = \int_{y=0}^{y=1} \int_{x=0}^{x=1-y} (1 - y - x)\, dx\, dy$$

$$= \int_0^1 \frac{(1-y)^2}{2}\, dy$$

$$= \frac{1}{6}$$

EXERCISES

With the notation of Theorem 5-4-1, for any $x \in [a, b]$,

$$\psi(x + h) - \psi(x) = \int_{\varphi_B(x+h)}^{\varphi_T(x+h)} f(x + h, y)\, dy - \int_{\varphi_B(x)}^{\varphi_T(x)} f(x, y)\, dy$$

$$= \left\{ \int_{\varphi_B(x+h)}^{\varphi_B(x)} + \int_{\varphi_T(x)}^{\varphi_T(x+h)} \right\} f(x + h, y)\, dy$$

$$+ \int_{\varphi_B(x)}^{\varphi_T(x)} [f(x + h, y) - f(x, y)]\, dy$$

1. The mean value theorem for integrals says if f is a continuous function on $[p, q]$ into the real numbers, then there exists $r \in [p, q]$ such that $\int_p^q f = f(r)(q - p)$. Apply this theorem to each of the three integrals above to find an expression for $\psi(x + h) - \psi(x)$.

2. Use the continuity of the functions involved to show that ψ is continuous at x.

3. Use the continuity of ψ given in Exercises 1 and 2 to construct another proof of Theorem 5-4-1.

4. Prove Theorem 5-4-2.

5. f is a continuous function on the three-dimensional set

$$D = \left\{ (x, y, z) \,\middle|\, x^2 + \frac{y^2}{4} + \frac{z^2}{9} \leq 1 \right\}$$

into the real numbers. Find all possible iterated integrals for $\int_D f$.

6. Give an analogue of Theorems 5-4-1 and 5-4-2 for a function which is continuous on a three-dimensional set.

Find all iterated integrals for $\int_D f$ where

7. $D = \{(x, y) \,|\, x^2 + y^2 \leq r^2\}$

8. D is that portion of the plane bounded by the graphs of $y = x^2$ and $y = x$.

9. D is that portion of the plane bounded by the graphs of $y = x^2$ and $x + y = 6$.

10. D is the three-dimensional right-circular cylinder of radius r and height h, whose axis is the z axis and whose base is the x-y plane.

11. D is the three-dimensional set common to the right-circular cylinders of radius 1, one of which has the x axis for an axis and the other has the y axis for an axis.

5-5   Changes in the Order of Integration

The theorems of the preceding section provide a method of evaluation of the integral on a quadrable two-dimensional set (with obvious extension to the case of functions whose domains are sets of higher dimension). Since the method requires successive integration of functions whose domains are intervals of numbers—that is, the evaluation of one-dimensional integrals—the method succeeds only if each and every one of these integrals can be evaluated.

Usually, the manner in which the quadrable two-dimensional set is described suggests the order in which the integrations can be performed. In some cases both possible orders of integration lend themselves to evaluation by the fundamental theorem of calculus, but one order provides less laborious manipulation than the other. For example, let f be an integrable function on the set A, which set is that portion of the x-y plane bounded by the graphs of $y = x^2$ and $x - y + 2 = 0$. The top boundary of the set A is given by the equation

$$y = \varphi_T(x) = x + 2, \qquad -1 \leq x \leq 2$$

and the bottom boundary is given by the equation

$$y = \varphi_B(x) = x^2, \qquad -1 \leq x \leq 2$$

Thus

$$\int_A f = \int_{x=-1}^{x=2} \left\{ \int_{y=x^2}^{y=x+2} f(x, y) \, dy \right\} dx$$

On the other hand, the left edge of A is given by

$$x = \varphi_G(y) = \begin{cases} -\sqrt{y}, & 0 \leq y \leq 1 \\ y - 2, & 1 \leq y \leq 4 \end{cases}$$

and the right edge of A is given by

$$x = \varphi_D(y) = \sqrt{y}, \qquad 0 \leq y \leq 4$$

In this case,

$$\int_A f = \int_{y=0}^{y=1} \left\{ \int_{x=-\sqrt{y}}^{x=\sqrt{y}} f(x, y) \, dx \right\} dy + \int_{y=1}^{y=4} \left\{ \int_{x=y-2}^{x=\sqrt{y}} f(x, y) \, dx \right\} dy$$

Unless the function f is rather special, the first order of integration (first vertically, then horizontally) will require less labor than the second.

In some cases, the form of the function being integrated calls for the order of integration to be used. That is, one may be faced with a function sufficiently awkward so that the one-dimensional integrals required in one order of integration can be evaluated by the fundamental theorem of calculus but those required in the other order cannot. For example, let f be given by

$$f(x, y) = e^{x/y}$$

and let

$$A = \{(x, y) \mid x \le y \le 1, 0 \le x \le 1\}$$
$$= \{(x, y) \mid 0 \le x \le y, 0 \le y \le 1\}$$

To illustrate the point being made on the order of integration, we ignore the misbehavior of f at $(0, 0)$. We have

$$\varphi_T(x) = 1, \qquad 0 \le x \le 1$$
$$\varphi_B(x) = x, \qquad 0 \le x \le 1$$
$$\int_A f = \int_{x=0}^{x=1} \left\{ \int_{y=x}^{y=1} e^{x/y} \, dy \right\} dx$$

We also have

$$\varphi_G(y) = 0, \qquad 0 \le y \le 1$$
$$\varphi_D(y) = y, \qquad 0 \le y \le 1$$
$$\int_A f = \int_{y=0}^{y=1} \left\{ \int_{x=0}^{x=y} e^{x/y} \, dy \right\} dx$$

For any fixed $x \in \,]0, 1]$, the function g_x, given by $g_x(y) = e^{x/y}$, is certainly integrable on the interval $[x, 1]$ (since g_x is continuous), but there is no elementary function which is an antiderivative of g_x. Thus, even though we know that the first evaluation of the integral is valid, the order of integration presented cannot be carried out.

For any fixed $y \in \,]0, 1]$, however, the function h_y, given by $h_y(x) = e^{x/y}$, is not only integrable on $[0, y]$, it has an antiderivative H_y, given by $H_y(x) = y e^{x/y}$. Thus

$$\int_{x=0}^{x=y} e^{x/y} \, dy = y(e - 1)$$

and

$$\int_A f = \int_{y=0}^{y=1} (e - 1) y \, dy = \frac{e - 1}{2}$$

[The method of approach which considers the misbehavior of f at $(0, 0)$ will be given in Chapter 8.]

For an integral on a three-dimensional set, the manner of description of the set again provides a way to express the integral as the result of three iterated integrations, each of them one-dimensional. Such a description has already been met in the classical Stokes' Theorem (Chapter 4). In three-dimensional integrals the basic type of quadrable set is one which has a boundary composed of a definite top and bottom, a left and right side, or a rear and front face, each of which is the graph of an equation involving a continuous function on a two-dimensional set.

For example, let A be that part of the first octant bounded by the co-ordinate planes and the graph of

$$\frac{x}{a} + \frac{y}{b} + \frac{z}{c} = 1 \qquad a > 0, b > 0, \text{ and } c > 0$$

Then six different iterated integrals can be written for an integral on A. These are left to the exercises.

EXERCISES

1. For the set A given above, find the projections onto the three coordinate planes and describe each of these projections in two ways.

2. Find functions which give the top and bottom of A.

3. Find functions which give the left and right sides of A.

4. Find functions which give the rear and front of A.

5. Write all six forms of iterated integrals for an integral on A.

Interchange the order of integration in

6. $\displaystyle\int_{x=1}^{x=2}\left\{\int_{y=0}^{y=x} f(x, y)\, dy\right\} dx$

7. $\displaystyle\int_{y=0}^{y=1}\left\{\int_{x=y^2}^{x=3-2y} f(x, y)\, dx\right\} dy$

8. $\displaystyle\int_{x=0}^{x=r}\left\{\int_{y=0}^{y=\sqrt{r^2-x^2}} f(x, y)\, dy\right\} dx$

Use iterated integrals and the result of Exercise 3, Section 5-2, to find $V_3(A)$ when A is

9. A right-circular cylinder.

10. A right-circular cone.

11. A sphere.

12. The tetrahedron bounded by the graphs of $x + y = 5, 8x - 12y + 15z = 0$, the x-y plane, and the y-z plane.

13. Any tetrahedron.

5-6   Nonrectangular Coordinate Systems

In the process of forming the integral of a function on a two- (or higher-) dimensional set, it may happen that the points of the set and a rule for the function are described by a nonrectangular coordinate system. The most common of such systems are polar coordinates for two-dimensional sets and cylindrical and spherical coordinates for three-dimensional sets. The purpose of this section is to examine methods of determining the integral in these cases. The general theory which considers arbitrary coordinate systems will be treated in Chapter 7.

Polar Coordinates. A polar coordinate system for a plane associates with each point an ordered pair of numbers and refers these numbers to a fixed half line, called the *polar axis*, and the end point of this half line, called the *origin*. If the point P has polar coordinates (r, θ), the first number r of the ordered pair (r, θ) has the property that the distance between P and the origin is $|r|$. The second number θ of the ordered pair (r, θ) has the property that the line through P and the origin makes an angle of θ radians with the polar axis. More specifically, if $r > 0$ and $\theta \geq 0$, the point with polar coordinates (r, θ) is $|r| = r$ units from the origin and the angle *from* the polar axis *to* the line segment joining P to the origin is $|\theta| = \theta$ radians. If $r > 0$ and $\theta < 0$, the point with polar coordinates (r, θ) is r units from the origin and the angle from the polar axis to the line segment joining P to the origin is $2\pi - |\theta| = 2\pi + \theta$ radians. If $r < 0$ and $\theta \geq 0$, then the point with polar coordinates (r, θ) is $-r$ units from the origin and the angle from the polar axis to the line segment joining P to the origin is $\pi + \theta$ radians. Finally if $r < 0$ and $\theta < 0$, the point with polar coordinates (r, θ) is $-r$ units from the origin and the angle from the polar axis to the line segment joining P to the origin is $\pi - |\theta| = \pi + \theta$ radians.

The basic type of two-dimensional quadrable set described by polar coordinates is one of the form

$$A = \{(r, \theta) \mid \Phi_i(\theta) \leq r \leq \Phi_o(\theta), \alpha \leq \theta \leq \beta\}$$
$$= \{(r, \theta) \mid \Phi_b(r) \leq \theta \leq \Phi_e(r), p \leq r \leq q\}$$

We require that the functions Φ_i, Φ_o, Φ_b, and Φ_e, which give the inner, outer, beginning, and ending parts, respectively, of the boundary of A, be continuous and that the set A be entirely contained in the angular section whose vertices have polar coordinates (p, α), (q, α), (q, β) and (p, β). A convenient method of providing both packings and coverings of the set A begins with forming partitions of the intervals $[\alpha, \beta]$ and $[p, q]$ by taking

$$\alpha = \theta_0 < \theta_1 < \theta_2 < \cdots < \theta_m = \beta$$

and

$$p = r_0 < r_1 < r_2 < \cdots < r_n = q$$

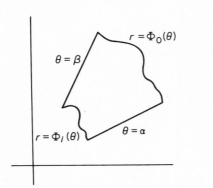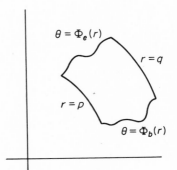

Figure 5-5

We then draw the line segments, for $i = 0, 1, 2, \ldots, m$,

$$\{(r, \theta) \mid \theta = \theta_i, \quad p \leq r \leq q\}$$

and the circular arcs, for $j = 0, 1, 2, \ldots, n$,

$$\{(r, \theta) \mid r = r_j, \quad \alpha \leq \theta \leq \beta\}$$

A typical angular section given by indices i and j will have vertices whose polar coordinates are (r_{j-1}, θ_{i-1}), (r_j, θ_{i-1}), (r_j, θ_i), and (r_{j-1}, θ_i) and its area will be

$$\frac{\theta_i - \theta_{i-1}}{2\pi} [\pi r_j^2 - \pi r_{j-1}^2] = \frac{1}{2}(r_j^2 - r_{j-1}^2)(\theta_i - \theta_{i-1})$$

$$= \frac{r_j + r_{j-1}}{2}(r_j - r_{j-1})(\theta_i - \theta_{i-1})$$

Now if F is a continuous function on A into the real numbers then $\int_A F$ exists and can be found by considering sums of the form

$$\sum_{i=1}^{m} \sum_{j=1}^{n} \sup F(A_{i,j}) \frac{r_j + r_{j-1}}{2}(r_j - r_{j-1})(\theta_i - \theta_{i-1})$$

and of the form

$$\sum_{i=1}^{m} \sum_{j=1}^{n} \inf F(A_{i,j}) \frac{r_j + r_{j-1}}{2}(r_j - r_{j-1})(\theta_i - \theta_{i-1})$$

We now let f be that function on the rectangle $[p, q] \times [\alpha, \beta] = R$ into the real numbers such that if (r, θ) is the rectangular coordinate label of a point of the rectangle R and (r, θ) is the polar coordinate label of a point in the set A, then the number which f pairs with the point with rectangular coordinates (r, θ) is also the number F pairs with the point with polar coordinates (r, θ).

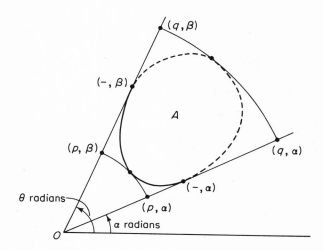

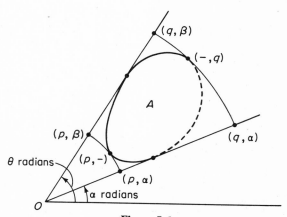

Figure 5-6

For $i = 1, 2, \ldots, m$ and $j = 1, 2, \ldots, n$, the angular section $A_{i,j}$ thus corresponds to a subrectangle, $R_{i,j}$ of the rectangle $R = [p, q] \times [\alpha, \beta]$. Obviously we have $\sup F(A_{i,j}) = \sup f(R_{i,j})$ and $\inf F(A_{i,j}) = \inf f(R_{i,j})$. We now let g be that function on the rectangle R into the real numbers given by

$$g(x, y) = xf(x, y)$$

For any point in $R_{i,j}$ with *rectangular* coordinates (r, θ), we have

$$\inf f(R_{i,j}) \leq f(r, \theta) \leq \sup f(R_{i,j})$$
$$\inf F(A_{i,j}) \leq f(r, \theta) \leq \sup F(A_{i,j})$$

Since we may always find polar coordinates with non-negative r coordinates, we can assume that the interval $[p, q]$ consists of non-negative numbers. Thus, for any $r \in [r_{j-1}, r_j]$,

$$r \inf F(A_{i,j}) \leq rf(r, \theta) \leq r \sup F(A_{i,j})$$
$$r_{j-1} \inf F(A_{i,j}) \leq rf(r, \theta) \leq r_j \sup F(A_{i,j})$$
$$r_{j-1} \inf F(A_{i,j}) \leq g(r, \theta) \leq r_j \sup F(A_{i,j})$$
$$r_{j-1} \inf F(A_{i,j}) \leq \inf g(R_{i,j}) \leq \sup g(R_{i,j}) \leq r_j \sup F(A_{i,j})$$

Further, for any point with rectangular coordinates (r, θ) in $R_{i,j}$,

$$r \inf F(A_{i,j}) \leq g(r, \theta) \leq \sup g(R_{i,j})$$

so that, for $r = r_j$,

$$r_j \inf F(A_{i,j}) \leq \sup g(R_{i,j})$$

Combining this with

$$r_{j-1} \inf F(A_{i,j}) \leq \sup g(R_{i,j})$$

yields

$$\frac{r_j + r_{j-1}}{2} \inf F(A_{i,j}) \leq \sup g(R_{i,j})$$

$$\sum_{i=1}^{m} \sum_{j=1}^{n} \inf F(A_{i,j}) \frac{r_j + r_{j-1}}{2} (r_j - r_{j-1})(\theta_i - \theta_{i-1}) \leq \sum_{i=1}^{m} \sum_{j=1}^{n} \sup g(R_{i,j}) V_2(R_{i,j})$$

which will imply that

$$\int_A F \leq \int_R g$$

But, in like manner, the inequality

$$r_{j-1}[\sup F(A_{i,j})] \geq \inf g(R_{i,j})$$

leads to the reverse inequality and we conclude that

$$\int_A F = \int_{\theta=\alpha}^{\theta=\beta} \left\{ \int_{r=\Phi_i(\theta)}^{r=\Phi_o(\theta)} f(r, \theta) r \, dr \right\} d\theta$$
$$= \int_{r=p}^{r=q} \left\{ \int_{\theta=\Phi_b(r)}^{\theta=\Phi_o(r)} f(r, \theta) \, d\theta \right\} r \, dr$$

EXAMPLE. A is that portion of the circle centered at the point with (rectangular or polar) coordinates $(1, 0)$, of radius 1, which lies outside the circle centered at the origin of radius 1.

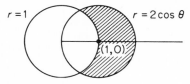

Figure 5-7

The circle of radius 1 centered at the origin is the graph of the polar coordinate equation $r = 1$. The circle of radius 1 centered at the point with coordinates $(1, 0)$ is the graph of the polar coordinate equation $r = 2 \cos \theta$. Then

$$A = \left\{ (r, \theta) \mid 1 \leq r \leq 2 \cos \theta, \quad \frac{-\pi}{4} \leq \theta \leq \frac{\pi}{4} \right\}$$

If F is a continuous function on A into the real numbers, then

$$\int_A F = \int_{\theta = -\pi/4}^{\theta = \pi/4} \left\{ \int_{r=1}^{r=2 \cos \theta} F(r, \theta) r \, dr \right\} d\theta$$

Cylindrical Coordinates A cylindrical coordinate system for a three-dimensional space associates with each point an ordered triple of numbers and refers these numbers to a fixed line, called the *z axis;* a fixed point on that line, called the *origin;* and a half line from the origin, perpendicular to the z axis, called the *polar axis.*

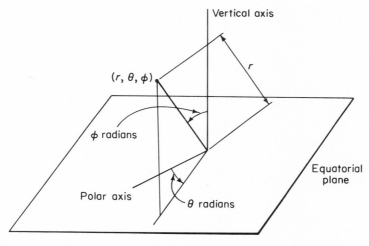

Figure 5-8

The plane through the origin containing the polar axis (and thus perpendicular to the z axis) is called the *polar plane.* If the point P has cylindrical coordinates (r, θ, z), then the ordered pair (r, θ) is the polar coordinate label of the projection of P onto the polar plane and the number z is the one-dimensional coordinate of the projection of P onto the z axis. The basic type of quadrable three-dimensional set described by cylindrical coordinates is one which is entirely contained within a segment of a cylindrical shell formed by two right-circular cylindrical surfaces whose axes are the

z axis, two planes containing the x axis, and two planes parallel to the polar plane,

$$\{(r, \theta, z) \,|\, p \leq r \leq q, \quad \alpha \leq \theta \leq \beta, \quad c \leq z \leq d\}$$

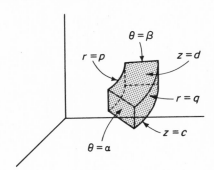

Figure 5-9

Within such a cylindrical shell we consider a three-dimensional set A with an inner surface given by

$$r = \Phi_i(\theta, z), \qquad \Phi_{rb}(z) \leq \theta \leq \Phi_{re}(z), \qquad c \leq z \leq d$$

or by

$$r = \Phi_i(\theta, z), \qquad \Phi_{rB}(\theta) \leq z \leq \Phi_{rT}(z), \qquad \alpha \leq \theta \leq \beta$$

an outer surface given by

$$r = \Phi_o(\theta, z), \qquad \Phi_{rb}(z) \leq \theta \leq \Phi_{re}(z), \qquad c \leq z \leq d$$

or by

$$r = \Phi_o(\theta, z), \qquad \Phi_{rB}(\theta) \leq z \leq \Phi_{rT}(\theta), \qquad \alpha \leq \theta \leq \beta$$

a top surface given by

$$z = \Phi_T(r, \theta), \qquad \Phi_{zb}(r) \leq \theta \leq \Phi_{ze}(r), \qquad p \leq r \leq q$$

or by

$$z = \Phi_T(r, \theta), \qquad \Phi_{zi}(\theta) \leq r \leq \Phi_{zo}(\theta), \qquad \alpha \leq \theta \leq \beta$$

a bottom surface given by

$$z = \Phi_B(r, \theta), \qquad \Phi_{zb}(r) \leq \theta \leq \Phi_{ze}(r), \qquad p \leq r \leq q$$

or by

$$z = \Phi_B(r, \theta), \qquad \Phi_{zi}(\theta) \leq r \leq \Phi_{zo}(\theta), \qquad \alpha \leq \theta \leq \beta$$

a beginning surface given by

$$\theta = \Phi_b(r, z), \qquad \Phi_{\theta i}(z) \leq r \leq \Phi_{\theta o}(z), \qquad c \leq z \leq d$$

or by

$$\theta = \Phi_b(r, z), \qquad \Phi_{\theta B}(r) \leq z \leq \Phi_{\theta T}(r), \qquad p \leq r \leq q$$

and an ending surface given by

$$\theta = \Phi_e(r, z), \qquad \Phi_{\theta i}(z) \le r \le \Phi_{\theta o}(z), \qquad c \le z \le d$$

or by

$$\theta = \Phi_e(r, z), \qquad \Phi_{\theta B}(r) \le z \le \Phi_{\theta T}(r), \qquad p \le r \le q$$

Then A has six possible descriptions and the integral of a continuous function on A can be found by using any of six distinct iterated integrals. The determination of the forms of these is left to the exercises.

Spherical Coordinates. A spherical coordinate system for a three-dimensional space associates with each point an ordered triple of numbers and refers these numbers to a fixed point, called the *origin;* a fixed half line beginning at the origin, called the *vertical axis;* a plane through the origin perpendicular to the vertical axis, called the *equatorial plane;* and a polar coordinate system (with a polar axis) in the equatorial plane. If the point P has spherical coordinates (r, θ, φ), the ordered pair (r, θ) are the polar coordinates of the projection of P onto the equatorial plane and the number φ, with the restriction $0 \le \varphi \le \pi$, has the property that the angle from the vertical axis to the line segment joining P to the origin is φ radians.

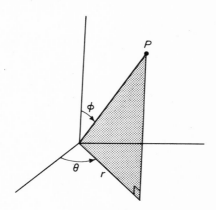

Figure 5-10

The basic type of quadrable three-dimensional sets described by spherical coordinates is one which is entirely contained within a segment of a spherical shell formed by two spheres centered at the origin, two planes containing the vertical axis, and two conical surfaces whose common vertex is the origin and whose common axis is the vertical axis,

$$\{(r, \theta, \varphi) \mid p \le r \le q, \quad \alpha \le \theta \le \beta, \quad \gamma \le \varphi \le \delta\}$$

Within such a spherical shell we consider a three-dimensional set an inner surface given by

$$r = \Phi_i(\theta, \varphi), \qquad (\theta, \varphi) \in R_{\theta, \varphi}$$
$$R_{\theta, \varphi} = \{(\theta, \varphi) \,|\, \Phi_{rb}(\varphi) \leq \theta \leq \Phi_{re}(\varphi), \gamma \leq \varphi \leq \delta\}$$
$$= \{(\theta, \varphi) \,|\, \Phi_{rn}(\theta) \leq \varphi \leq \Phi_{rs}(\theta), \alpha \leq \theta \leq \beta\}$$

and outer surface given by

$$r = \Phi_o(\theta, \varphi), \qquad (\theta, \varphi) \in R_{\theta, \varphi}$$

a "northern" edge given by

$$\varphi = \Phi_n(r, \theta), \qquad (r, \theta) \in R_{r, \theta}$$
$$R_{r, \theta} = \{(r, \theta) \,|\, \Phi_{\varphi i}(\theta) \leq r \leq \Phi_{\varphi o}(\theta), \alpha \leq \theta \leq \beta\}$$
$$= \{(r, \theta) \,|\, \Phi_{\varphi b}(r) \leq \theta \leq \Phi_{\varphi e}(r), p \leq r \leq q\}$$

a "southern" edge given by

$$\varphi = \Phi_s(r, \theta), \qquad (r, \theta) \in R_{r, \theta}$$

a "western" edge given by

$$\theta = \Phi_w(r, \varphi), \qquad (r, \varphi) \in R_{r, \varphi}$$
$$R_{r, \varphi} = \{(r, \varphi) \,|\, \Phi_{\theta i}(\varphi) \leq r \leq \Phi_{\theta o}(\varphi), \gamma \leq \varphi \leq \delta\}$$
$$= \{(r, \varphi) \,|\, \Phi_{\theta n}(r) \leq \varphi \leq \Phi_{\theta s}(r), p \leq r \leq q\}$$

and an "eastern" edge given by

$$\theta = \Phi_e(r, \varphi), \qquad (r, \varphi) \in R_{r, \varphi}$$

Then the set A can be described by

$$A = \{(r, \theta, \varphi) \,|\, \Phi_i(\theta, \varphi) \leq r \leq \Phi_o(\theta, \varphi), \quad (\theta, \varphi) \in R_{\theta, \varphi}\}$$
$$= \{(r, \theta, \varphi) \,|\, \Phi_n(r, \theta) \leq \varphi \leq \Phi_s(r, \theta), \quad (r, \theta) \in R_{r, \theta}\}$$
$$= \{(r, \theta, \varphi) \,|\, \Phi_w(r, \varphi) \leq \theta \leq \Phi_e(r, \varphi), \quad (r, \varphi) \in R_{r, \varphi}\}$$

Packings and coverings of A can be achieved by partitioning the three intervals $[p, q]$, $[\alpha, \beta]$, and $[\gamma, \delta]$ by

$$p = r_0 < r_1 < r_2 < \cdots < r_l = q$$
$$\alpha = \theta_0 < \theta_1 < \theta_2 < \cdots < \theta_m = \beta$$
$$\gamma = \varphi_0 < \varphi_1 < \varphi_2 < \cdots < \varphi_n = \delta$$

We construct the segments of spherical shells, for $i = 0, 1, 2, \ldots, l$,

$$\{(r, \theta, \varphi) \,|\, r = r_i, \alpha \leq \theta \leq \beta, \gamma \leq \varphi \leq \delta\}$$

the vertical plane annular segments, for $j = 0, 1, 2, \ldots, m$,

$$\{(r, \theta, \varphi) \,|\, \theta = \theta_j, p \leq r \leq q, \gamma \leq \varphi \leq \delta\}$$

and the segments of conical surfaces, for $k = 0, 1, 2, \ldots, n,$

$$\{(r, \theta, \varphi) \mid \varphi = \varphi_k, p \le r \le q, \alpha \le \theta \le \beta\}$$

We let $A_{i,j,k}$ be the subdivision of the spherical shell surrounding A which has inner face given by $r = r_{i-1}$, outer face given by $r = r_i$, a western face given by $\theta = \theta_{j-1}$, an eastern face given by $\theta = \theta_j$, a northern face given by $\varphi = \varphi_{k-1}$, and a southern face given by $\varphi = \varphi_k$. Then

$$V_3(A_{i,j,k}) = \frac{1}{3}(r_i^3 - r_{i-1}^3)(\theta_j - \theta_{j-1})(\cos \varphi_{k-1} - \cos \varphi_k)$$

$$= \frac{r_i^2 + r_i r_{i-1} + r_{i-1}^2}{3}(r_i - r_{i-1})(\theta_j - \theta_{j-1})(\cos \varphi_{k-1} - \cos \varphi_k)$$

Since the cosine function is differentiable, the mean value theorem tells us that there exists a number ϵ_k in the open interval $]\varphi_{k-1}, \varphi_k[$ such that

$$\cos \varphi_{k-1} - \cos \varphi_k = (\varphi_{k-1} - \varphi_k)(-\sin \epsilon_k) = (\varphi_k - \varphi_{k-1})(\sin \epsilon_k)$$

Thus

$$V_3(A_{i,j,k}) = \frac{r_i^2 + r_i r_{i-1} + r_{i-1}^2}{3}(\sin \epsilon_k)(r_i - r_{i-1})(\theta_j - \theta_{j-1})(\varphi_k - \varphi_{k-1})$$

Now if f is a continuous function on A into the real numbers, we may consider a new function on the rectangular box given by considering (r, θ, φ) as rectangular coordinates and, as in the case of polar coordinates, arrive at the conclusion that

$$\int_A F = \int_{\varphi=\gamma}^{\varphi=\delta} \left\{ \int_{\theta=\Phi_{rw}(\varphi)}^{\theta=\Phi_{re}(\varphi)} \left\{ \int_{r=\Phi_i(\theta,\varphi)}^{r=\Phi_o(\theta,\varphi)} r^2 f(r, \theta, \varphi)\, dr \right\} d\theta \right\} \sin \varphi\, d\varphi$$

as well as five other forms of iterated integral.

EXERCISES

1. Carry out the argument for upper and lower integrals of a continuous function described by cylindrical coordinates.

2. Write the six forms of iterated integral for a function described by cylindrical coordinates.

3. Carry out the argument for upper and lower integrals of a continuous function described by spherical coordinates.

4. Write the five remaining forms of iterated integral for a function described by spherical coordinates.

Write an iterated integral for $\int_A f$ when

5. A is the circle centered at the point with polar coordinates $(a, 0)$, of radius $a > 0$.

6. A is the portion of the plane inside the graph of $r = 1 + \sin \theta$.

7. A is the cylinder given by rectangular coordinates $x^2 + y^2 \leq 1, 0 \leq z \leq 1$.

8. A is the sphere centered at the origin, of radius $a > 0$.

9. Use the iterated integral in cylindrical coordinates to find the volume of a right-circular cylinder.

10. Use the iterated integral in spherical coordinates to find the volume of a sphere.

11. Use the iterated integral in spherical coordinates to find the volume of the portion of a sphere cut off by a plane.

LIMITS AND CONVERGENCE 6

6-1 Limits

In Section 2-1 we considered the concept of limit and local continuity for a function on an n-dimensional set into the real numbers. In this section we review these concepts.

If f is a function on the n-dimensional set D into the real numbers and $\mathbf{a} = (a_1, a_2, \ldots, a_n)$ is a fixed point of D, then we can construct, for $k = 1, 2, \ldots, n$, the function $^k f$ given by

$$^k f(t) = f(a_1, a_2, \ldots, a_{k-1}, t, a_{k+1}, \ldots, a_n)$$

The domain of $^k f$ is

$$\{t \mid (a_1, a_2, \ldots, a_{k-1}, t, a_{k+1}, \ldots, a_n) \in D\}$$

The definition of "f is continuous at $\mathbf{a}$" requires that for every $\epsilon > 0$ there exists $\delta_\epsilon > 0$ such that if $d_n(\mathbf{x}, \mathbf{a}) < \delta_\epsilon$, then $\mathbf{x} \in D$ and $|f(\mathbf{x}) - f(\mathbf{a})| < \epsilon$. In other words, "$f$ is continuous at $\mathbf{a}$" means that

$$\lim_{\mathbf{x} \to \mathbf{a}} f(\mathbf{x}) = f(\mathbf{a})$$

We have seen that if f is continuous at $\mathbf{a}$, then, for $k = 1, 2, \ldots, n$, $^k f$ will be continuous at a_k and have noted that the converse of this theorem is false.

In Chapter 5 we examined the concept of the integral, since integrals were involved in the classical vector theorems on which we are focusing our attention. We now turn to an examination of the functions which might be integrated and begin by looking at the concept of continuity.

6-2 Continuity

The most immediate use of the concept of limit occurs in forming definitions which use the word *continuous*. The definition we have seen thus far is equivalent to

Definition 6-2-1. f is a function on the n-dimensional set D into the real numbers. $\mathbf{c} \in D$. f *is continuous at* $\mathbf{c}$ means $\lim\limits_{\mathbf{x} \to \mathbf{c}} f(\mathbf{x}) = f(\mathbf{c})$.

The equation in this definition says three things: $\lim_{x \to c} f(\mathbf{x})$ exists (that is, it is some real number); $\mathbf{c}$ is in the domain of f (that is, $f(\mathbf{c})$ is some real number); and these two real numbers are the same.

Another use of the word continuous occurs in

> **Temporary definition.** f is a function on the n-dimensional set D into the real numbers. *f is continuous* means f is continuous at every point of D.

In this way, continuous, when used alone, refers to a "global" property of a function—that is, a property which applies throughout the domain, whereas the phrase *continuous at* refers to a "local" property. For example, the function f, given by

$$f(x) = 2x, \qquad 0 < x < 1$$

is continuous at every number in its domain since, if $0 < c < 1$, then $\lim_{x \to c} 2x = 2c$. On the other hand, the function g, given by

$$f(x) = \begin{cases} x, & 0 < x < 1 \text{ and } x \text{ rational} \\ 1 - x, & 0 < x < 1 \text{ and } x \text{ irrational} \end{cases}$$

is continuous at $\frac{1}{2}$, but it is not continuous at any other number in its domain.

An awkwardness now arises with our temporary definition of the word *continuous* as a global property of a function in trying to apply the definition of limit to a boundary point of the domain of a function. Since a boundary point of any set, by definition, has the property that every one of its neighborhoods intersects both the set and the complement of the set, if one has a boundary point of the domain of a function, then one can never find a neighborhood of such a point which lies entirely within the domain. But the definition of $\lim_{x \to c} f(\mathbf{x})$ requires, among other things, that some deleted neighborhood of the point $\mathbf{c}$ be entirely in the domain of f. The definition of "f is continuous at $\mathbf{c}$" requires that some (nondeleted) neighborhood of the point $\mathbf{c}$ lie entirely within the domain of f. Then, according to our temporary definition of *continuous* as a global property of functions, the function f, given by

$$f(x) = 2x, \qquad 0 \le x \le 1$$

cannot be continuous since this function is not continuous at either 0 or 1.

It is not unreasonable that we construct our definitions in such a manner that the technical mathematical meaning given a word does not do too much violence to the usual English meanings of that word. Thus one would expect the definition of *continuous at* to result in a situation in which a segment of a curve is not continuous at the end points of that segment. One would also expect, however, that the definition of *continuous* should allow a segment of a curve, considered in its entirety, to be called *continuous*. In order to have this happen, we need to alter the temporary definition to allow for boundary points of the domain. In order to allow for special behavior at boundary points, we begin by examining the behavior of a function whose domain includes none of its boundary points and which function is continuous at each of the points actually in the domain. If f is continuous at the point $\mathbf{c}$ of $\mathbf{V_n}$ and is a function into the real numbers, then the definition of *continuous at* provides us with the following equivalent statements:

    1. For every $\epsilon > 0$ there exists $\delta_\epsilon > 0$ such that if $d_n(\mathbf{x}, \mathbf{c}) < \delta_\epsilon$, then $\mathbf{x}$ is in the domain of f and $|f(\mathbf{x}) - f(\mathbf{c})| < \epsilon$.

    2. For every $\epsilon > 0$ there exists $\delta_\epsilon > 0$ such that if $d_n(\mathbf{x}, \mathbf{c}) < \delta_\epsilon$, then $\mathbf{x}$ is in the domain of f and $d_1(f(\mathbf{x}), f(\mathbf{c})) < \epsilon$.

    3. For every V_ϵ, an ϵ-neighborhood of $f(\mathbf{c})$, there exists a corresponding W_ϵ, an n-dimensional neighborhood of $\mathbf{c}$, such that if $\mathbf{x} \in W_\epsilon$, then $\mathbf{x}$ is in the domain of f and $f(\mathbf{x}) \in V$.

    4. For every V, a one-dimensional neighborhood of $f(\mathbf{c})$, there exists a corresponding W_V, an n-dimensional neighborhood of $\mathbf{c}$, such that W_V is a subset of the domain of f and $f(W_V) \subseteq V$.

    For any set of real numbers A, and a function f on an n-dimensional set into the real numbers, the *inverse image* $f^{-1}(A)$ of the set A under the function f is defined by

$$f^{-1}(A) = \{\mathbf{x} \mid \mathbf{x} \text{ is in the domain of } f \text{ and } f(\mathbf{x}) \in A\}$$

(This notation does *not* imply that the function f has an inverse.) The fourth of the statements above may now be rephrased as

    4. For every V, a one-dimensional neighborhood of $f(\mathbf{c})$, there exists a corresponding W_V, an n-dimensional neighborhood of $\mathbf{c}$, such that W_V is a subset of the domain of f and $W_V \subseteq f^{-1}(V)$.

    We recall that a set is open if, and only if, it consists exclusively of interior points, so we can prove

    Theorem 6-2-1. f is a function on the n-dimensional set D into the real numbers. If, for every $\mathbf{c} \in D$, f is continuous at $\mathbf{c}$, then for every open set of real numbers G, $f^{-1}(G)$ is an open n-dimensional set.

Proof. Let G be a given open set of real numbers and let $\mathbf{c}$ be a point of $f^{-1}(G)$. By the definition of the inverse image of a set, we must have $\mathbf{c} \in D$ and $f(\mathbf{c}) \in G$.

    Since $f(\mathbf{c})$ is a number in the open set G, there exists V, a neighborhood of $f(\mathbf{c})$, such that $f(\mathbf{c}) \in V \subseteq G$. [That is, $f(\mathbf{c})$ is an interior point of G.] Since V is a neighborhood of $f(\mathbf{c})$ and f is continuous at $\mathbf{c}$, then there exists

W, an n-dimensional neighborhood of c, such that $W \subseteq D$ and $W \subseteq f^{-1}(V)$. But, since W is a neighborhood of c and $W \subseteq f^{-1}(V)$, then c is an interior point of $f^{-1}(V)$. But $V \subseteq G$ implies $f^{-1}(V) \subseteq f^{-1}(G)$ so that c is an interior point of $f^{-1}(G)$. Since c was chosen arbitrarily in $f^{-1}(G)$, every point of this set must be an interior point and the set is open.   ■

In this way the definition of *continuous at* requires that a function can be continuous at every point in its domain only in the case that the domain itself is an open set, since every point in the domain must be an interior point.

In order to determine how we might construct a definition for *continuous* as a global property for a function, which definition will give appropriate local behavior at interior *and* boundary points of the domain, we examine the function f, given by

$$f(x) = 2x, \qquad 0 \le x \le 4$$

The domain of this function is the closed interval $[0, 4]$ and the range is the closed interval $[0, 8]$. If G is any open set of real numbers and c is a number in the set $f^{-1}(G)$, then c is in the closed interval $[0, 4]$—the domain of f—and $f(c) = 2c$ is in the closed interval $[0, 8]$—the range of f. Since G is an open set and $2c$ is a number in G, there exists $\epsilon > 0$ such that the open interval $]2c - \epsilon, 2c + \epsilon[$ is a subset of G. Then

$$f^{-1}(]2c - \epsilon, 2c + \epsilon[) = \left]c - \frac{\epsilon}{2}, c + \frac{\epsilon}{2}\right[\cap \,]0, 4[$$

Now if c is an interior point of $[0, 4]$, then $0 < c < 4$ and $0 < 2c < 8$ so that we may take ϵ less than both $2c$ and $8 - 2c$ in order that $f^{-1}(]2c - \epsilon, 2c + \epsilon[)$ be an open set. For the two end points of the domain, however, we have, for $\epsilon < 8$,

$$f^{-1}(]0 - \epsilon, 0 + \epsilon[) = \left]-\frac{\epsilon}{2}, \frac{\epsilon}{2}\right[\cap [0, 4] = \left[0, \frac{\epsilon}{2}\right[$$

$$f^{-1}(]8 - \epsilon, 8 + \epsilon[) = \left]4 - \frac{\epsilon}{2}, 4 + \frac{\epsilon}{2}\right[\cap [0, 4] = \left]4 - \frac{\epsilon}{2}, 4\right]$$

Neither of these two inverse images is an open set, but each is the intersection of an open set with the domain of the function. Accordingly, in constructing a definition for *continuous* as a global property of functions, we will not require that the function be continuous at every point of its domain, but will require that it be continuous at all interior points of the domain and will require at those boundary points of the domain which are actually in the domain a form of behavior similar to continuity. We have

Definition 6-2-2. f is a function on the n-dimensional set D into the real numbers. *f is continuous* means for every open set of real numbers G there exists an open n-dimensional set H such that $f^{-1}(G) = H \cap D$.

A consequence of this definition of continuity as a global property of a function is that one can easily construct continuous functions which are not continuous at any points of their domains. This is done simply by having every point of the domain be a boundary point. Examples are the functions given by

$$f(x) = 3x, \qquad 0 \le x \le 1, x \text{ rational}$$
$$g(x) = x^2, \qquad x \text{ any integer}$$
$$h = \{(3, 2), (4, 1)\}$$

Because of the manner in which the definition is given, a continuous function may have a graph which is not the path of a curve. This results from the fact that the path of a curve is defined to be the range of a function which is continuous at every number of an interval.

EXERCISES

1. Prove if f is a function on the n-dimensional set D into the real numbers and f is continuous at every point of D, then f is continuous.

2. $f(x) = 2x, 0 < x < 1$. For $c \in]0, 1[$, given $\epsilon > 0$, find $\delta_{\epsilon,c} > 0$ such that $|x - c| < \delta_{\epsilon,c}$ implies that $x \in]0, 1[$ and $|f(x) - f(c)| < \epsilon$.

3. g is given by

$$g(x) = \begin{cases} x, & 0 < x < 1, x \text{ rational} \\ 1 - x, & 0 < x < 1, x \text{ irrational} \end{cases}$$

Given $\epsilon > 0$, find $\delta_\epsilon > 0$ such that $|x - \frac{1}{2}| < \delta_\epsilon$ implies that $x \in]0, 1[$ and $|g(x) - \frac{1}{2}| < \epsilon$.

4. For g in Exercise 3 and $c \in]0, 1[$, $c \ne \frac{1}{2}$, find an $\epsilon_0 > 0$ such that for all $\delta > 0$ there exists x_δ such that $|x_\delta - c| < \delta$ but either $x \notin]0, 1[$ or $|f(x_\delta) - f(c)| > \epsilon_0$.

5. For the functions f and g of Exercises 2 and 3, find $f^{-1}(]a, b[)$.

6. Prove that if f is a function on the set of all real numbers into the real numbers and f is continuous, then every restriction of f is continuous.

7. Prove that all constant functions are continuous.

8. $f(x) = 3x, 0 \le x \le 1$, x rational. Prove that f is continuous. At which numbers is f continuous?

9. $g(x) = x^2$, x any integer. Prove that g is continuous. At which numbers is g continuous?

10. $h = \{(3, 2), (4, 1)\}$. Prove that f is continuous. At which numbers is f continuous?

11. $f(x) = x^2, 0 < x < 1$. For $c \in]0, 1[$, find $\delta_{\epsilon,c} > 0$ such that $|x - c| < \delta_{\epsilon,c}$ implies that $x \in]0, 1[$ and $|f(x) - f(c)| < \epsilon$.

12. For the $\delta_{\epsilon,c}$ found in Exercise 11, find inf $\{\delta_{\epsilon,c} \mid c \in]0, 1[\}$.

13. For the function f of Exercise 11, show that there exists $\delta_\epsilon > 0$ such that, for all $c \in]0, 1[$, $|x - c| < \delta_\epsilon$ implies that $x \in]0, 1[$ and $|f(x) - f(c)| < \epsilon$.

6-3 Uniform Continuity

We consider here two rather simple functions, given by

$$f(x) = \frac{1}{x}, \qquad 0 < x < 1$$

and

$$g(x) = 3x, \qquad 0 < x < 1$$

The range of f is the interval $]1, +\infty[$. The range of g is the interval $]0, 3[$. For any open interval of real numbers $]p, q[$, we examine $f^{-1}(]p, q[)$ and $g^{-1}(]p, q[)$.

If $q \leq 1$, then $f^{-1}(]p, q[) = \varnothing$, since no number in $]p, q[$ is in the range of f. If $p \leq 1 < q$, then $f^{-1}(]p, q[) =]1/q, 1[$, since $]1, q[$ is the only part of $]p, q[$ which is in the range of f. If $1 < p < q$, then $f^{-1}(]p, q[) =]1/q, 1/p[$. Thus the inverse image of any open interval is an open set. Since any open set is the union of open intervals, the inverse image under f of any open set is the intersection of an open set with the domain of f and we conclude that f is continuous.

For g we have $g^{-1}(]p, q[) =]p/3, q/3[\cap]0, 1[$, which is the intersection of an open set with the domain of g and g is also continuous.

We want to examine more closely the manner in which f and g are continuous at each number in $]0, 1[$. For this, it is convenient to expand the notation we used in the definition of limit so that, for any number $a \in]0, 1[$, we define $\lim_{x \to a} f(x) = f(a)$ to mean for every $\epsilon > 0$, there exists $\delta_{\epsilon,a,f} > 0$ such that if $|x - a| < \delta_{\epsilon,a,f}$, then $x \in]0, 1[$ and $|f(x) - f(a)| < \epsilon$; and we define $\lim_{x \to a} g(x) = g(a)$ to mean for every $\epsilon > 0$, there exists $\delta_{\epsilon,a,g} > 0$ such that if $|x - a| < \delta_{\epsilon,a,g}$, then $x \in]0, 1[$ and $|g(x) - g(a)| < \epsilon$.

For the function f, a fixed $\epsilon > 0$, and x and a in $]0, 1[$, the following statements are all equivalent:

$$|f(x) - f(a)| < \epsilon$$

$$\left| \frac{1}{x} - \frac{1}{a} \right| < \epsilon$$

$$\left| \frac{a - x}{ax} \right| < \epsilon$$

$$|x - a| < |a| \cdot |x|\epsilon$$

$$|x - a| < ax\epsilon$$

For the function g, a fixed $\epsilon > 0$, and x and a in $]0, 1[$, the following statements are all equivalent:

$$|g(x) - g(a)| < \epsilon$$

$$|3x - 3a| < \epsilon$$

$$|x - a| < \frac{\epsilon}{3}$$

In addition, $x \in]0, 1[$ means, among other things, $x > 0$.

Now for any $a \in]0, 1[$ and any $\epsilon > 0$ if $|x - a| < \delta_{\epsilon,a,f}$ implies $x \in]0, 1[$ and $|f(x) - f(a)| < \epsilon$, then $|x - a| < \delta_{\epsilon,a,f}$ implies $x > 0$ and $|x - a| < axe$. The requirement about $x \in]0, 1[$ means that $\delta_{\epsilon,a,f} \leq a$ and the requirement about $|f(x) - f(a)|$ means that $\delta_{\epsilon,a,f} \leq axe$. But $|x - a| < \delta_{\epsilon,a,f}$ and $\delta_{\epsilon,a,f} \leq a$ means that $x < 2a$ so that we have, from the requirement about x in the domain of f, that $\delta_{\epsilon,a,f} \leq a$ and, from the requirement about $|f(x) - f(a)|$, that $\delta_{\epsilon,a,f} \leq 2a^2$.

Considering the function g, we have, for any $a \in]0, 1[$ and any $\epsilon > 0$, if $|x - a| < \delta_{\epsilon,a,g}$ implies $x \in]0, 1[$ and $|g(x) - g(a)| < \epsilon$, then $|x - a| < \delta_{\epsilon,a,g}$ implies $x \in]0, 1[$ and $|x - a| < \delta/3$. The requirement $x \in]0, 1[$ means that $\delta_{\epsilon,a,g} \leq a$ and the requirement about $|g(x) - g(a)|$ means that $\delta_{\epsilon,a,g} \leq \epsilon/3$.

Now for both of these functions we have

$$\inf \{\delta_{\epsilon,a,f} \mid 0 < a < 1\} = 0$$

and

$$\inf \{\delta_{\epsilon,a,g} \mid 0 < a < 1\} = 0$$

but in the case of f this occurs because of the requirement that we be in the domain *and* the behavior of f, while in the case of g this occurs only because of the requirement that we be in the domain. There is thus revealed a rather basic difference in the manner in which f and g are continuous at each number in their domains.

We now consider how we could have, for any two numbers r and s in $[0, 1]$, both

$$|f(r) - f(s)| < \epsilon$$

and

$$|g(r) - g(s)| < \epsilon$$

Suppose there are positive numbers $\delta_{\epsilon,r,s,f}$ and $\delta_{\epsilon,r,s,g}$ such that

$$|r - s| < \delta_{\epsilon,r,s,f} \text{ implies } |f(r) - f(s)| < \epsilon$$

and

$$|r - s| < \delta_{\epsilon,r,s,g} \text{ implies } |g(r) - g(s)| < \epsilon$$

This means that

$$|r - s| < \delta_{\epsilon,r,s,f} \quad \text{implies} \quad |r - s| < rs\epsilon$$

and

$$|r - s| < \delta_{\epsilon,r,s,g} \quad \text{implies} \quad |r - s| < \frac{\epsilon}{3}$$

Then we must have

$$\delta_{\epsilon,r,s,f} \leq rs\epsilon$$

and

$$\delta_{\epsilon,r,s,g} \leq \frac{\epsilon}{3}$$

Now

$$\inf \{\delta_{\epsilon,r,s,f} \mid r, s \in \,]0, 1[\} = 0$$

from the first inequality. But for every $\epsilon > 0$ there exists $\delta_\epsilon > 0$; namely, $\delta_\epsilon = \epsilon/3$, such that for all r and s in $]0, 1[$

$$|r - s| < \delta_\epsilon \quad \text{implies} \quad |g(r) - g(s)| < \frac{\epsilon}{3}$$

Thus we may take $\delta_{\epsilon,r,s,g} = \epsilon/3$ for every r and s in $]0, 1[$, and if we do, then

$$\inf \{\delta_{\epsilon,r,s,g} \mid r, s \in \,]0, 1[\} = \frac{\epsilon}{3} > 0$$

In this way, by considering the relation between the closeness of two points in the domain and the closeness between the corresponding points in the range, we can see a basic difference between the local behavior of these two functions. We establish another kind of nice behavior for a function in

Definition 6-3-1. f is a function on the n-dimensional set D into the real numbers. *f is uniformly continuous* means that for every $\epsilon > 0$ there exists $\delta_\epsilon > 0$ such that if $\mathbf{r}$ and $\mathbf{s}$ are any two points of D and $d_n(\mathbf{r}, \mathbf{s}) < \delta_\epsilon$, then $|f(\mathbf{r}) - f(\mathbf{s})| < \epsilon$.

Roughly, to say a function is continuous means that any desired closeness of points of the range can be attained by an appropriate closeness of the domain points but the relation between these closenesses may change widely from point to point. To say that a function is uniformly continuous means that one relation between range closeness and domain closeness will do throughout.

EXERCISES

1. Prove that a uniformly continuous function is continuous.

2. Show that the functions f and g of this section are continuous at each number in their domains.

For the function f of this section we take, for $n = 1, 2, \ldots, r_n = 1/n^2$ and $s_n = 2/n^2$.

3. Find $|r_n - s_n|$.

4. Find $\epsilon_0 > 0$ such that, for $n = 1, 2, \ldots, |f(r_n) - f(s_n)| \geq \epsilon_0$.

5. Show that f is not uniformly continuous.

$h(x) = x^2, \qquad 0 < x < 1$

6. Show that h is continuous at every number in its domain.

7. Show that h is continuous.

8. Show that h is uniformly continuous.

9. Find, for $\epsilon > 0$ and $0 < a < 1$, $\delta_{\epsilon,a,h}$ such that

$|x - a| < \delta_{\epsilon,a,h} \qquad \text{implies} \qquad x \in \,]0, 1[\qquad \text{and} \qquad |h(x) - h(a)| < \epsilon$

$H(x) = x^2, \qquad 0 \leq x \leq 1$

10. Is H continuous at every number in its domain?

11. Is H continuous?

12. Is H uniformly continuous?

6-4 Heine-Borel Theorems and Uniform Continuity

In this section we examine certain properties of the set of real numbers and their implications for n-dimensional sets. We begin with

> **Definition 6-4-1.** A is a set of real numbers. b and c are real numbers. *A is bounded above by b* means, for all $x \in A$, $b \geq x$. *A is bounded below by c* means, for all $x \in A$, $c \leq x$.

> **Definition 6-4-2.** A is a set of real numbers. b and c are real numbers. b is the *supremum* of A, written $b = \sup A$, means b is an upper bound of A and if $d < b$, then d is not an upper bound of A. c is the *infimum*, written $c = \inf A$, means c is a lower bound of A and if $d > c$, then d is not a lower bound of A.

Thus the supremum, $\sup A$, of the set A is that real number which is the smallest of all the upper bounds of A; and the infimum, $\inf A$, of the set A is that real number which is the largest of all the lower bounds of A. Obviously if a set is not bounded above, then it has no supremum; and if a set is not bounded below, then it has no infimum. In terms of the ordering of the real numbers, we have, as an immediate consequence of the definition,

Theorem 6-4-1. A is a set of real numbers and b is a real number. $b = \sup A$ if, and only if,
   (i) For every $x \in A$, $b \geq x$.
   (ii) For every $\epsilon > 0$, there exists $a_\epsilon \in A$ such that $b - \epsilon < a_\epsilon \leq b$.

Proof. Since, for $\epsilon > 0$, $b - \epsilon < b$, $b = \sup A$ if, and only if, b is an upper bound of A and $b - \epsilon$ is not an upper bound of A. But, to say that $b - \epsilon$ is not an upper bound of A is equivalent to the existence of some number $a_\epsilon \in A$ such that $a_\epsilon > b - \epsilon$. Since $a_\epsilon \in A$ and b is an upper bound of A, we must have $a_\epsilon \leq b$. ∎

The analogous theorem for infimum is

Theorem 6-4-2. A is a set of real numbers and c is a real number. $c = \inf A$ if, and only if,
   (i) For every $x \in A$, $c \leq x$.
   (ii) For every $\epsilon > 0$, there exists $a_\epsilon \in A$ such that $c \leq a_\epsilon < c + \epsilon$.

We assume as a basic property of the real numbers

Postulate   Any nonempty set of real numbers which is bounded above has a supremum.

An immediate consequence of this postulate is

Theorem 6-4-3. Any nonempty set of real numbers which is bounded below has an infimum.

Proof. Let A be a nonempty set of real numbers and let m be a lower bound of A. Then, for all $x \in A$, $m \leq x$. Further, for all $x \in A$, $-m \geq -x$. The real number $-m$ is thus an upper bound of $\{-x \mid x \in A\}$. Since A is not empty, $\{-x \mid x \in A\}$ is a nonempty set of real numbers which is bounded above. Thus there exists a real number b such that $b = \sup \{-x \mid x \in A\}$. For every $x \in A$, $b \geq -x$ so that $-b \leq x$. For every $\epsilon > 0$, there exists $a_\epsilon \in A$ such that $b - \epsilon < -a_\epsilon \leq b$ so that $-b \leq a_\epsilon < -b + \epsilon$. Thus $-b = \inf A$. ∎

We are now ready to examine an important consequence of the postulate on the existence of a supremum for a nonempty set of real numbers which is bounded above.

Theorem 6-4-4. p and q are two real numbers such that $p < q$. If, for every γ in some set Γ of indices, there is an open interval $]a_\gamma, b_\gamma[$

such that

$$[p, q] \subseteq \bigcup_{\gamma \in \Gamma}]a_\gamma, b_\gamma[$$

then there exists a finite set of these indices,

$$\{\gamma_k \mid k = 1, 2, \ldots, n\}$$

such that

$$[p, q] \subseteq \bigcup_{k=1}^{n}]a_{\gamma_k}, b_{\gamma_k}[$$

Proof. Let $M = \{x \mid x \in [p, q]$ and there exists a finite number of indices, $\{\gamma_{x,k} \mid k = 1, 2, \ldots, n_x\}$ such that

$$[p, x] \subseteq \bigcup_{k=1}^{n_x}]a_{\gamma_{x,k}}, b_{\gamma_{x,k}}[$$

Part 1: The real number p is in the closed interval $[p, q]$. Thus, by hypothesis, there exists an index γ_p such that

$$p \in]a_{\gamma_p}, b_{\gamma_p}[$$

That is,

$$a_{\gamma_p} < p < b_{\gamma_p}$$

Then

$$\left[p, \frac{p + b_{\gamma_p}}{2} \right] \subseteq]a_{\gamma_p}, b_{\gamma_p}[$$

Since the closed interval $[p, (p + b_{\gamma_p})/2]$ is a subset of a finite union of intervals from the given collection of open intervals (in this case consisting of exactly one of these open intervals), the number $(p + b_{\gamma_p})/2$ is in M and M is not empty.

Part 2: By its definition, $M \subseteq [p, q]$ so that M is bounded above by the real number q (or, for that matter, by any real numbers larger than q). The first part of the proof showed that M was not empty. Thus, by the postulate, sup M exists. We call this number c, giving $c = $ sup M.

Since q is an upper bound of M, we must have $c \leq q$. Since $(p + b_{\gamma_p})/2 \in M$, no number smaller that this one can be an upper bound of M. In particular, p is not an upper bound of M so that $p < c$. Then $c \in [p, q]$.

By hypothesis there exists an index γ_c such that

$$c \in]a_{\gamma_c}, b_{\gamma_c}[$$

That is

$$a_{\gamma_c} < c < b_{\gamma_c}$$

Since $c = $ sup M and $a_{\gamma_c} < c$, there exists $d \in M$ such that

$$a_{\gamma_c} < d \leq c$$

Since $d \in M$, there exists a finite set of indices

$$\{\gamma_{d,k} \mid k = 1, 2, \ldots, n_d\}$$

such that

$$[a, d] \subseteq \bigcup_{k=1}^{n_d}]a_{\gamma_{d,k}}, b_{\gamma_{d,k}}[$$

But then

$$[a, c] \subseteq \bigcup_{k=1}^{n_d}]a_{\gamma_{d,k}}, b_{\gamma_{d,k}}[\cup]a_{\gamma_c}, b_{\gamma_c}[$$

so that $c \in M$.

Part 3: We now know that $c = \sup M$ and $c \in M$ and, since q is an upper bound of M, that $c \leq q$. We assume that $c < q$. Then $q \notin M$ and thus the interval $]a_{\gamma_c}, b_{\gamma_c}[$ cannot extend so far to the right as to include q. In other words, the assumption $c < q$ means

$$c < \frac{c + b_{\gamma_c}}{2} < c + b_{\gamma_c} \leq q$$

But then the number $(c + b_{\gamma_c})/2$ is in M since

$$\left[a, \frac{c + b_{\gamma_c}}{2}\right] \subseteq \bigcup_{k=1}^{n_d}]a_{\gamma_{d,k}}, b_{\gamma_{d,k}}[\cup]a_{\gamma_c}, b_{\gamma_c}[$$

But $c = \sup M$ so we must have $c \geq (c + b_{\gamma_c})/2$, which is a contradiction. Thus $c = q$ and $q \in M$. But $q \in M$ is the conclusion of the theorem. ∎

This theorem may be rephrased by stating that any covering of a given closed bounded interval by a collection of open intervals may be reduced to a finite covering. Roughly, this means that no matter how small the open intervals in a given covering may become, only a finite number of them are required to cover the fixed closed bounded interval.

While it is usually more convenient to deal with open intervals rather than open sets, the theorem can be immediately extended to consider the case of coverings by open sets. We have

Corollary 6-4-4-1. p and q are two real numbers such that $p < q$. For every γ in some set Γ of indices, G_γ is an open set of real numbers. If

$$[p, q] \subseteq \bigcup_{\gamma \in \Gamma} G_\gamma$$

then there exists a finite set of indices

$$\{\gamma_k \mid k = 1, 2, \ldots, n\}$$

such that

$$[p, q] \subseteq \bigcup_{k=1}^{n} G_{\gamma_k}$$

Proof. It is only necessary to show that the covering of $[p, q]$ by the collection of open sets $\{G_{\gamma} \mid \gamma \in \Gamma\}$ can be replaced by a covering of open intervals. But since, for every $x \in [p, q]$, there is an index γ_x for which $x \in G_{\gamma_x}$, and since G_{γ_x} is open, there is an open interval $]a_{\gamma_x}, b_{\gamma_x}[$ such that

$$x \in]a_{\gamma_x}, b_{\gamma_x}[\subseteq G_{\gamma_x}$$

Thus

$$[p, q] \subseteq \bigcup_{\gamma \in \Gamma}]a_{\gamma_x}, b_{\gamma_x}[$$

Since the covering by these open intervals may be reduced to a finite sub-covering, we need only take the (finite number) of open sets containing each of the intervals in the finite subcovering in order to complete the proof. ∎

We may extend the theorem still more by considering any closed bounded set rather than merely a closed interval.

Corollary 6-4-4-2. F is a closed bounded set of real numbers. For every γ in some set Γ of indices, G_{γ} is an open set of real numbers. If

$$F \subseteq \bigcup_{\gamma \in \Gamma} G_{\gamma}$$

then there exists a finite set of indices,

$$\{\gamma_k \mid k = 1, 2, \ldots, n\}$$

such that

$$F \subseteq \bigcup_{k=1}^{n} G_{\gamma_k}$$

Proof. Since F is bounded, there exist real numbers p and q such that $p < q$ and $F \subseteq [p, q]$. Since F is closed, $[p, q] - F$ is an open set of real numbers. The open set $[p, q] - F$, together with the given open sets in $\{G_{\gamma} \mid \gamma \in \Gamma\}$, form a covering of $[p, q]$ by open sets. By Corollary 6-4-4-1, this covering may be reduced to a finite subcovering of $[p, q]$. Discarding the open set $[p, q] - F$ gives a covering of F. ∎

Finally, we may easily extend this theorem to n-dimensional sets:

Theorem 6-4-5(the Heine-Borel Theorem). If F is a closed bounded n-dimensional set, for every index γ in a set of indices Γ, G_{γ} is an open

n-dimensional set such that

$$F \subseteq \bigcup_{\gamma \in \Gamma} G$$

then there exists a finite set of indices,

$$\{\gamma_k \,|\, k = 1, 2, \ldots, n\}$$

such that

$$F \subseteq \bigcup_{k=1}^{n} G_{\gamma_k}$$

Proof. Since an open n-dimensional set may be expressed as the union of n-dimensional open rectangles, we may, without loss of generality, assume that the given open sets G_γ are in fact open n-dimensional rectangles. For an n-dimensional set A, we adopt the notation

$$A^{(k)} = \{x \,|\, x \text{ is the } k\text{th coordinate of a point of } A\}$$

Under this notation, the sets of

$$\{F^{(k)} \,|\, k = 1, 2, \ldots, n\}$$

are all closed bounded sets of real numbers, and the sets of

$$\{G_\gamma^k \,|\, k = 1, 2, \ldots, n, \gamma \in \Gamma\}$$

are all open intervals of real numbers.
For $k = 1, 2, \ldots, n$,

$$F^{(k)} \subseteq \bigcup_{\gamma \in \Gamma} G_\gamma^k$$

Then by the theorem for real numbers there exists a finite set of indices

$$\{\gamma_{k,j} \,|\, j = 1, 2, \ldots, m_k\}$$

such that

$$F^{(k)} \subseteq \bigcup_{j=1}^{m_k} G_{\gamma_{k,j}}^k$$

We let

$$G_k = \bigcup_{j=1}^{m_k} G_{\gamma_{k,j}}$$

Then G_k is an n-dimensional open set and

$$F^{(k)} \subseteq G^{(k)}$$

We do not necessarily know that $F \subseteq G_k$ but we can show indirectly that

$$F \subseteq \bigcup_{k=1}^{n} G_k$$

Assuming there exists a point $\mathbf{x} = (x_1, x_2, \ldots, x_n) \in \mathbf{V_n}$ which is in F but not in $\bigcup\limits_{k=1}^{n} G_k$, then, for $k = 1, 2, \ldots, n$,

$$x_k \notin G_k^{(k)}$$

But $x_k \in F^{(k)}$ and $F^{(k)} \subseteq G_k^{(k)}$, which gives a contradiction and the theorem is proved. ∎

We now proceed to apply the Heine-Borel theorem to continuous functions.

Theorem 6-4-6. f is a function on the closed bounded n-dimensional set D into the real numbers. If f is continuous, then f is uniformly continuous.

Proof. Since f is continuous, given any open set of real numbers G, the inverse image under f, $f^{-1}(G)$, is either itself an open n-dimensional open set or the intersection of such a set with D. Thus for each $\mathbf{x} \in D$ the inverse image of any open neighborhood of $f(\mathbf{x})$ must be the intersection of an open n-dimensional neighborhood of $\mathbf{x}$ and the domain D.

We pick $\epsilon > 0$. For each $\mathbf{x} \in D$, there exists $\delta_{\mathbf{x},\epsilon} > 0$ such that if $d_n(\mathbf{x}, \mathbf{z}) < \delta_{\mathbf{x},\epsilon}$ and $\mathbf{z} \in D$, then

$$|f(\mathbf{x}) - f(\mathbf{z})| < \frac{\epsilon}{2}$$

For each $\mathbf{x} \in D$, we let

$$G_\mathbf{x} = \{\mathbf{z} \mid d_n(\mathbf{x}, \mathbf{z}) < \delta_{\mathbf{x},\epsilon}\}$$

Thus each $G_\mathbf{x}$ is an open n-dimensional sphere, centered at $\mathbf{x}$, with radius $\delta_{\mathbf{x},\epsilon}$. Obviously

$$D \subseteq \bigcup_{\mathbf{x} \in D} G_\mathbf{x}$$

By the Heine-Borel theorem there exists a finite set of points

$$\{\mathbf{x}_k \mid k = 1, 2, \ldots, m\}$$

such that

$$D \subseteq \bigcup_{k=1}^{m} G_{\mathbf{x}_k}$$

Whenever $G_{\mathbf{x}_j} \cap G_{\mathbf{x}_k} \neq \varnothing$, we let $\delta_{\epsilon,j,k}$ be the diameter of this set. We let $\delta_\epsilon = \min \{\delta_{\epsilon,j,k} \mid j, k = 1, 2, \ldots, m \text{ and } G_{\mathbf{x}_j} \cap G_{\mathbf{x}_k} \neq \varnothing\}$. Thus the positive number δ_ϵ is the diameter of the smallest of the overlaps of the open n-dimensional spheres in $\{G_{\mathbf{x}_k} \mid k = 1, 2, \ldots, m\}$.

Now if **r** and **s** are any two points of D such that $d_n(\mathbf{r}, \mathbf{s}) < \delta_\epsilon$, then there exists at least one index $k_{\mathbf{r},\mathbf{s}}$ such that **r** and **s** are both in the open n-dimensional sphere $G_{\mathbf{x}_{k_{\mathbf{r},\mathbf{s}}}}$. Then

$$d_n(\mathbf{r}, \mathbf{s}) < \delta_\epsilon \text{ implies } d_n(\mathbf{r}, \mathbf{x}_{k_{\mathbf{r},\mathbf{s}}}) < \delta_{\mathbf{x}_{k_{\mathbf{r},\mathbf{s}}}}$$

and

$$d_n(\mathbf{s}, \mathbf{x}_{k_{\mathbf{r},\mathbf{s}}}) < \delta_{\mathbf{x}_{k_{\mathbf{r},\mathbf{s}}}}$$

so that

$$|f(\mathbf{r}) - f(\mathbf{x}_{k_{\mathbf{r},\mathbf{s}}})| < \frac{\epsilon}{2}$$

and

$$|f(\mathbf{s}) - f(\mathbf{x}_{k_{\mathbf{r},\mathbf{s}}})| < \frac{\epsilon}{2}$$

which means

$$|f(\mathbf{r}) - f(\mathbf{s})| < \epsilon$$

We then conclude that f is uniformly continuous. ∎

The theorem says that continuity on a closed bounded set implies uniform continuity. But the fact that a function is uniformly continuous need not mean that its domain must be closed and bounded. One immediate example is provided by taking the restriction of a continuous function on a closed bounded set to an open subset of the domain. There are also examples of uniformly continuous functions whose domains are not bounded—constant functions being the most glaring.

EXERCISES

1. Prove Theorem 6-4-2.

Find infimum and supremum for the following sets:

2. $[p, q]$

3. $]p, q[$

4. $[0, +\infty[$

5. $]0, +\infty[$

6. $\{1/n \mid n = 1, 2, \ldots\}$

7. $\{1/n + 1/m \mid n, m = 1, 2, \ldots\}$

8. $\{n^{(-1)^n} \mid n = 1, 2, \ldots\}$

9–15. If $b = \sup A$ and $c = \inf A$ (where these exist) for the sets in Exercises 2–8, find, for $\epsilon > 0$, $b_\epsilon \in A$ such that $b - \epsilon < b_\epsilon \le b$ and $c_\epsilon \in A$ such that $c \le c_\epsilon < c + \epsilon$.

16. Prove that if $A \subseteq B$, then $\sup A \le \sup B$.

17. State and prove the theorem analogous to that of Exercise 16 for infima.

18. Prove $\sup \{x + y \mid x \in A$ and $y \in B\} \le \sup A + \sup B$.

19. For $f(x) = e^x$, $x \in [0, 1]$, find δ_x such that $|t - x| < \delta_x$ and $t \in [0, 1]$ implies $|f(t) - f(x)| < 0.5$. *Hint:* For $r \in \,]-1, 1[$, there exists θ, $0 < \theta < 1$ such that $e^r = 1 + re^{\theta r}$.

20. For the δ_x found in Exercise 19, find $\{x_k \mid k = 1, 2, \ldots, n\}$ such that

$$[0, 1] \subseteq \bigcup_{k=1}^{n} \,]x_k - \delta_{x_k}, x_k + \delta_{x_k}[$$

21. Use the numbers δ_{x_k} found in Exercise 20 to prove that f is uniformly continuous.

6-5   Uniform Convergence

We turn now to an idea concerning iterated limits which concern a uniform type of behavior more general than that of uniform continuity. We saw in Section 6-1 that for a function on a two-dimensional set into the real numbers we can consider the three limits:

$$\lim_{(x,y) \to (a,b)} f(x, y)$$

$$\lim_{x \to a} \lim_{y \to b} f(x, y)$$

and

$$\lim_{y \to b} \lim_{x \to a} f(x, y)$$

If the first limit exists, then the other two must exist and be this number; but it is possible to have a function for which the first limit does not exist even though the other two do.

Examining the latter two iterated limits more closely, we see that

$$\lim_{x \to a} \lim_{y \to b} f(x, y)$$

will exist if there is a function g, whose domain is at least a deleted neighborhood of the number a such that

$$g(x) = \lim_{y \to b} f(x, y)$$

and that this function g is sufficiently well-behaved so that

$$\lim_{x \to a} g(x) = \lim_{x \to a} \lim_{y \to b} f(x, y)$$

We have a similar situation for the other iterated limit.
  Using

$$L = \lim_{x \to a} \lim_{y \to b} f(x, y) = \lim_{x \to a} g(x)$$

we have, for every $\epsilon > 0$, the existence of $\delta_{\epsilon,a} > 0$ such that

$$0 < |x - a| < \delta_{\epsilon,a} \text{ implies } |g(x) - L| < \epsilon$$

Further, for each fixed value of x, $\lim_{y \to b} f(x, y) = g(x)$ means that for every $\epsilon > 0$ there exists $\delta_{\epsilon,b,x} > 0$ such that

$$0 < |y - b| < \delta_{\epsilon,b,x} \text{ implies } |f(x, y) - g(x)| < \epsilon$$

We consider the particular example given by $f(x, y) = 3xy$, with attention to the point $(2, 3)$. We have, for this case,

$$\lim_{(x,y) \to (2,3)} 3xy = 18$$

$$\lim_{x \to 2} \lim_{y \to 3} 3xy = \lim_{x \to 2} 9x = 18$$

$$\lim_{y \to 3} \lim_{x \to 2} 3xy = \lim_{y \to 3} 6y = 18$$

Here $g(x) = 9x$. For definiteness we take the restriction of f to the rectangle

$$\{(x, y) \mid 1 \le x \le 3 \text{ and } 2 \le y \le 4\}$$

In this rectangle we have $|x| = x \le 3$ so that

$$|f(x, y) - g(x)| = |3xy - 9x| = 3 |x| \cdot |y - 3| \le 9 |y - 3|$$

For every $\epsilon > 0$ there then exists $\delta_{\epsilon,3,x} > 0$; namely, $\delta_{\epsilon,3,x} = \epsilon/9$, such that

$$|y - 3| < \delta_{\epsilon,3,x} \text{ implies } |f(x, y) - g(x)| < \epsilon$$

But since $\delta_{\epsilon,3,x} = \epsilon/9$ does not depend on the value of x in the closed interval $[1, 3]$, we in fact can state for every $\epsilon > 0$ there exists $\delta_{\epsilon,3} > 0$ such that for all $x \in [1, 3]$

$$|y - 3| < \delta_{\epsilon,3} \text{ implies } |f(x, y) - g(x)| < \epsilon$$

On the other hand, we let f be the function given by

$$f(x, y) = \begin{cases} \dfrac{3y}{x}, & x \ne 0 \\ 0, & x = 0 \end{cases}$$

Considering the point $(0, 0)$, we have for $x \neq 0$,

$$g(x) = \lim_{y \to 0} \frac{3y}{x} = 0$$

$$g(0) = \lim_{x \to 0} 0 = 0$$

$$\lim_{x \to 0} g(x) = 0$$

Thus $\lim_{x \to 0} \lim_{y \to 0} f(x, y)$ exists and is the number 0. For the reverse order of taking limits, we find

$$\lim_{x \to 0} f(x, y)$$

exists only for $y = 0$ so that

$$\lim_{y \to 0} \lim_{x \to 0} f(x, y)$$

does not exist.

Limit processes also occur in differentiation and integration. For a differentiable function f on a set of real numbers into the real numbers, the derivative f' is the function given by

$$f'(x) = \lim_{h \to 0} \frac{f(x + h) - f(x)}{h}$$

We consider two examples, f given by

$$f(x) = x^2$$

and g given by

$$g(x) = \frac{1}{x}$$

For any x in the open interval $]0, 2[$,

$$f'(x) = \lim_{h \to 0} \frac{(x + h)^2 - x^2}{h}$$
$$= \lim_{h \to 0} \frac{h}{h}(2x + h)$$
$$= 2x$$

Thus, for $h \neq 0$ we have

$$\left| \frac{f(x + h) - f(x)}{h} - f'(x) \right| = |h|$$

For any x in the open interval $]0, 2[$, we have

$$g'(x) = \lim_{h \to 0} \frac{1/(x + h) - 1/x}{h}$$

$$= \lim_{h \to 0} \frac{h}{h} \frac{-1}{x(x + h)}$$

$$= -\frac{1}{x^2}$$

Thus, for $h \neq 0$ we have

$$\left| \frac{g(x + h) - g(x)}{h} - g'(x) \right| = \frac{|h|}{x^2 |x + h|}$$

Now if

$$0 < |h| < \delta_{\epsilon,x,g} \quad \text{implies} \quad \left| \frac{g(x + h) - g(x)}{h} - g'(x) \right| < \epsilon$$

then

$$0 < |h| < \delta_{\epsilon,x,g} \quad \text{implies} \quad \frac{|h|}{x^2 |x + h|} < \epsilon$$

or

$$|h| < \epsilon x^2 |x + h|$$
$$\leq \epsilon x^2 (|x| + |h|)$$
$$\leq \epsilon x^2 (2 |x|)$$

since we must have $|h| < x$ in order to be in $[0, 2]$. But if

$$0 < |h| < \delta_{\epsilon,x,g} \quad \text{implies} \quad |h| < \epsilon(2x^3)$$

then we must have $\delta_{\epsilon,x,g} \leq 2x^2\epsilon$. Thus for a given $\epsilon > 0$, values of x near 0 require smaller values of $\delta_{\epsilon,x,g}$ than values of x more distant from 0; and since successively smaller values of x require even smaller values of $\delta_{\epsilon,x,g}$, there is no one $\delta_{\epsilon,g} > 0$ for which all the difference quotients are within ϵ of the value of the derivative.

On the other hand, for the function f, if

$$0 < |h| < \delta_{\epsilon,x,f} \quad \text{implies} \quad \left| \frac{f(x + h) - f(x)}{h} - f'(x) \right| < \epsilon$$

then

$$0 < |h| < \delta_{\epsilon,x,f} \quad \text{implies} \quad |h| < \epsilon$$

so that $\delta_{\epsilon,x,f} \leq \epsilon$ and we find that for every $\epsilon > 0$ there exists $\delta_{\epsilon,f} > 0$; namely, $\delta_{\epsilon,f} = \epsilon$ (or any smaller fixed positive number), such that for all x in the interval $[0, 2]$ the difference quotient will be with ϵ of the value of the derivative.

For integration we consider two functions on the rectangle

$$\{(x, y) \mid 0 < x < 2 \text{ and } 0 \le y \le 1\}$$

the function f, given by

$$f(x, y) = xy$$

and the function g, given by

$$g(x, y) = \frac{y}{x}$$

We define the functions F and G by

$$F(x) = \int_0^1 f(x, y)\, dy, \qquad 0 < x < 2$$

and

$$G(x) = \int_0^1 g(x, y)\, dy, \qquad 0 < x < 2$$

Integration yields

$$F(x) = \frac{x}{2}, \qquad 0 < x < 2$$

and

$$G(x) = \frac{1}{2x}, \qquad 0 < x < 2$$

Partitioning the interval of integration $[0, 1]$ into n equal subintervals yields the approximating upper sums

$$\bar{S}_{n,f}(x) = x\left[\frac{1}{2} + \frac{1}{2n}\right]$$

$$\bar{S}_{n,g}(x) = \frac{1}{x}\left[\frac{1}{2} + \frac{1}{2n}\right]$$

Then

$$F(x) = \lim_{n \to \infty} x\left[\frac{1}{2} + \frac{1}{2n}\right] = \frac{x}{2}, \qquad 0 < x < 2$$

and

$$G(x) = \lim_{n \to \infty} \frac{1}{x}\left[\frac{1}{2} + \frac{1}{2n}\right] = \frac{1}{2x}, \qquad 0 < x < 2$$

Further,

$$|\bar{S}_{n,f}(x) - F(x)| = \frac{|x|}{2n}$$

$$|\bar{S}_{n,g}(x) - G(x)| = \frac{1}{2n\,|x|}$$

Now if

$$n \ge N_{\epsilon,x,f} \quad \text{implies} \quad |\bar{S}_{n,f}(x) - F(x)| < \epsilon$$

then

$$n \geq N_{\epsilon,x,f} \quad \text{implies} \quad \frac{|x|}{2n} < \epsilon \quad \text{or} \quad n > \frac{|x|}{2\epsilon}$$

so that

$$N_{\epsilon,x,f} \geq \frac{|x|}{2\epsilon}$$

But $x \in [0, 2]$ so we need only take $N_{\epsilon,x,f} \geq 2/2\epsilon = 1/\epsilon$ in order to have the approximating sum be within ϵ of the integral.

On the other hand if

$$n \geq N_{\epsilon,x,g} \quad \text{implies} \quad |\bar{S}_{n,g}(x) - G(x)| < \epsilon$$

then

$$n \geq N_{\epsilon,x,g} \quad \text{implies} \quad \frac{1}{2n\,|x|} < \epsilon \quad \text{or} \quad n > \frac{1}{2\,|x|\,\epsilon}$$

so that $N_{\epsilon,x,g} \geq (1/2)\,|x|\,\epsilon$. Hence, for a given $\epsilon > 0$, the index of the upper sum $\bar{S}_{n,g}(x)$ needed to give this approximating sum a value within ϵ of the integral depends on the value of x, and the closer to 0 the value of x is, the larger the index which must be taken.

In all three situations considered—iterated limits, differentiation, and integration—we see that one limit process may occur uniformly with respect to the points of a given set or that the manner in which a limit process occurs may depend on which points of a given set are considered. As a generalized definition which will include all limit processes, we have

> *Definition 6-5-1.* M is a set. $\prec$ *is a partial ordering in M* means $\prec$ is a relation between points of M or between subsets of M such that
>
>   if p, q, and r are points (subsets) of M and
>   if $p \prec q$ and $q \prec r$, then $p \prec r$
> and
>   for any p and q which are points (subsets) of M there exists a point (subset) r of M such that $p \prec r$ and $q \prec r$.

> *Definition 6-5-2.* M is a set. $\prec$ is a partial ordering for M. f is a function on M into the real numbers. L is a real number. $\lim_{x,\prec} f(x) = L$ means for every $\epsilon > 0$ there exists a point (subset) p_ϵ of M such that if $p \succ p_\epsilon$ and x is (is in) the point (subset) p_ϵ, then $|f(x) - L| < \epsilon$.

EXAMPLES. $\{a_n \mid n = 1, 2, \ldots\}$ is a sequence of real numbers. $\lim_{n \to \infty} a_n = A$ may be considered as a limit over the partial ordering on the set M of positive integers where the partial ordering is the natural ordering $<$ of real numbers.

f is a function on a set of real numbers into the set of real numbers. $\lim\limits_{x \to a} f(x) = L$ may be considered as a limit over the partial ordering on the set M of real numbers where the partial ordering relates deleted neighborhoods of the number a by $V \succ W$ means $V \subseteq W$.

For a function on a two-dimensional set, one of whose coordinates forms a partially ordered set, we have two kinds of limits, given by

Definition 6-5-3. M is a set with the partial ordering $\prec$. A is a set. f is a function on $A \times M$ into the real numbers. g is a function on A into the real numbers. $\lim\limits_{y, \prec} f(x, y) = g(x)$ *pointwise with respect to* $x \in A$ means for every $\epsilon > 0$ and for every $x \in A$ there exists a point (subset) $p_{\epsilon, x}$ of M such that if $p \succ p_{\epsilon, x}$ and y is (is in) the point (subset) p_ϵ, then

$$|f(x, y) - g(x)| < \epsilon$$

$\lim\limits_{y, \prec} f(x, y) = g(x)$ *uniformly with respect to* $x \in A$ means for every $\epsilon > 0$ there exists a point (subset) p_ϵ of M such that for all $x \in A$ if $p \succ p_\epsilon$ and y is (is in) the point (subset) p, then

$$|f(x, y) - g(x)| < \epsilon$$

The basic theorem concerning the uniform convergence of one limit process with respect to another and giving a criterion for the interchange of the order of iterated limits is

Theorem 6-5-1. M is a set with partial ordering $\succ\limits_{M}$. N is a set with partial ordering $\succ\limits_{N}$. f is a function on $M \times N$ into the real numbers. g is a function on M into the real numbers. h is a function on N into the real numbers. If

$\lim\limits_{x, \succ \atop M} f(x, y) = h(y)$ uniformly with respect to $y \in N$

$\lim\limits_{y, \succ \atop N} f(x, y) = g(x)$ pointwise with respect to $x \in M$

$\lim\limits_{x, \succ \atop M} g(x) = B$ and $\lim\limits_{y, \succ \atop N} h(y) = A$

then $A = B$.

Proof. Pick $\epsilon > 0$.

There exists p_ϵ, a point (subset) of M, such that if $p \succ\limits_{M} p_\epsilon$, then for all $y \in N$ and for any x which is (is in) the point (subset) p, $|f(x, y) - h(y)| < \epsilon/4$.

For each $x \in M$ there exists a point (subset) $q_{\epsilon, x}$ of N such that if $q \succ\limits_{M} q_{\epsilon, x}$ and y is (is in) the point (subset) q, then $|f(x, y) - g(x)| < \epsilon/4$.

There exists p'_ϵ, a point (subset) of M, such that if $p \underset{M}{\succ} p'_\epsilon$ and x is (is in) the point (subset) p, then $|g(x) - B| < \epsilon/4$.

There exists q'_ϵ, a point (subset) of N, such that if $q \underset{N}{\succ} q'_\epsilon$ and y is (is in) the point (subset) p, then $|h(y) - A| < \epsilon/4$.

Fix the point (subset) p_0 in M such that $p_0 \underset{M}{\succ} p'$ and $p_0 \underset{M}{\succ} p$. Fix x_0 to be (be in) the point (subset) p_0. Then for all $y \in N$ we have $|f(x_0, y) - h(y)| < \epsilon/4$ and $|g(x_0) - B| < \epsilon/4$.

Now fix q_0, a point (subset) of N, such that $q_0 \underset{N}{\succ} q'_\epsilon$ and $q_0 \underset{N}{\succ} q_{\epsilon, x_0}$. Fix y_0 to be (be in) the point (subset) q_0. We then have

$$|f(x_0, y_0) - h(y_0)| < \frac{\epsilon}{4}$$

$$|f(x_0, y_0) - g(y_0)| < \frac{\epsilon}{4}$$

$$|h(y_0) - A| < \frac{\epsilon}{4}$$

Thus

$$|A - B| = |A - h(y_0) + h(y_0) - f(x_0, y_0) + f(x_0, y_0) - g(x_0) + g(x_0) - B|$$
$$\leq |A - h(y_0)| + |h(y_0) - f(x_0, y_0)| + |f(x_0, y_0) - g(x_0)|$$
$$+ |g(x_0) - B|$$
$$< \frac{\epsilon}{4} + \frac{\epsilon}{4} + \frac{\epsilon}{4} + \frac{\epsilon}{4} = \epsilon$$

Since the non-negative number $|A - B|$ is less than every positive number, we must have $A = B$. ∎

The conclusion of this theorem may be summarized by saying that when one of the limit processes in an iterated limit is uniform with respect to the other, then the order of taking limits may be reversed.

EXERCISES

1. Find $\delta_{\epsilon, x}$ such that $|y - 3| < \delta_{\epsilon, x}$ implies $|4xy - 12x| < \epsilon$.

2. Find $\delta_{\epsilon, y}$ such that $|x - 1| < \delta_{\epsilon, y}$ implies $|4xy - 4y| < \epsilon$.

3. Show that $\lim_{y \to 3} 4xy = 12x$ uniformly with respect to $x \in [1, 2]$.

4. Show that $\lim_{x \to 1} 4xy = 4y$ uniformly with respect to $y \in [2, 4]$.

5. Prove that if f is a function on $R = [a, b] \times [c, d]$ into the real numbers and is continuous, then for every interior point (p, q) of R

$$\lim_{y \to q} f(x, y) = f(x, q)$$

uniformly with respect to $x \in [a, b]$ and

$$\lim_{x \to p} f(x, y) = f(p, y)$$

uniformly with respect to $y \in [c, d]$.

6. For $g(x) = 2x^2 + 5x - 1$, find $g'(x)$.

7. For g the function of Exercise 6, find $\delta_{\epsilon, x}$ such that

$$0 < |h| < \delta_{\epsilon, x} \quad \text{implies} \quad \left| \frac{g(x + h) - g(x)}{h} - g'(x) \right| < \epsilon$$

8. Show that for a and b fixed, $a < b$, and g the function of Exercise 6

$$\lim_{h \to 0} \frac{g(x + h) - g(x)}{h} = g'(x)$$

uniformly with respect to $x \in [a, b]$.

9. Sketch the proof of: if P is any polynomial function, then

$$\lim_{h \to 0} \frac{P(x + h) - P(x)}{h} = P'(x)$$

uniformly with respect to x in a closed bounded interval.

10. Show that the set of deleted neighborhoods of a fixed real number is partially ordered under set inclusion.

11. Show that a family tree is partially ordered.

12. Show that for every $\delta > 0$

$$\lim_{n \to \infty} \sum_{k=0}^{n} x^k = \frac{1}{1 - x}$$

uniformly with respect to $x \in [\delta, 1 - \delta]$.

13. Is the limit in Exercise 12 uniform with respect to x in $[0, 1]$?

6-6   Sequences

In this section we examine some useful consequences of combining the idea of uniform convergence of one limit process with respect to another with the idea of a sequence of functions. We begin with the basic definitions for sequences.

Definition 6-6-1. A *sequence* is a function whose domain is the set of all integers greater than or equal to some fixed integer.

Definition 6-6-2. The n-dimensional set of points $\{\mathbf{a}_k \mid k = 1, 2, \ldots\}$ is the range of a sequence. $\mathbf{A}$ is a point of $\mathbf{V_n}$. $\mathbf{A}$ *is the limit of the sequence given by* $\{\mathbf{a}_k \mid k = 1, 2, \ldots\}$, written $\mathbf{A} = \lim\limits_{k \to \infty} \mathbf{a}_k$, means

for every $\epsilon > 0$ there exists an integer N_ϵ such that $k > N_\epsilon$ implies $d_n(\mathbf{a}_k, \mathbf{A}) < \epsilon$.

In many cases we are more concerned with the existence of the limit than with determining the exact number or point which is the limit. This is especially true in those sequences called series. For this purpose we have the basic theorem:

Theorem 6-6-1(the Cauchy Convergence Criterion). The set of real numbers $\{a_k \mid k = 1, 2, \ldots\}$ is the range of a sequence. $\lim\limits_{k \to \infty} a_k$ exists if, and only if, for every $\epsilon > 0$ there exists an integer N_ϵ such that $m > N_\epsilon$ and $n > N_\epsilon$ implies $|a_m - a_n| < \epsilon$.

(Roughly, this criterion says that a sequence is convergent if, and only if, the numbers in the range get closer together as one proceeds through the domain.)

Proof

Part 1: We assume that $\lim\limits_{k \to \infty} a_k$ exists and is the number A. Then, given $\epsilon > 0$, there exists an integer N_ϵ such that $n > N_\epsilon$ implies $|a_n - A| < \epsilon/2$. Then $n > N_\epsilon$ and $m > N_\epsilon$ implies

$$|a_m - a_n| = |a_m - A + A - a_n|$$
$$\leq |a_m - A| + |A - a_n|$$
$$< \frac{\epsilon}{2} + \frac{\epsilon}{2} = \epsilon$$

Part 2: We assume that for every $\epsilon > 0$ there exists N_ϵ such that $m > N_\epsilon$ and $n > N_\epsilon$ implies $|a_m - a_n| < \epsilon$.

For the particular value $\epsilon = 1$ there exists N_1 such that $m > N_1$ and $n > N_1$ implies $|a_m - a_n| < 1$. This means that, for $n = N_1 + 1, N_1 + 2, \ldots$,

$$|a_n - a_{N_1+1}| < 1$$

We let

$$M = \max \{|a_1|, |a_2|, \ldots, |a_{N_1}|, |a_{N_1+1}| + 1\}$$

Then, for $k = 1, 2, \ldots$,

$$-M \leq a_k \leq M$$

Since the set of real numbers $\{a_k \mid k = 1, 2, \ldots\}$ is bounded both above and below,

$$L = \inf \{a_k \mid k = 1, 2, \ldots\}$$

and

$$U = \sup \{a_k \mid k = 1, 2, \ldots\}$$

both exist.

Since the range of the given sequence is bounded above, any subset of the range will also be bounded above and thus will have a supremum. We let, for $n = 1, 2, \ldots$,

$$b_n = \sup \{a_m \mid m = n, n + 1, n + 2, \ldots\}$$

We must then have, for $n = 1, 2, \ldots$,

$$L \leq b_n \leq U$$

The new sequence formed by $\{b_n \mid n = 1, 2, \ldots\}$ is bounded below by L and thus its range has an infimum. We let

$$A = \inf \{b_n \mid n = 1, 2, \ldots\}$$

and conclude that

$$L \leq A \leq U$$

(Since $\{m \mid m \geq n\} \supseteq \{m \mid m \geq n + 1\}$, we have $b_n \geq b_{n+1}$ so that, in fact, $A = \lim_{n \to \infty} b_n$.)

In a similar manner we let, for $n = 1, 2, \ldots$,

$$c_n = \inf \{a_m \mid m = n, n + 1, n + 2, \ldots\}$$

giving, for $n = 1, 2, \ldots$,

$$L \leq c_n \leq U$$

Further we let

$$C = \sup \{c_n \mid n = 1, 2, \ldots\}$$

so that

$$L \leq C \leq U$$

(Since $\{m \mid m \geq n\} \supseteq \{m \mid m \geq n + 1\}$, we have $c_n \leq c_{n+1}$ so that, in fact, $C = \lim_{n \to \infty} c_n$.)

Further, since, for $n = 1, 2, \ldots$,

$$\inf \{a_m \mid m = n, n + 1, \ldots\} \leq \sup \{a_m \mid m = n, n + 1, \ldots\}$$

we have, for $n = 1, 2, \ldots$, $c_n \leq b_n$. This implies

$$A \leq C$$

We now assume $A < C$. Then $C - A > 0$ and, from the construction of C, we know there exists an integer N_2 such that

$$n > N_2 \quad \text{implies} \quad A \le b_n < A + \frac{C-A}{3}$$

From the construction of the b_n we must then have

$$k > N_2 \quad \text{implies} \quad a_k \le A + \frac{C-A}{3}$$

Similarly there exists an integer N_3 such that

$$n > N_3 \quad \text{implies} \quad C - \frac{C-A}{3} < c_n \le C$$

so that

$$k > N_3 \quad \text{implies} \quad a_k \ge C - \frac{C-A}{3}$$

We now let N_4 be the larger of N_2 and N_3. Then

$$m > N_4 \quad \text{and} \quad n > N_4 \quad \text{implies} \quad |a_m - a_n| \ge \frac{C-A}{3}$$

But, by the hypothesis of this part of the proof, there exists an integer N_5 such that

$$m > N_5 \quad \text{and} \quad n > N_5 \quad \text{implies} \quad |a_m - a_n| < \frac{C-A}{3}$$

Letting N_6 be the larger of N_4 and N_5, we see that

$$m > N_6 \quad \text{and} \quad n > N_6 \quad \text{implies} \quad \frac{C-A}{3} \le |a_m - a_n| < \frac{C-A}{3}$$

which is impossible. Thus the assumption $A < C$ is false and we conclude $A = C$. That is,

$$A = \inf_n \sup_{m \ge n} a_n = \sup_n \inf_{m \ge n} a_n$$

Now, for any $\epsilon > 0$, there exists an integer N_ϵ such that

$$n > N_\epsilon \quad \text{implies} \quad A \le b_n < A + \frac{\epsilon}{3} \quad \text{and} \quad A - \frac{\epsilon}{3} < c_n \le A$$

Thus

$$m > N \quad \text{implies} \quad a_m \le A + \frac{\epsilon}{3} \quad \text{and} \quad a_m \ge A - \frac{\epsilon}{3}$$

That is,

$$m > N \quad \text{implies} \quad |a_m - A| \le \frac{2\epsilon}{3} < \epsilon$$

and we conclude that

$$A = \lim_{n \to \infty} a_n \qquad \blacksquare$$

When dealing with sequences of functions, there are two theorems which consider the implications of uniform convergence:

Theorem 6-6-2. For $n = 1, 2, \ldots$, u_n is a function on the closed interval $[a, b]$ into the real numbers. For $n = 1, 2, \ldots$, u_n is continuous. f is a function on the closed interval $[a, b]$ into the real numbers. If $\lim_{n \to \infty} u_n(x) = f(x)$ uniformly with respect to $x \in [a, b]$, then f is continuous.

Proof. For any c in the open interval $]a, b[$, we have, for $n = 1, 2, \ldots$,

$$\lim_{x \to c} u_n(x) = u_n(c)$$

since u_n is continuous. Further,

$$\lim_{n \to \infty} u_n(c) = f(c)$$

by hypothesis. Also by hypothesis

$$\lim_{n \to \infty} u_n(x) = f(x)$$

uniformly with respect to $x \in [a, b]$. By Theorem 6-5-1,

$$\lim_{x \to c} f(x) = \lim_{x \to c} \lim_{n \to \infty} u_n(x)$$
$$= \lim_{n \to \infty} \lim_{x \to c} u_n(x)$$
$$= \lim_{n \to \infty} u_n(c)$$
$$= f(c)$$

so that f is continuous at c.

A similar argument holds for the end points a and b with the insertion of one-sided limits. Thus f is continuous. $\blacksquare$

The conclusion of this theorem may be summarized by saying that the uniform limit of a sequence of continuous functions is itself continuous.

For the purposes of calculus operations, the following theorem has endless consequences:

Theorem 6-6-3. For $n = 1, 2, \ldots$, u_n is an integrable function on the closed interval $[a, b]$ into the real numbers. f is a function on $[a, b]$ into the real numbers. If $\lim_{n \to \infty} u_n(x) = f(x)$ uniformly with respect to

$x \in [a, b]$, then f is integrable and

$$\int_a^b f = \lim_{n \to \infty} \int_a^b u_n$$

Proof. Pick $\epsilon > 0$. Since $\lim\limits_{n \to \infty} u_n(x) = f(x)$ uniformly with respect to $x \in [a, b]$, there exists an integer N_ϵ such that, for all $x \in [a, b]$,

$$n > N_\epsilon \quad \text{implies} \quad |u_n(x) - f(x)| < \frac{\epsilon}{b - a}$$

Part 1: $u_{N_\epsilon+1}$ is integrable on $[a, b]$. Thus there exist Π_ϵ, a partition of $[a, b]$, such that

$$\bar{S}(u_{N_\epsilon+1}; \Pi_\epsilon) - \underline{S}(u_{N_\epsilon+1}; \Pi_\epsilon) < \epsilon$$

If $[x_{k-1}, x_k]$ is a subinterval of the partition Π_ϵ, then, for all $x \in [x_{k-1}, x_k]$, we have

$$u_{N_\epsilon+1}(x) - \frac{\epsilon}{b - a} < f(x) < u_{N_\epsilon+1}(x) + \frac{\epsilon}{b - a}$$

Thus

$$\inf u_{N_\epsilon+1}([x_{k-1}, x_k]) - \frac{\epsilon}{b - a} \leq \inf f([x_{k-1}, x_k])$$
$$\leq \sup f([x_{k-1}, x_k])$$
$$\leq \sup u_{N_\epsilon+1}([x_{k-1}, x_k]) + \frac{\epsilon}{b - a}$$

$$\bar{S}(f; \Pi_\epsilon) - \underline{S}(f; \Pi_\epsilon) \leq \bar{S}(u_{N+1}; \Pi_\epsilon) - \underline{S}(u_{N+1}; \Pi_\epsilon) < \epsilon$$

We conclude that f is integrable.

Part 2

$$n > N \quad \text{implies} \quad \left| \int_a^b f - \int_a^b u_n \right| = \left| \int_a^b (f - u_n) \right|$$
$$\leq \int_a^b |f - u_n|$$
$$< \frac{\epsilon}{b - a}(b - a) = \epsilon$$

Thus

$$\lim_{n \to \infty} \int_a^b u_n = \int_a^b f \qquad \blacksquare$$

Theorem 6-6-4. For $n = 1, 2, \ldots$, u_n is a function on the closed interval $[a, b]$ into the real numbers with the property that u'_n is continuous. For $n = 1, 2, \ldots$, $v_n = u'_n$. f and g are functions on $[a, b]$

into the real numbers. If $\lim\limits_{n \to \infty} u_n(x) = f(x)$ pointwise with respect to $x \in [a, b]$ and $\lim\limits_{n \to \infty} v_n(x) = g(x)$ uniformly with respect to $x \in [a, b]$, then $f' = g$ and $\lim\limits_{n \to \infty} u_n(x) = f(x)$ uniformly with respect to $x \in [a, b]$.

Proof

Part 1: For each $x \in [a, b]$,

$$u_n(x) = \int_a^x u_n' = \int_a^x v_n$$

But $\lim\limits_{n \to \infty} v_n(t) = g(t)$ uniformly with respect to $t \in [a, b]$. By Theorem 6-6-3, g is integrable and

$$\int_a^x g = \lim_{n \to \infty} \int_a^x v_n = \lim_{n \to \infty} u_n(x) = f(x)$$

By the Fundamental Theorem of Calculus, $f'(x) = g(x)$.

Since this last equation holds for all $x \in [a, b]$, we have $f' = g$.

Part 2: For any $x \in [a, b]$,

$$|u_n(x) - f(x)| = \left| \int_a^x v_n - \int_a^x g \right|$$

$$= \left| \int_a^x (v_n - g) \right|$$

$$\leq \int_a^x |v_n - g|$$

$$\leq \int_a^b |v_n - g|$$

Since $\lim\limits_{n \to \infty} v_n(x) = g(x)$ uniformly with respect to $x \in [a, b]$, given $\epsilon > 0$, there exists an integer N_ϵ such that for all $x \in [a, b]$,

$$n > N_\epsilon \text{ implies } |v_n(x) - g(x)| < \frac{\epsilon}{b - a}$$

Thus for all $x \in [a, b]$,

$$n > N_\epsilon \text{ implies } |u_n(x) - f(x)| < \frac{\epsilon}{b - a} (b - a) = \epsilon$$

and $\lim\limits_{n \to \infty} u_n(x) = f(x)$ uniformly with respect to $x \in [a, b]$. ∎

EXERCISES

Find $A = \lim\limits_{n \to \infty} a_n$ and N_ϵ such that $n > N_\epsilon$ implies $|a_n - A| < \epsilon$ for

1. $a_n = n^{-1}$

2. $a_n = 2^{-n}$

3. $a_n = 3 + (-1)^n n^{-2}$

For $n = 1, 2, \ldots$, we have $a_n = \cos(n\pi/3) + (-1)^n 1/n$.

4. Find $b_n = \sup\{a_m \mid m = n, n+1, n+2, \ldots\}$.

5. Find $A = \inf\{b_n \mid n = 1, 2, \ldots\}$.

6. Find $c_n = \inf\{a_m \mid m = n, n+1, n+2, \ldots\}$.

7. Find $C = \sup\{c_n \mid n = 1, 2, \ldots\}$.

8–12. Repeat Exercises 4–7 for $a_n = n^{-2}$.

DIFFERENTIATION 7

7-1   The Derivative

In manufacturing the material from which the Divergence Theorem and Stokes' Theorem were constructed, we found it necessary to consider the divergence and curl of a function on a three-dimensional set into $\mathbf{V}_3$, the set of three-dimensional vectors. The concepts of divergence and curl, in their turn, were involved with the existence of partial derivatives for functions on n-dimensional sets into the real numbers. These functions were the component functions of the functions into $\mathbf{V}_3$.

The underlying concept was given in Definition 2-3-1 for the differentiability at a point of a function on an n-dimensional set into the real numbers. For the particularly simple case $n = 1$, this definition becomes

> *Definition 7-1-1(Special Case of Definition 2-3-1).* f is a function on a set of real numbers into the real numbers. a is a real number. f *is differentiable at* a means there exists $\delta > 0$; there exists η_f, a function on $\{h \mid |h| < \delta\}$ into the real numbers; and there exists a real number A such that
>
> (i) $|h| < \delta$ implies $f(a + h) - f(a) = hA + h\eta_f(h)$
> (ii) $\lim\limits_{h \to 0} \eta_f(h) = 0$

Examining this definition closely, the first part yields, for $h \neq 0$,

$$\eta_f(h) = \frac{f(a + h) - f(a)}{h} - A$$

Thus the requirement $\lim\limits_{h \to 0} \eta_f(h) = 0$ is equivalent to

$$\lim\limits_{h \to 0} \frac{f(a + h) - f(a)}{h} = A$$

The requirement in the definition of the differentiability of the function f at the number a which calls for the existence of a real number A satisfying

173

property (i) is equivalent to the requirement that the limit of the difference quotient exist. At each number in the domain of f for which this limit does exist, we are able to give a rule for a new function, which new function is then called the derivative of f. We adopt the usual notation f' to indicate the derivative of the function f and arrive at

Definition 7-1-2. f is a function on a set of real numbers into the real numbers. f' *is the derivative of f* means that f' is the function whose domain is the set of all numbers a in the domain of f such that

$$\lim_{h \to 0} \frac{f(a+h) - f(a)}{h}$$

exists, and, for any such number, this limit is $f'(a)$.

The basic theorems concerning the relation between the derivative of algebraic combinations of functions and the derivatives of the functions being combined are usually first encountered when the main goal is manipulative. That is, we need tools which enable us actually to find the derivative of given algebraic combinations of given functions. Here, however, our object is to examine the structure of the theory. It will then be useful to look at exact statements of these theorems. The manner of looking depends heavily on the idea that a function (and derivatives are themselves functions) is a *set* of ordered pairs. Thus a statement which says that two functions are equal to each other is also a statement that two sets are equal to each other, that each is a subset of the other. But it may happen that, given two sets, one is a proper subset of the other. With this in mind, we begin.

Theorem 7-1-1. f and g are functions on a set of real numbers into the real numbers. f' is the derivative of f, and g' is the derivative of g.

$$f' + g' \subseteq \{f + g\}'$$

Proof. Let (a, b) be an ordered pair of the function $f' + g'$. By the definition of the sum of two functions, a is in the domain of f' and also in the domain of g' and $b = f'(a) + g'(a)$.

Since a is in the domain of the function f',

$$\lim_{h \to 0} \frac{f(a+h) - f(a)}{h}$$

exists and is the number $f'(a)$. Since a is in the domain of the function g',

$$\lim_{h \to 0} \frac{g(a+h) - g(a)}{h}$$

exists and is the number $g'(a)$. By the theorem concerning the limit of the sum of two functions,

$$\lim_{h \to 0} \left[\frac{f(a + h) - f(a)}{h} + \frac{g(a + h) - g(a)}{h} \right]$$

exists and is the number $f'(a) + g'(a) = b$. That is,

$$\lim_{h \to 0} \frac{\{f + g\}(a + h) - \{f + g\}(a)}{h}$$

exists and is the number b. By the definition of derivative, (a, b) is an ordered pair of the function $\{f + g\}'$.

The converse of this theorem is false. Thus it is not always true that the sum of the derivatives of two functions is the derivative of their sum. An example showing this is provided by taking f to be the function given by

$$f(x) = \begin{cases} 0, & \text{if } x \text{ is rational} \\ 1, & \text{if } x \text{ is irrational} \end{cases}$$

and g to be the function given by

$$g(x) = \begin{cases} 1, & \text{if } x \text{ is rational} \\ 0, & \text{if } x \text{ is irrational} \end{cases}$$

Neither of the functions f and g is continuous at any number so, since differentiability implies continuity, neither f nor g is differentiable at any number. f' and g' are thus empty sets of ordered pairs and $f' + g'$ is also an empty set of ordered pairs. The sum $f + g$, however, is given by

$$\{f + g\}(x) = 1, \quad x \text{ any real number}$$

which constant function is differentiable at every number and has as its derivative the function given by

$$\{f + g\}'(x) = 0, \quad x \text{ any real number}$$

Thus we have $f' + g' = \varnothing$ and $\{f + g\}' = \{(x, 0) \mid x \text{ any real number}\}$ so that $f' + g'$ is a proper subset of $\{f + g\}'$. ∎

One theorem in which we do have equality between derivatives is

Theorem 7-1-2. f is a function on a set of real numbers into the real numbers. k is a fixed nonzero real number. f' is the derivative of f.

$$\{kf\}' = kf'$$

Proof

Part 1:   Let (a, b) be an ordered pair of the function $\{kf\}'$. By the definition of derivative,

$$\lim_{h \to 0} \frac{\{kf\}(a + h) - \{kf\}(a)}{h}$$

exists and is the number b. Thus

$$\lim_{h \to 0} \frac{kf(a + h) - kf(a)}{h} = k \lim_{h \to 0} \frac{f(a + h) - f(a)}{h}$$

exists and is the number b. But then, since $k \neq 0$,

$$\lim_{h \to 0} \frac{f(a + h) - f(a)}{h}$$

exists and is the number b/k. The ordered pair $(a, b/k)$ must then be in the function f', the derivative of f. From the definition of a constant multiple of a function, we conclude that (a, b) is an element of the function kf', so that $\{kf\}' \subseteq kf'$.

Part 2:   Let (a, c) be an ordered pair of the function kf'. By the definition of a constant multiple of a function, a is in the domain of f' and $c = kf'(a)$. Since $k \neq 0$, we then have $f'(a) = c/k$. By the definition of derivative,

$$\lim_{h \to 0} \frac{f(a + h) - f(a)}{h}$$

exists and is the number c/k. By the theorem on the limit of a constant multiple of a function,

$$\lim_{h \to 0} \frac{\{kf\}(a + h) - \{kf\}(a)}{h}$$

will exist and be the number $k(c/k) = c$. Thus (a, c) is an element of the function $\{kf\}'$ so that $kf' \subseteq \{kf\}'$.   ∎

We now state theorems applicable to other algebraic combinations of functions.

Theorem 7-1-3. f is a function on a set of real numbers into the real numbers. f' is the derivative of f.

$$2ff' \subseteq \{f^2\}'$$

An example showing that we cannot replace the set inclusion by equality is provided by the function f, given by

$$f(x) = \begin{cases} \sqrt{x}, & x \text{ rational}, x > 0 \\ -\sqrt{x}, & x \text{ irrational}, x > 0 \end{cases}$$

Theorem 7-1-4. f and g are two functions on a set of real numbers into the real numbers. f' is the derivative of f and g' is the derivative of g.

$$fg' + f'g \subseteq \{fg\}'$$

The example given above shows also that we cannot have equality here.

Theorem 7-1-5. f is a function on a set of real numbers into the real numbers. f' is the derivative of f.

$$\left\{\frac{1}{f}\right\}' = \left\{-\frac{f'}{f^2}\right\}$$

Theorem 7-1-6. f and g are two functions on a set of real numbers into the real numbers. f' is the derivative of f, and g' is the derivative of g.

$$\frac{gf' - fg'}{g^2} \subseteq \left\{\frac{f}{g}\right\}'$$

An example showing we cannot have set equality is given by taking f to be the function given by

$$f(x) = \begin{cases} 1, & x \text{ irrational} \\ 2, & x \text{ rational} \end{cases}$$

and taking g to be the function given by

$$g(x) = 3f(x)$$

Neither f nor g is differentiable at any number so that f' and g' are empty sets. Then $(gf' - fg')/g^2$ is also empty. However, the quotient f/g is the constant function given by

$$\frac{f}{g}(x) = \frac{1}{3}$$

so that

$$\left\{\frac{f}{g}\right\}' = \{(x, 0) \mid x \text{ any real number}\}$$

which is not empty.

EXERCISES

1. Prove Theorem 7-1-3.

2. Prove Theorem 7-1-4. *Hint:* $fg = \frac{1}{4}[(f+g)^2 - (f-g)^2]$.

3. Prove Theorem 7-1-5.

4. Prove Theorem 7-1-6.

In Exercises 5–8, for the function f, given by

$$f(x) = \begin{cases} 0, & x \text{ rational} \\ 1, & x \text{ irrational} \end{cases}$$

5. Prove that, given any real number a, there exists $\epsilon_1 > 0$ such that for all $\delta > 0$ there exists x_δ with the properties that $|x_\delta - a| < \delta$ and $|f(x_\delta) - 1| \geq \epsilon_1$.

6. Prove that, given any real number a and given $b \neq 1$, there exists $\epsilon_b > 0$ such that for all $\delta > 0$ there exists x_δ with the properties that $|x_\delta - a| < \delta$ and $|f(x_\delta) - b| \geq \epsilon_b$.

7. Prove that, given any real number a, f is not continuous at a.

8. Prove that f is not continuous.

9. Let g be the restriction of f to the set of rational numbers. Show that g is continuous, but that it is not continuous at any rational number.

10. For h the function given by

$$h(x) = \begin{cases} \sqrt{x}, & x \text{ rational}, x > 0 \\ -\sqrt{x}, & x \text{ irrational}, x > 0 \end{cases}$$

show that $2hh'$ is a proper subset of $\{h^2\}'$.

Find f' when

11. $f = \{(x, |x|) \mid x \text{ any real number}\}$

12. $f = \{(x, |x|) \mid x \geq 0\}$

13. $f = \{(x, \sqrt{x}) \mid x \geq 0\}$

14. $f = \{(x, x^2) \mid x \geq 0\}$

7-2 The Chain Rule

In order to form any nonempty algebraic combination of two functions, it is necessary that the domains of the functions intersect and that the ranges consist of entities on which the algebraic operation can be performed. The composite of two functions—often referred to as a "function of a function"— may be formed whenever the range of one function intersects the domain of the other. In the case of functions whose domains and ranges are sets of real numbers, we have the following basic theorem, usually known as "the chain rule":

Theorem 7-2-1. f and g are functions on a set of real numbers into the real numbers. f' is the derivative of f, and g' is the derivative of g.

$$f'(g) \cdot g' \subseteq \{f(g)\}'$$

More explicitly, this theorem says that if x is any number in the domain of g' and the number $g(x)$ is in the domain of f', then the composite $f(g)$ is differentiable at x and

$$\{f(g)\}'(x) = f'(g(x))g'(x)$$

It is convenient to use the following lemma in the proof of the chain rule:

Lemma 7-2-1. f is a function on a set of real numbers into the real numbers. b is a number in the domain of f', the derivative of f. If the function G is given by

$$G(t) = \begin{cases} \dfrac{f(t) - f(b)}{t - b}, & \text{for } t \neq b \\[2mm] f'(b), & \text{for } t = b \end{cases}$$

then G is continuous at b and, for all z in the domain of G,

$$f(z) - f(b) = G(z)(z - b)$$

Proof. Since f is differentiable at b,

$$\lim_{z \to b} G(z) = \lim_{z \to b} \frac{f(z) - f(b)}{z - b}$$

$$= \lim_{h \to 0} \frac{f(b + h) - f(b)}{h}$$

$$= f'(b)$$

$$= G(b)$$

so that G is continuous at b.

If z is in the domain of G and $z \neq b$, then

$$G(z) = \frac{f(z) - f(b)}{z - b}$$

so that $(z - b)G(z) = f(z) - f(b)$. The number b is in the domain of G and $(b - b)G(b) = f(b) - f(b)$ so that for all z in the domain of G

$$(z - b)G(z) = f(z) - f(b) \qquad ∎$$

Proof of Theorem 7-2-1. Let (a, c) be an ordered pair of the function $f'(g)g'$. By the definition of the product of two functions,

$$c = \{f'(g)\}(a)g'(a)$$

By the definition of the composite of two functions,

$$c = f'(g(a))g'(a)$$

Let $b = g(a)$ and let G be the function given by

$$G(z) = \begin{cases} \dfrac{f(z) - f(b)}{z - b}, & \text{for } z \neq b \\ f'(b), & \text{for } z = b \end{cases}$$

By Lemma 7-2-1, G is continuous at b and, for any x in the domain of the composite $f(g)$,

$$f(g(x)) - f(g(a)) = [g(x) - b]G(g(x))$$

Thus, if $x \neq a$,

$$\frac{f(g(x)) - f(g(a))}{x - a} = \frac{g(x) - g(a)}{x - a} G(g(x))$$

Since a is in the domain of g',

$$\lim_{x \to a} \frac{g(x) - g(a)}{x - a}$$

exists and is the number $g'(a)$. Since a is in the domain of g', g is continuous at a, so that $\lim_{x \to a} g(x)$ exists and is the number $g(a) = b$. Since G is continuous at b, $\lim_{z \to b} G(z)$ exists and is the number $G(b) = f'(b) = f'(g(a))$. By the theorem concerning the limit of the composite of two functions, $\lim_{x \to a} G(g(x))$ exists and is the number $G(b) = f'(g(a))$. By the theorem concerning the limit of the product of two functions,

$$\lim_{x \to a} \frac{g(x) - g(a)}{x - a} G(g(x))$$

exists and is the number $g'(a)f'(g(a)) = c$.

Thus a is in the domain of $\{f(g)\}'$ and the ordered pair (a, c) is an element of the function $\{f(g)\}'$. $\qquad ∎$

An example which shows that one cannot always have equality between the two functions in the theorem is provided by taking f to be the function given by

$$f(x) = \begin{cases} 1, & \text{if } x \text{ is rational} \\ 0, & \text{if } x \text{ is irrational} \end{cases}$$

and g to be the function given by

$$g(z) = \begin{cases} 2, & \text{if } z \text{ is rational} \\ 3, & \text{if } z \text{ is irrational} \end{cases}$$

Since neither f nor g is continuous, f' and g' are empty and the function $f'(g)g'$ is also empty. The composite $f(g)$ is the function given by

$$\{f(g)\}(x) = 1, \qquad x \text{ any real number}$$

which constant function has an exceedingly nonempty derivative.

In the following sections we examine the idea of differentiability and an analogue of the chain rule for functions whose domains are n-dimensional sets rather than sets of real numbers.

EXERCISES

1. Prove that if $\lim\limits_{x \to a} g(x) = b$ and $\lim\limits_{z \to b} f(z) = L$, then $\lim\limits_{x \to a} \{f(g)\}(x) = L$.

What follows is an alternate proof of a modification of the chain rule; this modification has stronger hypotheses. Give a justification for each of the steps:

2. $\{f(g)\}(a + h) - \{f(g)\}(a) = f(g(a + h)) - f(g(a))$

3. There exists θ_1, $0 < \theta_1 < 1$, such that

$$g(a + h) = g(a) + hg'(a + \theta_1 h)$$

4. $\{f(g)\}(a + h) - \{f(g)\}(a) = f(g(a) + hg'(a + \theta_1 h)) - f(g(a))$

5. There exists θ_2, $0 < \theta_2 < 1$, such that

$$\{f(g)\}(a + h) - \{f(g)\}(a) = hg'(a + \theta_1 h)f'(g(a) + \theta_2 hg'(a + \theta_1 h))$$

6. $\dfrac{\{f(g)\}(a + h) - \{f(g)\}(a)}{h} = g'(a + \theta_1 h)f'(g(a) + \theta_2 hg'(a + \theta_1 h))$

7. $\lim\limits_{h \to 0} g'(a + \theta_1 h) = g'(a)$

8. $\lim\limits_{h \to 0} [g(a) + \theta_2 hg'(a + \theta_1 h)] = g(a)$

9. $\lim\limits_{h \to 0} [f'(g(a) + \theta_2 hg'(a + \theta_1 h))] = f'(g(a))$

10. $\{f(g)\}'(a) = g'(a)f'(g(a))$

11. Give an *exact* statement of the modification of the chain rule to which the steps in Exercises 2–10 form a proof.

12. One "proof" of the chain rule proceeds as follows:

$$\frac{\{f(g)\}(a + h) - \{f(g)\}(a)}{h}$$

$$= \frac{f(g(a) + g(a + h) - g(a)) - f(g(a))}{g(a + h) - g(a)} \frac{g(a + h) - g(a)}{h}$$

$$\lim_{h \to 0} \frac{f(g(a) + g(a + h) - g(a)) - f(g(a))}{g(a + h) - g(a)} = f'(g(a)), \text{ etc.}$$

Why is this last equation not valid? (Consider the case in which g is a constant function.)

7-3 Differentiability in General

In Chapter 2 we saw that the differentiability of a function whose domain was an n-dimensional set implied the existence of the n distinct partial derivatives of the first order. In this chapter we examine the consequence of differentiability for vector-algebraic combinations of functions whose ranges consist of vectors. First, however, we examine a sufficient condition for differentiability.

Recalling Definition 2-3-1, if f is a function on an n-dimensional set into the real numbers, f is said to be differentiable at the point $\mathbf{a}$ provided there exists a vector $\mathbf{A}$ of $\mathbf{V}_n$, a positive number δ, and a function η, on the n-dimensional set $\{\mathbf{h} \mid \|\mathbf{h}\| < \delta\}$ into the real numbers such that

$$\|\mathbf{h}\| < \delta \text{ implies } f(\mathbf{a} + \mathbf{h}) - f(\mathbf{a}) = \mathbf{h} \cdot \mathbf{A} + \|\mathbf{h}\| \, \eta(\mathbf{h})$$

and

$$\lim_{\mathbf{h} \to 0} \eta(\mathbf{h}) = 0$$

We know that if f is differentiable at $\mathbf{a}$, then the n partial derivatives $f_1, f_2, \ldots, f_n$ all exist at $\mathbf{a}$. The converse of this theorem is false, as shown by the example of the function f given by

$$f(x, y) = \begin{cases} 1, & \text{if } x \neq 0 \text{ and } y \neq 0 \\ 2x, & \text{if } y = 0 \\ 3y, & \text{if } x = 0 \end{cases}$$

Clearly f is not continuous at $(0, 0)$ so that it cannot be differentiable at $(0, 0)$. However,

$$f_1(0, 0) = \lim_{h \to 0} \frac{f(0 + h, 0) - f(0, 0)}{h} = \lim_{h \to 0} \frac{2h}{h} = 2$$

and

$$f_2(0, 0) = \lim_{k \to 0} \frac{f(0, 0 + k) - f(0, 0)}{k} = \lim_{k \to 0} \frac{3k}{k} = 3$$

A condition on the partial derivative which is sufficient to guarantee the differentiability of the function is given in

Theorem 7-3-1. f is a function on the n-dimensional set D into the real numbers. $\mathbf{a} = (a_1, a_2, \ldots, a_n) \in D$. If the partial derivatives f_1, $f_2, \ldots, f_n$ are all continuous at $\mathbf{a}$, then f is differentiable at $\mathbf{a}$.

Proof. By hypothesis, for $k = 1, 2, \ldots, n, f_k$ is continuous at $\mathbf{a}$. There thus exists $\delta > 0$ such that if $\|\mathbf{h}\| < \delta$, then, for $k = 1, 2, \ldots, n, f_k(\mathbf{a} + \mathbf{h})$ exists. We have

$$\begin{aligned}
f(\mathbf{a} + \mathbf{h}) - f(\mathbf{a}) &= f(a_1 + h_1, a_2 + h_2, \ldots, a_n + h_n) - f(a_1, a_2, \ldots, a_n) \\
&= [f(a_1 + h_1, a_2 + h_2, \ldots, a_n + h_n) \\
&\quad - f(a_1, a_2 + h_2, a_3 + h_3, \ldots, a_n + h_n)] \\
&\quad + [f(a_1, a_2 + h_2, a_3 + h_3, \ldots, a_n + h_n) \\
&\quad - f(a_1, a_2, a_3 + h_3, a_4 + h_4, \ldots, a_n + h_n)] + \cdots \\
&\quad + [f(a_1, a_2, \ldots, a_{k-1}, a_k + h_k, a_{k+1} + h_{k+1}, \ldots, a_n + h_n) \\
&\quad - f(a_1, a_2, \ldots, a_{k-1}, a_k, a_{k+1} + h_{k+1}, \ldots, a_n + h_n)] + \cdots \\
&\quad + [f(a_1, a_2, \ldots, a_{n-1}, a_n + h_n) - f(a_1, a_2, \ldots, a_n)]
\end{aligned}$$

By the mean value theorem for functions differentiable on an interval, if $\|\mathbf{h}\| < \delta$, then there exist n numbers $\theta_1, \theta_2, \ldots, \theta_n$ such that, for $k = 1, 2, \ldots, n, 0 < \theta_k < 1$, and

$$\begin{aligned}
&f(a_1, a_2, \ldots, a_{k-1}, a_k + h_k, a_{k+1} + h_{k+1}, \ldots, a_n + h_n) \\
&\quad - f(a_1, a_2, \ldots, a_{k-1}, a_k, a_{k+1} + h_{k+1}, \ldots, a_n + h_n) \\
&= h_k f_k(a_1, a_2, \ldots, a_{k-1}, a_k + \theta_k h_k, a_{k+1} + h_{k+1}, \ldots, a_n + h_n)
\end{aligned}$$

Denoting the point at which f_k is evaluated by $\mathbf{a_k} + \mathbf{b_k}$, we have thus found n points $\mathbf{b_1}, \mathbf{b_2}, \ldots, \mathbf{b_n}$ such that, for $k = 1, 2, \ldots, n$,

$$\|\mathbf{b_k}\| \leq \|\mathbf{h}\| < \delta$$

and

$$f(\mathbf{a} + \mathbf{h}) - f(\mathbf{a}) = h_1 f_1(\mathbf{a} + \mathbf{b_1}) + h_2 f_2(\mathbf{a} + \mathbf{b_2}) + \cdots + h_n f_n(\mathbf{a} + \mathbf{b_n})$$

Thus, for $\|\mathbf{h}\| < \delta$,

$$
\begin{aligned}
f(\mathbf{a} + \mathbf{h}) - f(\mathbf{a}) &= \mathbf{h} \cdot (f_1(\mathbf{a}), f_2(\mathbf{a}), \ldots, f_n(\mathbf{a})) \\
&\quad + h_1[f_1(\mathbf{a} + \mathbf{b}_1) - f_1(\mathbf{a})] + h_2[f_2(\mathbf{a} + \mathbf{b}_2) - f_2(\mathbf{a})] \\
&\quad + \cdots + h_n[f_n(\mathbf{a} + \mathbf{b}_\mathbf{n}) - f_n(\mathbf{a})] \\
&= \mathbf{h} \cdot (f_1(\mathbf{a}), f_2(\mathbf{a}), \ldots, f_n(\mathbf{a})) + \|\mathbf{h}\| \eta(\mathbf{h})
\end{aligned}
$$

provided that we take η to be the function given by

$$
\eta(\mathbf{h}) = \frac{h_1}{\|\mathbf{h}\|} [f_1(\mathbf{a} + \mathbf{b}_1) - f_1(\mathbf{a})] + \frac{h_2}{\|\mathbf{h}\|} [f_2(\mathbf{a} + \mathbf{b}_2) - f_2(\mathbf{a})] + \cdots
$$

$$
+ \frac{h_n}{\|\mathbf{h}\|} [f_n(\mathbf{a} + \mathbf{b}_\mathbf{n}) - f_n(\mathbf{a})]
$$

Now, for $k = 1, 2, \ldots, n$,

$$
\frac{|h_k|}{\|\mathbf{h}\|} \leq 1
$$

and, since f_k is continuous at $\mathbf{a}$, by hypothesis,

$$
\lim_{\mathbf{h} \to 0} [f_k(\mathbf{a} + \mathbf{b}_\mathbf{k}) - f_k(\mathbf{a})] = 0
$$

As a result, $\lim\limits_{\mathbf{h} \to 0} \eta(\mathbf{h}) = 0$ and f is differentiable at $\mathbf{a}$.   ∎

Clearly this theorem can be immediately extended to obtain a similar theorem for a function whose range is an n-dimensional set.

Theorem 7-3-2. $\mathbf{f}$ is a function on the n-dimensional set D into $\mathbf{V_m}$. $\mathbf{a} \in D$. If, for $k = 1, 2, \ldots, n$, $\mathbf{f}_k$ is continuous at $\mathbf{a}$, then $\mathbf{f}$ is differentiable at $\mathbf{a}$.

The theorem concerning vector-algebraic combinations of differentiable vector-valued functions follows the pattern of the theorems for algebraic combinations of numerically valued functions.

Theorem 7-3-3. $\mathbf{f}$ and $\mathbf{g}$ are functions on the n-dimensional set D into $\mathbf{V_m}$. If $\mathbf{f}$ and $\mathbf{g}$ are differentiable at $\mathbf{a}$, then $\mathbf{f} + \mathbf{g}$ is differentiable at $\mathbf{a}$.

Proof. For any fixed i, $i = 1, 2, \ldots, m$, since $\mathbf{f}$ and $\mathbf{g}$ are differentiable at $\mathbf{a}$, the component function f^i and g^i are also differentiable at $\mathbf{a}$.

Thus there exist vectors $\mathbf{A}_{f^i}$ and $\mathbf{A}_{g^i}$ in $\mathbf{V_n}$, there exists a positive number δ_i, and there exist functions η_{f^i} and $\eta_g^{\,i}$ on $\{\mathbf{h} \mid \|\mathbf{h}\| < \delta_i\}$ into the real numbers

such that

$$\lim_{\mathbf{h}\to 0} \eta_{f^i}(\mathbf{h}) = 0$$

$$\lim_{\mathbf{h}\to 0} \eta_{g^i}(\mathbf{h}) = 0$$

and

$$f^i(\mathbf{a}+\mathbf{h}) - f^i(\mathbf{a}) = \mathbf{h}\cdot\mathbf{A}_{f^i} + \|\mathbf{h}\|\eta_{f^i}(\mathbf{h})$$

$$g^i(\mathbf{a}+\mathbf{h}) - g^i(\mathbf{a}) = \mathbf{h}\cdot\mathbf{A}_{g^i} + \|\mathbf{h}\|\eta_{g^i}(\mathbf{h})$$

Letting δ be the smallest of the n numbers $\delta_1, \delta_2, \ldots, \delta_n$, we see that, for $i = 1, 2, \ldots, m$ and $\|\mathbf{h}\| < \delta$,

$$\{f+g\}^i(\mathbf{a}+\mathbf{h}) - \{f+g\}^i(\mathbf{a}) = \mathbf{h}\cdot(\mathbf{A}_{f^i}+\mathbf{A}_{g^i}) + \|\mathbf{h}\|\{\eta_{f^i}+\eta_{g^i}\}(\mathbf{h})$$

and

$$\lim_{\mathbf{h}\to 0} \{\eta_{f^i}+\eta_{g^i}\}(\mathbf{h}) = 0$$

so that $\{f+g\}^i$ is differentiable at **a**. But this means that **f** + **g** is differentiable at **a**. ∎

A slightly different method of proof is needed for the theorem concerning the scalar multiplication of a numerically valued function and a vector-valued function.

Theorem 7-3-4. **f** is a function on the *n*-dimensional set D into $\mathbf{V_m}$. φ is a function on D into the real numbers. $\mathbf{a} \in D$. If **f** and φ are differentiable at **a**, then $\varphi\mathbf{f}$ is differentiable at **a**.

Proof (in outline).

$$\mathbf{f} = (f^1, f^2, \ldots, f^n)$$

$$\begin{aligned}
\{\varphi\mathbf{f}\}^i(\mathbf{a}+\mathbf{h}) - \{\varphi\mathbf{f}\}^i(\mathbf{a}) &= \varphi(\mathbf{a}+\mathbf{h})f^i(\mathbf{a}+\mathbf{h}) - \varphi(\mathbf{a})f^i(\mathbf{a}) \\
&= [\varphi(\mathbf{a}+\mathbf{h})f^i(\mathbf{a}+\mathbf{h}) - \varphi(\mathbf{a})f^i(\mathbf{a}+\mathbf{h})] \\
&\quad + [\varphi(\mathbf{a})f^i(\mathbf{a}+\mathbf{h}) - \varphi(\mathbf{a})f^i(\mathbf{a})] \\
&= [\mathbf{h}\cdot\mathbf{A}_\varphi + \|\mathbf{h}\|\,\eta_\varphi(\mathbf{h})]f^i(\mathbf{a}+\mathbf{h}) \\
&\quad + \varphi(\mathbf{a})[\mathbf{h}\cdot\mathbf{A}_{f^i} + \|\mathbf{h}\|\,\eta_{f^i}(\mathbf{h})] \\
&= [\mathbf{h}\cdot\mathbf{A}_\varphi + \|\mathbf{h}\|\,\eta_\varphi(\mathbf{h})][f^i(\mathbf{a}+\mathbf{h}) - f^i(\mathbf{a}) + f^i(\mathbf{a})] \\
&\quad + \varphi(\mathbf{a})[\mathbf{h}\cdot\mathbf{A}_{f^i} + \|\mathbf{h}\|\,\eta_{f^i}(\mathbf{h})] \\
&= \mathbf{h}\cdot\mathbf{A}_{\varphi f} + \|\mathbf{h}\|\,\eta_{\varphi f}(\mathbf{h}) \quad ∎
\end{aligned}$$

Similar proofs establish

Theorem 7-3-5. **f** and **g** are functions on the *n*-dimensional set D into $\mathbf{V_m}$. $\mathbf{a} \in D$. If **f** and **g** are differentiable at **a**, then $\mathbf{f}\cdot\mathbf{g}$ is differentiable at **a**.

Theorem 7-3-6. **f** and **g** are functions on the *n*-dimensional set *D* into **V₃**. **a** ∈ *D*. If **f** and **g** are differentiable at **a**, then **f** × **g** and **g** × **f** are differentiable at **a**.

Since, in the particular case that the domains of these functions are real numbers, differentiability implies the existence of the derivative, we can use these theorems immediately to establish the following:

Theorem 7-3-7. **f** and **g** are functions on a set of real numbers into V_m. If **f**′ is the derivative of **f** and **g**′ is the derivative of **g**, then

$$\mathbf{f}' + \mathbf{g}' \subseteq \{\mathbf{f} + \mathbf{g}\}'$$

Theorem 7-3-8. **f** is a function on a set of real numbers into V_m. φ is a function on the same set of real numbers into the real numbers. If **f**′ is the derivative of **f** and φ' is the derivative of φ, then

$$\varphi\mathbf{f}' + \varphi'\mathbf{f} \subseteq \{\varphi\mathbf{f}\}'$$

Theorem 7-3-9. **f** and **g** are functions on a set of real numbers into V_m. If **f**′ is the derivative of **f** and **g**′ is the derivative of **g**, then

$$\mathbf{f} \cdot \mathbf{g}' + \mathbf{f}' \cdot \mathbf{g} \subseteq \{\mathbf{f} \cdot \mathbf{g}\}'$$

Theorem 7-3-10. **f** and **g** are functions on a set of real numbers into **V₃**. If **f**′ is the derivative of **f** and **g**′ is the derivative of **g**, then

$$\mathbf{f} \times \mathbf{g}' + \mathbf{f}' \times \mathbf{g} \subseteq \{\mathbf{f} \times \mathbf{g}\}'$$

and

$$\mathbf{g} \times \mathbf{f}' + \mathbf{g}' \times \mathbf{f} \subseteq \{\mathbf{g} \times \mathbf{f}\}'$$

Clearly we have corollaries for all these theorems for the case in which the domain is an *n*-dimensional set and the concern is with the partial derivatives.

EXERCISES

1. Prove Theorem 7-3-2.

2. Complete the proof of Theorem 7-3-4, giving the reasons for the steps.

3. Prove Theorem 7-3-5.

4. Prove Theorem 7-3-6.

5. Prove Theorem 7-3-7, using the appropriate theorem of this section.

6. Prove Theorem 7-3-8.

7. Prove Theorem 7-3-9.

8. Prove Theorem 7-3-10.

9. Give exact statements of the limit theorem used in the proofs above.

10. Give exact statements of the corollaries to Theorems 7-3-7 through 7-3-10 which consider partial derivatives.

7-4 Differentiability of Composites

In this section we examine the consequences of differentiability of composites of functions which have domains and/or ranges which are n-dimensional sets. Suppose D is an n-dimensional set and $\mathbf{g}$ is a function on D into $\mathbf{V_m}$. We let $R = \mathbf{g}(D)$ be that m-dimensional set of vectors which is the range of $\mathbf{g}$ and let f be a function on R into the real numbers.

Since the range of $\mathbf{g}$ is an m-dimensional set, $\mathbf{g}$ has m component functions, expressed by

$$\mathbf{g} = (g^1, g^2, \ldots, g^m)$$

We consider one specific point $\mathbf{a} = (a_1, a_2, \ldots, a_n) \in D$ and let the vector $\mathbf{g(a)}$ of $\mathbf{V_m}$ be called $\mathbf{b} = (b_1, b_2, \ldots, b_m)$. Thus, for $i = 1, 2, \ldots, m$, we have

$$g^i(\mathbf{a}) = b_i$$

If $\mathbf{g}$ is differentiable at $\mathbf{a}$, then, for $i = 1, 2, \ldots, m$, g^i is differentiable at $\mathbf{a}$. Thus, for $i = 1, 2, \ldots, m$, there exists a vector $\mathbf{A_i}$ of $\mathbf{V_n}$ [which is, in fact, $\{\operatorname{grad} g^i\}(\mathbf{a})$], and there exists $\delta_i > 0$ together with a function η_{g^i} on $\{\mathbf{h} \mid \|\mathbf{h}\| < \delta_i\}$ into the real numbers with the properties that

$$g^i(\mathbf{a + h}) - g^i(\mathbf{a}) = \mathbf{h \cdot A_i} + \|\mathbf{h}\| \, \eta_{g^i}(\mathbf{h})$$

and

$$\lim_{\mathbf{h} \to 0} \eta_g(\mathbf{h}) = 0$$

We let δ be the smallest of the numbers $\delta_1, \delta_2, \ldots, \delta_m$, so that $\{\mathbf{h} \mid \|\mathbf{h}\| < \delta\}$ will act as a common domain for all the functions $\eta_{g^1}, \eta_{g^2}, \ldots, \eta_{g^m}$.

Similarly, if f is differentiable at $\mathbf{b}$, then there exists a vector $\mathbf{B}$ of $\mathbf{V_m}$ [which is, in fact, $\{\operatorname{grad} f\}(\mathbf{b})$], and there exists $\delta^* > 0$ together with a function η_f on $\{\mathbf{k} \mid \|\mathbf{k}\| < \delta^*\}$ into the real numbers with the properties that

$$f(\mathbf{b + k}) - f(\mathbf{b}) = \mathbf{k \cdot B} + \|\mathbf{k}\| \, \eta_f(\mathbf{k})$$

and

$$\lim_{\mathbf{k} \to 0} \eta_f(\mathbf{k}) = 0$$

Since, for $i = 1, 2, \ldots, m$, we have $\lim\limits_{h\to 0} \eta_{g^i}(h) = 0$, we may, without loss of generality, assume that δ is sufficiently small so that

$$\|\mathbf{h}\| < \delta \text{ implies } \|\mathbf{g}(\mathbf{a} + \mathbf{h}) - \mathbf{g}(\mathbf{a})\| < \delta^*$$

This is, of course, merely a consequence of the fact that the differentiability of $\mathbf{g}$ implies its continuity.

For the composite function $f(\mathbf{g})$ which is a function on D into the real numbers, we then have, for $\|\mathbf{h}\| < \delta$,

$$\begin{aligned}
\{f(\mathbf{g})\}(\mathbf{a} + \mathbf{h}) - \{f(\mathbf{g})\}(\mathbf{a}) &= f(\mathbf{g}(\mathbf{a} + \mathbf{h})) - f(\mathbf{g}(\mathbf{a})) \\
&= f(\mathbf{g}(\mathbf{a}) + \mathbf{g}(\mathbf{a} + \mathbf{h}) - \mathbf{g}(\mathbf{a})) - f(\mathbf{g}(\mathbf{a})) \\
&= f(\mathbf{b} + \mathbf{g}(\mathbf{a} + \mathbf{h}) - \mathbf{g}(\mathbf{a})) - f(\mathbf{b}) \\
&= [\mathbf{g}(\mathbf{a} + \mathbf{h}) - \mathbf{g}(\mathbf{a})] \cdot \mathbf{B} \\
&\quad + \|\mathbf{g}(\mathbf{a} + \mathbf{h}) - \mathbf{g}(\mathbf{a})\| \, \eta_f(\mathbf{g}(\mathbf{a} + \mathbf{h}) - \mathbf{g}(\mathbf{a}))
\end{aligned}$$

But we have

$$\begin{aligned}
[\mathbf{g}(\mathbf{a} + \mathbf{h}) - \mathbf{g}(\mathbf{a})] \cdot \mathbf{B} &= [g^1(\mathbf{a} + \mathbf{h}) - g^1(\mathbf{a})]B_1 + [g^2(\mathbf{a} + \mathbf{h}) - g^2(\mathbf{a})]B_2 + \cdots \\
&\quad + [g^m(\mathbf{a} + \mathbf{h}) - g^m(\mathbf{a})]B_m \\
&= [\mathbf{h} \cdot \mathbf{A_1} + \|\mathbf{h}\| \, \eta_{g^i}(\mathbf{h})]B_1 \\
&\quad + [\mathbf{h} \cdot \mathbf{A_2} + \|\mathbf{h}\| \, \eta_{g^2}(\mathbf{h})]B_2 + \cdots \\
&\quad + [\mathbf{h} \cdot \mathbf{A_m} + \|\mathbf{h}\| \, \eta_{g^m}(\mathbf{h})B_m \\
&= \mathbf{h} \cdot (B_1\mathbf{A_1} + B_2\mathbf{A_2} + \cdots + B_m\mathbf{A_m}) \\
&\quad + \|\mathbf{h}\| \, \{B_1\eta_{g^1} + B_2\eta_{g^2} + \cdots + B_m\eta_{g^m}\}(\mathbf{h})
\end{aligned}$$

and also

$$\|\mathbf{g}(\mathbf{a} + \mathbf{h}) - \mathbf{g}(\mathbf{a})\| = \left\{ \sum_{i=1}^{m} [\mathbf{h} \cdot \mathbf{A}_i + \|\mathbf{h}\|\eta_{g^i}(\mathbf{h})]^2 \right\}^{1/2}$$

Thus

$$\|\mathbf{h}\| < \delta \text{ implies } \{f(\mathbf{g})\}(\mathbf{a} + \mathbf{h}) - \{f(\mathbf{g})\}(\mathbf{a}) = \mathbf{h} \cdot \mathbf{C} + \|\mathbf{h}\| \, \eta_{f(\mathbf{g})}(\mathbf{h})$$

where

$$\mathbf{C} = B_1\mathbf{A_1} + B_2\mathbf{A_2} + \cdots + B_m\mathbf{A_m}$$

and

$$\begin{aligned}
\eta_{f(\mathbf{g})}(\mathbf{h}) &= \{B_1\eta_{g^1} + B_2\eta_{g^2} + \cdots + B_m\eta_{g^m}\}(\mathbf{h}) \\
&\quad + \left\{ \sum_{i=1}^{m} [\mathbf{h} \cdot \mathbf{A}_i + \eta_{g^i}(\mathbf{h})]^2 \right\}^{1/2} \eta_f(\mathbf{g}(\mathbf{a} + \mathbf{h}) - \mathbf{g}(\mathbf{a}))
\end{aligned}$$

Clearly $\lim\limits_{h\to 0} \eta_{f(g)}(\mathbf{h}) = 0$ so that the differentiability of $\mathbf{g}$ at $\mathbf{a}$ and the differentiability of f at $\mathbf{b} = \mathbf{g}(\mathbf{a})$ imply the differentiability of the composite $f(\mathbf{g})$ at $\mathbf{a}$ and we have proved

> **Theorem 7-4-1.** $\mathbf{g}$ is a function on the n-dimensional set D into $\mathbf{V_m}$.
> f is a function on $\mathbf{g}(D)$ into the real numbers. $\mathbf{a} \in D$. If f is differentiable at $\mathbf{g}(\mathbf{a})$ and $\mathbf{g}$ is differentiable at $\mathbf{a}$, then $f(\mathbf{g})$ is differentiable at $\mathbf{a}$.

While it is rather elementary to show that the differentiability of the two functions involved implies the differentiability of their composite, the determination of the derivatives or partial derivatives of the composite in terms of the derivatives or partial derivatives of the given functions presents a slightly more formidable task.

Once more we take $\mathbf{g}$ to be a function on the n-dimensional set D and f to be a function on $R = \mathbf{g}(D)$ into the real numbers. We fix the point $\mathbf{a} = (a_1, a_2, \ldots, a_n) \in D$.

Now $\mathbf{g} = (g^1, g^2, \ldots, g^m)$ has m component functions, each of which is a function on an n-dimensional set into the real numbers. Each of these component functions will have n partial derivatives of the first order, giving the mn functions

$$g_i^j; \quad i = 1, 2, \ldots, n; \quad j = 1, 2, \ldots, m$$

The function f is a function on the m-dimensional set R into the real numbers and will have the m partial derivatives

$$f_j; \quad j = 1, 2, \ldots, m$$

The composite function $f(\mathbf{g})$ is a function on D into the real numbers so that it has n partial derivatives

$$\{f(\mathbf{g})\}_i; \quad i = 1, 2, \ldots, n$$

Assuming that all these partial derivatives not only exist at a fixed point but also are continuous there, we have

$$\{f(\mathbf{g})\}_i(\mathbf{a}) = \lim_{h_i \to 0} \frac{\{f(\mathbf{g})\}(\mathbf{a} + h_i\mathbf{e_i}) - \{f(\mathbf{g})\}(\mathbf{a})}{h_i}$$

where $\mathbf{e_i}$ is the element of $\mathbf{V_n}$ whose ith component is 1 and whose other components are 0. Thus

$$\mathbf{a} + h_i\mathbf{e_i} = (a_1, a_2, \ldots, a_{i-1}, a_i + h_i, a_{i+1}, a_{i+2}, \ldots, a_n)$$

We then have

$$\{f(\mathbf{g})\}(\mathbf{a} + h_i\mathbf{e}_i) - \{f(\mathbf{g})\}(\mathbf{a}) = f(g^1(\mathbf{a} + h_i\mathbf{e}_i), g^2(\mathbf{a} + h_i\mathbf{e}_i), \ldots, g^m(\mathbf{a} + h_i\mathbf{e}_i))$$
$$- f(g^1(\mathbf{a}), g^2(\mathbf{a}), \ldots, g^m(\mathbf{a}))$$
$$= [f(g^1(\mathbf{a} + h_i\mathbf{e}_i), g^2(\mathbf{a} + h_i\mathbf{e}_i), \ldots, g^m(\mathbf{a} + h_i\mathbf{e}_i))$$
$$- f(g^1(\mathbf{a}), g^2(\mathbf{a} + h_i\mathbf{e}_i), \ldots, g^m(\mathbf{a} + h_i\mathbf{e}_i))]$$
$$+ [f(g^1(\mathbf{a}), g^2(\mathbf{a} + h_i\mathbf{e}_i), \ldots, g^m(\mathbf{a} + h_i\mathbf{e}_i))$$
$$- f(g^1(\mathbf{a}), g^2(\mathbf{a}), g^3(\mathbf{a} + h_i\mathbf{e}_i),$$
$$g^4(\mathbf{a} + h_i\mathbf{e}_i), \ldots, g^m(\mathbf{a} + h_i\mathbf{e}_i))] + \cdots$$
$$+ [f(g^1(\mathbf{a}), g^2(\mathbf{a}), \ldots, g^{k-1}(\mathbf{a}),$$
$$g^k(\mathbf{a} + h_i\mathbf{e}_i), \ldots, g^m(\mathbf{a} + h_i\mathbf{e}_i))$$
$$- f(g^1(\mathbf{a}), g^2(\mathbf{a}), \ldots, g^k(\mathbf{a}),$$
$$g^{k+1}(\mathbf{a} + h_i\mathbf{e}_i), \ldots, g^m(\mathbf{a} + h_i\mathbf{e}_i))] + \cdots$$
$$+ [f(g^1(\mathbf{a}), g^2(\mathbf{a}), \ldots, g^{m-1}(\mathbf{a}), g^m(\mathbf{a} + h_i\mathbf{e}_i))$$
$$- f(g^1(\mathbf{a}), g^2(\mathbf{a}), \ldots, g^m(\mathbf{a}))]$$

Considering each of the m differences above, if all the partial derivatives involved exist in a neighborhood of $\mathbf{a}$ or of $\mathbf{b}$, then, for $j = 1, 2, \ldots, m$, there exists θ_j, $0 < \theta_j < 1$ such that

$$f(g^1(\mathbf{a}), \ldots, g^{j-1}(\mathbf{a}), g^j(\mathbf{a} + h_i\mathbf{e}_i), \ldots, g^m(\mathbf{a} + h_i\mathbf{e}_i))$$
$$- f(g^1(\mathbf{a}), \ldots, g^j(\mathbf{a}), g^{j+1}(\mathbf{a} + h_i\mathbf{e}_i), \ldots, g^m(\mathbf{a} + h_i\mathbf{e}_i))$$
$$= [g^j(\mathbf{a} + h_i\mathbf{e}_i) - g^j(\mathbf{a})]\{f_j(g^1(\mathbf{a}), \ldots, g^{j-1}(\mathbf{a}), g^j(\mathbf{a})$$
$$+ \theta_j[g^j(\mathbf{a} + h_i\mathbf{e}_i) - g^j(\mathbf{a})], g^{j+1}(\mathbf{a} + h_i\mathbf{e}_i), \ldots, g^m(\mathbf{a} + h_i\mathbf{e}_i))\}$$

and also, for $j = 1, 2, \ldots, m$, there exists θ_j^*, $0 < \theta_j^* < 1$ such that

$$g^j(\mathbf{a} + h_i\mathbf{e}_i) - g^j(\mathbf{a}) = h_i g_i^j(\mathbf{a} + \theta_j^* h_i\mathbf{e}_i)$$

Thus, under appropriate differentiability conditions,

$$\frac{\{f(\mathbf{g})\}(\mathbf{a} + h_i\mathbf{e}_i) - \{f(\mathbf{g})\}(\mathbf{a})}{h_i}$$

$$= f_1(g^1(\mathbf{a}) + \theta_1 h_i g_i^1(\mathbf{a} + \theta_1^* h_i\mathbf{e}_i),$$
$$g^2(\mathbf{a} + h_i\mathbf{e}_i), \ldots, g^m(\mathbf{a} + h_i\mathbf{e}_i))g_i^1(\mathbf{a} + \theta_1^* h_i\mathbf{e}_i)$$
$$+ f_2(g^1(\mathbf{a}), g^2(\mathbf{a}) + \theta_2 h_i g_i^2(\mathbf{a} + \theta_2^* h_i\mathbf{e}_i),$$
$$g^3(\mathbf{a} + h_i\mathbf{e}_i), \ldots, g^m(\mathbf{a} + h_i\mathbf{e}_i))g_i^2(\mathbf{a} + \theta_2^* h_i\mathbf{e}_i)$$
$$+ \cdots + f_j(g^1(\mathbf{a}), \ldots, g^{j-1}(\mathbf{a}), g^j(\mathbf{a}) + \theta_j h_i g_i^j(\mathbf{a} + \theta_j^* h_i\mathbf{e}_i),$$
$$g^{j+1}(\mathbf{a} + h_i\mathbf{e}_i), \ldots, g^m(\mathbf{a} + h_i\mathbf{e}_i))g_i^j(\mathbf{a} + \theta_j^* h_i\mathbf{e}_i)$$
$$+ \cdots + f_m(g^1(\mathbf{a}), \ldots, g^{m-1}(\mathbf{a}), g^m(\mathbf{a}) + \theta_m h_i g_i^m(\mathbf{a} + \theta_m^* h_i\mathbf{e}_i))g_i^m(\mathbf{a} + \theta_m^* h_i\mathbf{e}_i)$$

If, further, all the partial derivatives involved are continuous at **a** or **b**, we conclude that

$$\{f(\mathbf{g})\}_i(\mathbf{a}) = f_1(\mathbf{g}(\mathbf{a}))g_i^1(\mathbf{a}) + f_2(\mathbf{g}(\mathbf{a}))g_i^2(\mathbf{a}) + \cdots + f_m(\mathbf{g}(\mathbf{a}))g_i^m(\mathbf{a})$$

$$= \{[\{\text{grad } f\}(\mathbf{g})] \cdot \mathbf{g}_i\}(\mathbf{a})$$

We have thus proved

Theorem 7-4-2. **g** is a function on the n-dimensional set D into $\mathbf{V_m}$. f is a function on $\mathbf{g}(D)$ into the real numbers. $\mathbf{a} \in D$. If all the partial derivatives of all the component functions of **g** are continuous at **a** and all the partial derivatives of f are continuous at $\mathbf{g}(\mathbf{a})$, then, for $i = 1, 2, \ldots, n$, the partial derivatives of the composite $f(\mathbf{g})$ are given by

$$\{f(\mathbf{g})\}_i(\mathbf{a}) = \{[\{\text{grad } f\}(\mathbf{g})] \cdot \mathbf{g}_i\}(\mathbf{a})$$

In the next section we examine the notational techniques used actually to compute partial derivatives of composites.

EXERCISES

The function **g** is given by $\mathbf{g}(u, v) = (u^2 + 2v, uv, 3u - v^2)$ and the function f is given by $f(x, y, z) = 2x - y^2 + z$.

1. Find $\mathbf{A_1} = \{\text{grad } g^1\} (0, 0)$ and η_{g^1} such that

$$g^1(0 + h, 0 + k) - g^1(0, 0) = (h, k) \cdot \mathbf{A_1} + \sqrt{h^2 + k^2} \; \eta_{g^1}(h, k)$$

and show that $\lim\limits_{(h,k) \to (0,0)} \eta_{g^1}(h, k) = 0$.

2. Find $\mathbf{A_2} = \{\text{grad } g^2\} (0, 0)$ and η_{g^2} with properties similar to those in Exercise 1.

3. Find $\mathbf{A_3} = \{\text{grad } g^3\} (0, 0)$ and η_{g^3} with properties similar to those in Exercise 1.

4. Find $\mathbf{B} = \{\text{grad } f\} (0, 0, 0)$ and η_f such that

$$f(0 + p, 0 + q, 0 + r) - f(0, 0, 0) = (p, q, r) \cdot \mathbf{B} + \sqrt{p^2 + q^2 + r^2} \; \eta_f(p, q, r)$$

and show that

$$\lim\limits_{(p,q,r) \to (0,0,0)} \eta_f(p, q, r) = 0$$

5. Find an explicit rule for $\{f(\mathbf{g})\}(u, v)$.

6. Find $\mathbf{C} = \{\text{grad } \{f(\mathbf{g})\}\}(0, 0)$ and $\eta_{f(\mathbf{g})}$ such that

$$\{f(\mathbf{g})\}(0 + h, 0 + k) - \{f(\mathbf{g})\}(0, 0) = (h, k) \cdot \mathbf{C} + \sqrt{h^2 + k^2} \; \eta_{f(\mathbf{g})}(h, k)$$

and show that

$$\lim_{(h,k)\to(0,0)} \eta_{f(\mathbf{g})}(h, k) = 0$$

7. Verify that $\mathbf{C} = B_1\mathbf{A}_1 + B_2\mathbf{A}_2 + B_3\mathbf{A}_3$.

8. Verify that $\eta_{f(\mathbf{g})}$ has the relation to $\mathbf{B}$, $\mathbf{A}_1$, $\mathbf{A}_2$, $\mathbf{A}_3$, η_{g^1}, η_{g^2}, and η_{g^3} found in the proof of Theorem 7-4-1.

9. Find all partial derivatives of f, $\mathbf{g}$, and $f(\mathbf{g})$, and verify Theorem 7-4-2.

10–18. Verify Theorem 7-4-1 for $\mathbf{g}(u, v, w) = (u^2 + v + w^2, u + v^2 + w^2)$ and $f(x, y) = x^2 + y^2$, where $\mathbf{a} = (0, 0, 0)$.

7-5 Differentiation by the Chain Rule

The chain rule for functions whose domains and ranges are sets of dimension greater than one provides the basic tool for finding derivatives and partial derivatives. When dealing with a specific function, one is usually given a rule in terms of variables. Since a variable is used to represent any element of a given set, we find it convenient to adopt a notation to indicate derivatives and partial derivatives; this notation incorporates the variables used.

In elementary calculus if f is a function on the set of real numbers D into the real numbers, and its range $f(D)$ is called R, then the equation $y = f(x)$ is used to indicate that x, an independent variable of f, represents any number in the domain D and that y, a dependent variable of f, represents any number in the range R. If f' is the derivative of f, common notations for a dependent variable of the function f' are y' and Dy. The notations $D_x y$, dy/dx, and $f'(x)$ not only serve as dependent variables for the function f' but also indicate that the variable x is being used simultaneously as an independent variable of both the functions f and f'. Since a variable, by definition, represents an element of a fixed, specific set, a possible confusion may arise in writing $y = f(x)$ and $y' = f'(x)$. Strictly speaking, this notation should be valid only when the domains of f and f' are the same set. Throughout this section we will assume that this is the case—that is, the domain of a derivative or partial derivative will be exactly the domain of the original function.

For the multidimensional case, if f is a function on the n-dimensional set D into the real numbers, we may write $w = f(\mathbf{v})$, in which notation $\mathbf{v}$ is a symbol for any element of the n-dimensional set D and w is a symbol for the corresponding number in the range of f. We may also introduce the n new variables, $v_1, v_2, \ldots, v_n$, to represent the numbers which are the components of the vector $\mathbf{v}$ of $\mathbf{V}_n$ and use the notation $w = f(v_1, v_2, \ldots, v_n)$. Strictly speaking, since we are writing $\mathbf{v} = (v_1, v_2, \ldots, v_n)$, we should perhaps make a direct substitution in the equation $w = f(\mathbf{v})$ and write $w = f((v_1, v_2, \ldots, v_n))$, but normally the extra pair of parentheses is not written.

Now if D is an n-dimensional set and $\mathbf{g}$ is a function on D into $\mathbf{V}_m$, then $\mathbf{g}$ has m component functions given by $\mathbf{g} = (g^1, g^2, \ldots, g^m)$. Each of these component functions is a function on D into the set of real numbers. Thus we write

$$\mathbf{w} = \mathbf{g}(\mathbf{v}) = (g^1(\mathbf{v}), g^2(\mathbf{v}), \ldots, g^m(\mathbf{v}))$$
$$\mathbf{w} = (w_1, w_2, \ldots, w_m)$$

and, for $j = 1, 2, \ldots, m$,

$$w_j = g^j(\mathbf{v}) = g^j(v_1, v_2, \ldots, v_n)$$

so that

$$\mathbf{w} = (g^1(v_1, v_2, \ldots, v_n), g^2(v_1, v_2, \ldots, v_n), \ldots, g^m(v_1, v_2, \ldots, v_n))$$

We will use subscripts to denote the *numbers* which are the components of a point or vector and superscripts to denote the component *functions* of a function whose range is an n-dimensional set. With such a notation we then use subscripts on symbols for *functions* to denote the partial derivatives of these functions.

For composites, if $\mathbf{g}$ is a function on the n-dimensional set D into $\mathbf{V}_m$ and f is a function on the m-dimensional set $\mathbf{g}(D)$ into the real numbers, then we write, for the composite,

$$z = f(\mathbf{w}) = f(\mathbf{g}(\mathbf{v}))$$
$$= f(w_1, w_2, \ldots, w_m)$$
$$= f(g^1(\mathbf{v}), g^2(\mathbf{v}), \ldots, g^m(\mathbf{v}))$$
$$= f(g^1(v_1, v_2, \ldots, v_n), g^2(v_1, v_2, \ldots, v_n), \ldots, g^m(v_1, v_2, \ldots, v_n))$$

In this case we are using z as a dependent variable both of the function f and of the composite function $f(\mathbf{g})$. The partial derivatives of the functions f, $\mathbf{g}, f(\mathbf{g})$, and the component functions of $\mathbf{g}$ are denoted by

$$\frac{\partial z}{\partial w_j} = f_j(\mathbf{w}), \qquad j = 1, 2, \ldots, m$$

$$\frac{\partial \mathbf{w}}{\partial v_i} = \mathbf{g}_i(\mathbf{v}), \qquad i = 1, 2, \ldots, n$$

$$\frac{\partial w_j}{\partial v_i} = g_i^j(\mathbf{v}), \qquad i = 1, 2, \ldots, n; \qquad j = 1, 2, \ldots, m$$

$$\frac{\partial z}{\partial v_i} = \{f(\mathbf{g})\}_i(\mathbf{v}), \qquad i = 1, 2, \ldots, n$$

The chain rule says that whenever all partial derivatives involved are continuous in neighborhoods of $\mathbf{v}$ and $\mathbf{g}(\mathbf{v})$, we have

$$\{f(\mathbf{g})\}_i(\mathbf{v}) = \{[\{\operatorname{grad} f\}(\mathbf{g})] \cdot \mathbf{g}_i\}(\mathbf{v})$$
$$= \{f_1(\mathbf{g})g_i^1 + f_2(\mathbf{g})g_i^2 + \cdots + f_m(\mathbf{g})g_i^m\}(\mathbf{v})$$

In terms of the variables introduced, this equation becomes

$$\frac{\partial z}{\partial v_i} = \frac{\partial z}{\partial w_1}\frac{\partial w_1}{\partial v_i} + \frac{\partial z}{\partial w_2}\frac{\partial w_2}{\partial v_i} + \cdots + \frac{\partial z}{\partial w_m}\frac{\partial w_m}{\partial v_i}$$

Particular interest arises when we are faced with an equation or equations relating several variables, together with further information relating certain combinations of these variables as dependent and independent variables of some function or functions. As an example, we consider the equation

$$uv + x^2u + 2vy - uz = 3$$

together with the information that u, v, and w are dependent variables of three functions, for each of which three functions x, y, and z are independent variables with the property that the ordered triple (x, y, z) represents any element of the domain of each of these three functions. [This last is to avoid the confusion resulting from a situation such as $u = f(x, y, z)$ but $v = g(z, y, x)$.] We then have the existence of three functions f, g, and h such that

$$u = f(x, y, z)$$
$$v = g(x, y, z)$$

and

$$w = h(x, y, z)$$

This changes our given equation into

$$f(x, y, z)g(x, y, z) + x^2f(x, y, z) + 2yg(x, y, z) - zf(x, y, z) = 3$$

Returning to the original equation, the expression on the left prescribes a function on a six-dimensional set into the real numbers, namely that function given by

$$F(u, v, w, x, y, z) = uv + x^2w + 2yv - uz$$

and the equation suggests that there is some six-dimensional set whose image under F is the set consisting of the single number 3. The existence of the functions f, g, and h tells us that

$$F(f(x, y, z), g(x, y, z), h(x, y, z), x, y, z) = 3$$

We now simplify the problem by making it slightly longer. We introduce three new functions ξ, η, and ζ, given by

$$\xi(x, y, z) = x$$
$$\eta(x, y, z) = y$$

and

$$\zeta(x, y, z) = z$$

We then have

$$F(f(x, y, z), g(x, y, z), h(x, y, z), \xi(x, y, z), \eta(x, y, z), \zeta(x, y, z)) = 3$$

This equation says there is some three-dimensional set whose image under the composite function $F(f, g, h, \xi, \eta, \zeta)$ is the set consisting of the single number 3. Introducing the intermediate function $\mathbf{G} = (f, g, h, \xi, \eta, \zeta)$, we now see that the composite function $F(\mathbf{G})$ is a constant function. Thus all partial derivatives of this composite must be the restriction of the function identically 0 to the domain of $\mathbf{G}$. By the chain rule we have

$$\{F_1(\mathbf{G})f_i + F_2(\mathbf{G})g_i + F_3(\mathbf{G})h_i + F_4(\mathbf{G})\xi_i + F_5(\mathbf{G})\eta_i + F_6(\mathbf{G})\zeta_i\}$$

is the restriction of the function identically 0 to the domain of $\mathbf{G}$.
Specifically,

$$F_1(u, v, w, x, y, z) = v - z$$
$$F_2(u, v, w, x, y, z) = u + 2y$$
$$F_3(u, v, w, x, y, z) = x^2$$
$$F_4(u, v, w, x, y, z) = 2xw$$
$$F_5(u, v, w, x, y, z) = 2v$$

and

$$F_6(u, v, w, x, y, z) = -u$$

By the rules given for the functions ξ, η, and ζ,

$$\xi_1(x, y, z) = 1; \quad \xi_2(x, y, z) = 0; \quad \xi_3(x, y, z) = 0$$
$$\eta_1(x, y, z) = 0; \quad \eta_2(x, y, z) = 1; \quad \eta_3(x, y, z) = 0$$
$$\zeta_1(x, y, z) = 0; \quad \zeta_2(x, y, z) = 0; \quad \zeta_3(x, y, z) = 1$$

We then have the three equations

$$(v - z)\frac{\partial u}{\partial x} + (u + 2y)\frac{\partial v}{\partial x} + x^2\frac{\partial w}{\partial x} + 2xw = 0$$

$$(v - z)\frac{\partial u}{\partial y} + (u + 2y)\frac{\partial v}{\partial y} + x^2\frac{\partial w}{\partial y} + 2v = 0$$

and

$$(v - z)\frac{\partial u}{\partial z} + (u + 2y)\frac{\partial v}{\partial z} + x^2\frac{\partial w}{\partial z} - u = 0$$

If we know some of the values of the functions or their partial derivatives, we may then compute the values of others. In the next section we examine criteria by which we can determine, given an equation or equations involving several variables, the existence of a function or functions relating some of the given variables to others of them.

EXERCISES

1. $t = f(x, y, z) = 3x - 2y + z$; $\mathbf{w} = (x, y, z)$; $x = g^1(u, v) = 4u - v$; $y = g^2(u, v) = 2u + 3v$; $z = g^3(u, v) = u - 2v$; $t = h(u, v) = \{f(\mathbf{g})\}(u, v)$. Find an explicit rule for h. Find rules for the partial derivatives h_1 and h_2. Find explicit rules for the partial derivatives $f_1, f_2,$ and f_3. Find rules for the composites $f_1(\mathbf{g})$, $f_2(\mathbf{g})$, and $f_3(\mathbf{g})$, and verify that, for $i = 1, 2$, $h_i = f_1(\mathbf{g})g_i^1 + f_2(\mathbf{g})g_i^2 + f_3(\mathbf{g})g_i^3$.

2. Repeat Exercise 1 for $t = x^2 - 2y + z^3$; $x = u^2 + v$; $y = u + v^2$; $z = 2uv$.

3. Given the equation $2x + 3y - z = 6$ together with the information that there exists a function f such that $z = f(x, y)$. Let F be the function given by $F(x, y, z) = 2x + 3y - z$. The domain of F is all of V_3. What three-dimensional sets have images consisting of the single number 6? What three-dimensional sets have images consisting of any given single number? If the functions ξ and η are given by $\xi(x, y) = x$ and $\eta(x, y) = y$, find a rule for f such that the composite $F(\xi, \eta, f)$ is the constant function 6. Find the partial derivatives of f.

4. Given the equation $2x + 3y - z = 6$ together with the information that there exists a function g such that $y = g(x, z)$. If the functions ξ and ζ are given by $\xi(x, z) = x$ and $\zeta(x, z) = z$, find a rule for g such that the composite $F(\xi, g, \zeta)$ is the constant function 6. Find the partial derivatives of g.

5. Given the equation $2x + 3y - z = 6$ together with the information that there exists a function h such that $x = h(y, z)$. If the functions η and ζ are given by $\eta(y, z) = y$ and $\zeta(y, z) = z$, find a rule for h such that the composite $F(h, \eta, \zeta)$ is the constant function 6. Find the partial derivatives of h.

6. In Exercise 3, discuss the image of a neighborhood of $(1, 2)$ under the intermediate function (ξ, η, f).

7. In Exercise 4, discuss the image of a neighborhood of $(1, 3)$ under the intermediate function (ξ, g, ζ).

8. In Exercise 4, discuss the image of a neighborhood of $(2, 3)$ under the intermediate function (h, η, ζ).

9. In Exercise 3, if we consider the restriction of f to the rectangle $[0, 1] \times [1, 2]$, which subset of the domain of F is used as the range of (ξ, η, f) in forming the composite $F(\xi, \eta, f)$?

10. In Exercise 4, if we consider the restriction of g to the rectangle $[0, 1] \times [2, 3]$, which subset of the domain of F is used as the range of (ξ, g, ζ) in forming the composite $F(\xi, g, \zeta)$?

11. In Exercise 5, if we consider the restriction of h to the rectangle $[1, 2] \times [2, 3]$, which subset of the domain of F is used as the range of (h, η, ζ) in forming the composite $F(h, \eta, \zeta)$?

12. Given the equation $x^3 + xy + y^3 + z - 3z^3 = 1$ together with the information that there exists a function f such that $z = f(x, y)$; if $f(1, 1) = 1$, find

$f_1(1, 1)$ and $f_2(1, 1)$. Letting F be the function on $\mathbf{V}_3$ given by the left side of the equation given, discuss the image of a neighborhood of $(1, 1)$ under f, under (ξ, η, f), and under $F(\xi, \eta, f)$.

13. Given the equation of Exercise 12 together with the information that there exists a function g such that $y = g(x, z)$; if $g(1, 1) = 1$, find $g_1(1, 1)$ and $g_2(1, 1)$. Discuss the image of a neighborhood of $(1, 1)$ under g, under (ξ, g, ζ), and under $F(\xi, g, \zeta)$.

14. Given the equation of Exercise 12 together with the information that there exists a function h such that $x = h(y, z)$; if $h(1, 1) = 1$, find $h_1(1, 1)$ and $h_2(1, 1)$. Discuss the image of a neighborhood of $(1, 1)$ under h, under (h, η, ζ), and under $F(h, \eta, \zeta)$.

15. Given the equations

$$uvy + uvx + vxy + uxy = 4 \quad \text{and} \quad x + 2y + 3u + 4v = 10$$

with the information that there exist functions f and g such that $u = f(x, y)$ and $v = g(x, y)$; if $f(1, 1) = 1$ and $g(1, 1) = 1$, find $f_1(1, 1)$, $g_1(1, 1)$, $f_2(1, 1)$, and $g_2(1, 1)$. If $\mathbf{F}$ is the function given by $\mathbf{F}(x, y, u, v) = (uvy + uvx + vxy + uxy, x + 2y + 3u + 4v)$, discuss the composite $\mathbf{F}(\xi, \eta, f, g)$ and the image of a neighborhood of $(1, 1)$ under the intermediate function (ξ, η, f, g).

7-6   Implicit and Inverse Functions

A question of general interest in analysis arises from one of the most elementary aspects of algebra; the solution of equations. In terms of variables the question may be phrased as follows: If F is a "function of two variables" and the variables x and y are related by an equation of the form $F(x, y) = 0$, what conditions on the function F are sufficient for this equation to be solvable for y in terms of x?

More explicitly, we begin with some two-dimensional set D and a function F on D into the real numbers with the property that, for every (x, y) in D, $F(x, y) = 0$ (or any other constant). (Usually F is the restriction to D of a function which is not identically zero so that we are not dealing with trivia.) For a fixed (a, b) in D we want a numerically valued function φ whose domain is a set of real numbers D^* with a as an interior point such that, for all $x \in D^*$, $(x, \varphi(x)) \in D$ so that

$$F(x, \varphi(x)) = 0$$

One particularly simple case occurs when we begin with a function f, on a set of real numbers into the real numbers, and construct the function F, on a two-dimensional set into the real numbers, by

$$F(x, y) = f(y) - x$$

in which case we are looking for a function φ with the property that

$$f(\varphi(x)) = x$$

That is, we are looking for a function which is the inverse of f, or the inverse of some restriction of f. Thus it appears that the question of the existence of an implicit function—a solution of $F(x, y) = 0$ for y in terms of x—includes consideration of the existence of an inverse, and any theorem about implicit functions will have application to the existence of inverses.

If we expand our view, however, to consider the question of the existence of an inverse to a function on a two-dimensional set into a two-dimensional set, we can see that in fact the question of the existence of an inverse also includes consideration of the existence of an implicit function.

Suppose D is a two-dimensional set and F is a function on D into the real numbers such that, for all (x, y) in D, $F(x, y) = 0$. We are looking for a set of numbers D^* and a function φ on D^* into the real numbers such that, for all $x \in D^*$,

$$F(x, \varphi(x)) = 0$$

We begin by constructing a new function $\mathbf{f}$ on D into $\mathbf{V_2}$ by

$$\mathbf{f}(x, y) = (x, F(x, y))$$

If there exists a function $\mathbf{g}$ on $\mathbf{f}(D)$ into $\mathbf{V_2}$ such that $\mathbf{g}$ is the inverse of $\mathbf{f}$, then, for all $(x, y) \in D$,

$$\mathbf{g}(\mathbf{f}(x, y)) = (x, y)$$

Using the component functions of $\mathbf{g} = (g^1, g^2)$, we have, for all $(x, y) \in D$,

$$x = g^1(\mathbf{f}(x, y)) = g^1(x, F(x, y))$$

and

$$y = g^2(\mathbf{f}(x, y)) = g^2(x, F(x, y))$$

The first equation tells us that, for all x and t such that $(x, t) \in \mathbf{f}(D)$,

$$g^1(x, t) = x$$

Then, for all (x, y) in D,

$$\mathbf{f}(\mathbf{g}(\mathbf{f}(x, y))) = \mathbf{f}(x, y) = (x, F(x, y))$$
$$\mathbf{f}(g^1(x, F(x, y)), g^2(x, F(x, y))) = (x, F(x, y))$$
$$\mathbf{f}(x, g^2(x, 0)) = (x, 0)$$
$$(x, F(x, g^2(x, 0))) = (x, 0)$$
$$F(x, g^2(x, 0)) = 0$$

Then, for any fixed point (a, b) in D, we take $D^* = \{x \mid (x, b) \in D\}$ and define φ on D^* into the real numbers by

$$\varphi(x) = g^2(x, F(x, b)) = g^2(x, 0)$$

Thus if the function inverse to **f** exists, then there will be a solution to the equation $F(x, y) = 0$ for y in terms of x and we see that the two questions, one on the existence of an inverse and the other on the existence of an implicit function, are in fact equivalent and any theorem which answers one question also answers the other. The general n-dimensional question of the existence of an inverse is easy to state. That of the existence of an implicit function can be stated as follows: We want to find properties of **F**, a function on an $(m + n)$-dimensional set into an m-dimensional set, such that if, at a particular point $\mathbf{a} = (a_1, a_2, \ldots, a_{m+n})$ of $\mathbf{V}_{m+n}$, we have $\mathbf{F}(\mathbf{a}) = \mathbf{0}$, then there will exist a function **g** on $D^* = \{(x_1, x_2, \ldots, x_m) | (x_1, x_2, \ldots, x_m, a_{m+1}, a_{m+2}, \ldots, a_{m+n}) \in D\}$ into $\mathbf{V}_n$ such that, for all $\mathbf{x} \in D^*$,

$$\mathbf{F}(x_1, x_2, \ldots, x_m, g^1(\mathbf{x}), g^2(\mathbf{x}), \ldots, g^n(\mathbf{x})) = \mathbf{0}$$

Our primary concern in this section will be with the differentiability properties of the functions involved in these questions. We begin with finding an analogue of the derivative.

Definition 7-6-1. **f** is a function on the n-dimensional set D into $\mathbf{V}_n$. The *Jacobian matrix* $\mathbf{J}_f$ of **f** is the function on D'—the set of points of D for which all partial derivatives of **f** exist, into the set of $n \times n$ matrices given by

$$\{\mathbf{J}_f\}_{i,j} = (f^i_j)$$

The *Jacobian determinant* of **f** is the function det $\mathbf{J}_f$, on D into the real numbers.

This definition allows a restatement of the definition of differentiability for functions on an n-dimensional set into $\mathbf{V}_n$.

Theorem 7-6-1. **f** is a function on the n-dimensional set D into $\mathbf{V}_n$. $\mathbf{a} \in D$. **f** is differentiable at **a** if, and only if, there exists $\delta > 0$ and there exists a function $\boldsymbol{\eta}$ on $\{\mathbf{h} \mid \|\mathbf{h}\| < \delta\}$ into $\mathbf{V}_n$ such that

$$\lim_{\mathbf{h} \to \mathbf{0}} \boldsymbol{\eta}(\mathbf{h}) = \mathbf{0}$$

and

$$\mathbf{f}(\mathbf{a} + \mathbf{h}) - \mathbf{f}(\mathbf{a}) = [\mathbf{J}_f(\mathbf{a})\mathbf{h}^*]^* + \|\mathbf{h}\|\boldsymbol{\eta}(\mathbf{h})$$

It should be noted that the vector $\mathbf{J}_f(\mathbf{a})\mathbf{h}^* \in \mathbf{V}_n^*$ is the result of multiplying the $n \times n$ matrix $\mathbf{J}_f(\mathbf{a})$ on the right by the "column vector" (i.e., $n \times 1$ matrix) $\mathbf{h}^*$. Since the Jacobian matrix of **f** has horizontal rows which are the gradients of the component functions of **f**, the multiplication yields a vector whose components are precisely the numbers which occur when the definition of differentiability is applied to each of the component functions.

Application of the chain rule to the component functions involved yields

Theorem 7-6-2. **g** is a function on the n-dimensional set D into $\mathbf{V_n}$. **f** is a function on $\mathbf{g}(D)$ into $\mathbf{V_n}$. $\mathbf{a} \in D$ and $\mathbf{b} = \mathbf{g}(\mathbf{a})$. If **g** is differentiable at **a** and **f** is differentiable at **b**, then **f(g)** is differentiable at **a** and

$$\mathbf{J}_{\mathbf{f(g)}}(\mathbf{a}) = \mathbf{J}_{\mathbf{f}}(\mathbf{g}(\mathbf{a}))\mathbf{J}_{\mathbf{g}}(\mathbf{a})$$

Proof. The number in the ith horizontal row and jth vertical column of the product of the matrices $\mathbf{J}_{\mathbf{f}}(\mathbf{g}(\mathbf{a}))$ and $\mathbf{J}_{\mathbf{g}}(\mathbf{a})$ is the inner product of the vector which is the ith horizontal row of $\mathbf{J}_{\mathbf{f}}(\mathbf{g}(\mathbf{a}))$ and the "column vector" which is the jth vertical column of $\mathbf{J}_{\mathbf{g}}(\mathbf{a})$; namely,

$$(f_1^i(\mathbf{g}(\mathbf{a})), f_2^i(\mathbf{g}(\mathbf{a})), \ldots, f_n^i(\mathbf{g}(\mathbf{a}))) \cdot (g_j^1(\mathbf{a}), g_j^2(\mathbf{a}), \ldots, g_j^n(\mathbf{a}))$$
$$= f_1^i(\mathbf{g}(\mathbf{a}))g_j^1(\mathbf{a}) + f_2^i(\mathbf{g}(\mathbf{a}))g_j^2(\mathbf{a}) + \cdots + f_n^i(\mathbf{g}(\mathbf{a}))g_j^n(\mathbf{a})$$
$$= \{f(g)\}_j^i(\mathbf{a})$$

In the particular case in which **f** and **g** are functions inverse to each other, the composite **f(g)** is the identity function **I** such that

$$\mathbf{I}(\mathbf{x}) = \mathbf{x}$$

or

$$\mathbf{I}(x_1, x_2, \ldots, x_n) = (x_1, x_2, \ldots, x_n)$$

The Jacobian matrix of the identity function is then given by

$$\{\mathbf{J_I}\}_{i,j} = \begin{cases} 1, & \text{if } i = j \\ 0, & \text{if } i \neq j \end{cases}$$

Since the Jacobian matrix of the identity function is the unit matrix, the Jacobian determinant is the function 1 identically, and we have

Theorem 7-6-3. **f** is a function on the n-dimensional set D into $\mathbf{V_n}$. **g** is the inverse of **f**. $\mathbf{a} \in D$. If **f** is differentiable at **a** and **g** is differentiable at **f(a)**, then

$$\det \mathbf{J}_{\mathbf{g}}(\mathbf{f}(\mathbf{a})) \det \mathbf{J}_{\mathbf{f}}(\mathbf{a}) = 1$$

For implicit functions, once we are assured of the differentiability of the functions involved, we can compute derivatives or partial derivatives by means of

Theorem 7-6-4. **F** is a function on the $(m + n)$-dimensional set D into $\mathbf{V_m}$. **g** is a function on the m-dimensional set D^* into $\mathbf{V_n}$. $\mathbf{a} \in D^*$. For all $\mathbf{x} \in D^*$, $\mathbf{F}(\mathbf{x}, \mathbf{g}(\mathbf{x})) = \mathbf{0}$. If **g** is differentiable at **a** and **F** is differentiable

at $(\mathbf{a}, \mathbf{g}(\mathbf{a}))$ and $\det(F^i_j(\mathbf{a}) \mid i = 1, 2, \ldots, n; j = m + 1, m + 2, \ldots,$
$m + n) \neq 0$, then, for $i = 1, 2, \ldots, n$ and $j = 1, 2, \ldots, m$,

$$g^i_j(\mathbf{a}) = -\frac{\begin{vmatrix} F^1_{m+1}(\mathbf{a}) & \cdots & F^1_{m+j-1}(\mathbf{a}) & F^1_j(\mathbf{a}) & F^1_{m+j+1}(\mathbf{a}) & \cdots & F^1_{m+n}(\mathbf{a}) \\ \vdots & & & & & & \\ F^n_{m+1}(\mathbf{a}) & \cdots & F^n_{m+j-1}(\mathbf{a}) & F^n_j(\mathbf{a}) & F^n_{m+j+1}(\mathbf{a}) & \cdots & F^n_{m+n}(\mathbf{a}) \end{vmatrix}}{\det(F^i_j(\mathbf{a}) \mid i = 1, 2, \ldots, n; j = m + 1, m + 2, \ldots, m + n)}$$

Proof. Let $\mathbf{H}$ be the function on D^* into $\mathbf{V}_n$ given by

$$\mathbf{H}(\mathbf{x}) = \mathbf{F}(\mathbf{x}, \mathbf{g}(\mathbf{x}))$$

Then, for all $\mathbf{x} \in D^*$, $\mathbf{H}(\mathbf{x}) = \mathbf{0}$. Thus, for $k = 1, 2, \ldots, n$ and all $\mathbf{x} \in D^*$,
$H^k(\mathbf{x}) = 0$. Using the chain rule, we have, for $k = 1, 2, \ldots, n$ and j fixed,
$j = 1, 2, \ldots,$ or m, the n equations

$$0 = H^k_j(\mathbf{a}) = \{F^k_j + F^k_{m+1}g^1_j + F^k_{m+2}g^2_j + \cdots + F^k_{m+n}g^n_j\}(\mathbf{a})$$

That is,

$$\{F^k_{m+1}g^1_j + F^k_{m+2}g^2_j + \cdots + F^k_{m+n}g^n_j\}(\mathbf{a}) = -F^k_j(\mathbf{a})$$

Since the determinant of the coefficients is not zero, Cramer's rule for a system
of n linear equations gives the values of the desired partial derivatives. ∎

EXERCISES

Given $F(x, y)$, $\mathbf{f}(x, y) = (x, F(x, y))$; find $\mathbf{g} = \mathbf{f}^{-1}$ such that $\mathbf{g}(\mathbf{f}(x, y)) = (x, y)$.
Find $D \subseteq \mathbf{V}_2$ such that, for all $(x, y) \in D$, $F(x, y) = 0$. Show that, for any fixed
$(a, b) \in D$ if $(x, b) \in D$, then $F(x, g^2(x, 0)) = 0$ in the following:

1. $F(x, y) = 2x + 3y$

2. $F(x, y) = Ax + By$

3. $F(x, y) = x^2 + 2x + 3y$

Find $\mathbf{J_f}$ and $\det \mathbf{J_f}$ for

4. $\mathbf{f}(x, y) = (2x, 3y)$

5. $\mathbf{f}(x, y) = (\varphi(x), \psi(y))$

6. $\mathbf{f}(x, y) = (x^2 - y^2, 2xy)$

7. $\mathbf{f}(x, y) = (x \cos y, x \sin y)$

8. $\mathbf{f}(x, y, z) = (x \cos y, x \sin y, z)$

9. $\mathbf{f}(x, y, z) = (x \sin y \cos z, x \sin y \sin z, x \cos z)$

Find J_f, J_g, and the composite $J_f(g)$. Find the product $J_f(g)J_g$. Then find an explicit rule for the composite $f(g)$ and find $J_{f(g)}$, thus verifying Theorem 7-6-3 for the following:

   10. $f(u, v) = (2u, 3v)$, $g(x, y) = (4x, 5y)$

   11. $f(u, v) = (Au, Bv)$, $g(x, y) = (Cx, Dy)$

   12. $f(u, v) = (\varphi(u), \psi(v))$, $g(x, y) = (F(x), G(y))$

   13. $f(u, v) = (u^2 - v^2, 2uv)$, $g(x, y) = (x \cos y, x \sin y)$

   14. $f(x, y) = (Ax + By, Cx + Dy)$ Find $g = f^{-1}$. Find J_f, J_g and the composite $J_f(g)$, then verify that the product $J_f(g)J_g$ is the unit matrix function.

   15. $F(x, y, z) = (2x + 3y - z, x - 2y + z)$. Find $D \subseteq V_3$ such that, for all $(x, y, z) \in D$, $F(x, y, z) = (0, 0)$. Find D^*, a set of real numbers and g on D^* into V_2 such that, for all $x \in D^*$, $F(x, g^1(x), g^2(x)) = (0, 0)$. Use Theorem 7-6-4 to find g'. Verify by using an explicit rule for g.

7-7   Inverse and Implicit Function Theorems

We now examine the question of the existence of an inverse of a function on an n-dimensional set into V_n. We begin by considering an n-dimensional analogue of the mean value theorem.

   Theorem 7-7-1. f is a differentiable function on the open n-dimensional set D into V_n. If a and b are points of D such that $\{a + t(b - a) \mid 0 \leq t \leq 1\} \subseteq D$, then there exist n numbers $t_1, t_2, \ldots, t_n$ such that, for $k = 1, 2, \ldots, n$, $0 < t_k < 1$ and

$$f(b) - f(a) = [(f_j^i(a + t_i(b - a)))(b - a)^*]^*$$

Proof. Fix i to be an integer, $i = 1, 2, \ldots$, or n. Since f is differentiable, the component function f^i is also differentiable. We define a new function g^i on $[0, 1]$ into the real numbers by

$$g^i(t) = f^i(a + t(b - a)), \qquad 0 \leq t \leq 1$$

Then g^i is differentiable and, by the mean value theorem, there exists a number t_i with $0 < t_i < 1$ and

$$g^i(1) - g^i(0) = g^{i\prime}(t_i)(1 - 0)$$

But this means

$$f^i(b) - f^i(a) = [\{\operatorname{grad} f^i\}(a + t_i(b - a))] \cdot (b - a)$$

Since this last equation holds for $i = 1, 2, \ldots, n$, we have the conclusion of the theorem. ∎

This theorem can now be used to give a condition on the function **f** to give the existence of an inverse to a suitable restriction of **f**.

Theorem 7-7-2. **f** is a function on the open n-dimensional set D into V_n with continuous partial derivatives. If, for $\mathbf{a} \in D$, $\{\det \mathbf{J_f}\}(\mathbf{a}) \neq 0$, then there exists $\delta > 0$ such that the restriction of **f** to $\{\mathbf{v} \mid \|\mathbf{v} - \mathbf{a}\| < \delta\}$ is one-to-one.

Proof. Let $D^n = D \times D \times \cdots \times D$, where D is used as a Cartesian product factor n times. We define a new function F on D^n into the real numbers by

$$F(\mathbf{v}_1, \mathbf{v}_2, \ldots, \mathbf{v}_n) = \det (f^i_j(\mathbf{v}_i))$$

Since **f** has continuous partial derivatives, the function F is continuous. By hypothesis,

$$F(\mathbf{a}, \mathbf{a}, \ldots, \mathbf{a}) = \det(f^i_j(\mathbf{a})) = \{\det \mathbf{J_f}\}(\mathbf{a}) \neq 0$$

Thus there exists $\delta > 0$ such that, for $i = 1, 2, \ldots, n$,

$$\|\mathbf{v}_i - \mathbf{a}\| < \delta \text{ implies } \mathbf{v}_i \in D \quad \text{and} \quad F(\mathbf{v}_1, \mathbf{v}_2, \ldots, \mathbf{v}_n) \neq 0$$

We now let

$$D^* = \{\mathbf{v} \mid \|\mathbf{v} - \mathbf{a}\| < \delta\}$$

For any **r** and $\mathbf{s} \in D^*$, the line segment $\{\mathbf{r} + t(\mathbf{s} - \mathbf{r}) \mid 0 \leq t \leq 1\} \subseteq D^*$. By Theorem 7-7-1 there will then exist n numbers $t_1, t_2, \ldots, t_n$ such that

$$\mathbf{f}(\mathbf{s}) - \mathbf{f}(\mathbf{r}) = [(f^i_j(\mathbf{r} + t_i(\mathbf{s} - \mathbf{r})))(\mathbf{s} - \mathbf{r})^*]^*$$

If $\mathbf{f}(\mathbf{s}) = \mathbf{f}(\mathbf{r})$, then

$$[(f^i_j(\mathbf{r} + t_i(\mathbf{s} - \mathbf{r})))(\mathbf{s} - \mathbf{r})^*]^* = \mathbf{0}$$

Since the determinant of this matrix is not zero, we must have $\mathbf{s} - \mathbf{r} = \mathbf{0}$ or $\mathbf{r} = \mathbf{s}$. This means that different points of D^* must have different images under **f** so that the restriction of **f** to D^* is one-to-one. ∎

The condition on **f** given in this theorem is thus sufficient to insure the existence of an inverse to a restriction of **f**. We next want to investigate the differentiability properties of this inverse. For convenience we will denote the restriction of **f** to $D^* = \{\mathbf{v} \mid \|\mathbf{v} - \mathbf{a}\| < \delta\}$ by $\mathbf{f}_{\mathbf{a},\delta}$ and denote the inverse of this restriction by **g**. Then the range of $\mathbf{f}_{\mathbf{a},\delta}$—which is the domain of **g**— must be an open n-dimensional set, since D^* is open and both $\mathbf{f}_{\mathbf{a},\delta}$ and **g** are continuous. This set $\mathbf{f}(D^*)$ is thus a neighborhood of the point $\mathbf{f}(\mathbf{a})$. We have

Theorem 7-7-3. **f** is a function on the open n-dimensional set D into V_n with continuous partial derivatives. $\mathbf{a} \in D$ and $\det \mathbf{J_f}(\mathbf{a}) \neq 0$. If δ is

a number such that $\mathbf{f}_{\mathbf{a},\delta}$—the restriction of $\mathbf{f}$ to $D^* = \{\mathbf{v} \mid \|\mathbf{v} - \mathbf{a}\| < \delta\}$—
is one-to-one, for all $\mathbf{v} \in D^*$, det $\mathbf{J}_{\mathbf{f}}(\mathbf{v}) \neq 0$, and $\mathbf{g}$ is the inverse of $\mathbf{f}_{\mathbf{a},\delta}$,
then $\mathbf{g}$ is differentiable and $\mathbf{J}_{\mathbf{g}}(\mathbf{f}_{\mathbf{a},\delta}) = [\mathbf{J}_{\mathbf{f}_{\mathbf{a},\delta}}]^{-1}$.

Proof. Let $G = \mathbf{f}(D^*)$ so that $\mathbf{g}(G) = D^*$. Since $\mathbf{f}$ and $\mathbf{g}$ are continuous and
$G = \mathbf{g}^{-1}(D^*)$, G is an open n-dimensional set.

Pick $\mathbf{b} \in G$. Since $\mathbf{f}$ is one-to-one on D^*, there exists a unique $\mathbf{c} \in D^*$
such that $\mathbf{b} = \mathbf{f}(\mathbf{c})$ and $\mathbf{c} = \mathbf{g}(\mathbf{b})$. Since G is open, there exists $\delta' > 0$ such that

$$\|\mathbf{w} - \mathbf{b}\| < \delta' \text{ implies } \mathbf{w} \in G$$

We pick $\mathbf{h}$ such that $0 < \|\mathbf{h}\| < \delta'$. Then there exists a unique $\mathbf{d} \in G$ such that

$$\mathbf{d} \neq \mathbf{c}$$

$$\mathbf{f}(\mathbf{d}) = \mathbf{b} + \mathbf{h}$$

and

$$\mathbf{g}(\mathbf{b} + \mathbf{h}) = \mathbf{d}$$

We let

$$\mathbf{k} = \mathbf{d} - \mathbf{c}$$

Then

$$\|\mathbf{k}\| < \delta$$

We now have, for $0 < \|\mathbf{h}\| < \delta'$,

$$\mathbf{k} = \mathbf{g}(\mathbf{b} + \mathbf{h}) - \mathbf{g}(\mathbf{b})$$
$$\mathbf{h} = \mathbf{f}(\mathbf{c} + \mathbf{k}) - \mathbf{f}(\mathbf{c})$$
$$\|\mathbf{k}\| < \delta$$

Since $\mathbf{f}$ is differentiable at $\mathbf{c}$, there exists $\delta'' > 0$ and there exists a function
$\boldsymbol{\eta}$ on $\{\mathbf{r} \mid \|\mathbf{r}\| < \delta''\}$ into $\mathbf{V_n}$ such that

$$\lim_{\mathbf{r} \to 0} \boldsymbol{\eta}(\mathbf{r}) = \mathbf{0}$$

and

$$\mathbf{f}(\mathbf{c} + \mathbf{r}) - \mathbf{f}(\mathbf{c}) = [\mathbf{J}_{\mathbf{f}}(\mathbf{c})\mathbf{r}^*]^* + \|\mathbf{r}\| \, \boldsymbol{\eta}(\mathbf{r})$$

If $\|\mathbf{k}\| < \delta''$, we will have

$$\mathbf{f}(\mathbf{c} + \mathbf{k}) - \mathbf{f}(\mathbf{c}) = [\mathbf{J}_{\mathbf{f}}(\mathbf{c})\mathbf{k}^*]^* + \|\mathbf{k}\| \, \boldsymbol{\eta}(\mathbf{k})$$

Since det $\mathbf{J}_{\mathbf{f}}(\mathbf{c}) \neq 0$, the inverse matrix $[\mathbf{J}_{\mathbf{f}}(\mathbf{c})]^{-1}$ exists.

Now if $\|\mathbf{k}\| < \delta''$ and $0 < \|\mathbf{h}\| < \delta'$, then

$$\mathbf{h} = \mathbf{f}(\mathbf{c} + \mathbf{k}) - \mathbf{f}(\mathbf{c}) = [\mathbf{J}_{\mathbf{f}}(\mathbf{c})\mathbf{k}^*]^* + \|\mathbf{k}\| \, \boldsymbol{\eta}(\mathbf{k})$$
$$\mathbf{h}^* = [\mathbf{J}_{\mathbf{f}}(\mathbf{c})\mathbf{k}^*] + \|\mathbf{k}\| \, \boldsymbol{\eta}^*(\mathbf{k})$$

Multiplying on the left yields

$$[\mathbf{J}_{\mathbf{f}}(\mathbf{c})]^{-1}\mathbf{h}^* = [\mathbf{J}_{\mathbf{f}}(\mathbf{c})]^{-1}[\mathbf{J}_{\mathbf{f}}(\mathbf{c})\mathbf{k}^*] + \|\mathbf{k}\| \, [\mathbf{J}_{\mathbf{f}}(\mathbf{c})]^{-1}\boldsymbol{\eta}^*(\mathbf{k})$$

But if $\mathbf{A}$ is an $n \times n$ matrix with inverse $\mathbf{A}^{-1}$ and $\mathbf{k}$ is an n-dimensional vector—that is, an $n \times 1$ matrix—then

$$\{\mathbf{A}^{-1}[\mathbf{Ak}^*]\}^* = \mathbf{k}$$

so that we have

$$\mathbf{k} = \mathbf{g(b + h)} - \mathbf{g(b)} = \{[\mathbf{J_f(c)}]^{-1}\mathbf{h}^*\}^* - \|\mathbf{k}\| \{[\mathbf{J_f(c)}]^{-1}\boldsymbol{\eta}^*(\mathbf{k})\}^*$$

We now define the function $\boldsymbol{\eta}'$ on $\{\mathbf{s} \mid 0 < \|\mathbf{s} - \mathbf{b}\| < \delta'\}$ into $\mathbf{V_n}$ by

$$\boldsymbol{\eta}'(\mathbf{s}) = -\frac{1}{\|\mathbf{s}\|} \|\mathbf{g(b + s)} - \mathbf{g(b)}\| \{[\mathbf{J_f(c)}]^{-1}\boldsymbol{\eta}^*(\mathbf{g(b + h)} - \mathbf{g(b)})\}^*$$

We will then have

$$\mathbf{g\ (b + h)} - \mathbf{g(b)} = \{[\mathbf{J_f(c)}]^{-1}\mathbf{h}^*\}^* + \|\mathbf{h}\|\boldsymbol{\eta}'(\mathbf{h})$$

and

$$\|\boldsymbol{\eta}'(\mathbf{h})\| = \frac{1}{\|\mathbf{h}\|} \|\mathbf{g(b + h)} - \mathbf{g(b)}\| \left| \det [\mathbf{J_f(c)}]^{-1}\right| \|\boldsymbol{\eta}(\mathbf{g(b + h)} - \mathbf{g(b)})\|$$

Now if we can prove that

$$\lim_{\mathbf{s} \to 0} \boldsymbol{\eta}'(\mathbf{s}) = 0$$

then $\mathbf{g}$ will be differentiable at $\mathbf{b}$ and $\mathbf{J_g(b)}$ will be $[\mathbf{J_f(c)}]^{-1}$.

We now pick $\epsilon > 0$ such that $\epsilon < 1$. We know that

$$\lim_{\mathbf{r} \to 0} \boldsymbol{\eta}(\mathbf{r}) = 0$$

Thus there exists $\delta''' > 0$ such that

$$0 < \|\mathbf{r}\| < \delta''' \text{ implies} \|\boldsymbol{\eta}(\mathbf{r})\| < \tfrac{1}{2} |\det \mathbf{J_f\ (c)}|\epsilon$$

Since $\mathbf{g}$ is continuous at $\mathbf{b}$, there exists $\delta'''' > 0$ such that

$$\|\mathbf{h}\| < \delta'''' \text{ implies } \|\mathbf{g(b + h)} - \mathbf{g(b)}\| < \delta'''$$

Without loss of generality we may assume $\delta''' < \delta'$ and $\delta'''' < \delta$. Thus

$$\|\mathbf{h}\| < \delta'''' \text{ implies } \|\boldsymbol{\eta}(\mathbf{g(b + h)} - \mathbf{g(b)})\| < \tfrac{1}{2} |\det \mathbf{J_f(c)}| \ \epsilon$$

Further

$$\|\mathbf{h}\| < \delta'''' \text{ implies } \|\mathbf{k}\| < \delta''' < \delta' \quad \text{and} \quad \|\mathbf{h}\| < \delta'$$

so that

$$\|\mathbf{g(b + h)} - \mathbf{g(b)}\| \leq |\det [\mathbf{J_f(c)}]^{-1}| \ \|\mathbf{h}\|$$
$$+ \|\mathbf{g(b + h)} - \mathbf{g(b)}\| \ |\det [\mathbf{J_f(c)}]^{-1}| \ \|\boldsymbol{\eta}(\mathbf{k})\|$$
$$< |\det [\mathbf{J_f(c)}]^{-1}| \ \|\mathbf{h}\| + \|\mathbf{g(b + h)} - \mathbf{g(b)}\| \ \frac{\epsilon}{2}$$
$$< |\det [\mathbf{J_f(c)}]^{-1}| \ \|\mathbf{h}\| + \tfrac{1}{2} \|\mathbf{g(b + h)} - \mathbf{g(b)}\|$$

so that

$$\|g(b + h) - g(b)\| < 2 \,|\det [J_f(c)]^{-1}| \, \|h\|$$

Thus if $0 < \|h\| < \delta''''$, we will have

$$\|\boldsymbol{\eta}'(h)\| < \frac{1}{\|h\|} \, 2 \left| \det [J_f(c)]^{-1} \right| \, \|h\| \det [J_f(c)] \frac{\epsilon}{2} = \epsilon$$

We have then proved that g is differentiable at b and also that

$$J_g(b) = J_g(f(c)) = [J_f(c)]^{-1} \qquad \blacksquare$$

A somewhat lengthy but not really difficult argument will lead to the conclusion that not only is g differentiable but also that the continuity of the partial derivatives of f will guarantee the continuity of the partial derivatives of g. The theorems just proved can now be used to prove implicit function theorems. Samples of these are left to the exercises.

EXERCISES

1. For all $(x, y) \in D$, we have $F(x, y) = 0$. If $f(x, y) = (x, F(x, y))$, find J_f. Use this result, together with the theorems of this section, to prove that if F has continuous partial derivatives and $F_2(a, b) \neq 0$, then there exists a function g, on a neighborhood of a into the real numbers such that $F(x, g(x)) = 0$.

2. In the situation described in Exercise 1, show that $g' = -F_1/F_2$.

Apply Exercises 1 and 2 to the following functions, finding explicit rules for g when possible.

3. $F(x, y) = 2x + 3y$

4. $F(x, y) = Ax + By$

5. $F(x, y) = x^2 + y^2$

6. $F(x, y) = x^2 + 2x + y^3$

7. If, for all $(x, y, z) \in D$, $F(x, y, z) = 0$ and $f(x, y, z) = (x, y, F(x, y, z))$, find J_f. Use this result, together with the theorems of this section, to formulate and prove a theorem giving a condition on F such that there exists a function g with $F(x, y, g(x, y)) = 0$.

Apply the theorem found in Exercise 7 to

8. $F(x, y, z) = 2x + 3y + 4z$

9. $F(x, y, z) = Ax + By + Cz$

10. $F(x, y, z) = x^2 + y^2 + z^2$

11. $F(x, y, z) = x + y^2 + z^3$

12. Formulate and prove a theorem which, in the conditions of Exercise 7, gives the existence of a function h with $F(x, h(x, z), z) = 0$.

13. Formulate and prove a theorem which, in the conditions of Exercise 7, gives the existence of a function k with $F(k(y, z), y, z) = 0$.

14. Give an exact statement of the general implicit function theorem (*cf.* Theorem 7-6-4).

7-8   The Jacobians and Their Fight for Independence

We have seen that whenever a continuously differentiable function $\mathbf{f}$ on an n-dimensional open set into $\mathbf{V}_n$ has the property that, at some point $\mathbf{a}$, $\{\det \mathbf{J_f}\}(\mathbf{a}) \neq 0$, there will be a suitable restriction of $\mathbf{f}$ which has an inverse and this inverse is also continuously differentiable. The opposite case, in which for all $\mathbf{x}$ in some n-dimensional open set $\{\det \mathbf{J_f}\}(\mathbf{x}) = 0$, will now be investigated.

In the case of linear transformations given by matrices, if a given n by n matrix has determinant zero, then the transformation given by this matrix has, as its range, an n-dimensional set which is the continuous image of some m-dimensional set where $m < n$. For example, if $n = 3$, the range of such a "singular" transformation could be a plane, a straight line, or even a single point. This means the coordinates of the points in the range of such a transformation would be related by one or more equations. We might expect then, if $\mathbf{f}$ is any function on an n-dimensional set into $\mathbf{V}_n$, not necessarily a linear one, that if, for all $\mathbf{x}$ in some open n-dimensional set D, $\det \mathbf{J_f}(\mathbf{x}) = 0$, then the coordinates of points in the image set $\mathbf{f}(D)$ would not be independent of each other but would be related. That is, we would expect that there exists a function $\boldsymbol{\Phi}$, whose domain includes the range of $\mathbf{f}$ and whose range is a set of dimension smaller than n such that the composite $\boldsymbol{\Phi}(\mathbf{f})$ is a constant. In other words, the range of $\mathbf{f}$ will be a "level surface" for the function $\boldsymbol{\Phi}$.

If we do have such a function $\boldsymbol{\Phi}$ relating the components of $\mathbf{f}$, and both $\mathbf{f}$ and $\boldsymbol{\Phi}$ are differentiable, then, for all $\mathbf{x} \in D$,

$$\{\boldsymbol{\Phi}(\mathbf{f})\}(\mathbf{x}) = \mathbf{0} \qquad \text{or some other constant}$$

so that, for $i = 1, 2, \ldots, m$ and $j = 1, 2, \ldots, n$,

$$\{\Phi_1^i(\mathbf{f})f_j^1 + \Phi_2^i(\mathbf{f})f_j^2 + \cdots + \Phi_n^i(\mathbf{f})f_j^n\}(\mathbf{x}) = 0$$

$$[\{\{\operatorname{grad} \Phi^i\}(\mathbf{f})\}(\mathbf{x})] \cdot \mathbf{f}_j(\mathbf{x}) = 0$$

But this means that, for $i = 1, 2, \ldots, m$,

$$[(\mathbf{J_f}(\mathbf{x}))[\{\{\operatorname{grad} \Phi^i\}(\mathbf{f})\}(\mathbf{x})]^*]^* = \mathbf{0}$$

Thus, for each $\mathbf{x} \in D$, either $\{\det \mathbf{J_f}\}(\mathbf{x}) = 0$ or, for $i = 1, 2, \ldots, m$, $\{\{\text{grad } \Phi^i\}(\mathbf{f})\}(\mathbf{x}) = \mathbf{0}$ or both. In order that Φ actually relate the component functions of $\mathbf{f}$ it is necessary that Φ not be constant on any open set so that grad Φ^i cannot have zero value throughout any open set for all $i = 1, 2, \ldots, m$. If, for any specific point $\mathbf{a}$ and for $i = 1, 2, \ldots, m$, $\{\text{grad } \Phi^i\}(\mathbf{f}(\mathbf{a})) = 0$ and $\{\det \mathbf{J_f}\}(\mathbf{a}) \neq 0$, there will be a neighborhood of $\mathbf{a}$ for which $\det \mathbf{J_f}$ also has nonzero value. For all the points in this neighborhood of $\mathbf{a}$ and for $i = 1, 2, \ldots, m$, grad Φ^i has constant zero value, which contradicts the assumption that Φ is not constant on any open set. Consequently, even though $\{\text{grad } \Phi^i\}(\mathbf{f})$ might have isolated zero values for certain values of i, we must have $\det \mathbf{J_f}$ identically zero. More formally, for $m = 1$, we have

> *Theorem 7-8-1.* $\mathbf{f}$ is a function on the open n-dimensional set D into $\mathbf{V_n}$ with continuous partial derivatives. D' is an n-dimensional set containing $\mathbf{f}(D)$. If Φ is a function on D' into the real numbers which is not constant on any open set and, for all $\mathbf{x} \in D$, $\Phi(\mathbf{f}(\mathbf{x})) = 0$, then, for all $\mathbf{x} \in D$, $\{\det \mathbf{J_f}\}(\mathbf{x}) = 0$.

Proof. Let g be the composite $\Phi(\mathbf{f})$. By hypothesis, g is a constant function so that, for all $\mathbf{x} \in D$,

$$\{\text{grad } g\}(\mathbf{x}) = [(\mathbf{J_f}(\mathbf{x}))[\{\text{grad } \Phi\}(\mathbf{f}(\mathbf{x}))]^*]^* = \mathbf{0}$$

Since Φ is not constant on any open set,

$$\{\mathbf{x} \mid \mathbf{x} \in D \text{ and } \{\text{grad } \Phi\}(\mathbf{f}(\mathbf{x})) = 0\}$$

has no interior points. Then

$$\{\mathbf{x} \mid \mathbf{x} \in D \text{ and } \{\det \mathbf{J_f}\}(\mathbf{x}) \neq 0\}$$

has no interior points.

Since $\det \mathbf{J_f}$ is a continuous function if there exists $\mathbf{a} \in D$ such that $\{\det \mathbf{J_f}\}(\mathbf{a}) \neq 0$, then there is a neighborhood of $\mathbf{a}$ for each point of which $\det \mathbf{J_f}$ also has nonzero value. Thus every point of

$$\{\mathbf{x} \mid \mathbf{x} \in D \text{ and } \{\det \mathbf{J_f}\}(\mathbf{x}) \neq 0\}$$

is an interior point. But then this open set with no interior points must be empty so that, for all $\mathbf{x} \in D$, $\{\det \mathbf{J_f}\}(\mathbf{x}) = 0$. ∎

Similar theorems apply when the coordinates of the points in the range of $\mathbf{f}$ are multiply dependent—that is, when $m > 1$.

In examining the possibility of a converse to theorems of this type, it is necessary to use more than merely the fact that the Jacobian determinant is identically zero. We have

Theorem 7-8-2. **f** is a function on the n-dimensional open set D into $\mathbf{V_n}$ with continuous partial derivatives. If, for all $\mathbf{x} \in D$, $\{\text{rank } \mathbf{J_f}\}(\mathbf{x}) = k$, $0 < k < n$, then there exists a function $\mathbf{\Phi}$ on an n-dimensional set which contains $\mathbf{f}(D)$, into $\mathbf{V_{n-k}}$, which function is not constant on any open set and has continuous partial derivatives such that, for all $\mathbf{x} \in D$, $\mathbf{\Phi(f(x))} = \mathbf{0}$.

Proof. Fix $\mathbf{a} \in D$. Since $\{\text{rank } \mathbf{J_f}\}(\mathbf{a}) = k$, with $0 < k < n$, there exists at least one k by k submatrix of $\mathbf{J_f}(\mathbf{a})$ which has a nonzero determinant. Without loss of generality we may assume

$$\{\det (f_j^i \mid i, j = 1, 2, \ldots, k)\}(\mathbf{a}) \neq 0$$

Since the function giving the determinant of this k by k matrix is continuous there exists $\delta > 0$ such that

$$\|\mathbf{x} - \mathbf{a}\| < \delta \text{ implies } \mathbf{x} \in D \text{ and } \{\det (f_j^i \mid i, j = 1, 2, \ldots, k)\}(\mathbf{x}) \neq 0$$

We let $D^* = \{\mathbf{x} \mid \|\mathbf{x} - \mathbf{a}\| < \delta\}$.

We now construct a new function $\mathbf{F}$ on D^* into $\mathbf{V_n}$ by

$$\mathbf{F} = (f^1, f^2, \ldots, f^k, pr_{k+1}, pr_{k+2}, \ldots, pr_n)$$

so that

$$\mathbf{F}(x_1, x_2, \ldots, x_n) = f^1(\mathbf{x}), f^2(\mathbf{x}), \ldots, f^k(\mathbf{x}), x_{k+1}, \ldots, x_n)$$

The Jacobian matrix of $\mathbf{F}$ is given by

$$\mathbf{J_F} = \begin{pmatrix} f_1^1 & f_2^1 & \cdots & f_k^1 & 0 & 0 & \cdots & 0 \\ f_1^2 & f_2^2 & \cdots & f_k^2 & 0 & 0 & \cdots & 0 \\ \cdot & \cdot & \cdot & \cdot & \cdot & \cdot & & \cdot \\ \cdot & \cdot & \cdot & \cdot & \cdot & \cdot & & \cdot \\ \cdot & \cdot & \cdot & \cdot & \cdot & \cdot & & \cdot \\ f_1^k & f_2^k & \cdots & f_k^k & 0 & 0 & \cdots & 0 \\ 0 & 0 & \cdots & 0 & 1 & 0 & \cdots & 0 \\ \cdot & \cdot & & \cdot & \cdot & \cdot & & \cdot \\ \cdot & \cdot & & \cdot & \cdot & \cdot & & \cdot \\ \cdot & \cdot & & \cdot & \cdot & \cdot & & \cdot \\ 0 & 0 & \cdots & 0 & 0 & 0 & \cdots & 1 \end{pmatrix}$$

where the first k entries of the first k horizontal rows are the partial derivatives with respect to the first k components of the first k component functions of **f**, the remaining $n - k$ entries of these rows are zeros; and the entries of the remaining $n - k$ horizontal rows have 1 on the principal diagonal and 0 elsewhere.

For all $\mathbf{x} \in D^*$,

$$\{\det \mathbf{J_F}\}(\mathbf{x}) = \{\det (f_j^i \mid i, j = 1, 2, \ldots, k)\}(\mathbf{x}) \neq 0$$

Thus there exists a function $\mathbf{G}$ on $\mathbf{f}(D^*)$ into $\mathbf{V_n}$ such that $\mathbf{G} = \mathbf{F}^{-1}$. We then have, for all $\mathbf{y} \in \mathbf{f}(D)$,

$$\mathbf{F}(\mathbf{G}(\mathbf{y})) = \mathbf{f}(\mathbf{G}(\mathbf{y})) = \mathbf{y}$$

We also know, from the construction of $\mathbf{F}$, that, for $i = k + 1, k + 2,$ $\ldots, n$, $G^i(\mathbf{y}) = y_i$. We now have, for $i = 1, 2, \ldots, n$ and all $\mathbf{y} \in \mathbf{f}(D^*)$,

$$f^i(G^1(\mathbf{y}), \ldots, G^k(\mathbf{y}), y_{k+1}, \ldots, y_n) - y_i = 0$$

We now consider the $n - k$ functions $h^{k+1}, h^{k+2}, \ldots, h^n$, given by

$$h^i(\mathbf{y}) = f^i(G^1(\mathbf{y}), \ldots, G^k(\mathbf{y}), y_{k+1}, \ldots, y_n)$$

Differentiation with respect to the jth component yields, for $i = 1, 2, \ldots, k$,

$$\{f^i_1(\mathbf{G})G^1_j + \cdots + f^i_k(\mathbf{G})G^k_j + f^i_j(\mathbf{G})\}(\mathbf{y}) = 0$$

and, for $i = k + 1, k + 2, \ldots, n$,

$$h^i_j(\mathbf{y}) = \{f^i_1(\mathbf{G})G^1_j + \cdots + f^i_k(\mathbf{G})G^k_j + f^i_j(\mathbf{G})\}(\mathbf{y})$$

Rearranging these equations and adding convenient forms of zero gives, for $i = 1, 2, \ldots, k$,

$$\{f^i_1(\mathbf{G})G^1_j + \cdots + f^i_k(\mathbf{G})G^k_j + 0h^{k+1}_j + \cdots + 0h^n_j\}(\mathbf{y}) = -f^i_j(\mathbf{G}(\mathbf{y}))$$

and, for $i = k + 1, k + 2, \ldots, n$,

$$\{f^i_1(\mathbf{G})G^1_j + \cdots + f^i_k(\mathbf{G})G^k_j + 0h^{k+1}_j + \cdots + 0h^{i-1}_j$$
$$+ (-1)h^i_j + 0h^{i+1}_j + \cdots + 0h^n_j\}(\mathbf{y}) = -f^i_j(\mathbf{G}(\mathbf{y}))$$

Solving these equations for $h^i_j(\mathbf{y})$ by Cramer's rule yields the quotient of two determinants. We examine these determinants separately.

The denominator is the determinant of a matrix whose first k vertical columns are the partial derivatives with respect to the first k components of the component functions of $\mathbf{f}$, taken in composite with $\mathbf{G}$. The remaining $n - k$ vertical columns of this matrix have entry -1 on the principal diagonal and 0 elsewhere. The determinant is the product of $(-1)^{n-k}$ and the determinant of the k by k matrix

$$\{(f^i_j \mid i, j = 1, 2, \ldots, k)\}(\mathbf{y})$$

Since we know that for all $\mathbf{y} \in \mathbf{f}(D^*)$ the determinant of this matrix is not zero, we do have a valid solution.

The numerator is the determinant of a matrix whose first k vertical columns are the partial derivatives with respect to the first k components of the n component functions of $\mathbf{f}$, taken in composite with $\mathbf{G}$. The next $i - k - 1$ vertical columns have entry -1 on the principal diagonal and 0 elsewhere. The ith vertical column has entries $-f^p_j(\mathbf{G}(\mathbf{y}))$, $p = 1, 2, \ldots, n$. The remaining $n - i$ vertical columns have entry -1 on the principal diagonal and

0 elsewhere. If the determinant is altered by interchanging the $(k + 1)$th column with the ith column and then interchanging the $(k + 1)$th row with the ith row, the original numerator will be the product of some power of (-1) and a determinant whose last $n - k - 1$ columns have entry -1 on the principal diagonal and 0 elsewhere. This determinant in turn is the product of some power of -1 and a $(k + 1)$ by $(k + 1)$ determinant whose entries are distinct elements of the matrix $\mathbf{J_f}(\mathbf{G(y)})$. Since, for all $\mathbf{y} \in \mathbf{f}(D^*)$, the rank of $\mathbf{J_f}(\mathbf{G(y)})$ is k, this $(k + 1)$ by $(k + 1)$ determinant must have value 0. We then conclude that, for $i = k + 1, k + 2, \ldots, n$ and $j = k + 1, k + 2, \ldots, n$, and all $\mathbf{y} \in \mathbf{f}(D^*)$, $h_j^i(\mathbf{y}) = 0$.

This means there exists, for $i = k + 1, k + 2, \ldots, n$, a function φ^i, on a k-dimensional set into the real numbers, such that, for all $\mathbf{y} \in \mathbf{f}(D^*)$,

$$\varphi^i(y_1, y_2, \ldots, y_k) = h^i(\mathbf{y})$$

Then, for $i = k + 1, k + 2, \ldots, n$ and all $\mathbf{x} \in D^*$,

$$\varphi^i(f^1(\mathbf{x}), f^2(\mathbf{x}), \ldots, f^k(\mathbf{x})) = h^i(\mathbf{f}(\mathbf{x}))$$
$$= G^i(\mathbf{f}(\mathbf{x}))$$

We now, for $i = k + 1, k + 2, \ldots, n$, let

$$\Phi^i(\mathbf{y}) = \varphi^i(y_1, y_2, \ldots, y_k) - G^i(\mathbf{y})$$

and we will have, for all $\mathbf{x} \in D^*$,

$$\Phi^i(\mathbf{f}(\mathbf{x})) = \varphi^i(f^1(\mathbf{x}), f^2(\mathbf{x}), \ldots, f^k(\mathbf{x})) - G^i(\mathbf{f}(\mathbf{x})) = 0$$

Finally, we let

$$\mathbf{\Phi} = (\Phi^{k+1}, \Phi^{k+2}, \ldots, \Phi^n)$$

and we have, for all $\mathbf{x} \in D^*$,

$$\mathbf{\Phi}(\mathbf{f}(\mathbf{x})) = \mathbf{0}$$

The only remaining part of the proof requires us to show that not all Φ^i have a zero gradient. This is left to the exercises.   ∎

EXERCISES

$\mathbf{f}(x, y, z) = (x + 2y - z, 3x - y + z, 5x + 3y - z)$

1. Find $\mathbf{J_f}$ and det $\mathbf{J_f}$.

2. Show that rank $\mathbf{J_f} = 2$.

3. For $\mathbf{F} = (f^1, f^2, pr_3)$, find $\mathbf{J_F}$ and det $\mathbf{J_F}$.

4. Find $\mathbf{G} = \mathbf{F}^{-1}$.

5. Find $h = f^3(G^1, G^2, pr_3)$, and show that $h_3 = 0$.

6. Find $\Phi(u, v, w) = \varphi(u, v) - G^{(3)}(u, v, w)$.

7. Show that $\Phi(\mathbf{f}(x, y, z)) = 0$.

8–14. Repeat Exercises 1–7 for $\mathbf{f}(x, y, z) = (x - y + z, x + 2y - z, 2x + y)$.

$\mathbf{f}(w, x, y, z) = (w + x + y + z, 2x - z, w - x + y + 2z, 2w + 2y + 3z)$

15. Find $\mathbf{J_f}$ and det $\mathbf{J_f}$.

16. Show that rank $\mathbf{J_f} = 2$.

17. For $\mathbf{F} = (F^1, F^2, pr_3, pr_4)$, find $\mathbf{J_F}$ and det $\mathbf{J_F}$.

18. Find $\mathbf{G} = \mathbf{F}^{-1}$.

19. Find $h^3 = f^3(G^1, G^2, pr_3, pr_4)$, and show that $h_3^3 = h_4^3 = 0$.

20. Find $h^4 = f^4(G^1, G^2, pr_3, pr_4)$, and show that $h_3^4 = h_4^4 = 0$.

21. Find $\Phi^3(r, s, t, u) = \varphi^3(r, s) - G^3(r, s, t, u)$ and $\varphi^4(r, s, t, u) = \varphi^4(r, s) - G^4(r, s, t, u)$.

22. For $\mathbf{\Phi} = (\Phi^3, \Phi^4)$, show that $\mathbf{\Phi}(\mathbf{f}(w, x, y, z)) = (0, 0)$.

23. Complete the proof of Theorem 7-8-2 by showing that if grad $\Phi^i = \mathbf{0}$ for $i = k + 1, k + 2, \ldots, n$, then det $\mathbf{J_G} = 0$.

IMPROPER INTEGRALS 8

8-1 Nonintegrable Functions

The classical vector theorems which form the core of our study were proved by using the differentiability and integrability properties of the functions involved. We have now explored some of the general ideas of differentiability and integrability for functions whose domains and ranges were bounded sets of numbers or bounded sets of points. We now examine functions for which this is not the case, with the ultimate goal of extending the classical vector theorems to apply to such functions.

We begin by investigating a specific function on the interval $]0, 1]$, namely the function f, given by

$$f(x) = x^{-1/2}, \qquad 0 < x \le 1$$

This function is continuous, and its restriction to the open interval $]0, 1[$ has derivatives of all orders. Further, since for every $B > 0$ there exists $\delta_B > 0$, namely, $\delta_B = B^{-2}$, such that $0 < t < \delta_B$ implies $f(t) > B$, we have

$$\lim_{t \to 0+} f(t) = +\infty$$

The range of f is then the unbounded interval $[1, +\infty[$.

We consider the set of points in the plane bounded by the graph of f, the positive y axis, the portion of the x axis between $(0, 0)$ and $(1, 0)$, and the vertical line segment joining $(1, 0)$ to $(1, 1)$. Calling this set S, we can see immediately that S is not a quadrable two-dimensional set under the definition of Chapter 5 since no finite collection of rectangles can cover S. Then S has no two-dimensional outer content. But S may well have a two-dimensional inner content, since we can find packings of S which consist of a finite number of rectangles. We will examine the possibility of the existence of a two-dimensional inner content for S by considering integrals of suitable restrictions of f.

If $0 < x < 1$, the restriction of f to the closed interval $[x, 1]$ is continuous so that

$$\int_x^1 f \text{ exists and is } \int_x^1 t^{-1/2}\, dt = 2(1 - x^{1/2})$$

We now construct a new function F on $[0, 2]$ into the real numbers by

$$F(x) = 2x^{1/2}, \qquad 0 \le x \le 2$$

We then have F differentiable at all numbers in its domain except for 0 and 2 and

$$F'(x) = x^{-1/2}, \qquad 0 < x < 2$$

The restriction of F' to the interval $]0, 1]$ is precisely f.

We now consider an extension of the given function f to the function f^* obtained by assigning an arbitrary value at 0; say,

$$f^*(x) = \begin{cases} f(x), & 0 < x \le 1 \\ 3, & x = 0 \end{cases}$$

If $\Pi = \{x_k \mid k = 0, 1, 2, \ldots, n\}$ is any set of partition points of $[0, 1]$ with

$$0 < x_0 < x_1 < \cdots < x_n = 1$$

we have

$$\sum_{k=1}^{n} [F(x_k) - F(x_{k-1})] = F(x_n) - F(x_0)$$
$$= F(1) - F(0)$$
$$= 2$$

Since F is differentiable on each subinterval given by the partition Π, by the mean value theorem we have, for $k = 1, 2, \ldots, n$, the existence of a number $\xi_k \in]x_{k-1}, x_k[$ such that

$$F(x_k) - F(x_{k-1}) = F'(\xi_k)(x_k - x_{k-1})$$
$$= f(\xi_k)(x_k - x_{k-1})$$
$$\ge [\inf f^*([x_{k-1}, x_k])](x_k - x_{k-1})$$

Thus

$$2 = \sum_{k=1}^{n} [F(x_k) - F(x_{k-1})] \ge \underline{S}(f^*; \Pi)$$

Thus the set of all lower sums of the function f^* is bounded above by the number 2 and we conclude that

$$\int_0^1 f^* \text{ exists and does not exceed } 2$$

We now examine a particular sequence of partitions, $\{\Pi_n \mid n = 1, 2, \ldots\}$, given by

$$\Pi_n = \left\{ \frac{k^2}{n^2} \,\middle|\, k = 0, 1, 2, \ldots, n \right\}$$

For any of these partitions,

$$S(f^*; \Pi_n) = \sum_{k=1}^{n} \frac{n}{k} \left[\frac{k^2}{n^2} - \frac{(k-1)^2}{n^2} \right]$$

$$= \sum_{k=1}^{n} \frac{1}{n} \left(2 - \frac{1}{k} \right)$$

$$= 2 - \frac{1}{n} \sum_{k=1}^{n} \frac{1}{k}$$

But, for $n = 2, 3, \ldots$,

$$\log n < \sum_{k=1}^{n} \frac{1}{k} < 1 + \log n$$

$$\frac{\log n}{n} < \frac{1}{n} \sum_{k=1}^{n} \frac{1}{k} < \frac{1 + \log n}{n}$$

Thus

$$\lim_{n \to \infty} S(f^*; \Pi_n) \text{ exists and is } 2$$

Since all lower sums for f^* are bounded above by 2 and since there is a specific sequence of lower sums whose limit is 2, we conclude that

$$\int_0^1 f^* \text{ exists and is } 2 = F(1) - F(0) = \lim_{\epsilon \to 0+} \int_\epsilon^1 f$$

The result developed for this particular case holds in general:

Theorem 8-1-1. f is a continuous function on $]a, b]$ into the real numbers with the property that $\lim_{x \to a+} f(x) = +\infty$. If $\lim_{\epsilon \to 0+} \int_{a+\epsilon}^b f$ exists and is the number I, and if f^* is any function on $[a, b]$ into the real numbers whose restriction to $]a, b]$ is f, then

$$\int_a^b f^* \text{ exists and is the number } I$$

Proof. Let $f^*(a) = c$. Since $\lim_{x \to a+} f(x) = +\infty$, there exists $\delta > 0$ such that $a < x \le a + \delta$ implies $f(x) > c$ and $f(x) > 0$.

Let $\Pi = \{x_k \mid k = 0, 1, 2, \ldots, n\}$ be any set of partition points of $[a, b]$ with the norm of Π less than δ.

We now construct a new function F on $[a, b]$ into the real numbers by

$$F(x) = -\int_x^b f \quad \text{for} \quad a < x \le b$$

$$F(a) = I$$

By hypothesis,

$$\lim_{x \to a+} F(x) \text{ exists and is the number } I$$

Further, F is differentiable on the open interval $]a, b[$ and thus satisfies the hypothesis of the mean value theorem on every subinterval of Π. Thus, for $k = 1, 2, \ldots, n$, there exists a number $\xi_k \in]x_{k-1}, x_k[$ such that

$$F(x_k) - F(x_{k-1}) = F'(\xi_k)(x_k - x_{k-1})$$
$$= f(\xi_k)(x_k - x_{k-1})$$
$$\geq [\inf f^*([x_{k-1}, x_k])](x_k - x_{k-1})$$

Therefore,

$$I = F(b) - F(a) = \sum_{k=1}^{n} [F(x_k) - F(x_{k-1})] \geq \underline{S}(f^*; \Pi)$$

Any partition of $[a, b]$ with norm not less than δ possesses a refinement with norm less than δ and this refinement will have a lower sum greater than or equal to the lower sum of the given partition. Thus for all partitions Π of $[a, b]$ we have

$$\underline{S}(f^*; \Pi) \leq I$$

Therefore,

$$\underline{\int_a^b} f^* \text{ exists and } \underline{\int_a^b} f^* \leq I$$

We now choose a sequence of numbers $\{x_p \mid p = 1, 2, \ldots\}$ such that, for $p = 1, 2, \ldots,$

$$a < x_p \leq a + \delta$$

and

$$x_{p+1} < x_p$$

with the property that

$$\lim_{p \to \infty} x_p = a$$

From the hypothesis,

$$\lim_{p \to \infty} \int_{x_p}^b f \text{ exists and is } I$$

Let Π_p be a partition of the interval $[x_p, b]$ given by

$$x_p = x_{p,0} < x_{p,1} < x_{p,2} < \cdots < x_{p,n} = b$$

with the property that

$$\int_{x_p}^b f - \frac{\epsilon}{2} < \underline{S}(f; \Pi_p) \leq \int_{x_p}^b f$$

Since f is continuous on $[x_p, b]$, the lower integral is in fact the integral so we have

$$\int_{x_p}^b f - \frac{\epsilon}{2} < \underline{S}(f; \Pi_p) \leq \int_{x_p}^b f$$

We now let Π_p^* be the partition of $[a, b]$ whose first subinterval is $[a, x_p]$ and whose remaining subintervals are those of Π_p. We then have

$$\underline{S}(f^*; \Pi_p^*) = \inf f^*([a, x_p])(x_p - a) + \underline{S}(f; \Pi_p)$$
$$= c(x_p - a) + \underline{S}(f; \Pi_p)$$
$$> c(x_p - a) + \int_{x_p}^b f - \frac{\epsilon}{2}$$

We know that $\int_a^b f^*$ exists so we must have, for $p = 1, 2, \ldots,$

$$\int_a^b f^* \geq c(x_p - a) + \int_{x_p}^b f - \frac{\epsilon}{2}$$

Taking limit on p gives

$$\int_a^b f^* \geq I - \frac{\epsilon}{2} > I - \epsilon$$

Since this last inequality is true for every $\epsilon > 0$, we conclude

$$\int_a^b f^* \geq I$$

Combining this with the reverse inequality previously obtained completes the proof. ∎

A converse to this theorem also holds:

Theorem 8-1-2. f is a continuous function on $]a, b]$ into the real numbers with the property that $\lim_{x \to a+} f(x) = +\infty$. If for any function f^* on $[a, b]$ into the real numbers whose restriction to $]a, b]$ is f,

$$\int_a^b f^* \text{ exists and is the number } I$$

then

$$\lim_{\epsilon \to 0+} \int_{a+\epsilon}^b f \text{ exists and is the number } I$$

The proof of this theorem is left to the exercises. These two theorems allow us to extend the definition of integral to allow a type of integrability for functions whose ranges are unbounded sets of numbers. Formally, we have

Definition 8-1-1. f is a continuous function on $]a, b]$ into the real numbers for which $\lim_{x \to a+} f(x) = +\infty$. The *improper integral* of f on $]a, b]$ is defined to be

$$\lim_{\epsilon \to 0+} \int_{a+\epsilon}^b f$$

whenever this limit exists, in which case f is said to be *improperly integrable* on $]a, b]$ and the improper integral $\int_a^b f$ is said to *converge*. Otherwise the integral is said to *diverge*.

Further definitions can now be made to cover the situations in which f is continuous on $]a, b]$ and $\lim\limits_{x \to a+} f(x) = -\infty$ and in which f is continuous on $[a, b[$ and either $\lim\limits_{x \to b-} f(x) = +\infty$ or $\lim\limits_{x \to b-} f(x) = -\infty$. In these cases appropriate theorems relating the existence of the improper integral to the existence of upper or lower integrals of extensions of f can be proved. The statements of these definitions and theorems are left to the exercises.

The situation in which the misbehavior occurs at an interior point of an interval is treated by

> **Definition 8-1-2.** f is a continuous function on $[a, c[\ \cup \ ]c, b]$ into the real numbers for which $\lim\limits_{x \to c} |f(x)| = +\infty$. f *is improperly integrable on* $[a, b]$ means that f is improperly integrable on $[a, c[$ and on $]c, b]$ and the improper integral is given by

$$\int_a^b f = \int_a^c f + \int_c^b f$$

We now turn to the question of integral for a function whose domain is an unbounded set of numbers but whose range is bounded. Examining the specific example we began with, we may extend the definition of the word "area" in such a manner that the improper integral in this case will be the area of an appropriate two-dimensional set. For the given function f, with

$$f(x) = x^{-1/2}, \qquad 0 < x \le 1$$

the set S, bounded by the graph of f, the positive y axis, the portion of the x axis between $(0, 0)$ and $(1, 0)$, and the vertical line segment joining $(1, 0)$ and $(1, 1)$, has area 2. For a fixed $\epsilon > 0$, $0 < \epsilon < 1$, the bounded set S_ϵ, consisting of that portion of S which lies to the right of the vertical line $x = \epsilon$, will have area A_ϵ, where $\lim\limits_{\epsilon \to 0+} A_\epsilon = 2$. Adjoining to S the rectangle with vertices $(0, 0)$, $(\epsilon, 0)$, $(\epsilon, \epsilon^{-1/2})$, and $(0, \epsilon^{-1/2})$ yields a portion of the plane with area $A_\epsilon + \epsilon(1/\sqrt{\epsilon}) = A_\epsilon + \sqrt{\epsilon}$. Removing from this set the square with vertices $(0, 0)$, $(1, 0)$, $(1, 1)$, and $(0, 1)$ yields a set with area $A_\epsilon + \sqrt{\epsilon} - 1$.

The portion of the plane bounded above by the graph of $y = x^{-2}$, below by the x axis, to the left by the graph of $x = 1$, and to the right by the graph of $x = B_\epsilon = \epsilon^{-1/2}$ will be congruent to the the last set constructed and thus also will have area $A_\epsilon + \sqrt{\epsilon} - 1$. But the area of this horizontally stretched set is

$$\int_1^{B_\epsilon} t^{-2}\, dt$$

Since $\lim\limits_{\epsilon \to 0+} B_\epsilon = +\infty$, we must then have

$$\lim_{B \to +\infty} \int_1^B t^{-2}\, dt \text{ exists and is 2}$$

This development leads naturally into

Definition 8-1-3. f is a continuous function on $[a, +\infty[$ (where a is fixed) into the real numbers. *f is improperly integrable on $[a, +\infty[$* means

$$\lim_{B \to +\infty} \int_a^B f \text{ exists}$$

and the *improper integral* $\int_a^{+\infty} f$ is defined to be this limit.

This definition can be extended in an obvious way to functions on $]-\infty,$ $a]$ and to functions whose domain is the set of all real numbers, in which case we require the two limits to exist independently of each other.

We conclude with theorems treating certain elementary functions:

Theorem 8-1-3. $a > 0$.

If $0 < p < 1$, then $\int_a^b t^{-p}\, dt$ converges.

If $p \geq 1$, then $\int_0^a t^{-p}\, dt$ diverges.

Corollary 8-1-3-1. $a > 0$.

If $0 < p < 1$, then $\int_{-a}^0 t^{-p}\, dt$ converges.

If $p \geq 1$, then $\int_{-a}^0 t^{-p}\, dt$ diverges.

Theorem 8-1-4. $a > 0$.

If $p > 1$, then $\int_a^{+\infty} t^{-p}\, dt$ converges.

If $p \leq 1$, then $\int_a^{+\infty} t^{-p}\, dt$ diverges.

Corollary 8-1-4-1. $a > 0$.

If $p > 1$, then $\displaystyle\int_{-\infty}^{-a} t^{-p}\, dt$ converges.

If $p \leq 1$, then $\displaystyle\int_{-\infty}^{-a} t^{-p}\, dt$ diverges.

EXERCISES

1. Prove Theorem 8-1-2.

2. State analogues to Theorems 8-1-1 and 8-1-2 for the cases
  (a) $\lim\limits_{x \to a+} f(x) = -\infty$
  (b) $\lim\limits_{x \to b-} f(x) = -\infty$
  (c) $\lim\limits_{x \to b+} f(x) = +\infty$

3. Extend Definition 8-1-3 to improper integrals on $]-\infty, a]$ and $]-\infty, +\infty[$.

4. Prove Theorem 8-1-3.

5. Prove Corollary 8-1-3-1.

6. Prove Theorem 8-1-4.

7. Prove Corollary 8-1-4-1.

8. If $a > 0$ and $0 < p < 1$, find $\displaystyle\int_0^a t^{-p}\, dt$.

9. If $a > 0$ and $p > 1$, find $\displaystyle\int_a^{+\infty} t^{-p}\, dt$.

10. Discuss $\displaystyle\int_{-\infty}^{\infty} \exp\left(-t^2 - \frac{1}{t^2}\right) dt$.

11. Construct an example for which $\displaystyle\int_1^{+\infty} f$ is convergent but $\lim\limits_{x \to +\infty} f(x)$ does not exist.

12. Prove that if $\lim\limits_{x \to +\infty} f(x) = c \neq 0$, then $\displaystyle\int_1^{+\infty} f$ is divergent.

8-2   Convergence Tests

We now examine various criteria which are sufficient for an improper integral to be convergent or divergent. We have, immediately from the definition of convergence of an integral on an infinite interval,

Theorem 8-2-1. If a is a fixed number and $\int_a^{+\infty} f$ is convergent, then, for every $r > 0$,

$$\lim_{m \to +\infty} \int_m^{m+r} f = 0$$

Proof. Let $\int_a^{+\infty} f$ be the number I. For any given $\epsilon > 0$ there exists $B_\epsilon > a$ such that

$$x > B \text{ implies } \left| I - \int_a^x f \right| < \frac{\epsilon}{2}$$

Thus, for any $r > 0$

$$m > B \text{ implies } \left| \int_m^{m+r} f \right| = \left| \int_a^{m+r} f - \int_a^m f \right|$$

$$\leq \left| \int_a^{m+r} f - I \right| + \left| I - \int_a^m f \right|$$

$$< \frac{\epsilon}{2} + \frac{\epsilon}{2} = \epsilon \qquad \blacksquare$$

Speaking loosely, this theorem tells us that integrating f over intervals of arbitrary length will yield numbers close to zero, provided only that those intervals are sufficiently "far to the right." Examining the graphs of examples leads one to the temptation of guessing that the convergence of the improper integral leads to the function's having zero limit "at infinity." Such a conclusion is false, as we can see by examining the function f given by

$$f(x) = \begin{cases} x^{-2} + k^3 x - 2k^4, & 2k \leq x < 2k + k^{-2} \\ x^{-2} - k^3 x + 2k^4 + 2k, & 2k + k^{-2} \leq x < 2k + 2k^{-2} \\ x^{-2}, & 2k + 2k^{-2} \leq x < 2k + 1 \\ x^{-2} - k^3 x + 2k^4 + k^3, & 2k + 1 \leq x < 2k + 1 + k^{-2} \\ x^{-2} + k^3 x - 2k^4 - k^3 - 2k, & 2k + 1 + k^{-2} \leq x < 2k + 1 + 2k^{-2} \\ x^{-2}, & 2k + 1 + 2k^{-2} \leq x < 2k + 2 \end{cases}$$

for $k = 1, 2, \ldots$.

If B is any number of the form $2k + h$, where $0 < h < 2$ and k is an integer, then

$$\int_2^B f = \int_2^B t^{-2} + g(h, k)$$

where $|g(h, k)| < k^{-1}$.

Thus

$$\int_2^{+\infty} f = \lim_{B \to +\infty} \int_2^B f$$

$$= \int_2^{+\infty} t^{-2}\, dt + \lim_{k \to +\infty} g(h, k)$$

$$= \frac{1}{2}$$

Even though the improper integral of this function converges, $\lim\limits_{x \to +\infty} f(x)$ does not even exist. In fact, for every real number r, there exists a sequence $\{x_n \mid n = 1, 2, \ldots\}$ of real numbers such that, for $n = 1, 2, \ldots$,

$$x_n < x_{n+1}$$
$$f(x_n) = r$$

and

$$\lim_{n \to +\infty} x_n = +\infty$$

While we cannot conclude that convergence of the improper integral on an infinite interval implies convergence of the function "at infinity," we can establish

Theorem 8-2-2. If f is a continuous function on $[a, +\infty[$ into the real numbers and $\lim\limits_{x \to +\infty} f(x)$ exists and is $L \neq 0$, then $\int_a^{+\infty} f$ is divergent.

Proof. Since $L \neq 0$, $|L| > 0$, so there exists $B > 0$ such that

$$x > B \text{ implies } |f(x)| > \frac{|L|}{2}$$

Then, for $n = 1, 2, \ldots$, we must have

$$\left| \int_{B+1}^{B+n+1} f \right| = \int_{B+1}^{B+n+1} |f| > \frac{n\,|L|}{2}$$

Consequently

$$\lim_{n \to +\infty} \left| \int_{B+1}^{B+n+1} f \right| = +\infty$$

and the improper integral is divergent. ∎

The theorems of the preceding section give us many specific functions whose improper integrals converge and many others whose improper integrals diverge. The next few theorems provide a useful tool in using these known facts to determine the behavior of the improper integral for other functions.

Theorem 8-2-3. f and g are continuous functions on $]a, b]$ into the real numbers such that, for all $x \in \,]a, b]$, $0 \leq f(x) \leq g(x)$. $\lim\limits_{x \to a+} f(x) = +\infty$.

If $\int_a^b g$ is convergent, then $\int_a^b f$ is convergent.

If $\int_a^b f$ is divergent, then $\int_a^b g$ is divergent.

Proof. We assume that $\int_a^b g$ is convergent. If x is any number in $]a, b]$, the restrictions of f and g to $[x, b]$ are continuous so that $\int_x^b f$ and $\int_x^b g$ both exist. Further, the hypothesis implies that, for any $x \in \,]a, b]$,

$$0 \leq \int_x^b f \leq \int_x^b g$$

By hypothesis,

$$\lim_{x \to a+} \int_x^b g \text{ exists and is the number } \int_a^b g$$

If F is the function given by $F(x) = \int_x^b f$, $a < x \leq b$, then for $a < x < b$, $F'(x) = -f(x) \leq 0$. Thus F is a monotone nonincreasing function which is bounded above by the number $\int_a^b f$. Consequently, $\lim\limits_{x \to a+} F(x)$ must exist.

For the second part, if $\int_a^b f$ is divergent, then $\int_a^b g$ must also be divergent since if it were not, the first part would require $\int_a^b f$ to be convergent. (That is, the statements in the conclusion of the theorem are contrapositives of each other.) ∎

For the cases of the other forms of improper integral, we have the following analogues:

Theorem 8-2-4. f and g are continuous functions on $[a, b[$ into the real numbers such that, for all $x \in [a, b[$, $0 \leq f(x) \leq g(x)$. $\lim\limits_{x \to b-} f(x) = +\infty$.

If $\int_a^b g$ is convergent, then $\int_a^b f$ is convergent.

If $\int_a^b f$ is divergent, then $\int_a^b g$ is divergent.

Theorem 8-2-5. a is a fixed number. f and g are continuous functions on $[a, +\infty[$ (or $]-\infty, a]$) into the real numbers such that, for all $x \geq a$, (or $x \leq a$), $0 \leq f(x) \leq g(x)$.

If $\int_a^{+\infty} g \left(\text{or } \int_{-\infty}^a g \right)$ is convergent, then $\int_a^{+\infty} f \left(\text{or } \int_{+\infty}^a f \right)$ is convergent.

If $\int_a^{+\infty} f$ or $\left(\int_{-\infty}^a f \right)$ is divergent, then $\int_a^{+\infty} g \left(\text{or } \int_{-\infty}^a g \right)$ is divergent.

An interesting consequence of Theorem 8-2-2, which provides a test for convergence usually somewhat easier to apply than direct comparison, is given in

Theorem 8-2-6. f and g are continuous functions on $]a, b]$ (or $[a, b[$, $[a, +\infty[$, $]-\infty, a]$) into the non-negative real numbers such that integrals of f and g are improper. If $\lim\limits_{x \to a+} [f(x)/g(x)]$ exists and is a positive number (or $\lim\limits_{x \to b-}$, $\lim\limits_{x \to +\infty}$, $\lim\limits_{x \to -\infty}$), then the improper integral of f is convergent if, and only if, the improper integral of g is convergent.

The proof of this theorem is left to the exercises.

The theorems thus far presented, which give useful tests to be applied to determine the behavior of an improper integral, apply only to functions whose ranges are sets of non-negative real numbers. In order to treat functions whose ranges may include both negative and positive numbers, we have

Theorem 8-2-7. f is a continuous function on $[a, b[$ (or $]a, b]$, $[a, +\infty[$, $]-\infty, a]$) into the real numbers such that the integral of f is improper. If the improper integral of $|f|$ converges, then the improper integral of f converges.

Proof. For all x in the domain of f,

$$-|f(x)| \leq f(x) \leq |f(x)|$$
$$0 \leq f(x) + |f(x)| \leq 2|f(x)|$$

Since the improper integral of $|f|$ exists, so does that of $2|f|$ and, by the appropriate preceding theorem, $f + |f|$ is improperly integrable. The function $-|f|$ is also improperly integrable so that by using the theorem on the limit of the sum of two functions we must have f improperly integrable. ∎

We present one final theorem as an indication of the interplay of the concept of the improper integral with the general ideas involving integration.

Theorem 8-2-8. f is a continuous function on $[a, +\infty[$ into the real numbers. g is a differentiable function on $[a, +\infty[$ into the real numbers with the property that g' is continuous. If $|g'|$ is improperly integrable on $[a, +\infty[$, $\lim\limits_{x \to +\infty} g(x) = 0$, and $\left\{ \left| \int_a^r f \right| \, r \geq a \right\}$ is a bounded set of numbers, then fg is improperly integrable on $[a, +\infty[$.

Proof. For $r \geq a$, fg is continuous on $[a, r]$ and thus is integrable. Integrating by parts yields

$$\int_a^r fg = g(r)F(r) - \int_a^r Fg'$$

where F is the function given by

$$F(x) = \int_a^x f, \qquad x \geq a$$

By hypothesis the range of F is bounded. Since $\lim\limits_{r \to +\infty} g(r) = 0$, we must then have $\lim\limits_{r \to +\infty} g(r)F(r) = 0$.

If M is an upper bound of the range of F, then

$$t \geq a \text{ implies } |F(t)g'(t)| \leq M|g'(t)|$$

By hypothesis, $|g'|$ is improperly integrable so that $M|g'|$ is improperly integrable. By the comparison test, $|Fg'|$ is improperly integrable and, by Theorem 8-2-7, so is Fg'. Thus, by the theorem on the limit of the sum of two functions, fg is improperly integrable. ∎

EXERCISES

1. Give a proof of Theorem 8-2-3 by proving directly that the divergence of the improper integral of f implies the divergence of the improper integral of g.

2. Prove Theorem 8-2-6.

Determine the convergence or divergence of the following improper integrals, finding the values of the convergent ones when possible.

3. $\displaystyle\int_0^1 \frac{dx}{\sqrt{1 - x^2}}$

4. $\displaystyle\int_0^1 \log x \, dx$

5. $\int_0^1 \dfrac{\sin x}{x^2} \, dx$

6. $\int_0^1 \dfrac{\sin x}{x^p} \, dx, \qquad p > 0$

7. $\int_0^2 \dfrac{x^2 + x + 1}{x(x-1)^2} \, dx$

8. $\int_1^{+\infty} \dfrac{\log x}{x^2} \, dx$

9. $\int_1^{+\infty} \dfrac{\log x}{x^p} \, dx, \qquad p > 0$

10. $\int_1^{+\infty} x^p e^{-x} \, dx, \qquad p > 0$

11. $\int_1^{+\infty} \dfrac{dx}{x^2 + 2}$

12. $\int_1^{+\infty} \dfrac{dx}{x^p(1 + x)}, \qquad p > -1$

8-3 Improper Integrals in the n-dimensional Case

In the preceding section we extended the definition of integral for functions on sets of real numbers into the real numbers to include cases in which the domain, the range, or both are unbounded sets. A closer examination of the results obtained will lead us to a similar extension of the definition of integral for functions on n-dimensional sets into the real numbers.

For convenience, we will consider a function f on a set D of real numbers into the non-negative real numbers. We will further assume that f is one-to-one, so that f^{-1} will exist and be a function of $f(D)$ onto D. Again, for convenience, we will assume that D is a set of non-negative real numbers. We let $g = f^{-1}$ and $D^* = f(D)$ so that g is a function on D^* onto D and f is a function on D onto D^*. We have an improper integral for f (and thus also for g) whenever D or D^* (or both) are unbounded.

If D is bounded, but $D^* = f(D)$ is unbounded, then f will be improperly integrable if, and only if, the lower integral $\underline{\int}_D f$ exists. If D is unbounded but D^* is bounded, then g will be improperly integrable if, and only if, the lower integral $\underline{\int}_{D^*} g$ exists.

In the first case, we have

$$\int_{D\delta} f = m_{2,i}(\{(x, y) \mid 0 \le y \le f(x) \quad \text{and} \quad x \in D\})$$

and in the second

$$\int_{D^*} g = m_{2,i}(\{(x, y) \mid 0 \le x \le g(y) \quad \text{and} \quad y \in D^*\})$$

Thus the existence of the improper integral in each of these cases is equivalent to the existence of the two-dimensional inner content of a particular set of points. But, for the functions under consideration, since $g = f^{-1}$, we must have

$$\{(x, y) \mid 0 \le y \le f(x) \text{ and } x \in D\} = \{(x, y) \mid 0 \le x \le g(y) \text{ and } y \in D^*\}$$

These two apparently different sets are in fact the set of points in that portion of the plane bounded by the coordinate axes, the graph of f [or the graph of $x = g(y)$], and certain vertical and horizontal lines determined by D and D^*. In the frequently occurring case in which D and D^* are intervals, these lines are determined by the end points. Here, with both D and D^* consisting of non-negative numbers, the graph might be asymptotic to a vertical line or to a horizontal line in order to have an improper integral situation.

This same two-dimensional set is also involved in the question of the existence of an improper integral for f (or for g) in the cases in which both D and D^* are unbounded. For this case we cannot consider the lower integral of either f or g by using partitions but are forced to use packings of the domain by a finite number of intervals. The existence of the lower integral of f on D and of g on D^* will be equivalent to the existence of

$$m_{2,i}(\{(x, y) \mid 0 \le y \le f(x) \text{ and } x \in D\})$$

If we drop the assumption that f has an inverse, and also the assumption that D consists only of non-negative numbers, but keep the assumption that the range of f consists only of non-negative numbers, then we may generalize this relation between improper integrability of a function on a set of numbers and the existence of the two-dimensional inner area to form

Definition 8-3-1. f is a function on the n-dimensional set D into the non-negative real numbers. D is an unbounded set or $f(D)$ is an unbounded set, or both. f is *improperly integrable on D* means

$$m_{n+1,i}(\{(\mathbf{x}, x_{n+1}) \mid 0 \le x_{n+1} \le f(\mathbf{x}) \text{ and } \mathbf{x} \in D\})$$

exists and this number is the improper integral $\int_D f$.

EXAMPLE. $n = 2$, D is the entire plane, and $f(D) =]0, +\infty[$. f is the function given by

$$f(x, y) = \begin{cases} (x^2 + y^2)^{-3/2}, & 0 < x^2 + y^2 \leq 1 \\ 5, & (x, y) = (0, 0) \\ (x^2 + y^2)^{-3}, & x^2 + y^2 > 1 \end{cases}$$

The $(n + 1 = 3)$-dimensional set we need to examine is that portion of three-dimensional space bounded below by the x-y plane and above the surface consisting of the graphs of

$$z = (x^2 + y^2)^{-3/2}, \qquad 0 < x^2 + y^2 \leq 1$$
$$z = (x^2 + y^2)^{-3}, \qquad x^2 + y^2 > 1$$

and the single point $(0, 0, 5)$.

We now consider a collection of two-dimensional sets given by

$$D_{p,q} = \left\{ (x, y) \,\middle|\, \frac{1}{p} \leq (x^2 + y^2)^{1/2} \leq q \right\}$$

where $p = 2, 3, \ldots$ and $q = 2, 3, \ldots$. For these values of p and q we let $f_{p,q}$ be the restriction of f to $D_{p,q}$. The domain and range of $f_{p,q}$ are closed sets and $f_{p,q}$ is continuous so that $\int_{D_{p,q}} f_{p,q}$ must exist. If f is improperly integrable, then

$$m_{3,i}(\{(x, y, z) \mid 0 \leq f(x, y) \leq z \text{ and } (x, y) \in D\})$$

exists and this number must necessarily be

$$\lim_{q \to +\infty} \lim_{p \to +\infty} \int_{D_{p,q}} f_{p,q}$$

But we have

$$\int_{D_{p,q}} f_{p,q} = \int_0^{2\pi} \int_{1/p}^1 (r^{-3/2}) r \, dr \, d\theta + \int_0^{2\pi} \int_1^q (r^{-3}) r \, dr \, d\theta$$
$$= 2\pi \left[\int_{1/p}^1 r^{-1/2} \, dr + \int_1^q r^{-2} \, dr \right]$$
$$= 2\pi [3 - 2p^{-1/2} - q^{-1}]$$

Therefore, if f is improperly integrable, we must have

$$\int_D f = 6\pi$$

Since any packing of the three-dimensional set given is contained in a set of the form

$$B_{p,q} = \{(x, y, z) \mid 0 \leq z \leq f(x, y) \text{ and } (x, y) \in D_{p,q}\}$$

for sufficiently large p and q, and conversely for each p and q there exists a packing of this set which contains $B_{p,q}$, the existence of limit for this particular collection of integrals implies the existence of the three-dimensional inner content of the set involved and thus the improper integrability of f on D.

The result obtained here for a specific example can be generalized to give

> **Theorem 8-3-1.** f is a function on the n-dimensional set D into the non-negative real numbers. f is improperly integrable on D if, and only if, there exists a sequence $\{D_k \mid k = 1, 2, \ldots\}$ of n-dimensional closed bounded sets such that, for $k = 1, 2, \ldots$,

$$D_k \subseteq D_{k+1}$$
$$D_k \subseteq \bar{D}$$
$$f(D_k) \text{ is bounded}$$

and for which

$$D \subseteq \operatorname{Int}\left(\bigcup_{k=1}^{\infty} D_k\right)$$

for which sequence $\displaystyle\lim_{k \to +\infty} \int_{D_k} f$ exists.

The proof of this theorem is left to the exercises.

It is important to note that, in the case in which the limit of the sequence of integrals exists, this limit is independent of the particular sequence of n-dimensional closed bounded sets used to determine the improper integral. For example, when $n = 2$ and D is the first quadrant of the plane, and f is improperly integrable on D with integral I, we might consider a collection of squares

$$S_p = \{(x, y) \mid 0 \le x \le p \text{ and } 0 \le y \le p\}, \qquad p > 0$$

and also a collection of quadrants of circles

$$C_q = \{(x, y) \mid 0 \le x^2 + y^2 \le q^2 \text{ and } x \ge 0 \text{ and } y \ge 0\}, \qquad q > 0$$

If $I = \displaystyle\lim_{p \to +\infty} \int_{S_p} f$ exists, then for any $\epsilon > 0$ there exists P_ϵ such that $r > s > P_\epsilon$ implies $\displaystyle\int_{S_r - S} f < \epsilon$. But

$$\int_{C_q} f = \int_{S_{q/\sqrt{2}}} f + \int_{C_q - S_{q/\sqrt{2}}} f$$

and

$$\int_{C_q - S_{q/\sqrt{2}}} f < \int_{R_q - R_{q/\sqrt{2}}} f$$

Consequently, $\displaystyle\lim_{q \to +\infty} \int_{C_q} f$ must exist and be the number I. Conversely, it can be shown that if $I = \displaystyle\lim_{q \to +\infty} \int_{C_q} f$, then $\displaystyle\lim_{p \to +\infty} \int_{S_p} f$ must exist and be the number I. This development is left to the exercises.

We conclude with a particularly impressive use of the improper integral in the two-dimensional case.

$\int_0^{+\infty} e^{-t^2}\, dt$ is convergent by comparison with $\int_0^{+\infty} e^{-t}\, dt$. We let $I = \int_0^{+\infty} e^{-t^2}\, dt$. Then all the following improper integrals will be convergent and we have

$$I^2 = \int_0^{+\infty} e^{-x^2}\, dx \int_0^{+\infty} e^{-y^2}\, dy$$

$$= \int_0^{+\infty} \int_0^{+\infty} e^{-(x^2+y^2)}\, dy\, dx$$

$$= \int_0^{\pi/2} \int_0^{+\infty} e^{-r^2} r\, dr\, d\theta$$

$$= \frac{\pi}{4}$$

Thus

$$I = \int_0^{+\infty} e^{-t^2}\, dt = \frac{1}{2}\sqrt{\pi}$$

EXERCISES

1. Prove Theorem 8-3-1.

2. Show that, for the squares and quadrants of circles given above, if $\lim_{q \to +\infty} \int_{C_q} f = I$, then $\lim_{p \to +\infty} \int_{S_p} f$ must exist and be the number I.

Determine the convergence or divergence of $\int_R f$ for the following:

3. $f(x, y) = -\log(x^2 + y^2);$ $\quad R = \{(x, y) \mid 0 < x^2 + y^2 \le 1\}$

4. $f(x, y) = -\dfrac{\log(x^2 + y^2)}{x^2 + y^2};$ $\quad R = \{(x, y) \mid 0 < x^2 + y^2 \le 1\}$

5. $f(x, y) = -\log(x^2 + y^2);$ $\quad R = \{(x, y) \mid x^2 + y^2 \ge 1\}$

6. $f(x, y) = x^2(x^2 + y^2)^{-p/2};$ $\quad R = \{(x, y) \mid x^2 + y^2 \le 1\};$ $\quad p > 0$

7. $f(x, y) = (x^2 + y^4)(x^2 + y^2)^{-p/2};$ $\quad R = \{(x, y) \mid x^2 + y^2 \le 1\};$ $\quad p > 0$

8. $f(x, y) = x^2 y^2 (x^2 + y^2)^{-p/2};$ $\quad R = \{(x, y) \mid x^2 + y^2 \le 1\};$ $\quad p > 0$

9. $f(x, y) = [(x + 1)^2 + y^2]^{-1/2};$ $\quad R = \{(x, y) \mid x^2 + y^2 \le 1\}$

10. $f(x, y) = (1 + x^2 + y^2)^{-1};$ $\quad R = \{(x, y) \mid x \ge 0 \text{ and } y \ge 0\}$

11. $f(x, y, z) = (x^2 + y^2 + z^2)^{-p/2}$; $R = \{(x, y, z) \mid x^2 + y^2 + z^2 \leq 1\}$;
$$p > 0$$

12. $f(x, y, z) = x^2 y^2 z^2 (x^2 + y^2 + z^2)^{-p/2}$;
$$R = \{(x, y, z) \mid x^2 + y^2 + z^2 \leq 1\}; \qquad p > 0$$

13. $f(x, y, z) = (x^2 + y^4 + z^6)(x^2 + y^2 + z^2)^{-p/2}$;
$$R = \{(x, y, z) \mid x^2 + y^2 + z^2 \leq 1\}; \qquad p > 0$$

8-4   Extension to Functions with Negative Values

The definition given for improper integrals of a function on an n-dimensional set applies only to functions whose ranges consist of non-negative numbers. If a function does have negative numbers in its range, but the range is bounded below, then it is easy to extend the definition of improper integral to apply to such functions when the domain is also bounded, but more difficult when this is not the case. Clearly the techniques which were used on functions whose ranges were sets of non-negative real numbers should also be applicable to functions whose ranges are any sets of real numbers, with the expectation that the contribution to the integral made by the portions of the domain whose points are paired with negative numbers should be negative contributions. We give the following chain of definitions:

Definition 8-4-1. f is a function on the n-dimensional set D into the real numbers.
$$D_f^+ = f^{-1}([0, +\infty[)$$
$$D_f^- = f^{-1}(]-\infty, 0])$$
$$f^+ \text{ is the restriction of } f \text{ to } D_f^+$$
$$f^- \text{ is the restriction of } f \text{ to } D_f^-$$

Definition 8-4-2. f is a function on the n-dimensional set D into the real numbers. D is unbounded or $f(D)$ is unbounded, or both. f *is improperly integrable on D* means f^+ is either integrable or improperly integrable on D_f^+ and $-f^-$ is either integrable or improperly integrable on D_f^-. In this case the improper integral is given by

$$\int_D f = \int_{D_f^+} f^+ - \int_{D_f^-} (-f^-)$$

This definition means that we must examine separately the $(n + 1)$-dimensional inner content of the two sets

$$\{(\mathbf{x}, x_{n+1}) \mid 0 \leq x_{n+1} \leq f(\mathbf{x}) \quad \text{and} \quad \mathbf{x} \in D_f^+\}$$

and

$$\{(\mathbf{x}, x_{n+1}) \mid f(\mathbf{x}) \leq x_{n+1} \leq 0 \quad \text{and} \quad \mathbf{x} \in D_f^!\}$$

From the preceding section we see that the inner content will exist if, and only if, we can find a sequence of closed bounded sets which approximate D_f^+ and another sequence of closed bounded sets which approximate D_f^- such that the two sequences of numbers obtained by integrating f over these closed bounded sets will be convergent. We have, more formally,

> **Theorem 8-4-1.** If f is a function on the n-dimensional set D into the real numbers and f is improperly integrable on D, then there exists a sequence $\{D_k \mid k = 1, 2, \ldots\}$ of closed bounded n-dimensional sets such that, for $k = 1, 2, \ldots$,
>
> $$D_k \subseteq D_{k+1}$$
> $$D_k \subseteq \bar{D}$$
> $$f(D_k) \text{ is bounded}$$
>
> and
>
> $$\text{Int } D \subseteq \text{Int} \bigcup_{k=1}^{\infty} D_k$$
>
> for which sequence
>
> $$\int_D f = \lim_{k \to \infty} \int_D f$$

Proof. Since f is improperly integrable on D, then f^+ is integrable or improperly integrable on D_f^+ and f^- is integrable or improperly integrable on D_f^-. From the first there exists a sequence $\{D_k^+ \mid k = 1, 2, \ldots\}$ of closed, bounded, n-dimensional sets with the required properties and another sequence $\{D_k^- \mid k = 1, 2, \ldots\}$, with similar properties, for which

$$\int_{D_f^+} f^+ = \int_{D_f^+} f = \lim_{k \to +\infty} \int_{D_k^+} f$$

and

$$\int_{D_f^-} (-f^-) = \int_{D_f^-} (-f) = \lim_{k \to +\infty} \int_{D_k^-} (-f)$$

Consequently the sequence given by $D_k = D_k^+ \cup D_k^-$ will have the properties required in the conclusion of the theorem. ∎

The converse of this theorem is false. There do exist functions for which both f^+ and f^- are not improperly integrable but for which one can find a sequence of closed bounded sets such that the limit of the sequence of integrals on these sets is convergent. For example, with $n = 1$, let $D = [-1, 1]$ and f be the function given by

$$f(x) = \begin{cases} x^{-1}, & -1 \le x < 0 \quad \text{and} \quad 0 < x \le 1 \\ 0, & x = 0 \end{cases}$$

Here $D_f^+ = [0, 1]$ and $D_f^- = [-1, 0]$. We let $D_k^+ = [k^{-1}, 1]$ and $D_k^- = [-1, -k^{-1}]$ for $k = 2, 3, \ldots$. We then have

$$\int_{D_k^+} f = \int_{1/k}^1 t^{-1} \, dt = \log k$$

Since $\lim_{k \to +\infty} \log k = +\infty$, f^+ is not improperly integrable on $[0, 1]$ and so f cannot be improperly integrable. A similar argument shows that f^- is not improperly integrable. If, however, we chose the sequence of closed bounded sets given by

$$D_k = D_k^+ \cup D_k^- = \left[-1, -\frac{1}{k}\right] \cup \left[\frac{1}{k}, 1\right], \qquad k = 2, 3, \ldots$$

we have

$$\int_{D_k} f = \log k - \log k = 0$$

so that

$$\lim_{k \to +\infty} \int_{D_k} f \text{ exists and is } 0$$

There are many other cases of functions on a set of real numbers into the real numbers for which the improper integral is divergent, but with the property that the sequence of integrals on certain special sets does in fact converge. Two such cases give rise to the concept of the "Cauchy principal value" of a divergent improper integral:

Definition 8-4-3. f is a continuous function on $[a, c[\, \cup \,]c, d]$ into the real numbers for which $\lim_{x \to c} |f(x)| = +\infty$. The improper integral of f on $[a, b]$ is divergent. The *Cauchy principal value* of the improper integral,

$$\text{pr.v.} \int_a^b f \text{ is } \lim_{\epsilon \to 0+} \left[\int_a^{c - \epsilon} f + \int_{c + \epsilon}^b f \right]$$

Definition 8-4-4. f is a continuous function on the set of all real numbers into the real numbers. The improper integral of f on $]-\infty, +\infty[$ is divergent. The *Cauchy principal value* of the improper integral,

$$\text{pr.v.} \int_{-\infty}^{+\infty} f \text{ is } \lim_{B \to +\infty} \int_{-B}^B f$$

We have now given definitions for improper integral for a function whose domain is an (possibly unbounded) n-dimensional set (including $n = 1$) and whose range is a (possibly unbounded) set of real numbers, which real numbers may be negative as well as positive. In the particular case in which the domain is a bounded set, the question of convergence of the improper integral has arisen only when the range is unbounded.

There is no need to concern ourselves here with the case in which the domain and range are both bounded but, for some points (or numbers) in the domain, the function fails to be continuous. In such cases, since the domain and range are bounded, whenever the domain is a quadrable set, both upper and lower integrals must exist and so such a function is either integrable or not in the usual sense. It may be, however, that the determination of the integrability of such a function may be best accomplished by introducing an improper integral. As an example, we consider the function f, on $[0, 1]$, given by

$$f(x) = \begin{cases} \sin x^{-1/3}, & 0 < x \le 1 \\ 5280, & x = 0 \end{cases}$$

Although f is not continuous at 0, the range of f is bounded so that f will be integrable provided

$$\lim_{\epsilon \to 0+} \int_\epsilon^1 f \text{ exists}$$

But

$$\lim_{\epsilon \to 0+} \int_\epsilon^1 \sin x^{-1/3} dx = \lim_{B \to +\infty} 3 \int_1^B u^{-2} \sin u \, du$$

which converges by comparison with the convergent improper integral $\int_1^{+\infty} u^{-2} \, du$.

EXERCISES

1. Find $\int_D f$ when $f(x, y) = xye^{-(x^2+y^2)}$ and D is the entire plane.

2. Determine the convergence or divergence of the improper integral of f, given by $f(x, y) = (x - y)/(x^2 + y^2), f(0, 0) = 0$, on $[-1, 1] \times [-1, 1]$.

3. $D = [-1, 1] \times [-1, 1]$. For which $p > 0$ will f, given by $f(x, y) = xy(x^2 + y^2)^{-p/2}, f(0, 0) = 0$, be improperly integrable on D?

4. Show that if f is a function on $[0, +\infty[$ into the non-negative real numbers and g is a function on $[0, +\infty[$ into the non-negative real numbers and $F(x, y) = f(x)g(y)$, then the improper integrability of f and g imply the improper integrability of F on the first quadrant of the plane.

5. $f(x) = (\sin x)/x$ and $g(y) = e^{-y}$. $F(x, y) = f(x)g(y)$. Consider the collection of squares given, for $p > 0$, by $S_p = [0, p] \times [0, p]$ and the collection of triangles given, for $q > 0$, by $T_q = \{(x, y) \mid 0 \le y \le q - x, 0 \le x \le q\}$. Discuss

$\int_{S_p} f$ and $\int_{T_q} f$ and their limits. Then discuss the improper integrability of F on the first quadrant of the plane.

6. Prove that if f is a function on the n-dimensional set D into the real numbers and $|f|$ is improperly integrable on D, then f is improperly integrable on D.

7. Prove that if f and g are functions on the n-dimensional set D into the real numbers such that, for all $\mathbf{x} \in D$, $|f(\mathbf{x})| \leq |g(\mathbf{x})|$ and g is improperly integrable, then f is improperly integrable. (Recall that f and g may have negative values.)

Find the Cauchy principal values for

8. $\displaystyle\int_{-1}^{1} x^{-(2p+1)} \, dx, \qquad p = 1, 2, \ldots$

9. $\displaystyle\int_{-\infty}^{+\infty} x^{(2p+1)} \, dx, \qquad p = 1, 2, \ldots$

10. For which values of p and q ($p > 0$ and $q > 0$) does $\displaystyle\int_{0}^{1} x^p \sin x^{-q} \, dx$ exist?

8-5   The Divergence Theorem with Improper Integrals

The classical Divergence Theorem concerns a closed bounded three-dimensional set B which is enclosed by a closed bounded trace S for which there exists a continuous function $\mathbf{n}$ on S into V_3 with the property that $\mathbf{n}$ is the unit normal function and any representation of $\mathbf{n}(\mathbf{x})$ with initial point $\mathbf{x} \in S$ is directed away from B. The theorem, as proved in Chapter 4, considered a function $\mathbf{v}$ on B into V_3 with the property that $\mathbf{v}$ was continuous on B and div $\mathbf{v}$ was continuous on S. In this case the conclusion of the theorem is

$$\iint_S \mathbf{v} \cdot \mathbf{n} = \iiint_B \operatorname{div} \mathbf{v}$$

Since both $\mathbf{v}$ and div $\mathbf{v}$ in the classical version of the theorem are continuous functions, they are bounded and both integrals involved are ordinary. We now consider possible extensions of the Divergence Theorem in which one or both of the integrals is improper. Such a situation can occur if B or S are unbounded sets, if $\mathbf{v}(S)$ is an unbounded set, if $\{\operatorname{div} \mathbf{v}\}(B)$ is an unbounded set, or in any combination of these events.

Clearly if S is unbounded, then B is unbounded, since S is a subset of B. It is possible for B to be unbounded with S bounded—for example, simply by taking B to be the complement of a bounded set enclosed by S. If $\mathbf{v}(S)$ is unbounded, then $\{\operatorname{div} \mathbf{v}\}(B)$ will also be unbounded; but again it is possible for $\mathbf{v}(S)$ to be bounded and $\{\operatorname{div} \mathbf{v}\}(B)$ to be unbounded, either by having $\mathbf{v}$

unbounded in the interior of B or by having $\mathbf{v}$ bounded everywhere in B but being nondifferentiable at some point of S. We will consider several of the possible cases, but we will not attempt an exhaustive treatment.

Case 1: *B is unbounded;* $\mathbf{v}$ *and* div $\mathbf{v}$ *are bounded.* Here we are concerned with the behavior of the functions involved in the unbounded portions of B. We will hope that our considerations apply whether or not S is bounded.

Regardless of what set B is, we may readily extend the domain of $\mathbf{v}$ to the entire space by giving it zero value outside B. Then certainly the restriction of this extension to the complement of S has a divergence which agrees with the divergence of $\mathbf{v}$ in the interior of B and has zero value on the complement of B. The fact that the divergence of the extension of $\mathbf{v}$ may not be continuous on S will not by itself affect the existence of any improper integrals.

We now consider the collection of spheres centered at the origin. For $r > 0$ and $m > 0$ we consider the spherical shell

$$\{\mathbf{x} \mid r \leq \|\mathbf{x}\| \leq r + m\}$$

This shell is a bounded set whose surface is the union of two spherical shells, one with radius r and the other with radius $r + m$. The divergence of the extension of $\mathbf{v}$ to the entire space is continuous at all points of this shell except possibly for those points in S. For the moment we will assume that these possible points of discontinuity do not affect the existence of the integral. The function $\mathbf{n}$, given by

$$\mathbf{n}(x, y, z) = (x^2 + y^2 + z^2)^{-1/2}(x\mathbf{i} + y\mathbf{j} + z\mathbf{k})$$

will provide us with a unit normal vector function for the surface of the shell, where we use $\mathbf{n}$ on the outer face and $-\mathbf{n}$ on the inner. The classical Divergence Theorem holds for this spherical shell and we have

$$\iiint\limits_{r \leq \|\mathbf{x}\| \leq r+m} \operatorname{div} \mathbf{v} = \iint\limits_{\|\mathbf{x}\|=r} \mathbf{v} \cdot (-\mathbf{n}) + \iint\limits_{\|\mathbf{x}\|=r+m} \mathbf{v} \cdot \mathbf{n}$$

For improper integrals we need to consider the positive and negative parts of the integrals separately, but here we do not have improper integrals so that

$$\left| \iiint\limits_{r \leq \|\mathbf{x}\| \leq r+m} \operatorname{div} \mathbf{v} \right| \leq 4\pi r^2 \max \{\|\mathbf{v}(\mathbf{x})\| \mid \|\mathbf{x}\| = r\} \\ + 4\pi(r + m)^2 \max \{\|\mathbf{v}(\mathbf{x})\| \mid \|\mathbf{x}\| = r + m\}$$

When S is unbounded, some portion of S must intersect each of these spherical shells so that the three-dimensional integral over the shell will have to be replaced by the integral over the intersection of B with the shell. This will change the right-hand side of the equation above by the addition of a contribution from a portion of S. Further, when S is unbounded, the surface integral mentioned in the Divergence Theorem is improper so that we must consider positive and negative parts of the integrands. In addition, since B is unbounded, we must consider the positive and negative parts of divergence. The task is not really difficult but it is extremely lengthy, so we content ourselves with investigating the case in which S is bounded. In this case, for sufficiently large r, the spherical shell under consideration lies entirely within B.

Even though S is bounded, we are still dealing with an improper integral on B. Thus we must consider separately the two sets $B^+ = \{\mathbf{x} \mid \mathbf{x} \in B$ and $\{\text{div } \mathbf{v}\}(\mathbf{x}) \geq 0\}$ and $B^- = \{\mathbf{x} \mid \mathbf{x} \in B$ and $\{\text{div } \mathbf{v}\}(\mathbf{x}) \leq 0\}$.

We assume that $B^+ \cap B^-$ is the trace of a surface. This is no restriction since any three-dimensional set with positive content for which div $\mathbf{v}$ has zero value will contribute 0 to the integral. We take $\mathbf{n}^*$ as a unit normal vector function for the surface $B^+ \cap B^-$ with representations directed away from B^+. Then we have

$$\iiint_{\substack{r \leq \|\mathbf{x}\| \leq r+m \\ \mathbf{x} \in B^+}} \text{div } \mathbf{v} = \iint_{\substack{\|\mathbf{x}\| = r \\ \mathbf{x} \in B^+}} \mathbf{v} \cdot (-\mathbf{n}) + \iint_{\substack{\|\mathbf{x}\| = r+m \\ \mathbf{x} \in B^+}} \mathbf{v} \cdot \mathbf{n} + \iint_{\substack{r \leq \|\mathbf{x}\| \leq r+m \\ \mathbf{x} \in B^+ \cap B^-}} \mathbf{v} \cdot \mathbf{n}^*$$

We have a similar equation for B^-, with $\mathbf{n}^*$ replaced by its opposite. Calling the spherical shell $A_{r,m}$, we have

$$\left| \iiint_{A_{r,m} \cap B^+} \text{div } \mathbf{v} \right| \leq 4\pi r^2 \max \{\|\mathbf{v}(\mathbf{x})\| \mid \|\mathbf{x}\| = r\}$$
$$+ 4\pi (r + m)^2 \max \{\|\mathbf{v}(\mathbf{x})\| \mid \|\mathbf{x}\| = r + m\}$$
$$+ A(A_{r,m} \cap B^+ \cap B^-) \max \{\|\mathbf{v}(\mathbf{x})\| \mid \mathbf{x} \in A_{r,m}\}$$

with a similar inequality for B^-.

In this way we see that the existence of the improper integral $\iiint_B \text{div } \mathbf{v}$

depends on the behavior of $\|\mathbf{x}\|^2 \|\mathbf{v}(\mathbf{x})\|$ for $\mathbf{x}$ outside some large sphere centered at the origin and also on the form of the trace which is the graph of $\{\text{div } \mathbf{v}\}(\mathbf{x}) = 0$. The inequalities we have derived form the basis for a proof of

Theorem 8-5-1. B is an unbounded three-dimensional set. The bounded three-dimensional surface is the boundary of B. $\mathbf{v}$ is a bounded, continuous function on B into $\mathbf{V}_3$ such that div $\mathbf{v}$ is continuous and bounded on B. There exists a unit normal vector function $\mathbf{n}$ for S with representations directed away from B. If $\lim\limits_{\|\mathbf{x}\| \to +\infty} \|\mathbf{x}\|^2 \|\mathbf{v}(\mathbf{x})\| = 0$ and, for $r > 0$,

$$A(\{\mathbf{x} \mid \|\mathbf{x}\| \leq r \text{ and } \{\text{div } \mathbf{v}\}(\mathbf{x}) = 0\}) \leq Kr^2$$

then

$$\iiint_B \text{div } \mathbf{v} = \iint_S \mathbf{v} \cdot \mathbf{n}$$

Case 2: *B and S are bounded,* $\mathbf{v}(S)$ *is bounded,* $\text{div } \mathbf{v}(B)$ *is unbounded.* In this case there are two typical subcases for each of which there is exactly one point **a** of *B* such that

$$\lim_{\mathbf{x} \to \mathbf{a}} |\{\text{div } \mathbf{v}\}(\mathbf{x})| = +\infty$$

One case occurs when $\mathbf{a} \in S$ and the other when **a** is an interior point of *B*.

We consider the subcase in which **a** is an interior point of *B*. Then there exists $\delta > 0$ such that

$$\{\mathbf{x} \mid \|\mathbf{x} - \mathbf{a}\| < \delta\}$$

lies entirely within the interior of *B*. For $0 < t < 1$ we consider

$$B_t = B - \{\mathbf{x} \mid \|\mathbf{x} - \mathbf{a}\| < t\delta\}$$

The Divergence Theorem applies to B_t and we have

$$\iiint_{B_t} \text{div } \mathbf{v} = \iint_S \mathbf{v} \cdot \mathbf{n} + \iint_{\|\mathbf{x}-\mathbf{a}\|=t\delta} \mathbf{v} \cdot \mathbf{n}^*$$

where $\mathbf{n}^*$ is the obvious unit normal vector function to the sphere centered at **a** of radius $t\delta$, which function has representations directed toward **a**.

Although div **v** is unbounded in neighborhoods of **a**, **v** is not, so that the second term on the right in the equation above becomes of interest. From the definition of divergence, there is a function g on $]0, 1]$ into the real numbers such that

$$\iint_{\|\mathbf{x}-\mathbf{a}\|=r} \mathbf{v} \cdot \mathbf{n}^* = -\pi r^2[\text{div } \mathbf{v}(\mathbf{a} + r\mathbf{e}) + g(t)]$$

where **e** is some fixed vector of unit length and $\lim\limits_{t \to 0+} g(t) = 0$. This suggests that

$$\lim_{\mathbf{x} \to \mathbf{a}} \|\mathbf{x} - \mathbf{a}\|^2 \{\text{div } \mathbf{v}\}(\mathbf{x}) = 0$$

will give a condition sufficient for the Divergence Theorem to hold. The exact statement and the proof are left to the exercises.

In case **a** is a point of *S*, a similar argument holds, where we surround **a** by the intersection of *B* with small spheres.

Other Cases: When *B* and *S* are unbounded or when *B* is unbounded and *S* is bounded and, further, div **v** is bounded at an interior point of *B* while **v** is bounded on S, we are essentially treating the preceding cases together. When div $\mathbf{v}$ becomes unbounded on unbounded portions of B, then we need to examine closely the exact manner of the unboundedness.

EXERCISES

1. Using the outline provided, give a detailed proof of Theorem 8-5-1.

2. Give a statement of a form of the Divergence Theorem for the cases in which B and S are bounded, $\mathbf{v}$ is bounded, but $\lim\limits_{\mathbf{x}\to\mathbf{a}} |\{\text{div } \mathbf{v}\}(\mathbf{x})| = +\infty$ where $\mathbf{a}$ is an interior point of B. Then prove the theorem, using the outline provided.

For the equation $\mathbf{v}(x, y, z) = (x^2 + y^2 + z^2)^{-p/2}(x\mathbf{i} + y\mathbf{j} + z\mathbf{k})$,

3. Find div $\mathbf{v}$.

4. When $B = \{(x, y, z) \mid x^2 + y^2 + z^2 \geq 1\}$, find the values of p for which $\iiint\limits_{B}$ div $\mathbf{v}$ is convergent. *Hint:* Use spherical coordinates.

5. When $S = \{(x, y, z) \mid x^2 + y^2 + z^2 = 1\}$ and $\mathbf{n}$ is a unit normal vector function for S with representations directed toward the origin, find

$$\iint\limits_{S} \mathbf{v} \cdot \mathbf{n}$$

6. For which values of p does the Divergence Theorem hold for B and S as in Exercises 4 and 5?

7. When $B = \{(x, y, z) \mid x^2 + y^2 + z^2 \leq 1\}$, find the values of p for which $\iiint\limits_{B}$ div $\mathbf{v}$ is convergent.

8. When $S = \{(x, y, z) \mid x^2 + y^2 + z^2 = 1\}$ and $\mathbf{n}$ is a unit normal vector function for S with representations directed away from the origin, find

$$\iint\limits_{S} \mathbf{v} \cdot \mathbf{n}$$

9. For which values of p does the Divergence Theorem hold for B and S as in Exercises 7 and 8?

8-6   Stokes' Theorem with Improper Integrals

We now examine the possibility of extending Stokes' Theorem to cover the situation in which one or both of the integrals involved are improper. For this we need the trace of a surface S bounded by the oriented path γ and a function $\mathbf{v}$ on S into $\mathbf{V_3}$ for which

$$\int_\gamma \mathbf{v} \cdot \mathbf{T} = \iint_S [\text{curl } \mathbf{v}] \cdot \mathbf{n}$$

These integrals become improper if the path γ is unbounded, in which case the trace S is necessarily unbounded, or if γ is bounded and S is unbounded or if the set of numbers $\{\mathbf{v} \cdot \mathbf{T}\}(\gamma)$ or $\{[\text{curl } \mathbf{v}] \cdot \mathbf{n}\}(S)$ are unbounded or with any combination of these circumstances.

We begin by considering the case in which γ is a bounded path, S is an unbounded trace, and both $\{\mathbf{v} \cdot \mathbf{T}\}(\gamma)$ and $\{[\text{curl } \mathbf{v}] \cdot \mathbf{n}\}(S)$ are bounded. We need to have some way of examining the unbounded portion of S and since we are dealing with an improper integral, we must consider separately those portions of S for which $[\text{curl } \mathbf{v}] \cdot \mathbf{n}$ has positive and negative values. For definiteness, we take

$$S^+ = \{\mathbf{x} \mid \mathbf{x} \in S \text{ and } \{[\text{curl } \mathbf{v}] \cdot \mathbf{n}\}(\mathbf{x}) \geq 0\}$$

and

$$S^- = \{\mathbf{x} \mid \mathbf{x} \in S \text{ and } \{[\text{curl } \mathbf{v}] \cdot \mathbf{n}\}(\mathbf{x}) \leq 0\}$$

In order that we may use the usual Stokes' Theorem, we must consider the boundary of S^+ and S^-. For these boundaries to be curves, we will require $\mathbf{v}$ to have the property that

$$\{\mathbf{x} \mid \mathbf{x} \in S \text{ and } \{[\text{curl } \mathbf{v}] \cdot \mathbf{n}\}(\mathbf{x}) = 0\}$$

is an orientable curve.

We now consider the collection of spheres centered at the origin given, for $t > 0$, by

$$B_t = \{\mathbf{x} \mid \|\mathbf{x}\| \leq t\}$$

and we let S_t be the surface of B_t.

The boundedness of the curve γ implies the existence of a positive number R such that, for $t \geq R$, $\gamma \subseteq B_t$. We then consider B_t and S_t for values of t which exceed R.

Again, in order to use the ordinary Stokes' Theorem, we will require that the boundary of $B_t \cap S$ be composed of curves so we assume that the given surface S has the property that, for all $t \geq R$, $S \cap S_t$ is an orientable curve.

We ignore the relative orientations of the normal to the surface and tangent to the curve in using the ordinary Stokes' Theorem and arrive at the conclusion that, for $t > R$,

$$\pm \iint_{S^+ \cap B} [\text{curl } \mathbf{v}] \cdot \mathbf{n} = \int_\gamma \mathbf{v} \cdot \mathbf{T} \pm \int_{S^+ \cap S^- \cap B_t} \mathbf{v} \cdot \mathbf{T} \pm \int_{S^+ \cap S_t} \mathbf{v} \cdot \mathbf{T}$$

Since we are concerned with limits as t increases, the middle term on the right may present the problem of an improper line integral, since $S^+ \cap S^-$ may be an unbounded curve. This would require us to consider separately the portions of the curve $S^+ \cap S^-$ for which $\mathbf{v} \cdot \mathbf{T}$ is positive and negative. One way to cope with this problem is to assume that $\mathbf{v}$ has the property that $S^+ \cap S^-$ is a bounded curve. Under that assumption, we may take t sufficiently large so that the middle term is not present.

With or without the middle term, we can investigate convergence for the left side by considering portions of spherical shells which lie on one side of S. For $r \geq R$ and $m > 0$, an assumption that $\mathbf{v}$ and curl $\mathbf{v}$ may be extended to bounded functions whose domain is the entire space and an application of the Divergence Theorem yield

$$\iint_{S^+ \cap B_t} [\text{curl } \mathbf{v}] \cdot \mathbf{n} \pm \iint_{\substack{\|x\|=r+m \\ x\,\text{"below"}\,S^+}} [\text{curl } \mathbf{v}] \cdot \mathbf{n} \pm \iint_{\substack{\|x\|=r \\ x\,\text{"below"}\,S^+}} [\text{curl } \mathbf{v}] \cdot \mathbf{n}$$

$$= \iiint_{\substack{B_{r+m}-B_r \\ x\,\text{"below"}\,S^+}} \text{div curl } \mathbf{v} = 0$$

Thus

$$\iint_{S^+ \cap B_t} [\text{curl } \mathbf{v}] \cdot \mathbf{n} = \iint_{\substack{\|x\|=r+m \\ x\,\text{"below"}\,S^+}} [\text{curl } \mathbf{v}] \cdot \mathbf{n} - \iint_{\substack{\|x\|=r \\ x\,\text{"below"}\,S^+}} [\text{curl } \mathbf{v}] \cdot \mathbf{n}$$

But on these spherical shells we may make the estimates

$$\left| \iint_{\substack{\|x\|=t \\ x\,\text{"below"}\,S^+}} [\text{curl } \mathbf{v}] \cdot \mathbf{n} \right| \leq 4\pi t^2 \max \{ \|\{[\text{curl } \mathbf{v}] \cdot \mathbf{n}\}(x)\| \mid x \in S_t \}$$

$$\leq 4\pi \max \{ \|x\|^2 \, \|\{\text{curl } \mathbf{v}\}(x)\| \mid \|x\| = t \}$$

Consequently the hypothesis that

$$\lim_{\|x\| \to +\infty} \|x\|^2 \, \|\{\text{curl } \mathbf{v}\}(x)\| = 0$$

will imply the existence of the improper integral

$$\iint_{S^+} [\text{curl } \mathbf{v}] \cdot \mathbf{n}$$

Under the assumption that the path $S^+ \cap S^-$ is bounded, this same hypothesis will then also assure the existence of

$$\lim_{\to +\infty} \int_{S^+ \cap S} \mathbf{v} \cdot \mathbf{T}$$

A similar argument holds for S^- and the boundedness assumption on $S^+ \cap S^-$ means that one of $S^+ \cap S_t$ and $S^- \cap S_t$ will be empty. Thus in order for Stokes' Theorem to be valid here, we need not only the existence of the limit of line integrals above but also that this limit be the number 0. One of the factors affecting this limit will be the behavior of the length of $S \cap S_t$ as t increases.

Since we may use the estimate

$$\left| \int_{S^+ \cap S_t} \mathbf{v} \cdot \mathbf{T} \right| \leq L(S \cap S_t) \max \{ \|\mathbf{v}(\mathbf{x})\| \mid \|\mathbf{x}\| = t \}$$

we would hope that the curve $S \cap S_t$, which lies on the surface of the sphere S_t, would have a length not too different from the length of a great circle of this sphere. One way to assure such behavior is to assume that, for $t \geq r$,

$$L(S \cap S_t) \leq Mt$$

where M is some constant. We would then have

$$\left| \int_{S^+ \cap S_t} \mathbf{v} \cdot \mathbf{T} \right| \leq Mt \max \{ \|\mathbf{v}(\mathbf{x})\| \mid \|\mathbf{x}\| = t \}$$

and we might take as a final hypothesis

$$\lim_{\|\mathbf{x}\| \to +\infty} \|\mathbf{x}\| \|\mathbf{v}(\mathbf{x})\| = 0$$

We have then outlined a proof of a version of Stokes' Theorem in which S is unbounded but $S^+ \cap S^-$ is bounded. The exact statement of the theorem is left to the exercises.

In case $S^+ \cap S^-$ is not a bounded path, we have to worry about the existence of

$$\lim_{t \to +\infty} \int_{S^+ \cap S^- \cap B_t} \mathbf{v} \cdot \mathbf{T}$$

The term of this form in the integral for S^+ will be the line integral over $S^+ \cap S^-$ with one orientation, and the term in the integral for S^- will be the integral with opposite orientation. In order for Stokes' Theorem to apply, it will be enough to assume that this last limit exists. Then all improper integrals will converge and, in the combining of the positive and negative parts, the contributions of $S^+ \cap S^-$ will add to 0. The statement of the theorem in this case is left to the exercises.

Finally we turn to the case in which γ and S are both bounded. We will examine one situation in which improper integrals appear because of the misbehavior of curl $\mathbf{v}$ at a single point $\mathbf{a} \in S$ for which $\mathbf{a} \notin \gamma$. That is, we have

$$\lim_{\mathbf{x} \to \mathbf{a}} |\{[\operatorname{curl} \mathbf{v}] \cdot \mathbf{n}\}(\mathbf{x})| = +\infty$$

Once again we are dealing with an improper surface integral and we must consider separately the subsurfaces S^+ and S^-. The assumption that $\mathbf{a} \in S$ but $\mathbf{a} \notin \gamma$ means that for t sufficiently small

$$\iint_{\substack{S^+ \\ \|\mathbf{x}-\mathbf{a}\| \geq t}} [\text{curl } \mathbf{v}] \cdot \mathbf{n} = \int_{\gamma \cap S^+} \mathbf{v} \cdot \mathbf{T} \pm \int_{S^+ \cap S^-} \mathbf{v} \cdot \mathbf{T} \pm \int_{C_t} \mathbf{v} \cdot \mathbf{T}$$

where $C_t = S \cap \{\mathbf{x} \mid \|\mathbf{x} - \mathbf{a}\| = t\}$ and

$$\iint_{S^-} [\text{curl } \mathbf{v}] \cdot \mathbf{n} = \int_{\gamma \cap S^-} \mathbf{v} \cdot \mathbf{T} \pm \int_{S^+ \cap S^-} \mathbf{v} \cdot \mathbf{T}$$

Attempting to formulate a theorem by hypotheses affecting the surface integral on the left of the first equation would still leave the need for further hypotheses on the line integral around the curve C_t. Such hypotheses need to consider the length of this curve. Again we would hope to encounter surfaces such that the intersection with the surface of a sphere would be a curve with length comparable to the radius of the sphere. If there is a constant M such that, for $0 < t < 1$,

$$L(C_t) \leq tM$$

and

$$\lim_{\mathbf{x} \to \mathbf{a}} \|\mathbf{x} - \mathbf{a}\| \, \|\mathbf{v}(\mathbf{x})\| = 0$$

then the improper line integral will exist and we will have an extension of Stokes' Theorem. Again the exact statement is left to the exercises.

EXERCISES

1. Give an exact statement of the version of Stokes' Theorem formulated for the case in which S is unbounded but $S^+ \cap S^-$ is bounded, then prove the theorem, using the outline given.

2. Give an exact statement of the version of Stokes' Theorem for the case in which S is unbounded and $S^+ \cap S^-$ is also unbounded, then prove the theorem.

3. Give an exact statement of the version of Stokes' Theorem for the case in which S is bounded but curl $\mathbf{v}$ misbehaves at a single point $\mathbf{a} \in S$, then prove the theorem.

$S = \{(x, y, 1 - x^2 - y^2) \mid x^2 + y^2 \geq 1\}$
$\gamma = \{(\cos\theta, \sin\theta, 0) \mid 0 \leq \theta \leq 2\pi\}$
$\mathbf{v}(x, y, z) = (x^2 + y^2 + z^2)^{-p/2}(\mathbf{i} + \mathbf{j} + \mathbf{k})$

4. Find $\displaystyle\int_\gamma \mathbf{v} \cdot \mathbf{T}$, where γ is oriented positively.

5. Find curl **v**.

6. Find a unit normal vector function **n** for S with representations directed toward the z axis.

7. Determine S^+ and S^-.

8. Follow through the steps in the section for the various limits involved for this particular function on this surface.

9. For which values of p does Stokes' Theorem apply here?

10. Now consider $S = \{(x, y, 1 - x^2 - y^2) \mid x^2 + y^2 \leq 1\}$ with γ and **v** as before. For what values of p does Stokes' Theorem apply here?

SERIES 9

9-1 Taylor's Theorem

Of the mathematical entities which occur in the classical vector theorems we have examined the integral, limits, derivatives and partial derivatives, and improper integrals. We turn now to an examination of the kinds of functions to which these ideas are applicable. We have already available a seemingly large stock of functions: algebraic, trigonometric, logarithmic, the inverses of these or of their restrictions, and combinations of all these by composition. The problem of extending this stock is the topic of investigation for this chapter. We begin with an extension of the mean value theorem:

Theorem 9-1-1(Taylor's Theorem). If f is a function into the real numbers such that, for the positive integer n, the closed interval $[a,b]$ is in the domain of $f^{(n+1)}$—the $(n+1)$th derivative of f—then there exists $c \in \,]a, b[$ such that

$$f(b) - f(a) = \sum_{k=1}^{n} \frac{(b-a)^k}{k!} f^{(k)}(a) + \frac{(b-a)^{n+1}}{(n+1)!} f^{(n+1)}(c)$$

Proof. We create a new function F into the real numbers by

$$F(x) = f(b) - f(x) - \sum_{k=1}^{n} \frac{(b-x)^k}{k!} f^{(k)}(x)$$

By hypothesis the interval $[a, b]$ is included in the domain of F' and thus for $x \in [a, b]$ we have

$$F'(x) = -f'(x) + \sum_{k=1}^{n} \frac{(b-x)^{k-1}}{(k-1)!} f^{(k)}(x) - \sum_{k=1}^{n} \frac{(b-x)^k}{k!} f^{(k+1)}(x)$$

$$= -\frac{(b-x)^n}{n!} f^{(n+1)}(x)$$

We now create a second function g into the real numbers by

$$g(x) = F(x) - \frac{(b-x)^{n+1}}{(b-a)^{n+1}} F(a)$$

Then $[a, b]$ is included in the domain of g' and for $x \in [a, b]$ we have

$$g'(x) = F'(x) + \frac{(n+1)(b-x)^n}{(b-a)^{n+1}} F(a)$$

$$= \frac{(n+1)(b-x)^n}{(b-a)^{n+1}} F(a) - \frac{(b-a)^{n+1}}{(n+1)!} f^{(n+1)}(x)$$

We note that $g(a) = 0$ and $g(b) = F(b) = 0$. Thus, by the mean value theorem, there exists a number $c \in]a, b[$ such that $g'(c) = 0$. This means

$$F(a) = \frac{(b-a)^{n+1}}{(n+1)!} f^{(n+1)}(c)$$

$$f(b) = f(a) + \sum_{k=1}^{n} \frac{(b-a)^k}{k!} f^{(k)}(a) + \frac{(b-a)^{n+1}}{(n+1)!} f^{(n+1)}(c) \qquad \blacksquare$$

An immediate corollary, which is an extremely useful form of the theorem, is

> **Theorem 9-1-2.** f is a function into the real numbers such that, for the positive integer n, the closed interval $[a, b]$ is included in the domain of $f^{(n+1)}$. $c \in]a, b]$. There exists $\delta > 0$ such that for any h with $|h| < \delta$ there exists θ, $0 < \theta < 1$, such that
>
> $$f(c + h) = f(c) + \sum_{k=1}^{n} \frac{f^{(k)}(c)}{k!} h^k + \frac{h^{n+1}}{(n+1)!} f^{(n+1)}(c + \theta h)$$

In order to have a reasonably concise notation in extending this theorem to a function whose domain is an n-dimensional set, we introduce

> **Definition 9-1-1.** F is a function on the n-dimensional set D into the real numbers. For every positive integer k, $F^{(k)}$ is the function on $D \times V_n$ into the real numbers given by
>
> $$F^{(k)}(\mathbf{x}, \mathbf{t}) = \left\{ \left[t_1 \frac{\partial}{\partial x_1} + \cdots + t_n \frac{\partial}{\partial x_n} \right]^k F \right\}(\mathbf{x})$$

EXAMPLE. For $n = 2$ and $k = 3$ we have

$$F^{(3)}(\mathbf{x}, \mathbf{t}) = F^{(3)}(x_1, x_2, t_1, t_2)$$

$$= \left\{ \left[t_1 \frac{\partial}{\partial x_1} + t_2 \frac{\partial}{\partial x_2} \right]^3 \right\} F(x_1, x_2)$$

$$= \left\{ t_1^3 \frac{\partial^3}{\partial x_1^3} + 3t_1^2 t_2 \frac{\partial^3}{\partial x_1^2 \, \partial x_2} \right.$$

$$\left. + 3t_1 t_2^2 \frac{\partial^3}{\partial x_1 \partial x_2^2} + t_2^3 \frac{\partial^3}{\partial x_2^3} \right\} F(x_1, x_2)$$

$$= t_1^3 F_{111}(x_1, x_2) + 3t_1^2 t_2 F_{112}(x_1, x_2)$$

$$+ 3t_1 t_2^2 F_{122}(x_1, x_2) + t_2^3 F_{222}(x_1, x_2)$$

With this notation we have, as an immediate consequence of Taylor's Theorem,

Theorem 9-1-3. F is a function on the n-dimensional set D into the real numbers with the property that F and all its partial derivatives of orders $1, 2, \ldots, m + 1$ are continuous. $\{\mathbf{a} + t\mathbf{h} \mid 0 \leq t \leq 1\} \subseteq D$. Then there exists θ, $0 < \theta < 1$, such that

$$F(\mathbf{a} + \mathbf{h}) = F(\mathbf{a}) + \sum_{k=1}^{m} \frac{1}{k!} F^{(k)}(\mathbf{a}, \mathbf{h}) + \frac{1}{(m + 1)!} F^{(m+1)}(\mathbf{a} + \theta\mathbf{h}, \mathbf{h})$$

The proof is left to the exercises.

We now discuss an example of the kind of thing we are going to consider. The exponential function given by

$$f(x) = e^x$$

has derivatives of all orders and, for $k = 1, 2, \ldots$,

$$f^{(k)}(x) = e^x$$

Considering the interval $[0, 1]$, Taylor's Theorem says that, for every $x \in [0, 1]$ and any positive integer n, there exists $t_{x,n} \in {]}0, x{[}$ such that

$$e^x = 1 + \sum_{k=1}^{n} \frac{x^k}{k!} + \frac{x^{n+1}}{(n + 1)!} e^{t_{x,n}}$$

But $x \in [0, 1]$ and $t_{x,n} \in {]}0, x{[}$ implies that, for all $x \in [0, 1]$ and for $n = 1, 2, \ldots$,

$$\left| \frac{x^{n+1}}{(n + 1)!} e^{t_{x,n}} \right| < \frac{e}{(n + 1)!}$$

Consequently, for any $\epsilon > 0$ there exists N_ϵ such that $n > N_\epsilon$ implies that for all $x \in [0, 1]$

$$\left| e^x - \sum_{k=0}^{n} \frac{x^k}{k!} \right| < \epsilon$$

(Recall that, for convenience, $0! = 1$.) Thus if we construct a sequence of functions $\{s_n \mid n = 1, 2, \ldots\}$ by

$$s_n(x) = \sum_{k=0}^{n} \frac{x^k}{k!}$$

we have $\lim_{n \to +\infty} s_n = f$ uniformly on $[0, 1]$.

We will spend the remainder of this chapter investigating sequences of functions, each of which is the sum of terms from some given sequence of functions, and we hope that there are such uniform convergence properties as allow us to differentiate and integrate.

EXERCISES

1. Prove Theorem 9-1-3.

Apply Taylor's Theorem to the following functions on the given intervals, for the given value of n, and find an estimate for the "remainder" term.

2. $\sin x$; $[-1, 1]$; $n = 3$

3. $\cos x$; $[-1, 1]$; $n = 3$

4. $\log x$; $[-\frac{1}{2}, \frac{3}{2}]$; $n = 4$

5. x; $[\frac{1}{2}, \frac{3}{2}]$; $n = 3$

6. $\sin^2 x$; $[-1, 1]$; $n = 3$

Apply the extension of Taylor's Theorem to the following functions in regard to $(0, 0)$ for $n = 2$, and find an estimate for the "remainder" term.

7. $\sin (x + y)$

8. $\log (1 + x + y)$

9. $(1 + x + y)^3$

Use Taylor's Theorem to find an estimate to each of the following integrals, and make this estimate accurate to two decimal places.

10. $\displaystyle\int_0^1 e^{-x^2} \, dx$

11. $\displaystyle\int_0^1 \frac{\sin x}{x} \, dx$

9-2 Sequence of Real Numbers

We recall from Chapter 6 that a sequence is a function whose domain is the set of all integers exceeding some fixed integer. Here we will restrict ourselves to sequences whose ranges are sets of real numbers. In Chapter 6 we were concerned with convergent sequences, that is, those which have a limit. Here we will investigate tools for treating sequences which do not necessarily converge.

We begin with

> **Definition 9-2-1.** The sequence given by $\{b_k \mid k = 1, 2, \ldots\}$ is a *subsequence* of the sequence given by $\{a_k \mid k = 1, 2, \ldots\}$ provided there exists a sequence given by $\{n_k \mid k = 1, 2, \ldots\}$ whose range is a set of integers with the properties that, for $k = 1, 2, \ldots$,
>
> $$n_k < n_{k+1}$$
>
> and
>
> $$b_k = a_{n_k}$$

In this definition we require more than merely that the set $\{a_{n_k} \mid k = 1, 2, \ldots\}$ be a subset of $\{a_n \mid n = 1, 2, \ldots\}$. In fact, we need $\{a_{n_k} \mid k = 1, 2, \ldots\}$ as the range of the composite function $f(g)$, where f is given by $f(n) = a_n$ and g is given by $g(k) = n_k$, and we also require g to be a strictly increasing function.

While a sequence may not be convergent, it is entirely possible that one or more of its subsequences will converge. This situation is given a name in

> **Definition 9-2-2.** The real number p is said to be a *limit point* of the sequence of real numbers given by $\{a_n \mid n = 1, 2, \ldots\}$ provided there exists a subsequence, given by $\{a_{n_k} \mid k = 1, 2, \ldots\}$, of the given sequence, for which
>
> $$\lim_{k \to \infty} a_{n_k} = p$$

An immediate consequence of the definition of limit for a sequence and the definition of subsequence is

> **Theorem 9-2-1.** The real number p is a limit point of the sequence of real numbers given by $\{a_n \mid n = 1, 2, \ldots\}$ if, and only if, for every $\epsilon > 0$ and for every integer m there exists an integer $n_m > m$ such that
>
> $$|a_{n_m} - p| < \epsilon$$

Proof

Case 1: Assume that p is a limit point of the sequence given by $\{a_n \mid n = 1, 2, \ldots\}$.

Then there exists a subsequence of the given sequence, which subsequence is given by $\{a_{n_k} \mid k = 1, 2, \ldots\}$, such that $\lim_{k \to \infty} a_{n_k} = p$. From the definition of limit we have, for any $\epsilon > 0$, the existence of an integer K_ϵ such that

$$k > K_\epsilon \text{ implies } |a_{n_k} - p| < \epsilon$$

The definition of subsequence requires that, for $k = 1, 2, \ldots, n_k \geq k$ so we can conclude that for every $\epsilon > 0$ and for every integer m there exists an integer $n_m > m$; namely, $n = n_{m+1}$, such that $|a_n - p| < \epsilon$.

Case 2: Conversely, we assume that for every integer n there exists an integer $n > m$ such that $|a_n - p| < \epsilon$.

Then for $m = 1$ and $\epsilon = 1$ there exists $n_1 > 1$ such that $|a_{n_1} - p| < 1$. For $n = n_1$ and $\epsilon = \frac{1}{2}$ there exists $n_2 > n_1$ such that $|a_{n_2} - p| < \frac{1}{2}$. We continue in this manner, finding the integers $n_3, n_4, \ldots, n_{k-1}$. For $n = n_{k-1}$ there exists $n_k > n_{k-1}$ such that $|a_{n_k} - p| < 1/k$.

We have thus constructed a sequence given by the set of integers $\{n_k \mid k = 1, 2, \ldots\}$, for which $\lim_{k \to \infty} a_{n_k} = p$. Thus p is a limit point of the original sequence. ∎

Clearly a convergent sequence has one and only one limit point, and this limit point is the limit. The converse of this statement is invalid unless we make provision for unbounded sequences. The result, of course, is that a bounded sequence is convergent if, and only if, it has exactly one limit point.

A sequence of real numbers is said to be properly divergent if either $\lim_{n \to \infty} a_n = +\infty$ or $\lim_{n \to \infty} a_n = -\infty$, the definitions of these concepts being rather obvious. When a divergent sequence is not properly divergent, then it has no limit points or more than one limit point, or is unbounded and has one or more limit points. Our concern here is with sequences which have more than one limit point and even with ones which have infinitely many limit points. Our first result is

Theorem 9-2-2. For $k = 1, 2, \ldots$, the real number p_k is a limit point of the sequence of real numbers given by $\{a_n \mid n = 1, 2, \ldots\}$. If q is a limit point of the sequence given by $\{p_k \mid k = 1, 2, \ldots\}$, then q is a limit point of the sequence given by $\{a_n \mid n = 1, 2, \ldots\}$.

Proof. Pick $\epsilon > 0$. For each integer m there exists an integer $k > m$ such that $|p_k - q| < \epsilon/2$.

Since p_k is a limit point of the sequence given by $\{a_n \mid n = 1, 2, \ldots\}$, there exists $n > k$ such that $|p_k - a_n| < \epsilon/2$.

Thus there exists $n > m$ such that $|a_n - q| < \epsilon$, so that q is a limit point of the sequence given by $\{a_n \mid n = 1, 2, \ldots\}$.   ∎

In order to have a way of discussing nonconvergent sequences, we introduce the following:

Definition 9-2-3. For the sequence of real numbers given by $\{a_n \mid n = 1, 2, \ldots\}$, the *limit superior*, written $\overline{\lim_n} \, a_n$, and the *limit inferior*, written $\underline{\lim_n} \, a_n$, are defined as follows:

(i) If $\{a_n \mid n = 1, 2, \ldots\}$ is not bounded above, $\overline{\lim_n} \, a_n = +\infty$.

(ii) If $\{a_n \mid n = 1, 2, \ldots\}$ is not bounded below, $\underline{\lim_n} \, a_n = -\infty$.

(iii) If $\{a_n \mid n = 1, 2, \ldots\}$ is bounded above, $\overline{\lim_n} \, a_n = \max \{p \mid p$ is a limit point of the sequence$\}$.

(iv) If $\{a_n \mid n = 1, 2, \ldots\}$ is bounded below, $\underline{\lim_n} \, a_n = \min \{p \mid p$ is a limit point of the sequence$\}$.

Under this definition the limit superior is the largest limit point and the limit inferior is the smallest limit point, with appropriate provision being made for unbounded sequences. One immediate consequence of the definition is

Theorem 9-2-3. If the sequence of real numbers given by $\{a_n \mid n = 1, 2, \ldots\}$ is bounded, then

$$\underline{\lim_n} \, (-a_n) = -\overline{\lim_n} \, a_n$$

and

$$\overline{\lim_n} \, (-a_n) = -\underline{\lim_n} \, a_n$$

The proof is left to the exercises.
A somewhat more revealing theorem is

Theorem 9-2-4. $A = \overline{\lim_n} \, a_n$ if, and only if, for every $\epsilon > 0$ there exists N such that

$$n > N \text{ implies } a_n > A - \epsilon$$

and for every $\epsilon > 0$ and every integer m there exists an integer $n > m$ such that

$$a_n < A + \epsilon$$

Proof. We assume A is the smallest limit point of the sequence given by $\{a_n \mid n = 1, 2, \ldots\}$.

Then no number smaller than A can be a limit point. But $A - \epsilon$ is smaller than A and thus if there were infinitely many numbers of the form a_n less than $A - \epsilon$, either the sequence would be unbounded below—which contradicts the hypothesis—or there would be a limit point smaller than A.

The second statement follows from the fact that A is a limit point. The details are left to the exercises. ∎

Roughly, this theorem says that, for every $\epsilon > 0$, the inequality $a_n < A - \epsilon$ will be true for only a finite number of integers n and the inequality $a_n < A + \epsilon$ must be true for infinitely many n. The obvious corollary is

Theorem 9-2-5. $B = \overline{\lim_n} \, a_n$ if, and only if, for every $\epsilon > 0$ there exists N such that

$$n > N \text{ implies } a_n < B + \epsilon$$

and for every $\epsilon > 0$ and every integer m there exists an integer $n > m$ such that

$$a_n > B - \epsilon$$

A somewhat deeper theorem, which is extremely useful, is

Theorem 9-2-6. If the sequence of real numbers given by

$$\{a_n \mid n = 1, 2, \ldots\}$$

is bounded below, then

$$\underline{\lim_n} \, a_n = \sup_n \left(\inf_{m \geq n} a_m \right)$$

Proof. Let $A = \underline{\lim_n} \, a_n$ and $B = \sup_n \left(\inf_{m \geq n} a_m \right)$. For $n = 1, 2, \ldots$, let $c_n = \inf_{m \geq n} a_m$.

Clearly, for $n = 1, 2, \ldots, c_n \leq c_{n+1}$.

From the definition of infimum, for $n = 1, 2, \ldots$, there exists a sequence of integers, given by $\{m_{n,k} \mid k = 1, 2, \ldots\}$ such that $c_n = \lim_{k \to \infty} a_{m_{n,k}}$. Thus c_n is a limit point of the original sequence. Since B is a limit point (in fact, the limit) of the sequence given by $\{c_n \mid n = 1, 2, \ldots\}$, B must also be a limit point of the original sequence. Since A is the smallest limit point, we conclude that $A \leq B$.

We now assume that $A < B$ and let $d = B - A > 0$. We have

$$B - d < B = \sup_n c_n$$

From the definition of supremum there exists N such that

$$n > N \quad \text{implies} \quad c_n > B - \frac{d}{2}$$

or

$$n > N \quad \text{implies} \quad \inf_{m \geq n} a_m > B - \frac{d}{2}$$

or

$$m > N \quad \text{implies} \quad a_m > B - \frac{d}{2}$$

Since the limit points of a sequence are unaffected by discarding a finite number of terms, A must also be the limit inferior of the sequence given by $\{a_m \mid m = N + 1, N + 2, \ldots\}$ and we must have

$$A \geq B - \frac{d}{2} = A + \frac{d}{2}$$

which is a contradiction. Thus $A = B$.   ∎

The obvious corollary is

Theorem 9-2-7. If the sequence of real numbers given by $\{a_n \mid n = 1, 2, \ldots\}$ is bounded above, then

$$\overline{\lim_n} \, a_n = \inf_n \sup_{m \geq n} a_m$$

Proof

$$\overline{\lim_n} \, a_n = -\underline{\lim_n} \, (-a_n)$$

$$= -\sup_n \left(\inf_{m \geq n} (-a_m) \right)$$

$$= -\sup_n \left(-\sup_{m \geq n} a_m \right)$$

$$= \inf_n \left(\sup_{m \geq n} a_m \right)$$

                                                    ∎

For a convergent sequence, we have

Theorem 9-2-8. $a = \lim\limits_{n \to \infty} a_n$ if, and only if,

$$\varliminf_{n} a_n = \varlimsup_{n} a_n = a$$

The proof is left to the exercises.

(An interesting sideline can be developed at this point by observing the analogy between taking the larger of two numbers and the union of two sets to form definitions for limit inferior, limit superior, and limit of a sequence whose range is a collection of sets. More in the line we are pursuing, however, is an investigation of these concepts with respect to algebraic combinations of sequences.) We turn now to

Theorem 9-2-9. If the sequences of real numbers given by $\{a_n \mid n = 1, 2, \ldots\}$ and $\{b_n \mid n = 1, 2, \ldots\}$ are bounded then

$$\varlimsup_{n} (a_n + b_n) \leq \varlimsup_{n} a_n + \varlimsup_{n} b_n$$

Proof. If $\{c_n \mid n = 1, 2, \ldots\}$ is a bounded sequence, then

$$\sup_{m > n} c_m \geq \sup_{m > n+1} c_m$$

which makes $\left\{ \sup\limits_{m > n} c_m \mid n = 1, 2, \ldots \right\}$ a monotone nondecreasing sequence.
Thus $\inf\limits_{n} \left(\sup\limits_{m > n} c_m \right) = \lim\limits_{n} \left(\sup\limits_{m > n} c_m \right)$. Thus

$$\varlimsup_{n} (a_n + b_n) = \inf_{n} \left[\sup_{m \geq n} (a_m + b_m) \right]$$

$$= \lim_{n} \left[\sup_{m > n} (a_m + b_m) \right]$$

$$\leq \lim_{n} \left[\sup_{m > n} a_m + \sup_{m > n} b_m \right]$$

$$= \lim_{n} \left(\sup_{m > n} a_m \right) + \lim_{n} \left(\sup_{m > n} b_m \right)$$

$$= \inf_{n} \left(\sup_{m > n} a_m \right) + \inf_{n} \left(\sup_{m > n} b_m \right)$$

$$= \varlimsup_{n} a_n + \varlimsup_{n} b_n.$$

EXERCISES

1. For a bounded sequence, prove that $\varlimsup_{n} (-a_n) = -\varliminf_{n} a_n$.

2. For bounded sequences, prove that

$$\varliminf_{n} a_n + \varliminf_{n} b_n \leq \varliminf_{n} (a_n + b_n) \leq \varliminf_{n} a_n + \varlimsup_{n} b_n$$

3. Complete the details of the proof of Theorem 9-2-4.

4. Prove Theorem 9-2-8.

Find all limit points, limit superior, and limit inferior for the sequences given by the following expressions for a_n:

5. $(-1)^n$ **10.** $\sin n\pi/5$

6. $\sin n\pi/3$ **11.** $n \sin n\pi/2$

7. $(-1)^n(1 + 1/n)$ **12.** $n^2 \sin^2 n\pi/2$

8. $\sin n$ **13.** x^n

9. $(-1)^n n$

9-3   Series

With the machinery developed for sequences in the preceding section, we can now investigate a new kind of mathematical entity:

> **Definition 9-3-1.** The set of real numbers $\{a_n \mid n = 1, 2, \ldots\}$ is the range of a sequence. The *series given by* $\{a_n \mid n = 1, 2, \ldots\}$ is the sequence given by $\{s_n \mid n = 1, 2, \ldots\}$, where, for $n = 1, 2, \ldots$,
>
> $$s_n = \sum_{k=1}^{n} a_k$$
>
> The number s_n is called the *nth partial sum* of the series. The series is denoted by the symbol
>
> $$\sum_{n=1}^{\infty} a_n$$

It should be noted at the outset that $\sum_{n=1}^{\infty} a_n$ is a symbol for the sequence of partial sums and is not a symbol for a number.

The words *convergent* and *divergent* apply to series, since each series is a sequence. Rather than the word *limit* in the case of a convergent series, however, it is more common to use

Definition 9-3-2. The real number S is the *sum* of the convergent series $\sum\limits_{n=1}^{\infty} a_n$ provided that $S = \lim\limits_{n \to \infty} \sum\limits_{k=1}^{n} a_k$.

EXAMPLE. We consider the sequence given by

$$a_n = \frac{1}{2^n}, \qquad n = 0, 1, 2, \ldots$$

Then

$$s_n = \sum_{k=0}^{n} \frac{1}{2^k} = \frac{1 - 2^{-(n+1)}}{1 - 2^{-1}} = 2 - 2^{-n}$$

Since $\lim\limits_{n \to \infty} s_n = 2$, the series is convergent and its sum is 2. It is not legitimate, however, to insert "=" between $\sum\limits_{n=0}^{\infty} 1/2^n$ and 2, since the first is a symbol for a sequence and the second is a number.

When coping with series, the first question of interest is that of convergence or divergence. Very often the question of convergence can be answered, but the determination of the sum (when there is one) in reasonable terms is not easy. For example, we consider the series

$$\sum_{n=1}^{\infty} \frac{1}{n^2}$$

For the partial sums, we have

$$s_n = \sum_{k=1}^{n} \frac{1}{k^2}$$

$$s_{n+1} - s_n = \frac{1}{(n+1)^2} > 0$$

$$s_n < s_{n+1}$$

Thus the sequence given by $\{s_n \mid n = 1, 2, \ldots\}$ is monotone increasing. Further, for $n = 1, 2, \ldots,$

$$s_n < 1 + \int_1^n \frac{dt}{t^2} = 2 - \frac{1}{n} < 2$$

Since the sequence of partial sums is monotone increasing and bounded above, it must be convergent. At this stage the only name available for the number which is the sum of this series is "the sum of $\sum\limits_{n=1}^{\infty} \frac{1}{n^2}$."

The method used to determine the convergence of this particular series generalizes to

Theorem 9-3-1. f is a continuous, monotone decreasing function on $[1, +\infty[$ into the non-negative real numbers. $\sum\limits_{n=1}^{\infty} f(n)$ is convergent if, and only if, $\int_1^{+\infty} f$ is convergent.

Proof. Since the range of f is a set of non-negative real numbers, the series, considered as a sequence of its partial sums, is monotone increasing.

Since the function f is monotone decreasing, we have, for $n = 1, 2, \ldots$ and $t \in [n, n+1]$,

$$f(n+1) \leq f(t) \leq f(n)$$

so that

$$f(n+1) \leq \int_n^{n+1} f \leq f(n)$$

For the partial sums,

$$s_{n+1} - f(1) \leq \int_1^{n+1} f \leq s_n$$

If $\int_1^{+\infty} f$ is convergent, then the sequence of partial sums is bounded above by the improper integral and thus the series is convergent. Conversely, if the improper integral is divergent, then

$$\lim_{B \to +\infty} \int_1^B f = +\infty$$

(since the range of f consists of non-negative numbers) and then $\lim_{n \to \infty} s_n = +\infty$, which makes the series divergent. ∎

This theorem allows us to establish the convergence or divergence of particular series:

Theorem 9-3-2. If $p > 1$, then $\sum_{n=1}^{\infty} \dfrac{1}{n^p}$ is convergent. If $p \leq 1$, then $\sum_{n=1}^{\infty} \dfrac{1}{n^p}$ is divergent.

Theorem 9-3-1 is usually referred to as "the integral test." We noted in the preceding chapter on improper integrals that it was possible for an integral of the form $\int_1^{+\infty} f$ to be convergent without having $\lim_{x \to +\infty} f(x)$ even existing. There is no such situation with series. In fact, we have

Theorem 9-3-3. If $\sum_{n=1}^{\infty} a_n$ is convergent, then $\lim_{n \to \infty} a_n = 0$.

Proof. For $n = 1, 2, \ldots$, let

$$s_n = \sum_{k=1}^{n} a_k$$

Then

$$a_n = s_n - s_{n-1}$$

By hypothesis, $\lim\limits_{n \to \infty} s_n = \lim\limits_{n \to \infty} s_{n-1} = S$ exists. Then

$$\lim_{n \to \infty} a_n = S - S = 0 \qquad \blacksquare$$

We now examine some tools which will help us determine the convergence or divergence of series.

Theorem 9-3-4 (the Comparison Test). For $n = 1, 2, \ldots$, $0 \le a_n \le b_n$.

If $\sum\limits_{n=1}^{\infty} a_n$ is divergent, then $\sum\limits_{n=1}^{\infty} b_n$ is divergent.

If $\sum\limits_{n=1}^{\infty} b_n$ is convergent, then $\sum\limits_{n=1}^{\infty} a_n$ is convergent.

Proof. The hypothesis implies that in both cases the sequence of partial sums is monotone increasing. For $n = 1, 2, \ldots$,

$$\sum_{k=1}^{n} a_k \le \sum_{k=1}^{n} b_k$$

If $\sum\limits_{n=1}^{\infty} a_n$ is divergent, then $\lim\limits_{n \to \infty} \sum\limits_{k=1}^{n} a_k = +\infty$. This implies that $\lim\limits_{n \to \infty} \sum\limits_{k=1}^{n} b_k = +\infty$ so that $\sum\limits_{n=1}^{\infty} b_n$ is divergent.

Conversely, if $\sum\limits_{n=1}^{\infty} b_n$ is convergent, then $\lim\limits_{n \to \infty} \sum\limits_{k=1}^{n} b_k$ must exist and this number is an upper bound for the partial sums of the series $\sum\limits_{n=1}^{\infty} a_n$. Since this series is a bounded monotone sequence, it must be convergent. $\qquad \blacksquare$

In order to use the comparison test, it is necessary to have a stock of series with known convergence properties. Theorem 9-3-2 gives us some series for this stock. We then can examine a new series by comparison with ones already known. One way in which we can avoid the inequalities involved in this comparison is given by

Theorem 9-3-5. For $n = 1, 2, \ldots$, $a_n > 0$ and $b_n > 0$. Further, $\lim\limits_{n \to \infty} a_n/b_n = L > 0$. Then $\sum\limits_{n=1}^{\infty} a_n$ converges if, and only if, $\sum\limits_{n=1}^{\infty} b_n$ converges.

The proof merely consists of noting the existence of an integer N such that

$$n > N \quad \text{implies that} \quad \frac{L}{2} < \frac{a_n}{b_n} < \frac{3}{2}L$$

and applying the comparison test.

In order further to build a stock of known series, we turn to

Theorem 9-3-6. If $|x| < 1$, then $\sum_{n=0}^{\infty} x^n$ is convergent and its sum is $1/(1-x)$. If $|x| \geq 1$, then $\sum_{n=0}^{\infty} x^n$ is divergent.

Proof. We let

$$s_n(x) = \sum_{k=0}^{n} x^k$$

For $x \neq 1$,

$$s_n(x) = \frac{1 - x^{n+1}}{1 - x}$$

$$s_n(1) = n + 1$$

If $|x| < 1$, then

$$\lim_{n \to \infty} s_n(x) = \frac{1}{1 - x}$$

If $|x| > 1$, then

$$\lim_{n \to \infty} s_n(x) = +\infty$$

$$\lim_{n \to \infty} s_n(1) = +\infty$$

$$\overline{\lim_{n}} \, s_n(-1) = 1, \qquad \underline{\lim_{n}} \, s_n(-1) = 0 \qquad \blacksquare$$

We now expand our arsenal of tests applicable to series with positive terms by

Theorem 9-3-7 (the Ratio Test). For $n = 1, 2, \ldots, a_n > 0$.

If $\overline{\lim_{n}} \, \frac{a_{n+1}}{a_n} < 1$, then $\sum_{n=1}^{\infty} a_n$ is convergent.

If $\underline{\lim_{n}} \, \frac{a_{n+1}}{a_n} > 1$, then $\sum_{n=1}^{\infty} a_n$ is divergent.

Proof. We assume $\overline{\lim_{n}} \, a_{n+1}/a_n = r < 1$. From the definition of limit inferior, there exists an integer N such that

$$n \geq N \quad \text{implies} \quad \frac{a_{n+1}}{a_n} < \frac{r+1}{2}$$

If $m > n \geq N$,

$$\sum_{k=n}^{m} a_k = \sum_{k=n}^{m} a_N \frac{a_{N+1}}{a_N} \frac{a_{N+2}}{a_{N+1}} \cdots \frac{a_{k-1}}{a_{k-2}} \frac{a_k}{a_{k-1}}$$

$$< a_N \sum_{k=n}^{m} \left(\frac{r+1}{2}\right)^{(k-N)}$$

$$= (\text{const.}) \sum_{k=n}^{m} \left(\frac{r+1}{2}\right)^{k}$$

Since $0 < (r+1)/2 < 1$, then $\sum_{n=0}^{\infty} [(r+1)/2]^n$ is convergent and thus $\sum_{n=1}^{\infty} a_n$ is convergent by the comparison test. The remainder of the proof, concerning limit inferior, is left to the exercises. ∎

An obvious corollary is

Theorem 9-3-8. For $n = 1, 2, \ldots, a_n > 0$. $\lim_{n \to \infty} a_{n+1}/a_n = r$.

If $r < 1$, then $\sum_{n=1}^{\infty} a_n$ is convergent.

If $r > 1$, then $\sum_{n=1}^{\infty} a_n$ is divergent.

In the particular case that $\lim_{n \to \infty} a_{n+1}/a_n = 1$, no conclusions can be drawn. This is illustrated in the case in which $a_n = 1/n^p$ where

$$\lim_{n \to \infty} \frac{a_{n+1}}{a_n} = \lim_{n \to \infty} \left(\frac{n}{n+1}\right)^{p} = 1$$

regardless of the value of p; but the series $\sum_{n=1}^{\infty} 1/n^p$ is convergent for $p > 1$ and divergent for $p \leq 1$.

Theorem 9-3-9 (the Root Test). For $n = 1, 2, \ldots, a_n \geq 0$.

If $\overline{\lim_{n}} \, (a_n)^{1/n} < 1$, then $\sum_{n=1}^{\infty} a_n$ is convergent.

If $\underline{\lim_{n}} \, (a_n)^{1/n} > 1$, then $\sum_{n=1}^{\infty} a_n$ is divergent.

Proof

Part 1: Assume $\underline{\lim_{n}} \, (a_n)^{1/n} = r > 1$. Then there exists an integer N such that

$$n \geq N \quad \text{implies} \quad \frac{1+r}{2} < (a_n)^{1/n}$$

or

$$a_n > \left(\frac{1+r}{2}\right)^n > 1$$

Then $\lim\limits_{n \to \infty} a_n \neq 0$ so that $\sum\limits_{n=1}^{\infty} a_n$ is divergent.

Part 2: Assume $\overline{\lim\limits_{n}}\, (a_n)^{1/n} = r < 1$. Then there exists an integer N such that

$$n \geq N \quad \text{implies} \quad (a_n)^{1/n} < \frac{1+r}{2}$$

or

$$a_n < \left(\frac{1+r}{2}\right)^n$$

Since $0 < (1+r)/2 < 1$, then $\sum\limits_{n=0}^{\infty} a_n$ is convergent. ∎

An obvious corollary is

Theorem 9-3-10. For $n = 1, 2, \ldots, a_n \geq 0$. $\lim\limits_{n \to \infty} (a_n)^{1/n} = r$.

If $r < 1$, then $\sum\limits_{n=1}^{\infty} a_n$ is convergent.

If $r > 1$, then $\sum\limits_{n=1}^{\infty} a_n$ is divergent.

As with the ratio test, no information is forthcoming if the limit is 1, with the same series' illustrating the point.

The tests thus far have applied to series given by sequences whose ranges consist, at the least, of non-negative numbers. A theorem of great value in treating series which involve infinitely many positive numbers and infinitely many negative numbers is

Theorem 9-3-11. If $\sum\limits_{n=1}^{\infty} |a_n|$ is convergent, then $\sum\limits_{n=1}^{\infty} a_n$ is convergent.

Proof

$$\left| \sum_{k=m}^{n} a_k \right| \leq \sum_{k=m}^{n} |a_k|$$ ∎

This situation is given a name in

Definition 9-3-3. The series $\sum\limits_{n=1}^{\infty} a_n$ is called *absolutely convergent* provided that the series $\sum\limits_{n=1}^{\infty} |a_n|$ is convergent. A series is *conditionally convergent* if it is convergent but not absolutely convergent.

We conclude this section with a theorem which applies to series called *alternating*:

Theorem 9-3-12. If, for $n = 1, 2, \ldots, a_n > 0$ and $a_{n+1} \leq a_n$, and if $\lim_{n \to \infty} a_n = 0$, then $\sum_{n=1}^{\infty} (-1)^{n+1} a_n$ is convergent.

Proof. We consider separately two subsequences of the sequence of partial sums; namely, those given by

$$\{s_{2k} \mid k = 1, 2, \ldots\}$$

and by

$$\{s_{2k+1} \mid k = 0, 1, 2, \ldots\}$$

We have

$$s_{2k+2} - s_{2k} = -a_{2k+2} + a_{2k+1} \geq 0$$

$$s_{2k} \leq s_{2k+2}$$

Further,

$$s_{2k} = \sum_{i=1}^{2k} (-1)^{i+1} a_i$$

$$= a_1 + \sum_{j=1}^{k-1} [-a_{2j} + a_{2j+1}] - a_{2k}$$

$$\leq a_1$$

Thus the sequence given by $\{s_{2k} \mid k = 1, 2, \ldots\}$ is monotone increasing and bounded above and so is convergent. We let $A = \lim_{k \to \infty} s_{2k}$.

Now, for $k = 0, 1, 2, \ldots,$

$$s_{2k+3} - s_{2k+1} = a_{2k+3} - a_{2k+2} \leq 0$$

$$s_{2k+1} \geq s_{2k+3}$$

Further,

$$s_{2k+1} = a_1 - a_2 + \sum_{j=1}^{k-1} [a_{2j+1} - a_{2j+2}] + a_{2k+1}$$

$$\geq a_1 - a_2$$

Thus the sequence given by $\{s_{2k+1} \mid k = 0, 1, 2, \ldots\}$ is monotone decreasing and bounded below and so is convergent.

We let $B = \lim_{k \to \infty} s_{2k+1}$. Since $a_{2k} = -s_{2k} + s_{2k-1}$, we have $\lim_{k \to \infty} a_{2k} = B - A$. But, by hypothesis, $\lim_{n \to \infty} a_n = 0$, so that $B = A$ and the sequence given by $\{s_n \mid n = 1, 2, \ldots\}$ must be convergent to A. ∎

In the next sections we investigate algebraic operations on series.

EXERCISES

1. Complete the proof of Theorem 9-3-7.

Determine the convergence or divergence of $\sum\limits_{n=1}^{\infty} a_n$ where a_n is given by the following expressions.

2. $1/n$

3. $1/\log n$

4. $1/n!$

5. $1/(1)(3)(5) \cdots (2n - 1)$

6. $n^2/(n^3 + 1)$

7. $(2n + 3)/(n^2 + 4n)$

8. $(3n + 1)/(n^3 + 5n)$

9. $(n + 1)/2^n$

10. $1/(n \log n)$

11. $n^n/n!$

12. $n!/2^n$

13. $(1)^{n+1}/n$

14. $(\sin n)/n^2$

15. $(-1)^{n+1}[n/(n + 1)]^n$

9-4   Operations with Series

One advantage gained from the particular manner in which the word *series* has been defined is that we need not make new definitions for algebraic combinations of series. Since a series is the sequence of its partial sums, and since a sequence is a function—in this case a function into the real numbers—we have all algebraic things for sequences which we have for such functions. Further, all limit theorems apply so that, for example, the result of adding two convergent series will be a convergent series. Before examining these algebraic operations, we look at certain operations which are peculiar to series.

Definition 9-4-1. The series $\sum\limits_{n=1}^{\infty} b_n$ is a *rearrangement* of the series $\sum\limits_{n=1}^{\infty} a_n$ provided there exists a one-to-one function g on the positive integers onto the positive integers such that for $n = 1, 2, \ldots, b_n = a_{g(n)}$, and for every positive integer m there exists a positive integer $m > n$ such that $g(m) \neq m$.

The last part of the definition restricts the use of the word *rearrangement* to the situation in which the position of infinitely many terms is changed.

EXAMPLE. We consider the "alternating harmonic series,"

$$\sum_{n=1}^{\infty} \frac{(-1)^{n+1}}{n}$$

This convergent series is given by the sequence described by

$$a_n = \frac{(-1)^{n+1}}{n}, \qquad n = 1, 2, \ldots$$

We form a new sequence by

$$b_n = \frac{(-1)^{n+1}}{2n}, \qquad n = 1, 2, \ldots$$

Let us denote by S the sum of the alternating harmonic series. That is,

$$\sum_{n=1}^{\infty} a_n \text{ is convergent to } S.$$

Then

$$\sum_{n=1}^{\infty} b_n \text{ is convergent to } S/2.$$

We now form a third sequence by

$$c_{2j-1} = 0, \qquad j = 1, 2, \ldots$$
$$c_{2j} = b_j, \qquad j = 1, 2, \ldots$$

The series $\sum_{n=1}^{\infty} c_n$ is not the same series as $\sum_{n=1}^{\infty} b_n$, but since

$$\sum_{k=1}^{2m} c_k = \sum_{k=1}^{m} b_k, \qquad m = 1, 2, \ldots$$

and

$$\sum_{k=1}^{2m+1} c_k = \sum_{k=1}^{m} b_k, \qquad m = 1, 2, \ldots$$

the series $\sum_{n=1}^{\infty} c_n$ must also be convergent and its sum is $S/2$.

Our fourth and final sequence is formed by taking

$$d_n = a_n + c_n, \qquad n = 1, 2, \ldots$$

We then have, for $j = 0, 1, 2, \ldots,$

$$d_{4j+1} = \frac{1}{4j+1} + 0 = \frac{1}{4j+1}$$

$$d_{4j+2} = -\frac{1}{4j+2} + \frac{1}{4j+2} = 0$$

$$d_{4j+3} = \frac{1}{4j+3} + 0 = \frac{1}{4j+3}$$

$$d_{4j+4} = -\frac{1}{4j+4} - \frac{1}{4j+4} = -\frac{1}{2j+2}$$

The numbers in the range of the sequence given by $\{d_n \mid n = 1, 2, \ldots\}$ include the reciprocals of all the odd positive integers, the opposites of the reciprocals of all the even positive integers, and the number 0 repeated infinitely often. If we form a new series by dropping all the zero terms in this sequence, then this new series is a rearrangement of the alternating harmonic series. Since

$$\sum_{k=1}^{n} d_k = \sum_{k=1}^{n} a_k + \sum_{k=1}^{n} c_k$$

this rearrangement of the alternating harmonic series must be convergent and its sum is $\frac{3}{2}S$.

Thus we see that a rearrangement of one particular series converges to a different sum from that of the original series. In fact one can easily find two series which are rearrangements of one another, with one convergent and the other divergent. One saving grace, however, is given by

Theorem 9-4-1. If $\sum_{n=1}^{\infty} a_n$ is absolutely convergent and has sum S, and $\sum_{n=1}^{\infty} b_n$ is a rearrangement of $\sum_{n=1}^{\infty} a_n$, then $\sum_{n=1}^{\infty} b_n$ is also absolutely convergent and has sum S.

Proof. Since $\sum_{n=1}^{\infty} b_n$ is a rearrangement of $\sum_{n=1}^{\infty} a_n$, there is a one-to-one function g on the positive integers into the positive integers such that, for $n = 1, 2, \ldots$,

$$b_n = a_{g(n)}$$

For a given $\epsilon > 0$, the absolute convergence of $\sum_{n=1}^{\infty} a_n$ implies the existence of an integer N_ϵ such that

$$\left| \sum_{k=1}^{N_\epsilon} a_k - S \right| < \frac{\epsilon}{2}$$

and, for $p = 1, 2, \ldots$,

$$\sum_{k=N}^{N+p} |a_k| < \frac{\epsilon}{2}$$

We let $M = \max \{g(k) \mid k = 1, 2, \ldots, N\}$. Then for $m > M$

$$\left| \sum_{k=1}^{m} b_k - S \right| \leq \left| \sum_{k=1}^{N} a_k - S \right| + \sum_{j \in A} |b_j|$$

where $A = \{j \mid 1 \leq j \leq m, g(j) > N\}$. Since A contains a finite number of integers, there exists an integer p such that $g(A) \subseteq [N, N + p]$, which gives

$$\left| \sum_{k=1}^{m} b_k - S \right| \leq \left| \sum_{k=1}^{N} a_k - S \right| + \sum_{k=N}^{N+p} |a_k| < \frac{\epsilon}{2} + \frac{\epsilon}{2} = \epsilon \qquad \blacksquare$$

Another operation which can be performed on series is given in

Definition 9-4-2. The series $\sum\limits_{n=1}^{\infty} b_n$ is a *grouping* of the series $\sum\limits_{n=1}^{\infty} a_n$ provided that there exists a strictly monotone increasing function g on the set of positive integers into the set of positive integers such that, for $n = 1, 2, \ldots$,

$$g(n) > n$$

$$b_1 = \sum_{k=1}^{g(1)} a_k$$

$$b_n = \sum_{k=g(n-1)+1}^{g(n)} a_k$$

Under this definition a grouping of a series is necessarily a subsequence of the sequence of partial sums of the given series, but with the further provision that infinitely many terms in the original sequence of partial sums have been omitted. Since a subsequence of a convergent sequence is necessarily convergent, and has the same limit, we have immediately

Theorem 9-4-2. A grouping of a convergent series is convergent and has the same sum.

It is not the case that grouping preserves divergence. The divergent series $\sum\limits_{n=1}^{\infty} (-1)^n$ has the grouping $\sum\limits_{n=1}^{\infty} [(-1)^{2n-1} + (-1)^{2n}]$ which is convergent with sum 0.

We now turn to algebraic operations with series. From the definition of a series as the sequence of its partial sums, we have immediately

Theorem 9-4-3. If $\sum\limits_{n=1}^{\infty} a_n$ is convergent to A and $\sum\limits_{n=1}^{\infty} b_n$ is convergent to B, then $\sum\limits_{n=1}^{\infty} (a_n + b_n)$ is convergent to $A + B$.

Theorem 9-4-4. If $\sum\limits_{n=1}^{\infty} a_n$ is convergent to A, then $\sum\limits_{n=1}^{\infty} (-a_n)$ is convergent to $-A$.

Theorem 9-4-5. If $\sum\limits_{n=1}^{\infty} a_n$ is convergent to A and $\sum\limits_{n=1}^{\infty} b_n$ is convergent to B, then $\sum\limits_{n=1}^{\infty} (a_n - b_n)$ is convergent to $A - B$.

Theorem 9-4-6. If $\sum_{n=1}^{\infty} a_n$ is convergent to A and $\sum_{n=1}^{\infty} b_n$ is convergent to B, then $\sum_{n=1}^{\infty} \left[\sum_{i=1}^{n} \sum_{j=1}^{n} a_i b_j \right]$ is convergent to AB.

This last theorem, concerning the product of two series, raises an interesting point. The series which is the product of two series arises from the sequence given by

$$\left\{ \sum_{i=1}^{n} \sum_{j=1}^{n} a_i b_j \,\middle|\, n = 1, 2, \ldots \right\}$$

The nth term of this sequence is the sum of n^2 numbers, which numbers may be conveniently arranged in a square array. This geometric display suggests the following technique for treating the product of two series.

We define a function f on $[0, +\infty[\times [0, +\infty[$ into the real numbers by requiring, for i and $j = 1, 2, \ldots$,

$$f(x, y) = a_i b_j; \quad i - 1 \leq x < i \quad \text{and} \quad j - 1 \leq y < j$$

Thus f has constant value on each unit square with lattice-point vertices, and the nth partial sum of the series which is the product of the two given series is the number

$$\sum_{i=1}^{n} \sum_{j=1}^{n} a_i b_j = \int_{[0,n] \times [0,n]} f$$

We are then examining the convergence of a sequence of integrals and are able to use the full machinery established for improper integrals. The result which comes from this machinery is called *the Cauchy product of two series:*

Theorem 9-4-7. If $\sum_{n=1}^{\infty} a_n$ is absolutely convergent, with sum A, and $\sum_{n=1}^{\infty} b_n$ is absolutely convergent, with sum B, and the sequence given by $\{c_n \mid n = 1, 2, \ldots\}$ is determined by

$$c_n = \sum_{j=1}^{n} a_j b_{n-j+1}$$

then $\sum_{n=1}^{\infty} c_n$ is absolutely convergent, with sum AB.

Proof. We consider the partial sums,

$$s_n = \sum_{k=1}^{n} a_k \quad \text{and} \quad t_n = \sum_{k=1}^{n} b_k$$

By hypothesis, $\lim_{n \to \infty} s_n = A$, $\lim_{n \to \infty} t_n = B$, so that $\lim_{n \to \infty} s_n t_n = AB$.

We now construct the function f on $[0, +\infty[\times [0, +\infty[$ into the real numbers by specifying, for i and $j = 1, 2, \ldots,$

$$f(x, y) = a_i b_j; \qquad i - 1 \leq x < i \quad \text{and} \quad j - 1 \leq y < j$$

Then

$$s_n t_n = \int_{[0,n] \times [0,n]} f$$

Since the given series are absolutely convergent, the positive and negative terms separately form convergent series so that the function $|f|$ is improperly integrable on the first quadrant of the plane. Thus f itself is improperly integrable on the first quadrant and its improper integral is $\lim_{n \to \infty} s_n t_n = AB$. But the value of the improper integral, when it exists, is independent of the method of approximating the domain so that we also have

$$AB = \lim_{n \to \infty} \int_{([0,n] \times [0,n]) \cap \{(x,y) \mid x + y \leq n\}} f$$

$$= \lim_{n \to \infty} \sum_{k=1}^{n} c_k \qquad\qquad \blacksquare$$

EXERCISES

1. Show that the rearrangement

$$\sum_{j=0}^{\infty} \left[\frac{1}{2j + 1} + \frac{1}{2j + 3} + \frac{1}{2j + 5} - \frac{1}{2j + 2} - \frac{1}{2j + 4} - \frac{1}{2j + 6} \right]$$

of the series $\sum_{n=1}^{\infty} (-1)^{n+1}/n$ is convergent to the same sum.

2. Show that the Cauchy product of the series $\sum_{n=1}^{\infty} (-1)^{n+1}/n$ with itself is divergent.

3. $\sum_{n=0}^{\infty} (-1)^n x^{2n+1}/(2n + 1)!$ converges to $\sin x$ and $\sum_{n=0}^{\infty} (-1)^n x^{2n}/(2n)!$ converges to $\cos x$. Use the Cauchy product to prove that $\sin 2x = 2 \sin x \cos x$.

4. $\sum_{n=0}^{\infty} x^n/n!$ converges to e^x. Use the Cauchy product to show that $e^x e^y = e^{x+y}$. For $|x| < 1$, $\sum_{n=0}^{\infty} x^n$ is convergent to $1/(x - 1)$. Use the Cauchy product to show that, for $|x| < 1$,

5. $\sum_{n=0}^{\infty} (n + 1)x^n$ converges to $1/(x - 1)^2$.

6. $\sum\limits_{n=0}^{\infty} \{[(n+1)(n+2)]/2\}x^n$ converges to $1/(x-1)^3$.

7. Find a series convergent to $1/(x-1)^p$, where p is a positive integer.

9-5 Estimates of Error

If we are able to determine that a particular series does converge, we are still left with the question of what number its sum is. In many cases we are content with being able to find a rational number estimate to the sum, provided that we also have some idea of the size of the error introduced by using the estimate in place of the actual sum. The following theorems give such estimates for each of the convergence tests we have established.

Theorem 9-5-1. If f is a function on $[1, +\infty[$ into the non-negative real numbers which is continuous and monotone nonincreasing, if $\int_{1}^{+\infty} f$ is convergent, and if $\sum\limits_{n=1}^{\infty} f(n)$ is convergent with sum S, then, for $n = 1, 2, \ldots$,

$$\left| S - \sum_{k=1}^{n} f(k) \right| \leq \int_{n}^{+\infty} f$$

Proof. The non-negative and nonincreasing character of f implies that, for $k = 1, 2, \ldots$,

$$f(k+1) \leq \int_{k}^{k+1} f$$

Thus, for $n = 1, 2, \ldots$ and $p = 1, 2, \ldots$, we have

$$\sum_{k=n+1}^{n+p} f(k) \leq \int_{n}^{n+p+1} f$$

$$\left| S - \sum_{k=1}^{n} f(k) \right| = \lim_{p \to \infty} \sum_{k=n+1}^{n+p} f(k)$$

$$\leq \lim_{p \to \infty} \int_{n}^{n+p+1} f$$

$$= \int_{n}^{+\infty} f \qquad \blacksquare$$

Theorem 9-5-2. If, for $n = 1, 2, \ldots$,

$$|a_n| \leq b_n$$

$\sum_{n=1}^{\infty} a_n$ is convergent to S, and $\sum_{n=1}^{\infty} b_n$ is convergent to T, then, for $n = 1, 2, \ldots,$

$$\left| S - \sum_{k=1}^{n} a_k \right| \leq \left| T - \sum_{k=1}^{n} b_k \right|$$

Proof. For $n = 1, 2, \ldots$ and $p = 1, 2, \ldots,$

$$\left| \sum_{k=n+1}^{n+p} a_k \right| \leq \sum_{k=n+1}^{n+p} |a_k| \leq \sum_{k=n+1}^{n+p} b_k$$

$$\left| S - \sum_{k=1}^{n} a_k \right| = \lim_{p \to \infty} \left| \sum_{k=n+1}^{n+p} a_k \right|$$

$$\leq \lim_{p \to \infty} \sum_{k=n+1}^{n+p} b_k$$

$$= \left| T - \sum_{k=1}^{n} b_k \right|$$

Theorem 9-5-3. If, for $n = 1, 2, \ldots, a_n > 0$ and

$$\frac{a_{n+1}}{a_n} \leq r < 1$$

and $\sum_{n=1}^{\infty} a_n$ is convergent to S, then, for $n = 1, 2, \ldots,$

$$\left| S - \sum_{k=1}^{n} a_k \right| \leq \frac{a_{n+1}}{1 - r}$$

Proof. For $n = 1, 2, \ldots$ and $p = 1, 2, \ldots,$

$$\sum_{k=n+1}^{n+p} a_k = \sum_{k=1}^{p} \left[a_{n+1} \frac{a_{n+2}}{a_{n+1}} \frac{a_{n+3}}{a_{n+2}} \cdots \frac{a_{n+k}}{a_{n+k-1}} \right]$$

$$\leq a_{n+1} \sum_{k=1}^{p} r^{k-1}$$

$$< \frac{a_{n+1}}{1 - r}$$

Theorem 9-5-4. If, for $n = 1, 2, \ldots, a_n > 0$ and

$$(a_n)^{1/n} \leq r < 1$$

and $\sum_{n=1}^{\infty} a_n$ is convergent to S, then, for $n = 1, 2, \ldots,$

$$\left| S - \sum_{k=1}^{n} a_k \right| \leq \frac{r^{n+1}}{1 - r}$$

Proof. For $n = 1, 2, \ldots$ and $p = 1, 2, \ldots$,

$$\sum_{k=n+1}^{n+p} a_k \leq \sum_{k=n+1}^{n+p} r^k$$

$$= r^{n+1} \sum_{j=0}^{p-1} r^j$$

$$< \frac{r^{n+1}}{1-r}$$ ∎

Theorem 9-5-5. If, for $n = 1, 2, \ldots$,

$$a_n \geq a_{n+1} \geq 0$$

$\lim\limits_{n \to \infty} a_n = 0$, and $\sum\limits_{n=1}^{\infty} (-1)^{n+1} a_n$ is convergent to S, then, for $n = 1, 2, \ldots$,

$$\left| S - \sum_{k=1}^{n} (-1)^{k+1} a_k \right| < a_{n+1}$$

Proof. Denoting the partial sums, for $n = 1, 2, \ldots$, by

$$s_n = \sum_{k=1}^{n} (-1)^{k+1} a_k$$

we have already determined that

$$s_{2n} < S < s_{2n-1}$$

Thus, for $n = 0, 1, 2, \ldots$ and $p = 1, 2, \ldots$,

$$0 < \sum_{k=2n+1}^{2n+p} (-1)^{k+1} a_k < s_{2n+1} - s_{2n} = a_{2n+1}$$

and

$$0 > \sum_{k=(2n-1)+1}^{2n+p} (-1)^{k+1} a_k > s_{2n} - s_{2n-1} = -a_{2n}$$

Therefore, whether m is odd or even, for $m = 1, 2, \ldots$,

$$\left| S - \sum_{k=1}^{m} (-1)^{k+1} a_k \right| < a_{m+1}$$ ∎

There are two basic uses for these estimates of error. The first is the obvious one of discovering how many terms are necessary to take in order that the partial sum be within a prescribed amount of the sum. For example, $\sum\limits_{n=1}^{\infty} 1/n^2$ is convergent but its sum is, with the machinery thus far developed, unknown. Theorem 9-5-1 says that

$$\left| S - \sum_{k=1}^{n} \frac{1}{k^2} \right| \leq \int_{n}^{+\infty} \frac{dt}{t_2} = \frac{1}{n}$$

Thus, in order that the nth partial sum be within 0.01 of S, it is necessary that $n \geq 100$.

The second major use for the estimates of error is to determine the relative "rapidity" of convergence of two or more series. For example, Theorem 9-5-3, applied to the series $\sum_{n=0}^{\infty} r^n$, yields (when $0 < r < 1$) the estimate

$$S - \sum_{k=0}^{n} r^k = \frac{r^{n+1}}{1-r}$$

But the inequality

$$\frac{r^{n+1}}{1-r} < \epsilon$$

is equivalent to

$$n + 1 > \frac{\log \epsilon + \log(1-r)}{\log r}$$

Clearly the number of terms in the partial sum which gives accuracy gets larger as r increases to 1.

EXERCISES

Find the sum of the following series accurate to three decimal places.

1. $\sum_{n=1}^{\infty} 1/n^4$
2. $\sum_{n=1}^{\infty} 1/n^5$

3. $\sum_{n=1}^{\infty} 1/(n^4 + n)$
4. $\sum_{n=1}^{\infty} 1/(n^5 + 5n^2)$

5. $\sum_{n=1}^{\infty} 1/n!$
6. $\sum_{n=1}^{\infty} n/[(n+1)2^n]$

7. $\sum_{n=1}^{\infty} 1/n^n$
8. $\sum_{n=2}^{\infty} 1/(\log n)^n$

9. $\sum_{n=1}^{\infty} (-1)^{n+1}/n^2$
10. $\sum_{n=1}^{\infty} (-1)^{n+1}3^n/(5^n + 4)$

11. Determine the number of terms necessary to find the sum of $\sum_{n=0}^{\infty} r^n$ accurate to three decimal places when $r = 0.5, 0.9, 0.99,$ and 0.999.

9-6 Series of Functions

Given a sequence of functions, the series of functions given by that sequence is the sequence of the partial sums formed by the functions in the given sequence. Since the domain of the sum of two functions is the intersection of their domains, we need only consider a sequence of functions, all of which have the same domain.

Thus if $\{f_n \mid n = 1, 2, \ldots\}$ is the range of a sequence of functions, each of which is a function on some fixed set into the real numbers, the series $\sum_{n=1}^{\infty} f_n$ is the sequence given by $\{s_n \mid n = 1, 2, \ldots\}$, where

$$s_n = \sum_{k=1}^{n} f_k$$

In Chapter 6 we have already established theorems about sequences of functions, which we recall here:

Theorem 9-6-1. For $n = 1, 2, \ldots$, u_n is a continuous function on $[a, b]$ into the real numbers. f is a function on $[a, b]$ into the real numbers. If $f = \lim_{n \to \infty} u_n$ uniformly with respect to numbers in $[a, b]$, then f is continuous.

Theorem 9-6-2. For $n = 1, 2, \ldots$, u_n is an integrable function on $[a, b]$ into the real numbers. f is a function on $[a, b]$ into the real numbers. If $f = \lim_{n \to \infty} u_n$ uniformly with respect to numbers in $[a, b]$, then f is integrable and

$$\int_a^b f = \lim_{n \to \infty} \int_a^b u_n$$

Theorem 9-6-3. For $n = 1, 2, \ldots$, u_n is a function whose domain includes $[a, b]$ and v_n is a function on $[a, b]$ into the real numbers such that, for $x \in [a, b]$, $v_n(x) = u'_n(x)$. f and g are functions on $[a, b]$ into the real numbers. If $f = \lim_{n \to \infty} u_n$ pointwise on $[a, b]$ and $g = \lim_{n \to \infty} v_n$ uniformly on $[a, b]$, then f is differentiable, $g = f'$, and $f = \lim_{n \to \infty} u_n$ uniformly on $[a, b]$.

These three results clearly apply to the sequence of partial sums which forms a series. Thus the function which is the sum of a uniformly convergent series of continuous functions is continuous. The function which is the sum of a uniformly convergent series of integrable functions is integrable and its integral is the sum of the series of numbers which are the integrals of the given functions. If the series of the derivatives of a given sequence of functions is uniformly convergent and the series of those functions is pointwise convergent, then the sum of the series of functions is differentiable and its derivative is the sum of the uniformly convergent series of derivatives.

All this may be summed up by saying that a uniformly convergent series of functions may be integrated term by term or differentiated term by term, taking derivatives of as high an order as desired, provided only that the series formed by the highest-order derivatives is uniformly convergent.

We then need only find some way of determining the uniform convergence of a series of functions. This is given in the "Weierstrass M-test":

> **Theorem 9-6-4.** For $n = 1, 2, \ldots, f_n$ is a function on $[a, b]$ into the real numbers. $\{M_n \mid n = 1, 2, \ldots\}$ is the range of a sequence of numbers with the property that, for all $x \in [a, b]$ and for $n = 1, 2, \ldots$,
>
> $$|f_n(x)| \le M_n$$
>
> If $\sum\limits_{n=1}^{\infty} M_n$ is convergent, then $\sum\limits_{n=1}^{\infty} f_n$ is uniformly convergent with respect to numbers in $[a, b]$.

Proof. The hypothesis implies, by the comparison test, that for each specific $x \in [a, b]$ the series of numbers $\sum\limits_{n=1}^{\infty} f_n(x)$ is convergent. Thus $\sum\limits_{n=1}^{\infty} f_n$ is pointwise convergent on $[a, b]$.

The convergence of the series of numbers $\sum\limits_{n=1}^{\infty} M_n$ implies that for a given $\epsilon > 0$ there exists an integer N such that $n > N$ and

$$p > 0 \text{ implies } \left| \sum_{k=n}^{n+p} M_k \right| < \epsilon$$

But this means that if $n > N$ and $p > 0$, then for all $x \in [a, b]$,

$$\left| \sum_{k=n}^{n+p} f_k(x) \right| \le \sum_{k=n}^{n+p} |f_k(x)|$$

$$\le \sum_{k=n}^{n+p} M_k < \epsilon$$

Thus the series $\sum\limits_{n=1}^{\infty} f_n$ is uniformly convergent on $[a, b]$. ∎

In effect, the Weierstrass M-test calls for a series of numbers which converges more "slowly" than every series of numbers of the form $\sum\limits_{n=1}^{\infty} f_n(x)$. We will be particularly concerned with series of the form $\sum\limits_{n=0}^{\infty} c_n x^n$, the partial sums of which are polynomials. These are given a formal name in

> **Definition 9-6-1.** The *power series centered at* a, *with coefficients* $\{c_n \mid n = 0, 1, 2, \ldots\}$ is the series
>
> $$\sum_{n=0}^{\infty} c_n (x - a)^n$$

For each specific value of x, a power series becomes a series of numbers and the convergence of this series of numbers will then depend on the value of x and the numbers in the sequence of coefficients. For convenience we will consider power series centered at 0.

Definition 9-6-2. The *radius of convergence* of the power series $\sum\limits_{n=0}^{\infty} c_n x^n$ is

(i) 0 if $\overline{\lim\limits_{n}} \, |c_n|^{1/n} = +\infty$.

(ii) $\dfrac{1}{\overline{\lim\limits_{n}} \, |c_n|^{1/n}}$ if $\overline{\lim\limits_{n}} \, |c_n|^{1/n} > 0$.

(iii) infinite if $\overline{\lim\limits_{n}} \, |c_n|^{1/n} = 0$.

The reason for the terminology becomes apparent in

Theorem 9-6-5. For the power series $\sum\limits_{n=0}^{\infty} c_n x^n$,

(i) If the radius of convergence is 0, then the series diverges for all $x \neq 0$.

(ii) If the radius of convergence is the positive number R, then the series is convergent when $|x| < R$ and is divergent when $|x| > R$.

(iii) If the radius of convergence is infinite, then the series is convergent for all x.

Proof. We consider only (ii), leaving (i) and (iii) to the exercises.

$$|x| < R \text{ implies } \overline{\lim_{n}} \, |c_n x^n|^{1/n} = |x| \, \overline{\lim_{n}} \, |c_n|^{1/n}$$
$$= \frac{|x|}{R}$$
$$< 1$$

so that the series converges by the root test.

$$|x| > R \text{ implies } \overline{\lim_{n}} \, |c_n x^n|^{1/n} = \frac{|x|}{R} > 1$$

which implies $\lim\limits_{n \to \infty} c_n x^n \neq 0$ so that the series diverges. ∎

For uniform convergence of a power series, we have

Theorem 9-6-6. If the positive number R is the radius of convergence of the power series $\sum_{n=0}^{\infty} c_n x^n$, then, for every δ such that $0 < \delta < R$, the power series is uniformly convergent on $[-R + \delta, R - \delta]$. If the radius of convergence of a power series is infinite, then the power series is uniformly convergent on every closed, bounded interval.

Proof. We consider only the case of a finite radius of convergence, leaving the infinite case to the exercises.

$$|x| \leq R - \delta \text{ implies } |c_n x^n| \leq |c_n| (R - \delta)^n$$

Since $0 < R - \delta < R$, the series of numbers $\sum_{n=0}^{\infty} c_n (R - \delta)^n$ is convergent, so that the uniform convergence of the power series on $[-R + \delta, R - \delta]$ follows from the Weierstrass M-test in which $M_n = c_n (R - \delta)^n$. ∎

The partial sums of a power series are polynomials and thus possess derivatives of all orders. For the series formed from the derivatives, we have

Theorem 9-6-7. The radius of convergence of the power series $\sum_{n=1}^{\infty} nc_n x^{n-1}$ is the same as the radius of convergence of the series $\sum_{n=0}^{\infty} c_n x^n$.

Proof. Again we consider only the case of a positive radius of convergence, leaving the other two cases to the exercises. We assume that the radius of convergence is the positive number R. Thus

$$\frac{1}{R} = \overline{\lim_n} |c_n|^{1/n}$$

We know

$$\lim_{n \to \infty} n^{1/n} = \lim_{n \to \infty} e^{(\log n)/n} = 1$$

For any $\epsilon > 0$, there exists an integer N such that

$$n > N \text{ implies } |1 - n^{1/n}| < \epsilon$$

$$1 - \epsilon < n^{1/n} < 1 + \epsilon$$

$$(1 - \epsilon) |c_n|^{1/n} < |nc_n|^{1/n} < (1 + \epsilon) |c_n|^{1/n}$$

Then we must have

$$\frac{1 - \epsilon}{R} \leq \overline{\lim_n} |nc_n|^{1/n} \leq \frac{1 + \epsilon}{R}$$

Thus, for every $\epsilon > 0$,

$$\left| R \,\overline{\lim_{n}}\, |nc_n|^{1/n} - 1 \right| < \epsilon \quad \text{or} \quad \overline{\lim_{n}}\, |nc_n|^{1/n} = \frac{1}{R}$$

which means that the two series have the same radius of convergence. ∎

Since this theorem applies to the power series formed of the derivatives of the functions forming the given power series, we must have the new series uniformly convergent on every closed subinterval of the interval of convergence (the same interval of convergence for both series). Thus if a given power series $\sum_{n=0}^{\infty} c_n x^n$ is convergent to the function f, then the power series $\sum_{n=1}^{\infty} nc_n x^{n-1}$ must be convergent to f'.

In other words, the theorems about uniformly convergent sequences of functions allow us to differentiate or integrate power series term by term, taking derivatives of all orders.

Putting this in reverse, a function which is the sum of a power series has derivatives of all orders, the domain of that function, of necessity, being the interval of convergence of the power series. For the relation between the function which is the sum and the coefficients of the power series, we have

Theorem 9-6-8. If the radius of convergence of the power series $\sum_{n=0}^{\infty} c_n x^n$ is not 0, and the series converges to the function f, then, for $m = 1, 2, \ldots$,

$$c_m = \frac{1}{m!} f^{(m)}(0)$$

Proof. Since the radius of convergence is not 0, there is some $P > 0$ such that the power series and all the series of derivatives of all orders are uniformly convergent on $[-P, P]$. We specify the functions s_n by

$$s_n(x) = \sum_{k=0}^{n} c_k x^k, \qquad n = 0, 1, 2, \ldots$$

If $n \leq m$ and $|x| \leq P$, then $s_n^{(m)}(x) = 0$. If $n > m$ and $|x| \leq P$, then

$$s_n^{(m)}(x) = \sum_{k=m}^{n} k(k-1)(k-2) \cdots (k-m+1)c_k x^{k-m}$$

Thus for $n > m$, $s_n^{(m)}(0) = m!\, c_m$ so that

$$f^{(m)}(0) = \lim_{n \to \infty} s_n^{(m)}(0) = m!\, c_m \qquad\qquad ∎$$

Finally we give a tool for determining the radius of convergence which is often more easily applied than the definition itself.

Theorem 9-6-9. $\{c_n \mid n = 0, 1, \ldots\}$ is the sequence of coefficients of a power series. If $\lim_{n \to \infty} |c_{n+1}/c_n| = L > 0$, then the radius of convergence of $\sum_{n=0}^{\infty} c_n x^n$ is $1/L$.

Proof. From the hypothesis, given $\epsilon > 0$, there exists an integer N such that

$$n > N \text{ implies } \left| \frac{c_{n+1}}{c_n} - 1 \right| < \epsilon$$

(Here, for convenience, we assume all $c_n > 0$.) Then, for $n > N$,

$$c_n = c_N \frac{c_{N+1}}{c_N} \frac{c_{N+2}}{c_{N+1}} \cdots \frac{c_n}{c_{n-1}}$$

$$(c_n)^{1/n} = (c_N)^{1/n} \left(\frac{c_{N+1}}{c_N} \right)^{1/n} \left(\frac{c_{N+2}}{c_{N+1}} \right)^{1/n} \cdots \left(\frac{c_n}{c_{n-1}} \right)^{1/n}$$

But, for $k = 1, 2, \ldots, n - N - 1$,

$$L - \epsilon < \frac{c_{N+k+1}}{c_{N+k}} < L + \epsilon$$

so that

$$(L - \epsilon)^{n-N-1} < \frac{c_{N+1}}{c_N} \frac{c_{N+2}}{c_{N+1}} \cdots \frac{c_n}{c_{n-1}} < (L + \epsilon)^{n-N-1}$$

$$(L - \epsilon)^{(n-N-1)/n} < \left(\frac{c_{N+1}}{c_N} \right)^{1/n} \left(\frac{c_{N+2}}{c_{N+1}} \right)^{1/n} \cdots \left(\frac{c_n}{c_{n-1}} \right)^{1/n} < (L + \epsilon)^{(n-N-1)/n}$$

Taking limits, limit inferior, and limit superior, we have

$$L - \epsilon \leq \varliminf_n \left(\frac{c_n}{c_N} \right)^{1/n} \leq \varlimsup_n \left(\frac{c_n}{c_N} \right)^{1/n} < L + \epsilon$$

Since this inequality is true for every $\epsilon > 0$, we conclude that $\lim_{n \to \infty} (c_n/c_N)^{1/n}$ exists and is L. Further, since N is fixed, $\lim_{n \to \infty} (c_N)^{1/n} = 1$. Thus, by the theorem on the limit of the product of two sequences, $\lim_{n \to \infty} |c_n|^{1/n}$ exists and is L. But this last limit is precisely the reciprocal of the radius of convergence. ∎

EXERCISES

1. Complete the proof of Theorem 9-6-5.

2. Complete the proof of Theorem 9-6-6.

3. Complete the proof of Theorem 9-6-7.

Determine the interval of convergence for the following power series:

4. $\sum_{n=1}^{\infty} x^n/n^2$

5. $\sum_{n=1}^{\infty} nx^n$

6. $\sum_{n=1}^{\infty} nx^n/2^n$

7. $\sum_{n=1}^{\infty} (x-3)^n/n^2$

8. $\sum_{n=0}^{\infty} x^n/n!$

9. $\sum_{n=0}^{\infty} (nx)^n$

10. $\sum_{n=0}^{\infty} [(2n)!/(n!)^2]x^n$

Show that each of the following series is uniformly convergent in the given interval:

11. $\sum_{n=1}^{\infty} x^n/n^3$, $\qquad [-1, 1]$

12. $\sum_{n=1}^{\infty} nx^n$, $\qquad [-\frac{1}{2}, \frac{1}{2}]$

13. $\sum_{n=1}^{\infty} n(n-1)x^n$, $\qquad [-a, a]$, where $0 < a < 1$

14. Prove that if, for $a \le x \le b$ and $n = 1, 2, \ldots, 0 < u_n(x) < 1/n$ and $u_{n+1}(x) \le u_n(x)$, then $\sum_{n=1}^{\infty} (-1)^{n+1}u_n(x)$ is uniformly convergent on $[a, b]$.

9-7 End Points and Applications

We have thus far determined that a power series with a positive radius of convergence converges to a function with derivatives of all orders, the domain of which function is the interior of the interval of convergence. The two series of numbers achieved by substituting the end points of the interval of convergence may be both divergent, both convergent, or one convergent and the other divergent. The basic result concerning end points is

Theorem 9-7-1. The power series $\sum_{n=0}^{\infty} c_n x^n$ has radius of convergence $R > 0$. If the series of numbers $\sum_{n=0}^{\infty} c_n R^n$ is convergent, then the original power series is uniformly convergent on $[0, R]$.

Proof. By hypothesis, the series of numbers $\sum\limits_{n=0}^{\infty} c_n R^n$ is convergent. We call its sum S and form a sequence by

$$E_n = S - \sum_{k=0}^{n} c_k R^k, \qquad n = 0, 1, 2, \ldots$$

Then $\lim\limits_{n \to \infty} E_n = 0$. For a given $\epsilon > 0$, there exists an integer N_ϵ such that

$$n > N_\epsilon \text{ implies } |E_n| < \frac{\epsilon}{3}$$

For $n = 0, 1, 2, \ldots, p = 1, 2, \ldots$, and $x \in [0, R]$,

$$\sum_{k=n}^{n+p} c_k x^k = \sum_{k=n}^{n+p} c_k R^k \left(\frac{x}{R}\right)^k$$

$$= \sum_{k=n}^{n+p} (E_k - E_{k+1}) \left(\frac{x}{R}\right)^k$$

$$= E_n \left(\frac{x}{R}\right)^n + \sum_{k=n+1}^{n+p} E_k \left(\frac{x}{R}\right)^k - \sum_{k=n+1}^{n+p} E_k \left(\frac{x}{R}\right)^{k-1} - E_{n+p+1}\left(\frac{x}{R}\right)^{n+p}$$

$$= E_n \left(\frac{x}{R}\right)^n + \left(\frac{x}{R} - 1\right) \sum_{k=n+1}^{n+p} E_k \left(\frac{x}{R}\right)^{k-1} - E_{n+p+1}\left(\frac{x}{R}\right)^{n+p}$$

If, in addition, $n > N_\epsilon$, then

$$\left| \sum_{k=n}^{n+p} c_k x^k \right| \le |E_n| \left(\frac{x}{R}\right)^n + \left(1 - \frac{x}{R}\right) \sum_{k=n+1}^{n+p} |E_k| \left(\frac{x}{R}\right)^{k-1} + E_{n+p+1}\left(\frac{x}{R}\right)^{n+p}$$

$$< \left(\frac{\epsilon}{3}\right) + \left(1 - \frac{x}{R}\right)\left(\frac{\epsilon}{3}\right) \sum_{j=0}^{p-1} \left(\frac{x}{R}\right)^{n+j} + \left(\frac{\epsilon}{3}\right)$$

$$< \left(\frac{\epsilon}{3}\right) + \left(1 - \frac{x}{R}\right)\left(\frac{\epsilon}{3}\right)\frac{1}{1 - (x/R)} + \left(\frac{\epsilon}{3}\right) = \epsilon$$

Thus $n > N_\epsilon$ implies that, for all $x \in [0, R]$,

$$\left| \sum_{k=n}^{n+p} c_k x^k \right| < \epsilon$$

and the series is uniformly convergent on $[0, R]$.   ∎

A proof essentially the same gives

Theorem 9-7-2. The power series $\sum\limits_{n=0}^{\infty} c_n x^n$ has radius of convergence $R > 0$. If the series of numbers $\sum\limits_{n=0}^{\infty} c_n(-R)^n$ is convergent, then the original power series is uniformly convergent on $[-R, 0]$.

We turn now to a few applications.

The geometric series $\sum\limits_{n=0}^{\infty} x^n$ has radius of convergence 1 and thus is convergent pointwise on the interval $]-1, 1[$ with uniform convergence on any closed subinterval of $]-1, 1[$. For $|x| < 1$,

$$\lim_{n \to \infty} \sum_{k=0}^{n} x^k = \frac{1}{1 - x}$$

Since a power series may be integrated term by term within the interval of convergence, for $|x| < 1$,

$$\sum_{n=0}^{\infty} \int_0^x t^n \, dt \text{ converges to } \int_0^x \frac{dt}{1 - t}$$

$$\sum_{n=0}^{\infty} \frac{x^{n+1}}{n + 1} \text{ converges to } -\log(1 - x)$$

$$\sum_{n=1}^{\infty} \frac{x^n}{n} \text{ converges to } -\log(1 - x)$$

For this last series, $\sum\limits_{n=1}^{\infty} (-1)^n/n$ is convergent (by the alternating series test) so that $\sum\limits_{n=1}^{\infty} x^n/n$ is uniformly convergent on $[-1, 0]$. Therefore, $\sum\limits_{n=1}^{\infty} (-1)^n/n$ must be convergent to $-\log[1 - (-1)] = -\log 2$. In more convenient terms, the alternating harmonic series $\sum\limits_{n=1}^{\infty} (-1)^{n+1}/n$ converges to $\log 2$.

Taking a modification of the geometric series, for $|x| < 1$,

$$\sum_{n=0}^{\infty} (-1)^n x^{2n} \text{ converges to } \frac{1}{1 + x^2}$$

$$\sum_{n=0}^{\infty} (-1)^n \int_0^x t^{2n} \, dt \text{ converges to } \int_0^x \frac{dt}{1 + t^2}$$

$$\sum_{n=0}^{\infty} \frac{(-1)^n x^{2n+1}}{2n + 1} \text{ converges to } \arctan x$$

Since the series of numbers $\sum\limits_{n=0}^{\infty} [(-1)^n (1)^{2n+1}]/(2n + 1)$ is convergent,

$$\sum_{n=0}^{\infty} \frac{(-1)^n}{2n + 1} \text{ converges to } \frac{\pi}{4}$$

For every real number z, $\sum\limits_{n=0}^{\infty} z^n/n!$ converges to e^z.

Thus, for every real number x,

$$\sum_{n=0}^{\infty} \frac{(-1)^n x^{2n}}{n!} \text{ converges to } e^{-x^2}$$

$$\sum_{n=0}^{\infty} \frac{(-1)^n x^{2n+1}}{n!\,(2n+1)} \text{ converges to } \int_0^x e^{-t^2}\,dt$$

We say in considering improper integrals that for very large values of x this integral is near $\frac{1}{2}\sqrt{\pi}$. This series representation allows us to find approximations to this integral for values of x near 0.

In the following, all series are absolutely convergent for every real number x and every real number y:

$$e^x e^y = \lim_{n \to \infty} \sum_{k=0}^{n} \frac{x^k}{k!} \sum_{k=0}^{n} \frac{y^k}{k!}$$

$$= \lim_{n \to \infty} \sum_{k=0}^{n} \sum_{j=0}^{n} \frac{x^j}{j!} \frac{y^{k-j}}{(k-j)!}$$

$$= \lim_{n \to \infty} \sum_{k=0}^{n} \frac{1}{k!} \sum_{j=0}^{k} \frac{k!}{j!\,(k-j)!} x^j y^{k-j}$$

$$= \lim_{n \to \infty} \sum_{k=0}^{n} \frac{1}{k!} (x+y)^k$$

$$= e^{x+y}$$

$$\sin x \cos x = \lim_{n \to \infty} \sum_{k=0}^{n} \frac{(-1)^k x^{2k+1}}{(2k+1)!} \sum_{k=0}^{n} \frac{(-1)^k x^{2k}}{(2k)!}$$

$$= \lim_{n \to \infty} \sum_{k=0}^{n} \sum_{j=0}^{k} \frac{(-1)^j x^{2j}}{(2j)!} \frac{(-1)^{k-j} x^{2k+1-2j}}{(2k-2j)!}$$

$$= \lim_{n \to \infty} \sum_{k=0}^{n} (-1)^k x^{2k+1} \sum_{j=0}^{k} \frac{1}{(2j)!\,(2k+1-2j)!}$$

$$= \lim_{n \to \infty} \sum_{k=0}^{n} \frac{(-1)^k x^{2k+1}}{(2k+1)!}$$

$$\times \frac{1}{2}\left[\sum_{i=0}^{2k+1} \frac{(2k+1)!}{i!\,(2k+1-i)!} + \sum_{i=0}^{2k+1} \frac{(2k+1)!}{i!\,(2k+1-i)!}(-1)^i\right]$$

$$= \lim_{n \to \infty} \sum_{k=0}^{n} \frac{(-1)^k x^{2k+1}}{(2k+1)!} \frac{1}{2}[(1+1)^{2k+1} + (1-1)^{2k+1}]$$

$$= \frac{1}{2} \lim_{n \to \infty} \sum_{k=0}^{n} \frac{(-1)^k (2x)^{2k+1}}{(2k+1)!}$$

$$= \tfrac{1}{2}\sin 2x$$

so that

$$\sin 2x = 2 \sin x \cos x$$

We conclude with a relation which is based on the fact that the theorems proved for series of real numbers have valid analogues for series of complex numbers, even though we have neither stated nor proved these theorems. Using only the statement $i^2 = -1$ and accepting that all manipulations are valid, we have

$$e^{ix} = \lim_{n \to \infty} \sum_{k=0}^{n} \frac{(ix)^k}{k!}$$

$$= \lim_{n \to \infty} \sum_{j=0}^{n} \frac{(ix)^{2j}}{(2j)!} + \lim_{n \to \infty} \sum_{j=0}^{n} \frac{(ix)^{2j+1}}{(2j+1)!}$$

$$= \lim_{n \to \infty} \sum_{j=0}^{n} \frac{(-1)^j x^{2j}}{(2j)!} + \lim_{n \to \infty} i \sum_{j=0}^{n} \frac{(-1)^j x^{2j+1}}{(2j+1)!}$$

$$= \cos x + i \sin x$$

From this we have, for $k = 1, 2, \ldots,$

$$e^{kix} = (\cos x + i \sin x)^k = \cos kx + i \sin kx$$

For example, for $k = 4$,

$$(\cos x + i \sin x)^4 = \cos 4x + i \sin 4x$$

which implies

$$\cos 4x = \cos^4 x - 6 \cos^2 x \sin^2 x + \sin^4 x$$

and

$$\sin 4x = 4 \cos^3 x \sin x - 4 \cos x \sin^3 x$$

EXERCISES

Discuss the intervals of convergence of the following series, including consideration of the end points.

1. $\displaystyle\sum_{n=1}^{\infty} (-1)^n \frac{(1)(3)(5) \cdots (2n-1)}{(2)(4)(6) \cdots (2n)} \frac{x^n}{n}$

2. $\displaystyle\sum_{n=2}^{\infty} \frac{[(n-1)!]^2}{(2n)!} \frac{x^{2n}}{2^{2n}}$

3. $\displaystyle\sum_{n=1}^{\infty} \frac{(n+1)^n}{n!} x^n$

4. The harmonic series $\displaystyle\sum_{n=1}^{\infty} 1/n$ is divergent. If we construct a sequence by $\left\{ c_n = \displaystyle\sum_{k=1}^{n} 1 - \log n \,\middle|\, n = 1, 2, \ldots \right\}$, show that this sequence is monotone and bounded and, thus, convergent. The limit of this sequence is called *Euler's constant*.

5. For the sequence given in Exercise 4, we form a new sequence by $b_n = c_{2n} - c_n$. Show that $\lim_{n \to \infty} b_n = \log 2$.

6. Use Exercises 4 and 5 to show that if, for $k = 1, 2, \ldots,$

$$a_{3k+1} = \frac{1}{3k+1}, \qquad a_{3k+2} = \frac{1}{3k+2}, \qquad a_{3k+3} = -\frac{1}{3k+3}$$

then $\sum_{n=1}^{\infty} a_n$ is divergent.

The Bessel function of the first kind, of order m, is given by

$$J_m(x) = \sum_{n=0}^{\infty} \frac{(-1)^n}{(n+m)!\, n!} \left(\frac{x}{2}\right)^{2n+m}$$

7. Show that $\dfrac{d}{dx}[xJ_1(x)] = xJ_0(x)$.

8. Show that $\dfrac{d}{dx}[x^2 J_2(x)] = x^2 J_1(x)$.

9. Generalize the results of Exercises 7 and 8.

10. Show that $\dfrac{d}{dx}\left[\dfrac{1}{x} J_1(x)\right] = -\dfrac{1}{x} J_2(x)$

11. Generalize the result of Exercise 10.

12. The power series $\sum_{n=0}^{\infty} c_n x^n$ is convergent to the function f on the interval $[-R, R]$. Show that if $f(x) = f(-x)$, then, for $k = 0, 1, 2, \ldots, c_{2k+1} = 0$. Show that if $f(-x) = -f(x)$, then, for $k = 0, 1, 2, \ldots, c_{2k} = 0$.

13. The power series $\sum_{n=0}^{\infty} x^n/n!$ converges to a function f whose domain is the set of all real numbers. Show that $f(0) = 1$ and $f' = f$, so that we must have $f(x) = e^x$.

14. Use a power series expansion for $\dfrac{d}{dx}(x^2 e^{-x})$ to show that

$$\sum_{n=1}^{\infty} \frac{n+2}{n!}(-2)^{n+1}$$

converges to 4.

REPRESENTATIONS 10
OF FUNCTIONS

10-1 Power Series Representations

We saw in the preceding chapter that a power series converges to a function which has derivatives of all orders and whose domain is the interval of convergence of the power series. If we begin with a function which does have—at least at one point—derivatives of all orders, we establish the following terminology.

> *Definition 10-1-1.* f is a function on a set of real numbers into the real numbers. At the real number a, f has derivatives of all orders. The *Taylor series of f, centered at a,* is the power series
>
> $$\sum_{n=0}^{\infty} \frac{f^{(n)}(a)}{n!} (x - a)^n$$
>
> The *Maclaurin series of f* is the Taylor series of f, centered at 0.

Directly from the definition, a function will have a Taylor series at each number for which it has derivatives of all orders. The basic question is concerned with what relations, if any, there are between the series and the function. We have already established, by the theorems on power series,

> *Theorem 10-1-1.* If the function f on $]a - r, a + r[$ into the real numbers has a Taylor series, centered at a, with radius of convergence R (where $r > 0$ and $R > 0$), then
>
> (i) On $]a - R, a + R[$, the Taylor series converges to a function which agrees with f on $]a - r, a + r[\cap]a - R, a + R[$.
>
> (ii) f has derivatives of all orders at each number in $]a - r, a + r[\cap]a - R, a + R[$.
>
> (iii) Any power series, centered at a, which converges to the restriction of f to some open interval containing a must be the Taylor series of f centered at a.

From the first part of the conclusion of this theorem, if $r > R$, then the Taylor series provides us with a method of approximating f by polynomials, which method is valid for only part of the domain of f. On the other hand, if $r < R$, the theorem allows us to view f as a restriction of some function F, with a larger domain, and to know that—from parts (ii) and (iii)—F is the only function with derivatives of all orders which can agree with f on $]a - r, a + r[$.

Part (ii) of the conclusion gives a way in which knowledge of the derivatives of f at one point will give the existence of the derivatives in a neighborhood of that point.

Part (iii), giving the uniqueness of the Taylor series, tells us that any power series representation of f on an interval—although possibly the result of multiplication of series, of term-by-term integration, or of other means—must necessarily be the Taylor series.

We now examine some specific examples.

EXAMPLE 1. f is the function on $]0, +\infty[$ given by

$$f(x) = x^{1/2}$$

f has derivatives of all orders on $[0, +\infty[$ and

$$f'(x) = \tfrac{1}{2}x^{-1/2}$$

Further, if

$$f^{(n)}(x) = (-1)^n \frac{(1)(3)(5) \cdots (2n - 3)}{2^n} x^{-(2n-1)/2}$$

then

$$f^{(n+1)}(x) = (-1)^{n+1} \frac{(1)(3)(5) \cdots (2n - 1)}{2^{n+1}} x^{-(2n-3)/2}$$

so that the expression given for $f^{(n)}$ is valid for $n = 2, 3, \dots$. If $a > 0$, then

$$f^{(n)}(a) = (-1)^{n+1} \frac{(1)(3)(5) \cdots (2n - 3)}{2^n} a^{-(2n-1)/2}$$

and the Taylor series, centered at a, of f is

$$\frac{1}{2} a^{-1/2} - \frac{1}{4} a^{-3/2} + \sum_{n=2}^{\infty} \frac{(-1)^n (2n - 2)!}{n!\, 2^{2n}(n - 1)!} a^{-(n-1/2)}(x - a)^n$$

The radius of convergence of this series is

$$\lim_{n \to \infty} \frac{(2n - 2)!\, a^{-(n-1/2)}}{2^{2n} n!\, (n - 1)!} \frac{2^{2n+2} n!\, (n + 1)!}{(2n)!\, a^{-(n+1/2)}} = \lim_{n \to \infty} \frac{4n(n + 1)a}{2n(2n + 1)} = a$$

This means that the Taylor series, centered at $a > 0$, for the function given by $f(x) = x^{-1/2}$ converges to the restriction of that function to the interval $[0, 2a]$.

EXAMPLE 2. f is the function on $]-\infty, +\infty[$ onto $]-\pi/2, \pi/2[$ given by

$$f(x) = \text{arc tan } x$$

Then f has derivatives of all orders and, in particular,

$$f'(x) = \frac{1}{1+x^2}$$

The power series $\displaystyle\sum_{n=0}^{\infty} (-1)^n x^{2n}$ converges to the restriction of f' to $]-1, 1[$. Thus the new power series obtained by integrating term by term,

$$\sum_{n=0}^{\infty} \int_0^x (-1)^n t^{2n}\, dt = \sum_{n=0}^{\infty} \frac{(-1)^n x^{2n+1}}{2n+1}$$

converges to the restriction of the arc tangent function to $]-1, 1[$. This power series is necessarily the Maclaurin series for the arc tangent function so that, for this function, we have, for $n = 0, 1, 2, \ldots$,

$$f^{(2n+1)}(0) = \frac{n!\,(-1)^n}{2n+1}$$

and

$$f^{(2n)}(0) = 0$$

Thus we have reversed the procedure and used the Taylor series to determine the values of the derivatives.

EXAMPLE 3. Since the Taylor series represents the function whenever the radius of convergence is positive, a function will fail to have such a representation when its Taylor series does not have a positive radius of convergence. Such a function is that given by

$$f(x) = \begin{cases} e^{-1/x^2} & \text{for } x \neq 0 \\ 0 & \text{for } x = 0 \end{cases}$$

For $p = 0, 1, 2, \ldots$,

$$\lim_{h \to 0+} \frac{1}{h^p} e^{-1/h^2} = \lim_{r \to +\infty} r^p e^{-r^2} = 0$$

and

$$\lim_{h \to 0-} \frac{1}{h^p} e^{-1/h^2} = 0$$

so that

$$\lim_{h \to 0} \frac{1}{h^p} e^{-1/h^2} = 0$$

For $p = 0$, this result implies that f is continuous at 0. For $p = 1$, this result implies that f is differentiable at 0 and $f'(0) = 0$. Further, if $f^{(n)}(0) = 0$, then

$$f^{(n+1)}(0) = \lim_{h \to 0} \frac{1}{h}\, f^{(n)}(h)$$

But, for $h \neq 0$,

$$f^{(n)}(h) = P\left(\frac{1}{h}\right)e^{-1/h^2}$$

where P is a polynomial. Thus $f^{(n+1)}(0)$ exists and is 0. Thus f has derivatives of all orders at 0, but since each of these is 0, the Maclaurin series of f has infinite radius of convergence and converges to the function identically zero which is far from a representation of f.

The use of Taylor series to represent functions becomes more powerful when one deals with functions whose domains and ranges are sets of complex numbers.

As a final example of the uses of power series, we consider

Theorem 10-1-2. If the power series $\sum_{n=0}^{\infty} c_n x^n$ has nonzero radius of convergence R and the function to which the series converges is a solution of the differential equation

$$a_2 y'' + a_1 y' + a_0 y = 0$$

then, for $n = 0, 1, 2, \ldots$,

$$a_2(n + 2)(n + 1)c_{n+2} + a_1(n + 1)c_{n+1} + a_0 c_n = 0$$

Proof. By hypothesis, the power series $\sum_{n=0}^{\infty} c_n x^n$ converges to the function f on the interval $]-R, R[$. Then the power series $\sum_{n=0}^{\infty} nc_n x^{n-1}$ converges to f' on this interval and the power series $\sum_{n=0}^{\infty} n(n - 1)c_n x^{n-2}$ converges to f'' on this interval. For every $x \in]-R, R[$,

$$0 = a_0 f''(x) + a_1 f'(x) + a_2 f(x)$$

$$= \lim_{n \to \infty} \left[a_0 \sum_{k=0}^{n} c_k x^k + a_1 \sum_{k=0}^{n} (k + 1)c_{k+1}x^k + a_2 \sum_{k=0}^{n} (k + 2)(k + 1)c_{k+2}x^k \right]$$

$$= \lim_{n \to \infty} \sum_{k=0}^{n} [a_2(k + 2)(k + 1)c_{k+2} + a_1(k + 1)c_{k+1} + a_0 c_k]x^k$$

Thus the power series with coefficients

$$a_2(n + 2)(n + 1)c_{n+2} + a_1(n + 1)c_{n+1} + a_0 c_n, \qquad n = 0, 1, 2, \ldots$$

converges to the restriction of the function identically zero to the interval $[-R, R]$. Since the function identically zero has derivatives of all orders, each one of which is also the function identically zero, the Maclaurin series of this function has all its coefficients zero. Since we now have two series, one with all zero coefficients and the other with the coefficients given above, both converging to the same function, each of the coefficients given above is zero and the theorem is proved.   ∎

The equations given in the conclusion of this theorem provide a way of determining a recursion relation between the coefficients.

EXAMPLE. We consider the differential equation

$$y'' + y = 0$$

The recursion relation for the coefficients of a power series, centered at 0, which power series converges to a solution of this differential equation, will be, for $n = 0, 1, 2, \ldots$,

$$(n + 2)(n + 1)c_{n+2} + c_n = 0$$

or

$$c_{n+2} = -\frac{c_n}{(n + 2)(n + 1)}$$

We then conclude that, for $k = 0, 1, 2, \ldots$,

$$c_{2k+2} = -\frac{c_{2k}}{(2k + 2)(2k + 1)}$$

$$= (-1)^k \frac{c_0}{(2k + 2)!}$$

and

$$c_{2k+3} = -\frac{c_{2k+1}}{(2k + 3)(2k + 1)}$$

$$= (-1)^k \frac{c_1}{(2k + 3)!}$$

Thus a solution of $y'' + y = 0$ is the function represented by the power series

$$c_0 \sum_{n=0}^{\infty} \frac{(-1)^n x^{2n}}{(2n)!} + c_1 \sum_{n=0}^{\infty} \frac{(-1)^n x^{2n+1}}{(2n + 1)!}$$

which is the function given by

$$c_0 \cos x + c_1 \sin x$$

E X E R C I S E S

Find the Maclaurin series for the functions given by the following, and determine their interval of convergence.

1. $P(x)$ where P is a polynomial of degree m.

2. $(1 - x)^{-1/2}$

3. $(1 - x)^{-(2p+1)/2}$,   where p is a positive integer

4. $(1 + x)^m$

5. $\int_0^x [(\sin t)/t] \, dt$

6. $\cosh x$

7. $\log (1 + x)$

8. $\cos^2 x$

Find a Maclaurin series solution to the following differential equations.

9. $y' = y$

10. $y'' - y = 0$

11. $y'' - 2y' - 3y = 0$

12. $y'' - 2y' + y = 0$

10-2   Representation by Integrals

The Fundamental Theorem of Calculus provides us with an elementary instance of a function's being represented by an integral. If g is continuous on $[a, b]$ and f is given by

$$f(x) = \int_a^x g$$

then, at least for $x \in \,]a, b[, f'(x) = g(x)$.

A slightly more complicated form of representation occurs when we begin with a function g on $[a, b] \times [c, d]$ into the real numbers and specify f, a function on this same rectangle into the real numbers, by

$$f(x, y) = \int_c^y g(x, t) \, dt$$

An immediate result of the Fundamental Theorem of Calculus is that, at least for (x, y) in the interior of $[a, b] \times [c, d]$,

$$f_2(x, y) = g(x, y)$$

Here the question of finding f_1 brings up the idea of "differentiation under the integral sign." As with so many mathematical things, we prefer to cope with a complicated situation in order that we may answer the given question and hopefully do still more.

Theorem 10-2-1. u and v are functions on $[a, b]$ into the real numbers which have continuous derivatives, and they have the property that, for all $x \in [a, b]$, $u(x) \leq v(x)$.

$$R = \{(x, y) \mid u(x) \leq y \leq v(x) \quad \text{and} \quad a \leq x \leq b\}$$

g is a continuous function on R with the property that g_1 and g_{11} are continuous. If the function f on $[a, b]$ into the real numbers is given by

$$f(x) = \int_{u(x)}^{v(x)} g(x, t) \, dt$$

then, for $x \in]a, b[$, f is differentiable at x and

$$f'(x) = g(x, v(x))v'(x) - g(x, u(x))u'(x) + \int_{u(x)}^{v(x)} g_1(x, t) \, dt$$

Proof. Fix $x \in]a, b[$. Then for h sufficiently small in absolute value (so that $x + h \in [a, b]$),

$$f(x + h) - f(x) = \int_{u(x+h)}^{v(x+h)} g(x + h, t) \, dt - \int_{u(x)}^{v(x)} g(x, t) \, dt$$

$$= \int_{u(x+h)}^{u(x)} g(x + h, t) \, dt + \int_{u(x)}^{v(x)} [g(x + h, t) - g(x, t)] \, dt$$

$$+ \int_{v(x)}^{v(x+h)} g(x + h, t) \, dt$$

Successive uses of the mean value theorem give the conclusions that

There exists θ_1, $0 < \theta_1 < 1$, such that $u(x + h) = u(x) + hu'(x + \theta_1 h)$
There exists θ_2, $0 < \theta_2 < 1$, such that $v(x + h) = v(x) + hv'(x + \theta_2 h)$

By the mean value theorem for integrals, there exists t_1, t_1 between $u(x)$ and $u(x + h)$ such that

$$\int_{u(x+h)}^{u(x)} g(x + h, t) \, dt = -\int_{u(x)}^{u(x+h)} g(x + h, t) \, dt$$

$$= -[u(x + h) - u(x)]g(x + h, t_1)$$

$$= -hu'(x + \theta_1 h)g(x + h, t_1)$$

Similarly, there exists t_2, t_2 between $v(x)$ and $v(x + h)$ such that

$$\int_{v(x)}^{v(x+h)} g(x + h, t) \, dt = hv'(x + \theta_2 h)g(x + h, t_2)$$

Further, for each $t \in [u(x), v(x)]$, there exists θ_t, $0 < \theta_t < 1$, such that

$$g(x + h, t) - g(x, t) = hg_1(x + \theta_t h, t)$$

Thus

$$\int_{u(x)}^{v(x)} [g(x + h, t) - g(x, t)] \, dt = h \int_{u(x)}^{v(x)} g_1(x + \theta_t h, t) \, dt$$

By the mean value theorem, for each $t \in [u(x), v(x)]$, there exists θ_t^*, $0 < \theta_t^* < 1$, such that

$$g_1(x + \theta_t^* h, t) = g_1(x, t) + \theta_t h g_{11}(x + \theta_t^* h, t)$$

Thus

$$\int_{u(x)}^{v(x)} [g(x + h, t) - g(x, t)]\, dt = h \int_{u(x)}^{v(x)} g_1(x, t)\, dt$$

$$+ h^2 \int_{u(x)}^{v(x)} \theta_t g_{11}(x + \theta_t^* h, t)\, dt$$

Combining, we have, for $h \neq 0$,

$$\frac{f(x + h) - f(x)}{h} = g(x + h, t_2)v'(x + \theta_2 h) - g(x + h, t_1)u'(x + \theta_1 h)$$

$$+ \int_{u(x)}^{v(x)} g_1(x, t)\, dt + h \int_{u(x)}^{v(x)} \theta_t g_{11}(x + \theta_t^* h, t)\, dt$$

The continuity of v' implies $\lim_{h \to 0} v'(x + \theta_2 h) = v'(x)$. The fact that t_2 is between $v(x)$ and $v(x + h)$ implies $\lim_{h \to 0} t_2 = v(x)$. These two, together with the continuity of g, imply that

$$\lim_{h \to 0} g(x + h, t_2)v'(x + \theta_2 h) = g(x, v(x))v'(x)$$

Similar reasoning yields

$$\lim_{h \to 0} g(x + h, t_1)u'(x + \theta_1 h) = g(x, u(x))u'(x)$$

Finally, the continuity of g_{11} and the fact that $0 < \theta_t < 1$ assures that the second integral is bounded so that

$$\lim_{h \to 0} h \int_{u(x)}^{v(x)} \theta_t g_{11}(x + \theta_t^* h, t)\, dt = 0$$

Consequently f is differentiable at x and

$$f'(x) = g(x, v(x))v'(x) - g(x, u(x))u'(x) + \int_{u(x)}^{v(x)} g_{11}(x, t)\, dt \quad \blacksquare$$

EXERCISES

Find f' when f is the function given in 1–7 below

1. $\displaystyle\int_1^x t^n\, dt$

2. $\displaystyle\int_1^{x^2} t^n\, dt$

3. $\displaystyle\int_{x^2}^{3} \log(1+t)\,dt$

4. $\displaystyle\int_{x}^{\tan x} e^{-t^2}\,dt$

5. $\displaystyle\int_{0}^{1/2x} x\sin tx\,dt$

6. $\displaystyle\int_{1}^{x^2} \sin t^2\,dt$

7. $\displaystyle\int_{\sin x}^{e^x} (1+t^3)\,dt$

8. $f(x) = \displaystyle\int_{0}^{4} \log(1-x^2t^2)\,dt$. Show that f has a maximum for $x=0$.

9. $f(x) = \displaystyle\int_{0}^{x} t^n(x-t)^m\,dt$, where m and n are positive integers. Find the mth derivative of f. Find the Maclaurin series for f.

10. f is continuous and has continuous partial derivatives. g is the function given by

$$g(x,y) = \int_{1/x}^{y} \int_{1/v}^{x} f(u,v)\,du\,dv$$

Find $g_{11}, g_{12},$ and g_{22}.

10-3   Representation by Improper Integrals

We now consider how the results of the preceding section are affected if the integrals involved are improper. We will only consider the case in which the interval of integration is unbounded, the results for other types of improper integrals being essentially the same. To begin with, we have

Definition 10-3-1. g is a continuous function on $[a,b] \times [c,+\infty[$ into the real numbers. F is a function on $[a,b]$ into the real numbers.

$$\int_{c}^{+\infty} g(x,\cdot)\ converges\ pointwise\ to\ F(x)\ on\ [a,b]$$

means that, for every $x \in [a,b]$, $\displaystyle\int_{c}^{+\infty} g(x,\cdot)$ is convergent to the number $F(x)$.

$$\int_{c}^{+\infty} g(x,\cdot)\ converges\ uniformly\ to\ F(x)\ on\ [a,b]$$

means that for every $\epsilon > 0$ there exists $B_\epsilon > c$ such that, for all $x \in [a, b]$,

$$\left| F(x) - \int_c^{B_\epsilon} g(x, \cdot) \right| < \epsilon$$

An immediate result of the definition of uniform convergence (and this result is not unexpected) is that the limit function itself is continuous:

Theorem 10-3-1. g is a continuous function on $[a, b] \times [c, +\infty[$ into the real numbers. F is a function on $[a, b]$ into the real numbers. If $\int_c^{+\infty} g(x, \cdot)$ converges uniformly to $F(x)$ on $[a, b]$, then F is continuous.

Proof. Pick $\epsilon > 0$. From the definition of uniform convergence there exists $B_\epsilon > c$ such that, for all $r \in [a, b]$,

$$\left| F(r) - \int_c^{B_\epsilon} g(r, \cdot) \right| < \frac{\epsilon}{3}$$

g is continuous and is thus uniformly continuous on $[a, b] \times [c, B_\epsilon]$. Then there exists $\delta > 0$ such that if $|h| < \delta$, then, for all $(x, y) \in [a, b] \times [c, B_\epsilon]$,

$$|g(x + h, y) - g(x, y)| < \frac{\epsilon}{3(B - c)}$$

For $|h| < \delta$,

$$F(x + h) - F(x) = \int_c^{+\infty} [g(x + h, \cdot) - g(x, \cdot)]$$

$$= \int_c^{B_\epsilon} [g(x + h, \cdot) - g(x, \cdot)]$$

$$+ \left[F(x + h) - \int_c^{B_\epsilon} g(x + h, \cdot) \right]$$

$$- \left[F(x) - \int_c^{B_\epsilon} g(x, \cdot) \right]$$

so that

$$|F(x + h) - F(x)| \leq \int_c^{B_\epsilon} |g(x + h, \cdot) - g(x, \cdot)|$$

$$+ \left| F(x + h) - \int_c^{B_\epsilon} g(x + h, \cdot) \right|$$

$$+ \left| F(x) - \int_c^{B_\epsilon} g(x, \cdot) \right|$$

$$< (B - c) \frac{\epsilon}{3(B - c)} + \frac{\epsilon}{3} + \frac{\epsilon}{3} = \epsilon$$

Thus F is continuous at x for $x \in \,]a, b[$ and has one-sided continuity at a and b. ∎

The method of determining the uniform convergence of a series of functions which we found was the Weierstrass M-test. An analogue for functions given by an improper integral is

Theorem 10-3-2. g is a continuous function on $[a, b] \times [c, +\infty[$ into the real numbers. F is a function on $[a, b]$ into the real numbers. $\int_c^{+\infty} g(x, \cdot\,)$ converges pointwise to F on $[a, b]$. M is a continuous function on $[c, +\infty[$ into the real numbers with the property that for all $(x, y) \in [a, b] \times [c, +\infty[$, $|g(x, y)| \leq M(y))$. If $\int_c^{+\infty} M$ is convergent, then $\int_c^{+\infty} g(x, \cdot\,)$ converges uniformly to $F(x)$ on $[a, b]$.

The proof is left to the exercises.

Pursuing the analogy with functions given by series, we have as a parallel to the term-by-term integration of a series

Theorem 10-3-3. g is a continuous function on $[a, b] \times [c, +\infty[$ into the real numbers. F is a function on $[a, b]$ into the real numbers. $\int_c^{+\infty} g(x, \cdot\,)$ converges uniformly to $F(x)$ on $[a, b]$. If h is the function on $[c, +\infty[$ into the real numbers given by $h(t) = \int_a^b g(\cdot\,, t)$, then $\int_c^{+\infty} h$ is convergent to $\int_a^b F$.

Proof. Pick $\epsilon > 0$. From the uniform convergence there exists $B_\epsilon > c$ such that for all $x \in [a, b]$,

$$\left| F(x) - \int_c^{B_\epsilon} g(x, \cdot\,) \right| < \frac{\epsilon}{b - a}$$

The uniform convergence also implies that F is continuous and, thus, is integrable.

Then

$$\int_a^b F = \int_a^b \left[\int_c^{B_\epsilon} g(x, \cdot\,) - \int_c^{B_\epsilon} g(x, \cdot\,) + F(x) \right] dx$$

$$= \int_a^b \int_c^{B_\epsilon} g(x, t)\, dt\, dx + \int_a^b \left[F(x) - \int_c^{B_\epsilon} g(x, \cdot\,) \right] dx$$

$$= \int_c^{B_\epsilon} \int_a^b g(x, t)\, dx\, dt + \int_a^b \left[F(x) - \int_c^{B_\epsilon} g(x, \cdot\,) \right] dx$$

$$= \int_c^{B_\epsilon} h + \int_a^b \left[F(x) - \int_c^{B_\epsilon} g(x, \cdot\,) \right] dx$$

Thus

$$\left| \int_a^b F - \int_c^{B_\epsilon} h \right| \le \int_a^b \left| F(x) - \int_c^{B_\epsilon} g(x, \cdot) \right| dx$$

$$< (b - a) \frac{\epsilon}{(b - a)} = \epsilon$$

and $\int_c^{+\infty} h$ is convergent to $\int_a^b F$.   ∎

For differentiation, the theorem about series requires the uniform convergence of the series formed by termwise differentiation. For improper integrals we have

Theorem 10-3-4. g is a function on $[a, b] \times [c, +\infty[$ into the real numbers such that g and g_1 are continuous. F and G are functions on $[a, b]$ into the real numbers. If $\int_c^{+\infty} g(x, \cdot)$ converges pointwise to $F(x)$ on $[a, b]$ and $\int_c^{+\infty} g_1(x, \cdot)$ converges uniformly to $G(x)$ on $[a, b]$, then F is differentiable, $F' = G$, and $\int_c^{+\infty} g(x, \cdot)$ converges uniformly to $F(x)$ on $[a, b]$.

Proof. The hypothesis implies that G is continuous and so, for any $x \in [a, b]$, G is integrable on $[a, x]$. We have

$$\int_a^x G = \int_a^x \int_c^{+\infty} g_1(s, t) \, dt \, ds$$

$$= \int_c^{+\infty} \int_a^x g_1(s, t) \, ds \, dt \qquad \text{by Theorem 10-3-3}$$

$$= \int_c^{+\infty} [g(x, t) - g(a, t)] \, dt$$

$$= F(x) - F(a)$$

By the Fundamental Theorem of Calculus, F is differentiable and $F' = G$.

For the uniform convergence and the convergence of $\int_c^{+\infty} g(a, \cdot)$ to $F(a)$, given $\epsilon > 0$, there exists $B_\epsilon > c$ such that

$$\left| F(a) - \int_c^{B_\epsilon} g(a, \cdot) \right| < \frac{\epsilon}{2}$$

and, for all $s \in [a, b]$,

$$\left| G(s) - \int_c^{B_\epsilon} g_1(s, \cdot) \right| < \frac{\epsilon}{2(b - a)}$$

Then, for all $x \in [a, b]$,

$$\left| F(x) - \int_c^{B_\epsilon} g(x, \cdot) \right| \leq \int_a^x \left| G(x) - \int_c^{B_\epsilon} g_1(s, t)\, dt \right| ds + \left| F(a) - \int_c^{B_\epsilon} g(a, \cdot) \right|$$

$$< (b - a)\, \frac{\epsilon}{2(b - a)} + \frac{\epsilon}{2} = \epsilon \qquad \blacksquare$$

EXERCISES

1. Prove Theorem 10-3-2.

2. Show that $\int_1^{+\infty} x^2\, dt/(1 + x^2 t^2)$ is pointwise convergent for all x. Investigate the uniform convergence.

3. For which values of p will $\int_1^{+\infty} dt/(x^2 + t^2)^{p/2}$ be uniformly convergent on $[0, 1]$?

4. Show that $\int_0^{+\infty} e^{-x t^2}\, dt$ is uniformly convergent on $[1, +\infty[$.

5. Show that, for $n = 2, 3, \ldots, \int_0^{+\infty} t^n e^{-x t^2}\, dt$ is uniformly convergent on $[1, +\infty[$.

6. Show that, for $n > 0$, $\int_0^{+\infty} t^n e^{-t^2} \cos(tx)\, dt$ and $\int_0^{+\infty} t^n e^{-t^2} \sin(tx)\, dt$ are uniformly convergent for all x.

7. If $F(x) = \int_0^{+\infty} e^{-t^2} \cos(tx)\, dt$, find F'.

8. Show that $\int_{-\infty}^{+\infty} [(e^{-xt} - e^{-yt})/(1 - e^{-t})]\, dt$ is pointwise convergent for $0 < x < y < 1$. Discuss the uniform convergence.

9. $F(x) = \int_0^{+\infty} e^{-t^2} e^{-x^2/t^2}\, dt$. Find F' and justify the procedure. Find an explicit rule for F. *Hint:* Make the substitution $y = t/x$ in the integral giving F'.

10-4 The Laplace Transform and the Gamma Function

One particular kind of function given by an improper integral which has been extensively studied is that given in

Definition 10-4-1. f is a continuous function on $[0, +\infty[$ into the real numbers. The *Laplace transform of f*, written Lf, is the function specified by

$$\{Lf\}(x) = \int_0^{+\infty} e^{-xt}f(t)\, dt$$

Since the definition calls for the convergence of an improper integral, the domain of the Laplace transform is the set of all values of x for which the improper integral above is convergent. In order to determine the kind of domain one could have, we examine

> ***Theorem 10-4-1.*** If f is a continuous function on $[0, +\infty[$ into the real numbers and the improper {integral $Lf\}(a)$ is convergent, then, for all $x > a$, the improper integral $\{Lf\}(x)$ is convergent.

Proof. For $B > 0$,

$$\int_0^B e^{-xt}f(t)\, dt = \int_0^B e^{-(x-a)t}e^{-at}f(t)\, dt$$

We form a new function g on $[0, +\infty[$ into the real numbers by

$$g(t) = \int_0^t e^{-as}f(s)\, ds$$

Then

$$\int_0^B e^{-xt}f(t)\, dt = \int_0^B e^{-(x-a)t}g'(t)\, dt$$

$$= -(x-a)e^{-(x-a)B} + (x-a)g(0)$$

$$+ (x-a)\int_0^B e^{-(x-a)t}g(t)\, dt$$

The fact that the improper integral $\{Lf\}(a)$ converges implies that $\lim_{B \to +\infty} g(B)$ exists. Thus, since $x - a > 0$, $\lim_{B \to +\infty} -(x-a)e^{-(x-a)B}g(B) = 0$. In addition, the convergence of $\{Lf\}(a)$ implies the existence of a constant M such that, for all $t \geq 0$,

$$|g(t)| \leq M$$

Then use of the comparison test with the convergent improper integral $\int_0^{+\infty} e^{-(x-a)t}\, dt$ shows that $\lim_{B \to +\infty} \int_0^B e^{-(x-a)t}g(t)\, dt$ exists so that $\{Lf\}(x)$ is convergent. ∎

We have two immediate corollaries of this theorem:

> ***Theorem 10-4-2.*** If $\{Lf\}(a)$ is divergent, then, for all $x < a$, $\{Lf\}(x)$ is divergent.

Theorem 10-4-3. If $\{Lf\}(a)$ is convergent, then, for all $R > 0$, $\{Lf\}(x)$ is uniformly convergent on $[a, a + R]$.

The proofs are left to the exercises. The second corollary allows us to integrate and differentiate under the integral sign whenever we are in any closed subinterval of the interval of convergence. (The interval of convergence is necessarily at least a half line.) One result of this fact is

Theorem 10-4-4. If $a > 0$ and $\{Lf\}(x)$ is convergent on $[a, +\infty[$, then, for all $x > 0$,

$$\{Lf'\}(x) = x\{Lf\}(x) - f(0)$$

Proof

$$\int_0^B e^{-xt} f'(t)\, dt = e^{-xB} f(B) - f(0) + x\int_0^B e^{-xt} f(t)\, dt \qquad \blacksquare$$

The theorem stated is not quite correct. The insertion of hypotheses needed to make the conclusion valid is left to the exercises.

An important variation on the concept of the Laplace transform is given by

Definition 10-4-2. The *gamma function* is that function on

$$[0, +\infty[\,\cup\, \bigcup_{k=1}^{\infty}]{-k}, -k + 1[$$

into the real numbers given by

$$\Gamma(x) = \begin{cases} \int_0^{+\infty} t^{x-1} e^{-t}\, dt, & x > 0 \\ \dfrac{1}{x}\Gamma(x + 1), & -k < x < -k + 1, k = 1, 2, \ldots \end{cases}$$

It is an easy exercise to show that the improper integral given in the definition of the gamma function converges for $x > 0$. The functional relation giving the values of the gamma function for negative numbers (nonintegers) is also valid for all positive numbers (including positive integers). This is shown in

Theorem 10-4-5. If $x > 0$, then $\Gamma(x + 1) = x\Gamma(x)$.

Proof

$$\int_0^B t^x e^{-t}\, dt = -Be^{-B} + x\int_0^B t^{x-1} e^{-t}\, dt$$

Taking $\lim_{B\to+\infty}$, we find $\Gamma(x+1) = x\Gamma(x)$. ∎

Theorem 10-4-6. For $k = 1, 2, \ldots$,

$$\Gamma(k+1) = k!$$

Proof

$$\Gamma(0) = 1$$ ∎

Theorem 10-4-7. For $n = 1, 2, \ldots$,

$$\Gamma\left(n + \frac{1}{2}\right) = \frac{(2n)!}{2^{2n}n!}\sqrt{\pi}$$

Proof

$$\Gamma\left(\frac{1}{2}\right) = \int_0^{+\infty} t^{-1/2} e^{-t}\, dt$$
$$= 2\int_0^{+\infty} u^{-1} e^{-u^2}\, du$$
$$= \sqrt{\pi}$$ ∎

A more detailed investigation of the behavior of the gamma function yields a useful approximation for factorials known as *Stirling's formula*:

Theorem 10-4-8

$$\lim_{x\to+\infty} \frac{\Gamma(x+1)}{\sqrt{2\pi}\, x^{x+1/2} e^{-x}} = 1$$

Proof

$$\Gamma(x+1) = \int_0^{+\infty} t^x e^{-t}\, dt = x^{x+1}\int_0^{+\infty} u^x e^{-xu}\, du$$
$$\frac{\Gamma(x+1)}{x^{x+1}} = \int_0^{+\infty} (ue^{-u})^x\, du$$

Examining the integrand, we find that the function given by ue^{-u} has a maximum value of $1/e$ when $u = 1$. We then consider three integrals.

For $0 < \delta < 1$,

$$\int_0^{1-\delta} (ue^{-u})^x \, du \leq (1 - \delta)[(1 - \delta)e^{-(1-\delta)}]^x$$

$$< [(1 - \delta)e^{-(1-\delta)}]^x$$

$$\int_{1+\epsilon}^{+\infty} (ue^{-u})^x \, du = \int_{1+\epsilon}^{+\infty} (ue^{-u})(ue^{-u})^{x-1} \, du$$

$$\leq [(1 + \epsilon)e^{-(1+\epsilon)}]^{x-1} \int_{1+\epsilon}^{+\infty} ue^{-u} \, du$$

$$< (\text{const.}) \, [(1 + \epsilon)e^{-(1+\epsilon)}]^{x-1}$$

$$\int_{1-\delta}^{1+\epsilon} (ue^{-u})^x \, du = e^{-x} \int_{-\delta}^{\epsilon} [(1 + t)e^{-t}]^x \, dt$$

For $|t| \leq \frac{1}{2}$, we have

$$\log(1 + t) = \lim_{n \to \infty} \sum_{k=1}^{n} \frac{(-1)^{k+1}t^k}{k}$$

$$\log(1 + t) - t = \lim_{n \to \infty} \sum_{k=2}^{n} \frac{(-1)^{k+1}t^k}{k}$$

$$= -\frac{t^2}{2} \lim_{n \to \infty} \sum_{k=0}^{n} \frac{2(-1)^k t^k}{k + 2}$$

$$(1 + t)e^{-t} = \exp\left[-\frac{t^2}{2} \lim_{n \to \infty} \sum_{k=0}^{n} \frac{2(-1)^k t^k}{k + 2}\right]$$

Since

$$\lim_{t \to 0} \lim_{n \to \infty} \sum_{k=0}^{n} \frac{2(-1)^k t^k}{k + 2} = 1, \text{ given } \eta > 0$$

we may take δ and ϵ sufficiently small so that

$$-\delta < t < \epsilon \text{ implies } \left| 1 - \lim_{n \to \infty} \sum_{k=0}^{n} \frac{2(-1)^k t^k}{k + 2} \right| < \eta$$

We then have

$$e^{-(t^2 x/2)(1+\eta)} < [(1 + t)e^{-t}]^x < e^{-(t^2 x/2)(1-\eta)}$$

$$\int_{-\delta}^{\epsilon} e^{-(t^2 x/2)(1+\eta)} \, dt < \int_{-\delta}^{\epsilon} [(1 + t)e^{-t}]^x \, dt$$

$$< \int_{-\delta}^{\epsilon} e^{-(t^2 x/2)(1-\eta)} \, dt$$

For the integrals on the two ends of this string of inequalities we have

$$\int_0^\epsilon e^{-kt^2}\, dt = \frac{1}{\sqrt{kx}} \int_0^{\epsilon\sqrt{kx}} e^{-t^2}\, dt$$

$$\sqrt{x}\int_0^\epsilon e^{-kxt^2}\, dt = \frac{1}{\sqrt{k}} \int_0^{\sqrt{kx}\,\epsilon} e^{-t^2}\, dt$$

$$\lim_{x\to+\infty} \sqrt{x}\int_0^\epsilon e^{-kxt^2}\, dt = \frac{1}{2}\sqrt{\frac{\pi}{k}}$$

Similarly,

$$\lim_{x\to+\infty} \sqrt{x}\int_{-\delta}^0 e^{-kxt^2}\, dt = \frac{1}{2}\sqrt{\frac{\pi}{k}}$$

Thus

$$\lim_{x\to+\infty} \sqrt{x}\int_{-\delta}^\epsilon e^{-kxt^2}\, dt = \sqrt{\frac{\pi}{k}}$$

Returning to the inequalities above, we have

$$\sqrt{x}\int_{-\delta}^\epsilon e^{-[(t^2x)(1+\eta)]/2}\, dt < \sqrt{x}\int_{-\delta}^\epsilon [(1+t)e^{-t}]^x\, dt$$

$$< \sqrt{x}\int_{-\delta}^\epsilon e^{-[(t^2x)(1-\eta)]/2}\, dt$$

Multiplying the term in the center by $e^x e^{-x}$ and changing variables there yields

$$\sqrt{x}\int_{-\delta}^\epsilon e^{-[(t^2x)(1+\eta)]/2}\, dt < \sqrt{x}\, e^x \int_{1-\delta}^{1+\epsilon} [ue^{-u}]^x\, du$$

$$< \sqrt{x}\int_{-\delta}^\epsilon e^{-[(t^2x)(1-\eta)]/2}\, dt$$

Taking $\lim\limits_{x\to+\infty}$ gives

$$\sqrt{\frac{2\pi}{1+\eta}} \le \lim_{x\to+\infty} \sqrt{x}\, e^x \int_{1-\delta}^{1+\epsilon} [ue^{-u}]^x\, du$$

$$\le \sqrt{\frac{2\pi}{1-\eta}}$$

$$\frac{\Gamma(x+1)}{x^{x+1/2}e^{-x}} = \left\{ \sqrt{x}\, e^x\int_0^{1-\delta} + \sqrt{x}\, e^x\int_{1-\delta}^{1+\epsilon} + \sqrt{x}\, e^x\int_{1+\epsilon}^{+\infty} \right\}(ue^{-u})^x\, du$$

$$\sqrt{x}\, e^x\int_0^{1-\delta} (ue^{-u})^x\, du < [(1-\delta)e^{-(1-\delta)}]^x\sqrt{x}\, e^x$$

$$= \exp\left[-x\left(-\log(1-\delta) - \frac{1}{2}\frac{\log x}{x} + \frac{\delta}{x}\right)\right]$$

Thus

$$\lim_{x \to +\infty} \sqrt{x}\, e^x \int_0^{1-\delta} [ue^{-u}]^x\, du = 0$$

Similarly,

$$\lim_{x \to +\infty} \sqrt{x}\, e^x \int_{1+\epsilon}^{+\infty} (ue^{-u})^x\, du = 0$$

We then conclude that

$$\sqrt{\frac{2\pi}{1+\eta}} \le \varliminf_{x \to +\infty} \frac{\Gamma(x+1)}{x^{x+1/2}e^{-x}} \le \varlimsup_{x \to +\infty} \frac{\Gamma(x+1)}{x^{x+1/2}e^{-x}} \le \sqrt{\frac{2\pi}{1-\eta}}$$

Since these inequalities are true for any $\eta > 0$, we arrive at the conclusion of the theorem. ∎

Stirling's formula itself expresses the result of this theorem for factorials of positive integers; namely, for large n,

$$n! \text{ is approximately } \sqrt{2\pi}\, n^{n+1/2}e^{-n}$$

Doing a little arithmetic gives $(1000)!$ as approximately $(7.9)(10)^{2672}$, a number finite but large.

EXERCISES

1. Prove Theorem 10-4-2.

2. Prove Theorem 10-4-3.

3. Correct the hypothesis given in Theorem 10-4-4, and complete the details of the proof.

4. Complete the proof of Theorem 10-4-6.

5. Complete the proof of Theorem 10-4-7.

In 6–8 find the Laplace transform Lf if f is given by $f(x) =$

6. e^{kx}

7. $\sin kx$

8. $\lim_{n \to \infty} \sum_{k=0}^{n} (1/k!)c_k x^k$

9. Show that $\int_0^{+\infty} t^{x-1}e^{-t}\, dt$ converges pointwise on $[0, +\infty[$.

10. Show that $\lim_{x \to 0+} \Gamma(x) = +\infty$.

11. Show that, for $n = 1, 2, \ldots,$ $\lim_{x \to -n} |\Gamma(x)| = +\infty$.

12. Find Γ' and Γ'' and use these to sketch the graph of the gamma function.

13. Prove that, for $r > 0$, $\Gamma(r) = 2 \int_0^{+\infty} x^{2r-1} e^{-x^2} \, dx$.

14. Show that

$$\Gamma(x)\Gamma(1-x) = \int_0^{+\infty} \frac{t^{x-1}}{1+t} \, dt$$

15. Prove that, for $r > 0$ and $s > 0$,

$$\frac{\Gamma(r)\Gamma(s)}{\Gamma(r+s)} = \int_0^1 t^{r-1}(1-t)^{s-1} \, dt$$

10-5 Representation by Fourier Series

The results we have attained for power series are a consequence of our earlier work on uniformly convergent sequences of functions. In the case of power series the functions in the sequence (the partial sums) are polynomials. We examine here series whose partial sums are "trigonometric polynomials":

Definition 10-5-1. f is a continuous function on $[a, b]$ into the real numbers. The *Fourier series of f on* $[a, b]$ is the series

$$\frac{a_0}{2} + \sum_{n=1}^{\infty} a_n \cos \frac{2n}{b-a}\left(x - \frac{a+b}{2}\right) + b_n \sin \frac{2n}{b-a}\left(x - \frac{a+b}{2}\right)$$

in which, for $n = 0, 1, 2, \ldots$,

$$a_n = \frac{2}{b-a} \int_a^b f(t) \cos \frac{2n}{b-a}\left(t - \frac{a+b}{2}\right) dt$$

and

$$b_n = \frac{2}{b-a} \int_a^b f(t) \sin \frac{2n}{b-a}\left(t - \frac{a+b}{2}\right) dt$$

For convenience in manipulations we make two assumptions. One, which does not affect our results, is that $a = -\pi$ and $b = \pi$. The other, which affects some of our results slightly, is that f in addition to being continuous is also periodic and has period $b - a = 2\pi$. We then have, as the Fourier series of a continuous function which is periodic, of period 2π,

$$\frac{a_0}{2} + \sum_{n=1}^{\infty} a_n \cos nx + b_n \sin nx$$

in which, for $n = 0, 1, 2, \ldots$,

$$a_n = \frac{1}{\pi} \int_{-\pi}^{\pi} f(t) \cos nt \, dt$$

and

$$b_n = \frac{1}{\pi} \int_{-\pi}^{\pi} f(t) \sin nt \, dt$$

We are now in the same situation we saw at the beginning of our consideration of Taylor series. Beginning with a function with certain properties, there exists a series of functions associated with the given function and the problem is to determine which properties of the given function insure convergence of the series—or, even better, uniform convergence—and to find connections between the function which is the sum of the series and the given function.

As an aid to computation, we note

Lemma 10-5-1. If p and q are integers, $p \neq q$, then

$$0 = \int_{-\pi}^{\pi} \cos px \cos qx \, dx = \int_{-\pi}^{\pi} \sin px \sin qx \, dx = \int_{-\pi}^{\pi} \sin px \cos qx \, dx$$

We begin our investigation by examining the consequences of uniform convergence of the Fourier series.

Theorem 10-5-1. If f is a continuous function, of period 2π, and the Fourier series of f on $[-\pi, \pi]$ converges uniformly to g on $[-\pi, \pi]$, then the Fourier series of g is also the Fourier series of f.

Proof. Since the Fourier series of f is assumed to be uniformly convergent on $[-\pi, \pi]$, this series can be integrated term by term. Then, for its sum g, we have for $n = 0, 1, 2, \ldots$,

$$a_n(g) = \frac{1}{\pi} \int_{-\pi}^{\pi} g(t) \cos nt \, dt$$

$$= \frac{1}{\pi} \int_{-\pi}^{\pi} \cos nt \left(\lim_{p \to \infty} \frac{a_0}{2} + \sum_{k=1}^{p} a_k \cos kt + b_k \sin kt \right) dt$$

For $n = 0$,

$$a_0(g) = \frac{1}{\pi} \int_{-\pi}^{\pi} \frac{a_0}{2} \, dt + \lim_{p \to \infty} \sum_{k=1}^{p} \int_{-\pi}^{\pi} (a_k \cos kt + b_k \sin kt) \, dt$$

$$= a_0$$

For $n = 1, 2, \ldots$,

$$a_n(g) = \frac{1}{\pi} \lim_{p \to \infty} \sum_{k=1}^{p} \int_{-\pi}^{\pi} (a_k \cos kt \cos nt + b_k \sin kt \cos nt)\, dt$$

$$= \frac{1}{\pi} \int_{-\pi}^{\pi} a_n \cos^2 nt\, dt$$

$$= a_n$$

In like manner we can show that, for $n = 1, 2, \ldots, b_n(g) = b_n.$ ■

Since we know that when uniform convergence occurs, the sum of the Fourier series and the original function both have the same Fourier series, our next task is to examine a function which has the property that all its Fourier coefficients are zero.

  Theorem 10-5-2. If f is continuous and has period 2π, and all the coefficients of the Fourier series of f on $[-\pi, \pi]$ are zero, then f is identically zero.

Proof. We assume there exists a number $a \in {]}{-\pi}, \pi[$ such that $f(a) > 0$. Since f is continuous at a, there exists $\delta > 0$ such that $\delta < \pi/2$ and

$$|t - a| < \delta \text{ implies } f(t) > \tfrac{1}{2}f(a)$$

  We now construct a new function g on the real numbers into the real numbers by

$$g(t) = 1 + \cos(t - a) - \cos \delta$$

Clearly g is differentiable and

$$g'(t) = -\sin(t - a)$$

so that $g'(a) = 0$. Further,

$$a - \delta < t < a \text{ implies } g'(t) > 0$$

and

$$a < t < a + \delta \text{ implies } g'(t) < 0$$

We can now determine the behavior of g on $]a - \delta, a + \delta[$.
  Coming slightly closer to a, we have

$$|t - a| \leq \frac{\delta}{2} \text{ implies } g\left(a + \frac{\delta}{2}\right) \leq g(t) \leq g(a)$$

or

$$g(t) \geq 1 + \cos\frac{\delta}{2} - \cos \delta > 1$$

and

$$\frac{\delta}{2} \leq |t - a| < \delta \text{ implies } g(a + \delta) < g(t) \leq g\left(a + \frac{\delta}{2}\right)$$

or

$$g(t) > 0$$

For the remainder of the interval $[-\pi, \pi]$,

$$-\pi \leq t \leq a - \delta \text{ implies } -1 \leq \cos(t - a) \leq \cos \delta$$

so that

$$-1 < -\cos \delta \leq g(t) \leq 1 - \cos \delta < 1$$

or

$$|g(t)| < 1$$

and, similarly,

$$a + \delta \leq t \leq \pi \text{ implies } |g(t)| < 1$$

Now, for m any positive integer,

$$\int_{-\pi}^{\pi} [g(t)]^m f(t)\, dt = \left\{ \int_{-\pi}^{a-\delta} + \int_{a-\delta}^{a-\delta/2} + \int_{a-\delta/2}^{a+\delta/2} + \int_{a+\delta/2}^{a+\delta} + \int_{a+\delta}^{\pi} \right\} [g(t)]^m f(t)\, dt$$

The fact that f and g have positive values on $[a - \delta, a - \delta/2]$ and $[a + \delta/2, a + \delta]$ implies

$$\int_{-\pi}^{\pi} [g(t)]^m f(t)\, dt > \left\{ \int_{-\pi}^{a-\delta} + \int_{a-\delta/2}^{a+\delta} + \int_{a+\delta}^{\pi} \right\} [g(t)]^m f(t)\, dt$$

The hypothesis that f is continuous means that f is bounded on $[-\pi, \pi]$, say by M. Since $g([-\pi, a - \delta]) \subseteq [-1, 1]$, we have

$$\int_{-\pi}^{a-\delta} [g(t)]^m f(t)\, dt \geq -M(a - \delta + \pi)$$

Since $g([a + \delta, \pi]) \subseteq [-1, 1]$, we also have

$$\int_{a+\delta}^{\pi} [g(t)]^m f(t)\, dt \geq -M(\pi - a - \delta)$$

For $t \in [a - \delta/2, a + \delta/2]$, we have

$$g(t) \geq 1 + \cos \frac{\delta}{2} - \cos \delta$$

and

$$f(t) > \tfrac{1}{2} f(a)$$

Thus

$$\int_{a-\delta/2}^{a+\delta/2} [g(t)]^m f(t)\, dt \geq \left(1 + \cos \frac{\delta}{2} - \cos \delta \right)^m \tfrac{1}{2}\, \delta f(a)$$

Combining, we arrive at

$$\int_{-\pi}^{\pi} [g(t)]^m f(t)\, dt \geq -M(2\pi - 2\delta) + \tfrac{1}{2}\, \delta f(a)\left(1 + \cos\frac{\delta}{2} - \cos\delta\right)^m$$

Since $1 + \cos(\delta/2) - \cos\delta > 1$, we have

$$\lim_{m \to \infty} \left(1 + \cos\frac{\delta}{2} - \cos\delta\right)^m = +\infty$$

and so there exists an integer N such that

$$\tfrac{1}{2}\, \delta f(a)\left(1 + \cos\frac{\delta}{2} - \cos\delta\right)^N > 2\pi M$$

or

$$\int_{-\pi}^{\pi} [g(t)]^N f(t)\, dt > 0$$

But g is a trigonometric polynomial so that $\displaystyle\int_{-\pi}^{\pi} g^N f$ must be the finite sum of integrals which are constant multiples of the Fourier coefficients of f. Since all the Fourier coefficients of f were assumed to be zero, we have arrived at a contradiction. Then f is identically zero on $]-\pi, \pi[$. Since f is continuous, we must also have $f(\pi) = f(-\pi) = 0$. ∎

One immediate result of this theorem is

Theorem 10-5-3. f is a continuous function with period 2π. If the Fourier series of f on $[-\pi, \pi]$ is uniformly convergent, then f is its sum.

Proof. Let g be the sum of the uniformly convergent Fourier series. Then the Fourier coefficients of g are precisely those of f. Therefore the Fourier coefficients of $f - g$ are all zero. Since f and g are continuous, so is $f - g$ and thus $f - g$ must be identically zero. ∎

We now need to examine conditions on a function which will insure that its Fourier series will be uniformly convergent. One such is given by

Theorem 10-5-4. If f is a continuous function with period 2π and f'' is continuous on $[-\pi, \pi]$, then the Fourier series of f on $[-\pi, \pi]$ will be uniformly convergent.

Proof. Examining the Fourier coefficients and integrating by parts yields, for $n = 1, 2, \ldots,$

$$a_n = \frac{1}{\pi} \int_{-\pi}^{\pi} f(t) \cos nt \, dt$$

$$= \frac{-1}{n\pi} \int_{-\pi}^{\pi} f'(t) \sin nt \, dt$$

$$= -\frac{1}{n^2\pi} \int_{-\pi}^{\pi} f''(t) \cos nt \, dt$$

Since f'' is continuous, it is bounded and we have, for $n = 1, 2, \ldots,$

$$|a_n| \leq \frac{\text{const.}}{n^2}$$

A similar application of integration by parts yields, for $n = 1, 2, \ldots,$

$$|b_n| \leq \frac{\text{const.}}{n^2}$$

Thus the Fourier series is uniformly convergent by comparison with the convergent series $\sum_{n=1}^{\infty} 1/n^2$.   ∎

EXERCISES

1. Prove Lemma 10-5-1.

2. Complete the proof of Theorem 10-5-1.

Find the Fourier series for the following functions which are assumed to have period 2π and are given for the interval $[-\pi, \pi]$:

3. $f(x) = -1$ for $-\pi \leq x < 0$; $f(x) = 1$ for $0 \leq x < \pi$

4. $f(x) = x,$ $-\pi \leq x < \pi$

5. $f(x) = x^2,$ $-\pi \leq x < \pi$

6. $f(x) = 0,$ for $-\pi \leq x < 0$; $f(x) = 1,$ for $0 \leq x < \pi$

Use the results above to show

7. $\sum_{n=1}^{\infty} (-1)^{n+1}/(2n - 1)$ converges to $\pi/4$.

8. $\sum_{n=1}^{\infty} 1/n^2$ converges to $\pi^2/6$.

9. $\sum\limits_{n=1}^{\infty} (-1)^{n+1}/n^2$ converges to $\pi^2/12$.

10. $\sum\limits_{n=1}^{\infty} 1/(2k-1)^2$ converges to $\pi^2/8$.

11. If the Fourier series of f is uniformly convergent to f on $[-\pi, \pi]$, use the multiplication of series to show that $a_0^2/2 + \sum\limits_{n=1}^{\infty} (a_n^2 + b_n^2)$ converges to $1/\pi \int_{-\pi}^{\pi} f^2$.

Use the result of Exercise 11 to show

12. $\sum\limits_{n=1}^{\infty} 1/n^4$ converges to $\pi^4/90$.

13. $\sum\limits_{n=1}^{\infty} 1/n^6$ converges to $\pi^6/945$.

14. An alternate development of Fourier series is given by $\sum\limits_{n=-\infty}^{\infty} c_n e^{nix}$, where, for $n = 0, \pm 1, \pm 2, \ldots, c_n = \dfrac{1}{2\pi} \int_{-\pi}^{\pi} f(t)e^{-nit}\, dt$. Use the relation $e^{ip} = \cos p + i \sin p$ to find the relations between the c_n and the a_n and b_n of this section.

10-6   Orthogonal Expansions

We will conclude our examination of representations of functions by observing some similarities between the Fourier series representation of a function and the rectangular component representation of a vector of $\mathbf{V_n}$.

The set of all continuous functions on $[a, b]$ into the real numbers forms a vector space in which vector addition is the addition of functions and scalar multiplication is multiplication by a constant function. In order that this vector space have further similarities to $\mathbf{V_n}$, we need to introduce a norm and an inner product which are related by

$$\|\mathbf{v}\|^2 = \mathbf{v} \cdot \mathbf{v}$$

Lemma 10-5-1, which states that, for $n \neq p$,

$$\int_{-\pi}^{\pi} \cos nx \cos px\, dx = \int_{-\pi}^{\pi} \cos nx \sin px\, dx = \int_{-\pi}^{\pi} \sin nx \sin px\, dx = 0$$

provides a link between the vector space of functions and $\mathbf{V_n}$. We have, in this vector space of functions, the (infinite) collection of functions

$$\{\varphi_n \mid n = 0, 1, 2, \ldots\}$$

given, for $k = 0, 1, 2, \ldots$, by

$$\varphi_{2k}(x) = \cos kx$$

and, for $k = 1, 2, \ldots,$ by

$$\varphi_{2k-1}(x) = \sin kx$$

The lemma provides us with a method of combining pairs of the functions in our collection which, when applied to two distinct functions, yields the number zero. This suggests forming

> **Definition 10-6-1.** f and g are continuous functions on $[a, b]$ into the real numbers. The *inner product* of f and g, written (f, g), is the number $\int_a^b fg$. The functions f and g are said to be *orthogonal* if $(f, g) = 0$.

An immediate consequence of this definition is

> **Theorem 10-6-1.** The vector space of all continuous functions on $[a, b]$ into the real numbers becomes a normed vector space with norm given by
> $$\|f\| = (f, f)^{1/2}$$

Proof. We need to show that

    (i) For all functions in this space, $\|f\| \geq 0$.
    (ii) $\|f\| = 0$ if, and only if, f is the function identically zero.
    (iii) For any two functions f and g in the space, $\|f + g\| \leq \|f\| + \|g\|$.
    (iv) For any function f in the space and any real number a, $\|af\| = |a| \cdot \|f\|$.

All except (iii) come immediately from the definition of norm. In Chapter 1 we proved the Cauchy-Schwartz inequality, which, in the terminology introduced here, says

$$(|f|, |g|)^2 \leq \|f\| \cdot \|g\|$$

For every $x \in [a, b]$,

$$|\{f + g\}(x)| \leq |f(x)| + |g(x)|$$

$$|\{f + g\}(x)|^2 \leq |f(x)|^2 + |g(x)|^2 + 2|f(x)g(x)|$$

Integrating,

$$\int_a^b |f + g|^2 \leq \int_a^b f^2 + \int_a^b g^2 + 2\int_a^b |fg|$$

$$\|f + g\|^2 \leq \|f\|^2 + \|g\|^2 + 2(|f|, |g|)$$

$$\leq \|f\|^2 + \|g\|^2 + 2\|f\| \cdot \|g\|$$

$$= (\|f\| + \|g\|)^2$$

so that

$$\|f + g\| \leq \|f\| + \|g\|$$

(This last is known as *Minkowski's inequality*.)   ∎

We now presuppose the existence of some collection $\{h_n \mid n = 1, 2, \ldots\}$ of continuous functions on $[a, b]$ into the real numbers, and these functions are pairwise orthogonal. Given any function f of this vector space, if we can find a sequence of numbers given by $\{c_n \mid n = 1, 2, \ldots\}$ with the property that the series $\sum_{n=1}^{\infty} c_n h_n$ is uniformly convergent to f, then we may integrate term by term to find

$$
\begin{aligned}
(f, h_n) &= \int_a^b f h_n \\
&= \lim_{p \to \infty} \sum_{k=1}^{p} \int_a^b c_k h_k h_n \\
&= c_n (h_n, h_n) \\
&= c_n \|h_n\|^2
\end{aligned}
$$

For convenience, we introduce

Definition 10-6-2. $\{h_n \mid n = 1, 2, \ldots\}$ is a collection of pairwise orthogonal continuous functions on $[a, b]$ into the real numbers. The collection is called *orthonormal* if, for $n = 1, 2, \ldots, \|h_n\| = 1$.

With an orthonormal collection of functions we then have, in the case of uniform convergence of the series $\sum_{n=1}^{\infty} c_n h_n$ to the function f, for $n = 1, 2, \ldots$,

$$
c_n = (f, h_n)
$$

This is completely analogous to the situation in $\mathbf{V_3}$ for which $\mathbf{e_1} = \mathbf{i}$, $\mathbf{e_2} = \mathbf{j}$, $\mathbf{e_3} = \mathbf{k}$; and, for any $\mathbf{x} = (x_1, x_2, x_3)$, we have, for $i = 1, 2, 3$,

$$
x_i = \mathbf{x} \cdot \mathbf{e_i}
$$

We give a name to the situation we have been considering in

Definition 10-6-3. $\{h_n \mid n = 1, 2, \ldots\}$ is an orthonormal collection of continuous functions on $[a, b]$ into the real numbers. f is a continuous function on $[a, b]$ into the real numbers. The *generalized Fourier series of f with respect to* $\{h_n \mid n = 1, 2, \ldots\}$ is the series $\sum_{n=1}^{\infty} c_n h_n$, in which, for $n = 1, 2, \ldots, c_n = (f, h_n)$.

We are now in the position of asking what the generalized Fourier series has to do with the function giving it. To begin with, we have

Theorem 10-6-2. If the generalized Fourier series of f with respect to the orthonormal collection $\{h_n \mid n = 1, 2, \ldots\}$ is uniformly convergent to g on $[a, b]$, then the generalized Fourier series of g with respect to this orthonormal collection is also the generalized Fourier series of f.

The proof results from term-by-term integration of the uniformly convergent series and is left to the exercises.

We now examine an interesting property of the generalized Fourier coefficients.

Theorem 10-6-3. If $\{c_n \mid n = 1, 2, \ldots\}$ are the coefficients of the generalized Fourier series of the function f with respect to the orthonormal collection $\{h_n \mid n = 1, 2, \ldots\}$ on $[a, b]$ and $\{d_n \mid n = 1, 2, \ldots\}$ gives any sequence of real numbers, then, for $n = 1, 2, \ldots$,

$$\left\| f - \sum_{k=1}^{n} c_k h_k \right\| \leq \left\| f - \sum_{k=1}^{n} d_k h_k \right\|$$

Proof

$$\left\| f - \sum_{k=1}^{n} d_k h_k \right\|^2 = \int_a^b \left(f - \sum_{k=1}^{n} d_k h_k \right)^2$$

$$= \int_a^b \left[f^2 - 2f \sum_{k=1}^{n} d_k h_k + \left(\sum_{k=1}^{n} d_k h_k \right)^2 \right]$$

$$= \int_a^b f^2 - 2 \sum_{k=1}^{n} c_k d_k + \sum_{k=1}^{n} d_k^2$$

$$= \| f \|^2 - \sum_{k=1}^{n} c_k^2 + \sum_{k=1}^{n} (c_k - d_k)^2$$

$$\geq \| f \|^2 - \sum_{k=1}^{n} c_k^2$$

$$= \| f \|^2 - 2 \sum_{k=1}^{n} c_k^2 + \sum_{k=1}^{n} c_k^2$$

$$= \| f \|^2 - 2 \sum_{k=1}^{n} c_k(f, h_k) + \sum_{k=1}^{n} c_k^2(f, h_k)$$

$$= \left\| f - \sum_{k=1}^{n} c_k h_k \right\|^2 \qquad \blacksquare$$

The generalized Fourier coefficients thus give a series whose partial sums give a better approximation—in terms of the norm for this vector space—to the given function than any other sequence of coefficients. In addition, we have

> **Theorem 10-6-4.** If $\{c_n \mid n = 1, 2, \ldots\}$ are the coefficients of the generalized Fourier series of the function f with respect to the orthonormal collection $\{h_n \mid n = 1, 2, \ldots\}$ on $[a, b]$, then, for $n = 1, 2, \ldots$,
>
> $$\sum_{k=1}^{n} c_k^2 \leq \|f\|^2$$

Proof

$$\left\| f^2 - \sum_{k=1}^{n} c_k^2 \right\| = \left\| f - \sum_{k=1}^{n} c_k h_k \right\|^2 \geq 0 \qquad \blacksquare$$

> **Theorem 10-6-5.** If $\{h_n \mid n = 1, 2, \ldots\}$ is an orthonormal collection of continuous functions on $[a, b]$ into the real numbers, then the coefficients of the generalized Fourier series of any continuous function form a sequence which converges to zero.

Proof. The series $\sum\limits_{n=1}^{\infty} c_n^2$ is convergent. $\blacksquare$

Whether or not the generalized Fourier series converges even pointwise, and if so, what connection there is between its sum and the given function, depends on the given orthonormal collection. We will not enter this large branch of mathematics in this book but will content ourselves by concluding with

> **Definition 10-6-4.** The orthonormal collection $\{h_n \mid n = 1, 2, \ldots\}$ of continuous functions on $[a, b]$ into the real numbers is called *complete* provided that the generalized Fourier series of every continuous function has the property
>
> $$\lim_{n \to \infty} \left\| f - \sum_{k=1}^{n} c_k h_k \right\| = 0$$

> **Theorem 10-6-6.** If $\{c_n \mid n = 1, 2, \ldots\}$ are the coefficients of the generalized Fourier series of the continuous function f with respect to the complete orthonormal collection $\{h_n \mid n = 1, 2, \ldots\}$ of continuous functions on $[a, b]$ into the real numbers, then $\sum\limits_{n=1}^{\infty} c_n^2$ is convergent to $\|f\|^2$.

(This equation is often called *Parseval's relation.*)

EXERCISES

1. Prove Theorem 10-6-2.

The Legendre polynomials are given on $[-1, 1]$ by $P_0(x) = 1$ and, for $n = 1, 2, \ldots$,

$$P_n(x) = \frac{1}{2^n n!} \frac{d^n}{dx^n} (x^2 - 1)^n$$

2. Show that $P_n'(x) = xP_{n-1}'(x) + nP_{n-1}(x)$

3. Show that $nP_n(x) = nxP_{n-1}(x) + (x^2 - 1)P_{n-1}'(x)$.

4. Prove that the Legendre polynomials form an orthogonal collection on $[-1, 1]$.

5. Use the Legendre polynomials to form an orthonormal collection on $[-1, 1]$.

6. Investigate the generalized Fourier series of the function given by $f(x) = x$, $-1 \leq x \leq 1$, with respect to the orthonormal system of Exercise 5.

11 CLASSICAL VECTOR THEOREMS, STRONG FORM

11-1 The Divergence Theorem

Now that we have examined the possible things which might enter into the versions of the classical vector theorems given in Chapter 4, we will re-examine those theorems in order to find stronger forms, that is, theorems with the same conclusion but much weaker hypotheses.

For the Divergence Theorem we certainly need to start with a three-dimensional set W which is closed and bounded. To avoid triviality, we also assume that this set is rectifiable and that $m_3(W) > 0$.

We assume further that S, the boundary of W, is the trace of a surface with the property that there exists a continuous function $\mathbf{n}$ on S into $\mathbf{V}_3$ such that, for every $\mathbf{x} \in S$, $\|\mathbf{n}(\mathbf{x})\| = 1$ and the representation of $\mathbf{n}(\mathbf{x})$ with initial point $\mathbf{x}$ is directed away from W.

Finally we consider a function $\mathbf{v}$ on W into $\mathbf{V}_3$ with the property that div $\mathbf{v}$ is integrable on W.

For every $\mathbf{x} \in W$ for which $\{\text{div } \mathbf{v}\}(\mathbf{x})$ exists, there is, by the definition of divergence, some $\delta_{\mathbf{x}} > 0$ such that for every three-dimensional set B with the properties

    (i) $\mathbf{x} \in B$
    (ii) $m_3(B) > 0$
    (iii) diam $B < \delta_{\mathbf{x}}$
    (iv) B', the boundary of B, is the trace of a surface for which there exists a continuous function $\mathbf{n}_B$ on B' into $\mathbf{V}_3$ with the properties that, for all $\mathbf{y} \in B'$, $\|\mathbf{n}_B(\mathbf{y})\| = 1$ and the representation of $\mathbf{n}(\mathbf{y})$ with initial point $\mathbf{y}$ is directed away from B,

we will have

$$\left| \{\text{div } \mathbf{v}\}(\mathbf{x}) - \frac{1}{m_3(B)} \iint_{B'} \mathbf{v} \cdot \mathbf{n}_B \right| < \frac{\epsilon}{4m_3(W)}$$

If div $\mathbf{v}$ is to be integrable on W, then the spheres of radius δ_x must cover the closed bounded set W. By the Heine-Borel Theorem there exist points

$\mathbf{x}_1, \mathbf{x}_2, \ldots, \mathbf{x}_p$ of W such that when $B_i = \{\mathbf{v} \mid \|\mathbf{v} - \mathbf{x}_i\| < \delta_{\mathbf{x}_i}\}$,

$$W \subseteq \bigcup_{i=1}^{p} B_i$$

We now let

$$\delta = \min \{\operatorname{diam}(B_i \cap B_j) \mid B_i \cap B_j \neq \varnothing \text{ and } i, j = 1, 2, \ldots, p\}$$

Then for all $\mathbf{x} \in W$ for which $\{\operatorname{div} \mathbf{v}\}(\mathbf{x})$ exists, any three-dimensional set B, for which properties (i)–(iv) above hold, has the property that

$$\left| \{\operatorname{div} \mathbf{v}\}(\mathbf{x}) - \frac{1}{m_3(B)} \iint_{B'} \mathbf{v} \cdot \mathbf{n}_B \right| < \frac{\epsilon}{2m_3(W)}$$

We have assumed that $\operatorname{div} \mathbf{v}$ is integrable on W. Thus there exists a decomposition of W into sets $W_1, W_2, \ldots, W_N$, each one of which is closed, and these sets intersect only in mutual boundary points and each one has properties (i)–(iv). In addition, we index these sets so that for $i = 1, 2, \ldots, M \leq N$,

$$W_i \cap S \neq \varnothing$$

and for $i = M + 1, M + 2, \ldots, N$,

$$W_i \cap S = \varnothing$$

Finally, this decomposition has the property that, for $i = 1, 2, \ldots, N$, there exists $\mathbf{p}_i \in W_i$ for which

$$\left| \iiint_W \operatorname{div} \mathbf{v} - \sum_{i=1}^{N} [\{\operatorname{div} \mathbf{v}\}(\mathbf{p}_i)] m_3(W_i) \right| < \frac{\epsilon}{2}$$

Using $\mathbf{n}_i$ to denote the unit normal vector function for W_i', the surface of W_i, we have, as a result of properties (i)–(iv),

$$\left| \{\operatorname{div} \mathbf{v}\}(\mathbf{p}_i) - \frac{1}{m_3(W_i)} \iint_{W_i'} \mathbf{v} \cdot \mathbf{n}_i \right| < \frac{\epsilon}{2m_3(W)}$$

$$\left| [\{\operatorname{div} \mathbf{v}\}(\mathbf{p}_i)] m_3(W_i) - \iint_{W_i'} \mathbf{v} \cdot \mathbf{n}_i \right| < \frac{m_3(W_i)}{2m_3(W)} \epsilon$$

$$\left| \sum_{i=1}^{N} [\{\operatorname{div} \mathbf{v}\}(\mathbf{p}_i)] m_3(W_i) - \sum_{i=1}^{N} \iint_{W_i'} \mathbf{v} \cdot \mathbf{n}_i \right| < \frac{\epsilon}{2}$$

Combining this with the preceding inequality gives

$$\left| \iiint_W \operatorname{div} \mathbf{v} - \sum_{i=1}^{N} \iint_{W_i'} \mathbf{v} \cdot \mathbf{n}_i \right| < \epsilon$$

For $i = 1, 2, \ldots, N$, we let $J_i = \{j \mid W_i \cap W_j \neq \varnothing \text{ and } j \neq i\}$. We then have

$$\iint_{W_i'} \mathbf{v} \cdot \mathbf{n}_i = \iint_{W_i' \cap S} \mathbf{v} \cdot \mathbf{n} + \sum_{j \in J_i} \iint_{W_i' \cap W_j'} \mathbf{v} \cdot \mathbf{n}_i$$

But whenever $\mathbf{x} \in W_i' \cap W_j'$ for $i \neq j$, we have $\mathbf{n}_i(\mathbf{x}) = -\mathbf{n}_j(\mathbf{x})$ so that

$$\iint_{W_i' \cap W_j'} \mathbf{v} \cdot \mathbf{n}_i + \iint_{W_i' \cap W_j'} \mathbf{v} \cdot \mathbf{n}_j = 0$$

Consequently,

$$\sum_{i=1}^{N} \sum_{j \in J_i} \iint_{W_i' \cap W_j'} \mathbf{v} \cdot \mathbf{n}_i = 0$$

We then have

$$\sum_{i=1}^{N} \iint_{W_i'} \mathbf{v} \cdot \mathbf{n}_i = \sum_{i=1}^{N} \iint_{W_i' \cap S} \mathbf{v} \cdot \mathbf{n}$$

$$= \sum_{i=1}^{M} \iint_{W_i' \cap S} \mathbf{v} \cdot \mathbf{n}$$

$$= \iint_{S} \mathbf{v} \cdot \mathbf{n}$$

since the W_i' form a decomposition of the surface S.

Our final result is then

$$\left| \iiint_{W} \operatorname{div} \mathbf{v} - \iint_{S} \mathbf{v} \cdot \mathbf{n} \right| < \epsilon$$

Since this holds for every $\epsilon > 0$ we have proved

Theorem 11-1-1(the Divergence Theorem). If W is a closed, bounded, three-dimensional set with a boundary S which is the trace of a surface for which there exists a continuous function $\mathbf{n}$ on S into $\mathbf{V}_3$ with the properties that, for all $\mathbf{x} \in S$, $\|\mathbf{n}(\mathbf{x})\| = 1$, and the representation of $\mathbf{n}(\mathbf{x})$ with initial point $\mathbf{x}$ is directed away from W, and $\mathbf{v}$ is a function on W into $\mathbf{V}_3$ for which div $\mathbf{v}$ is integrable on W, then

$$\iiint_{W} \operatorname{div} \mathbf{v} = \iint_{S} \mathbf{v} \cdot \mathbf{n}$$

EXERCISE

Prove that the integrability of div **v** assures that the given spheres of radius δ_x actually cover W.

11-2 Green's Theorem

The method of proof used in the preceding section for a strengthened version of the Divergence Theorem suggests a procedure for a similar proof of Stokes' Theorem. The structure of such a proof is somewhat complicated, however, so that we will first consider a special case in which the surface and bounding curve lie in a plane. This result is known as Green's Theorem:

> ***Theorem 11-2-1.*** If R is a closed bounded plane set and its boundary is the simple, closed, differentiable plane curve C, with positive (i.e., counterclockwise) orientation, and P and Q are functions on R into the real numbers with continuous partial derivatives, then

$$\int_C (P\mathbf{i} + Q\mathbf{j}) \cdot \mathbf{T} = \iint_R (Q_1 - P_2)$$

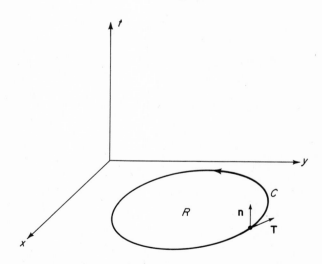

Figure 11-1

Proof. We let $S = \{(x, y, 0) \,|\, (x, y) \in R\}$ be the three-dimensional set, $\gamma = \{(x, y, 0) \,|\, (x, y) \in C\}$ be the path, and $\mathbf{v} = P^*\mathbf{i} + Q^*\mathbf{j}$ be functions to which Stokes' Theorem applies, where P^* is that function on S into the real numbers given by

$$P^*(x, y, z) = P(x, y)$$

and Q^* is that function on S into the real numbers given by

$$Q^*(x, y, z) = Q(x, y)$$

We then have

$$\text{curl } \mathbf{v} = -Q_3^*\mathbf{i} + P_3^*\mathbf{j} + (Q_1^* - P_2^*)\mathbf{k}$$
$$= (Q_1^* - P_2^*)\mathbf{k}$$

and

$$\iint_S [\text{curl } \mathbf{v}] \cdot \mathbf{n} = \iint_R (Q_1 - P_2)$$

In addition,

$$\int_\gamma \mathbf{v} \cdot \mathbf{T} = \int_C (P\mathbf{i} + Q\mathbf{j}) \cdot \mathbf{T}$$

so that the conclusion of this theorem is a result of Stokes' Theorem. ∎

We now consider the situation in which S is the plane trace given by

$$S = \{(x, y, 0) \mid (x, y) \in R\}$$

where R is a two-dimensional closed bounded set whose boundary is the simple closed differentiable path C with positive orientation. We assume that the "space" path γ is given by

$$\gamma = \{(x, y, 0) \mid (x, y) \in C\}$$

and that C has unit tangent vector function $\mathbf{T}$, unit principal normal vector function $\mathbf{N}$, and unit binormal vector function $\mathbf{B}$; the last, in this special case, is the constant function $\mathbf{k}$.

We consider the function $\mathbf{v} = P\mathbf{i} + Q\mathbf{j}$ whose domain is some open set enclosing S, which function has the properties

$$P_3 = Q_3 \text{ is the function identically } 0$$

and

$$\text{curl } \mathbf{v} \text{ is integrable on } S$$

The integrability of curl $\mathbf{v}$ implies the existence of $\delta > 0$ such that for all $\mathbf{p} \in S$ for which $\{\text{curl } \mathbf{v}\}(\mathbf{p})$ exists and for any three-dimensional set B with the properties

(i) $\mathbf{p} \in B$
(ii) diam $B < \delta$
(iii) $m_3(B) > 0$
(iv) the boundary of B is the trace B' which has a unit normal vector function $\mathbf{n}_B$ with the properties that, for all $\mathbf{y} \in B'$, $\|\mathbf{n}_B(\mathbf{y})\| = 1$ and the representation of $\mathbf{n}_B(\mathbf{y})$ with initial point $\mathbf{y}$ is directed away from B,

we have

$$\left\| \{\text{curl } \mathbf{v}\}(\mathbf{p}) - \frac{1}{m_3(B)} \int\!\!\int_{B'} \mathbf{n}_B \times \mathbf{v}_B \right\| < \frac{\epsilon}{2A(S)}$$

Further, the integrability of curl $\mathbf{v}$ on S implies the existence of a decomposition of S into the closed, bounded sets $S_1, S_2, \ldots, S_N$, which are pairwise disjoint except for boundary points with the following properties:

For $i = 1, 2, \ldots, N$, the boundary of S_i is an oriented path C_i with positive orientation, for which the unit tangent and normal vector functions $\mathbf{T}_i$ and $\mathbf{N}_i$ exist.

The diameter of S_i is less than $\delta/5$.

For $i = 1, 2, \ldots, M \leq N$, $S_i \cap \gamma \neq \varnothing$, and for $i = M+1, M+2, \ldots, N, S_i \cap \gamma = \varnothing$.

$$\left| \int\!\!\int_{S} [\text{curl } \mathbf{v}] \cdot \mathbf{n} - \sum_{i=1}^{N} [\{\text{curl } \mathbf{v}\}(\mathbf{p}_i)] \cdot \mathbf{k} A(S_i) \right| < \frac{\epsilon}{2}$$

where $\mathbf{p}_i$ is chosen arbitrarily in S_i.

We now construct N three-dimensional sets, $W_1, W_2, \ldots, W_N$ by fixing t, $0 < t < \delta/5$ and by

$$W_i = \{(x, y, z) \mid (x, y, 0) \in S_i, 0 \leq z \leq t\}$$

We let

$$S_i^T = \{(x, y, t) \mid (x, y, 0) \in S_i\}$$

and

$$S_i^E = \{(x, y, z) \mid (x, y, 0) \in C_i, \quad 0 \leq z \leq t\}$$

Then the boundary of W_i is the trace W_i', given by

$$W_i' = S_i \cup S_i^T \cup S_i^E$$

A unit normal vector function for the trace W_i', $\mathbf{n}_i$, will then be given by

$$\mathbf{n}_i(x, y, 0) = -\mathbf{k} \quad \text{for} \quad (x, y, 0) \in S_i$$
$$\mathbf{n}_i(x, y, t) = \mathbf{k} \quad \text{for} \quad (x, y, t) \in S_i^T$$
$$\mathbf{n}_i(x, y, z) = \mathbf{N}_i(x, y, 0) \quad \text{for} \quad (x, y, 0) \in C_i, 0 \leq z \leq t$$

Then W_i satisfies requirements (i)–(iv) above so that

$$\left\| \{\text{curl } \mathbf{v}\}(\mathbf{p}_i) - \frac{1}{tA(S_i)} \iint\limits_{W_i'} \mathbf{n}_i \times \mathbf{v} \right\| < \frac{\epsilon}{2A(S)}$$

$$\left\| [\{\text{curl } \mathbf{v}\}(\mathbf{p}_i)]A(S_i) - \frac{1}{t} \iint\limits_{W_i'} \mathbf{n}_i \times \mathbf{v} \right\| < \frac{\epsilon A(S_i)}{2A(S)}$$

$$\left\| \sum_{i=1}^{N} [\{\text{curl } \mathbf{v}\}(\mathbf{p}_i)]A(S_i) - \frac{1}{t} \sum_{i=1}^{N} \iint\limits_{W_i'} \mathbf{n}_i \times \mathbf{v} \right\| < \frac{\epsilon}{2}$$

$$\left| \sum_{i=1}^{N} [\{\text{curl } \mathbf{v}\}(\mathbf{p}_i)] \cdot \mathbf{k}A(S_i) - \frac{1}{t}\left[\sum_{i=1}^{N} \iint\limits_{W_i'} \mathbf{n}_i \times \mathbf{v} \right] \cdot \mathbf{k} \right| < \frac{\epsilon}{2}$$

Consequently,

$$\left| \iint\limits_{S} [\text{curl } \mathbf{v}] \cdot \mathbf{n} - \frac{1}{t} \sum_{i=1}^{N} \left[\iint\limits_{W_i'} \mathbf{n}_i \times \mathbf{v} \right] \cdot \mathbf{k} \right| < \epsilon$$

Now, for $i = 1, 2, \ldots, N$,

$$\iint\limits_{W_i'} \mathbf{n}_i \times \mathbf{v} = \left\{ \iint\limits_{S_i} + \iint\limits_{S_i^T} + \iint\limits_{S_i^E} \right\} \mathbf{n}_i \times \mathbf{v}$$

$$= \iint\limits_{S_i} (-\mathbf{k}) \times (\mathbf{v}) + \iint\limits_{S_i} \mathbf{k} \times \mathbf{v} + \iint\limits_{S_i^E} \mathbf{N}_i \times \mathbf{v}$$

$$= t \int_{C_i} \mathbf{N}_i \times \mathbf{v}$$

But

$$\sum_{i=1}^{N} \int_{C_i} \mathbf{N}_i \times \mathbf{v} = \sum_{i=1}^{M} \int_{C_i \cap \gamma} \mathbf{N}_i \times \mathbf{v}$$

$$= \int_{\gamma} \mathbf{N} \times \mathbf{v}$$

Substitution yields

$$\left| \iint\limits_{S} [\text{curl } \mathbf{v}] \cdot \mathbf{n} - \left[\int_{\gamma} [\mathbf{N} \times \mathbf{v}] \right] \cdot \mathbf{k} \right| < \epsilon$$

But, for every $\mathbf{x} \in \gamma$,

$$[\{\mathbf{N} \times \mathbf{v}\}(\mathbf{x})] \cdot \mathbf{k} = \{[\mathbf{N} \times \mathbf{v}] \cdot \mathbf{B}\}(\mathbf{x})$$

$$= \{\mathbf{v} \cdot [\mathbf{N} \times \mathbf{B}]\}(\mathbf{x})$$

$$= \{\mathbf{v} \cdot \mathbf{T}\}(\mathbf{x})$$

Thus

$$\left[\int_\gamma [\mathbf{N} \times \mathbf{v}]\right] \cdot \mathbf{k} = \int_\gamma \mathbf{v} \cdot \mathbf{T}$$

so that, for every $\epsilon > 0$,

$$\left| \iint_S [\text{curl } \mathbf{v}] \cdot \mathbf{n} - \int_\gamma \mathbf{v} \cdot \mathbf{T} \right| < \epsilon$$

and we conclude

Theorem 11-2-2(*Green's Theorem*). If R is a closed bounded plane set whose boundary is the twice differentiable curve C, which curve has positive orientation, and P and Q are two functions on R into the real numbers for which $P_3 = Q_3$ is the zero function and for which $Q_1 - P_2$ is integrable on R, then

$$\iint_R (Q_1 - P_2) = \int_C (P\mathbf{i} + Q\mathbf{j}) \cdot \mathbf{T}$$

11-3 Investigation of Stokes' Theorem

We will now attempt to construct a proof of a strong version of Stokes' Theorem, using the proof of Green's Theorem as a guide. We begin with a trace S for which there exists a continuous unit normal vector function $\mathbf{n}$ on S into $\mathbf{V}_3$ with the properties that, for all $\mathbf{y} \in S$, $\|\mathbf{n}(\mathbf{y})\| = 1$ and the representation of $\mathbf{n}(\mathbf{y})$ with initial point $\mathbf{y}$ is directed away from S.

We further assume that S is bounded by the simple closed path γ for which the unit tangent vector function $\mathbf{T}$, the unit principal normal vector function $\mathbf{N}$, and the binormal vector function $\mathbf{B}$, all exist.

We finally assume that the relative orientations of the curve and surface are such that, for all $\mathbf{y} \in \gamma$,

$$\mathbf{n}(\mathbf{y}) \cdot [\mathbf{T}(\mathbf{y}) \times \mathbf{N}(\mathbf{y})] = 1$$

As with Green's Theorem, an assumption that curl $\mathbf{v}$ is integrable on S implies that there exists $\delta > 0$ such that for every $\mathbf{p} \in S$ for which $\{\text{curl } \mathbf{v}\}(\mathbf{p})$ exists we have, for any three-dimensional set B with properties

(i) $\mathbf{p} \in B$
(ii) diam $B < \delta$
(iii) $m_3(B) > 0$
(iv) the boundary of B is the trace B' for which there exists a unit normal

vector function $\mathbf{n}_B$ with representations directed away from B,

$$\left\| \{\text{curl } \mathbf{v}\}(\mathbf{p}) - \frac{1}{m_3(B)} \iint\limits_{B'} \mathbf{v} \times \mathbf{n}_B \right\| < \frac{\epsilon}{4A(S)}$$

Further, the integrability of $\{\text{curl } \mathbf{v}\}$ on S implies a decomposition of S into N closed bounded sets $S_1, S_2, \ldots, S_N$ with the properties, for $i = 1, 2, \ldots, N$,

(i) diam $S_i < \delta/5$

(ii) the boundary of S_i is the simple closed, oriented path C_i for which unit tangent and normal vector functions $\mathbf{T}_i$ and $\mathbf{N}_i$ exist and such that, for every $\mathbf{x} \in C_i$, $\mathbf{n}(\mathbf{x}) \cdot [\mathbf{T}_i(\mathbf{x}) \times \mathbf{N}_i(\mathbf{x})] = 1$.

For $i = 1, 2, \ldots, M \leq N$, $S_i \cap \gamma \neq \varnothing$ and, for $i = M + 1, M + 2, \ldots, N$, $S_i \cap \gamma = \varnothing$. Finally, for $\mathbf{p}_i \in S_i$,

$$\left| \iint\limits_{S} \{\text{curl } \mathbf{v}\} \cdot \mathbf{n} - \sum_{i=1}^{N} [\{\text{curl } \mathbf{v}\}(\mathbf{p}_i)] \cdot \mathbf{n}(\mathbf{p}_i) A(S_i) \right| < \frac{\epsilon}{4}$$

In proving Green's Theorem, we used the decomposition of S to construct N three-dimensional sets by "lifting" S upward t units. Since, in this theorem, S is a plane set, we are assured that this procedure will yield small three-dimensional sets satisfying requirements (i)–(iv) given by the existence of curl $\mathbf{v}$. Here we must be much more careful.

Given the surface S, the set of points

$$\{\mathbf{p} + t\mathbf{n}(\mathbf{p}) \mid \mathbf{p} \in S\}$$

will necessarily (for fixed t) be a trace. Whether or not there is a three-dimensional "region" between this trace and S will depend on the value of t and will also depend on how "wrinkled" the trace S is. Let us assume that there does exist a fixed value of t, $0 < t < \delta/5$, such that this set does not intersect S. We then construct, for $i = 1, 2, \ldots, N$,

$$W_i = \{\mathbf{p} + r\mathbf{n}(\mathbf{p}) \mid \mathbf{p} \in S \text{ and } 0 \leq r \leq t\}$$

Under our assumption, the boundary of W_i will be a trace. Let us call this trace W_i' and consider the three parts of it which are of interest:

$$W_i' = S_i \cup S_i^T \cup S_i^E$$

where

$$S_i^T = \{\mathbf{p} + t\mathbf{n}(\mathbf{p}) \mid \mathbf{p} \in S\}$$

and

$$S_i^E = \{\mathbf{p} + r\mathbf{n}(\mathbf{p}) \mid \mathbf{p} \in C_i \text{ and } 0 \leq r \leq t\}$$

An appropriate unit normal vector function for the surface W_i' is then given by

$$\mathbf{n}_i(\mathbf{p}) = -\mathbf{n}(\mathbf{p}), \qquad \text{for } \mathbf{p} \in S_i$$

$$\mathbf{n}_i(\mathbf{p} + t\mathbf{n}(\mathbf{p})) = \mathbf{n}(\mathbf{p}), \qquad \text{for } \mathbf{p} + t\mathbf{n}(\mathbf{p}) \in S_i^T$$

$$\mathbf{n}_i(\mathbf{p} + r\mathbf{n}(\mathbf{p})) = \mathbf{N}_i(\mathbf{p}), \qquad \text{for } \mathbf{p} + r\mathbf{n}(\mathbf{p}) \in S_i^E$$

We have then

$$\iint_{W_i} \mathbf{n}_i \times \mathbf{v} = \iint_{S_i} (-\mathbf{n}) \times \mathbf{v} + \iint_{S_a^T} \mathbf{n}_i(\mathbf{p} + t\mathbf{n}) \times \mathbf{n} + \iint_{S_i^E} \mathbf{N}_i \times \mathbf{v}$$

Thus, using the estimate for curl $\mathbf{v}$ and the estimate for the surface integral, we have

$$\left| \iint_S [\text{curl } \mathbf{v}] \cdot \mathbf{n} - \sum_{i=1}^N \frac{A(S_i)}{m_3(W_i)} \left[\iint_{W_i'} \mathbf{n}_i \times \mathbf{v} \right] \cdot \mathbf{n}(\mathbf{p}_i) \right| < \frac{\epsilon}{2}$$

In the proof of Green's Theorem, we had $m_3(W_i) = tA(S_i)$ since S_i is a plane surface. In our present situation this need not occur. We will adopt the following plan of attack: We consider not merely one subdivision of S but a sequence of subdivisions such that

$$\lim_{N \to \infty} \sum_{k=1}^N [\{\text{curl } \mathbf{v}\}(\mathbf{p}_i)] \cdot \mathbf{n}(\mathbf{p}_i)A(S_i) = \iint_S [\text{curl } \mathbf{v}] \cdot \mathbf{n}$$

We then have

$$\lim_{N \to \infty} \sum_{k=1}^N \frac{A(S_i)}{m_3(W_i)} \left[\iint_{W_i'} \mathbf{n}_i \times \mathbf{v} \right] \cdot \mathbf{n}(\mathbf{p}_i) = \iint_S [\text{curl } \mathbf{v}] \cdot \mathbf{n}$$

where we of course also require that

$$\lim_{N \to \infty} \max \{A(S_i) \mid i = 1, 2, \ldots, N\} = 0$$

Under these circumstances it is not difficult to prove

$$\lim_{N \to \infty} \frac{A(S_i)}{m_3(W_i)} = \frac{1}{t}$$

where we take S_i from successive subdivisions all containing a fixed point $\mathbf{p} \in S$. We then hope to investigate

$$\lim_{N \to \infty} \sum_{k=1}^N \frac{1}{t} \left[\iint_{W_i'} \mathbf{n}_i \times \mathbf{v} \right] \cdot \mathbf{n}(\mathbf{p}_i)$$

Under some assumptions we could expect

$$\lim_{N \to \infty} \sum_{k=1}^{N} \frac{1}{t} \left[\iint_{S_i} \mathbf{n}_i \times \mathbf{v} \right] \cdot \mathbf{n}(\mathbf{p}_i) = \lim_{N \to \infty} \frac{1}{t} \iint_{S_i} [(\mathbf{n}_i \times \mathbf{v}) \cdot \mathbf{n}]$$

But we have, for $\mathbf{x} \in S_i$, $\{[\mathbf{n}_i \times \mathbf{v}] \cdot \mathbf{n}(\mathbf{x})\} = \{(\mathbf{n}_i \times \mathbf{v}) \cdot \mathbf{v}\}(\mathbf{x}) = 0$. Similarly, we would have

$$\lim_{N \to \infty} \sum_{k=1}^{N} \frac{1}{t} \left[\iint_{S_i^T} \mathbf{n}_i \times \mathbf{v} \right] \cdot \mathbf{n}(\mathbf{p}_i) = 0$$

This results in

$$\lim_{N \to \infty} \frac{1}{t} \sum_{k=1}^{N} \left[\iint_{S_i^E} \mathbf{N}_i \times \mathbf{v} \right] \cdot \mathbf{n}(\mathbf{p}_i) = \iint_{S} [\text{curl } \mathbf{v}] \cdot \mathbf{n}$$

Now in each subdivision, $S_1, S_2, \ldots, S_M$ do not intersect the path γ and portions of $C_{M+1}, C_{M+2}, \ldots, C_N$ are interior to S. We can easily decompose S_i^E into two parts, one intersecting γ and the other not. We then reindex so that $S_1^E, S_2^E, \ldots, S_M^E$ do intersect and $S_{M+1}^E, S_{M+2}^E, \ldots, S_N^E$ do not intersect. Then

$$\lim_{N \to \infty} \frac{1}{t} \sum_{k=M+1}^{N} \left[\iint_{S_k^E} \mathbf{N}_k \times \mathbf{v} \right] \cdot \mathbf{n}(\mathbf{p}_k) = 0$$

so that

$$\lim_{N \to \infty} \frac{1}{t} \sum_{k=1}^{N} \left[\iint_{S_k^E} \mathbf{N}_k \times \mathbf{v} \right] \cdot \mathbf{n}(\mathbf{p}_k) = \iint_{S} [\text{curl } \mathbf{v}] \cdot \mathbf{n}$$

Again we hope that the S_i are sufficiently small so that

$$\lim_{N \to \infty} \frac{1}{t} \sum_{k=1}^{N} \left[\iint_{S_k^E} \mathbf{N}_k \times \mathbf{v} \right] \cdot \mathbf{n}(\mathbf{p}_k) = \lim_{N \to \infty} \frac{1}{t} \sum_{k=1}^{N} \iint_{S_k^E} (\mathbf{N}_k \times \mathbf{v}) \cdot \mathbf{n}$$

$$= \lim_{N \to \infty} \frac{1}{t} \sum_{k=1}^{N} t \int_{C_k} (\mathbf{N}_k \times \mathbf{v}) \cdot \mathbf{n}$$

$$= \lim_{N \to \infty} \sum_{k=1}^{N} \int_{C_k} (\mathbf{N}_k \times \mathbf{v}) \cdot \mathbf{B}_k$$

$$= \lim_{N \to \infty} \sum_{k=1}^{N} \int_{C_k} \mathbf{v} \cdot \mathbf{T}_k$$

$$= \int_{\gamma} \mathbf{v} \cdot \mathbf{T}$$

That it is possible to find conditions on the surface S, the curve γ, and the function $\mathbf{v}$ so that all these steps are valid will be left, not to the exercises, but as an article of faith.

MATRICES A
AND DETERMINANTS

This appendix is intended to set forth those elementary properties of linear algebra which are needed for our treatment of Jacobians.

Definition A-1. When m and n are positive integers, the m by n matrix

$$A = (a_{i,j} \mid i = 1, 2, \ldots, m \text{ and } j = 1, 2, \ldots, n)$$

is a function on $\{1, 2, \ldots, m\} \times \{1, 2, \ldots, n\}$ into the real numbers. For $i = 1, 2, \ldots, m$, the 1 by n matrix $(a_{i,j} \mid j = 1, 2, \ldots, n)$ is the *ith horizontal row* of A. For $j = 1, 2, \ldots, n$, the m by 1 matrix $(a_{i,j} \mid i = 1, 2, \ldots, m)$ is the *jth vertical column* of A.

It is customary to display a matrix by writing a rectangular array of its entries:

$$\begin{bmatrix} a_{1,1} & a_{1,2} & \cdots & a_{1,n} \\ a_{2,1} & a_{2,2} & \cdots & a_{2,n} \\ \cdot & \cdot & \cdot & \cdot \\ \cdot & \cdot & \cdot & \cdot \\ \cdot & \cdot & \cdot & \cdot \\ a_{m,1} & a_{m,2} & \cdots & a_{m,n} \end{bmatrix}$$

Matrix addition is given by

Definition A-2. For the m by n matrices $A = (a_{i,j})$ and $B = (b_{i,j})$, the *sum $A + B$* is the m by n matrix $(a_{i,j} + b_{i,j})$.

EXAMPLE

$$\begin{bmatrix} 2 & 3 & -1 \\ 5 & -2 & 4 \end{bmatrix} + \begin{bmatrix} -1 & 2 & 5 \\ 4 & 7 & -3 \end{bmatrix} = \begin{bmatrix} 1 & 5 & 4 \\ 9 & 5 & 1 \end{bmatrix}$$

With this addition the set of all m by n matrices has the following properties:

327

Theorem A-1

(i) For any m by n matrices A and B, $A + B = B + A$.

(ii) For any m by n matrices A, B, and C, $A + (B + C) = (A + B) + C$.

(iii) If $0_{m,n}$ is the m by n matrix all of whose entries are 0, and A is any m by n matrix, then $A + 0_{m,n} = 0_{m,n} + A = A$.

(iv) For the m by n matrix $A = (a_{i,j})$, if $-A = (-a_{i,j})$, then $A + (-A) = (-A) + A = 0_{m,n}$.

The proof follows from the analogous properties of the real numbers.

It is clear that a scalar multiplication can be introduced which, together with the given addition, makes the set of all m by n matrices a vector space. We will not concern ourselves with such a digression but merely observe that the familiar n-dimensional vector space $\mathbf{V_n}$ is then merely the set of 1 by n matrices. Our major concern here will be with two further operations involving matrices.

Definition A-3. The *adjoint* of the m by n matrix $A = (a_{i,j})$ is the n by m matrix $A^* = (a_{j,i})$.

EXAMPLE

$$\begin{bmatrix} 2 & 3 & -1 \\ 5 & -2 & 4 \end{bmatrix}^* = \begin{bmatrix} 2 & 5 \\ 3 & -2 \\ -1 & 4 \end{bmatrix}$$

The operation of forming the adjoint of an m by n matrix is related to matrix addition by

Theorem A-2. For any m by n matrices A and B, $(A + B)^* = A^* + B^*$.

The proof is obvious.

The forming of the adjoint clearly has the following property

Theorem A-3. For any m by n matrix A, $(A^*)^* = A$.

We now turn to the more complicated matter of matrix multiplication:

Definition A-4. If $A = (a_{i,j} \mid i = 1, 2, \ldots, m$ and $j = 1, 2, \ldots, n)$ is an m by n matrix and $B = (b_{j,k} \mid j = 1, 2, \ldots, n$ and $k = 1, 2, \ldots, p)$ is an n by p matrix, then the *product* AB is the m by p matrix $(c_{i,k} \mid i = 1, 2, \ldots, m$ and $k = 1, 2, \ldots, p)$ with entries given by

$$c_{i,k} = \sum_{j=1}^{n} a_{i,j} b_{j,k}$$

A convenient way of handling matrix multiplication is to consider the entry $c_{i,k}$ of the product AB as the number which results from taking the dot product of the n-dimensional vector which is the ith horizontal row of A and the n-dimensional vector which is the adjoint of the kth vertical column of B.

EXAMPLE

$$\begin{bmatrix} 2 & 1 & 3 \\ 4 & -2 & 5 \end{bmatrix} \begin{bmatrix} 1 & -2 \\ -1 & 3 \\ 0 & 5 \end{bmatrix} = \begin{bmatrix} 2-1+0 & -4+3+15 \\ 4+2+0 & -8-6+25 \end{bmatrix}$$

$$= \begin{bmatrix} 1 & 14 \\ 6 & 11 \end{bmatrix}$$

This operation of matrix multiplication has its peculiarities. If $m \neq n$, $m \neq p$, and $n \neq p$, then "$AB = BA$" is not only false but there is no such product as BA. There is a sort of associativity, however, as given in

Theorem A-4. If A is an m by n matrix, B is an n by p matrix, and C is a p by q matrix, then $A(BC) = (AB)C$.

Proof. Let

$$A = (a_{i,j} \mid i = 1, 2, \ldots, m \text{ and } j = 1, 2, \ldots, n)$$
$$B = (b_{j,k} \mid j = 1, 2, \ldots, n \text{ and } k = 1, 2, \ldots, p)$$

and

$$C = (c_{k,r} \mid k = 1, 2, \ldots, p \text{ and } r = 1, 2, \ldots, q)$$

$$(AB)C = \left(\sum_{j=1}^{n} a_{i,j} b_{j,k} \right) C$$

$$= \left(\sum_{k=1}^{p} \left[\sum_{j=1}^{n} a_{i,j} b_{j,k} \right] c_{k,r} \right)$$

$$= \left(\sum_{k=1}^{p} \sum_{j=1}^{n} a_{i,j} b_{j,k} c_{k,r} \right)$$

$$= \left(\sum_{j=1}^{n} \sum_{k=1}^{p} a_{i,j} b_{j,k} c_{k,r} \right)$$

$$= \left(\sum_{j=1}^{n} a_{i,j} \left[\sum_{k=1}^{p} b_{j,k} c_{k,r} \right] \right)$$

$$= A \left(\sum_{k=1}^{p} b_{j,k} c_{k,r} \right)$$

$$= A(BC)$$

∎

The operation of matrix multiplication does distribute over matrix addition:

> **Theorem A-5.** If A is an m by n matrix and B and C are n by p matrices, then
> $$A(B + C) = AB + AC$$

The proof is left to the exercises.

The relation between matrix multiplication and the adjoint operation is given in

> **Theorem A-6.** If A is an m by n matrix and B is an n by p matrix, then $(AB)^* = B^*A^*$.

The proof is left to the exercises.

We now turn to the matter of the determinant of a square matrix.

> **Definition A-5.** If f is a one-to-one function on $\{1, 2, \ldots, n\}$ onto $\{1, 2, \ldots, n\}$, then the n-tuple $(f(1), f(2), \ldots, f(n))$ is a *permutation* of the n-tuple $(1, 2, \ldots, n)$. The permutation $(f(1), f(2), \ldots, f(n))$ is a permutation *by inversion of a pair* if one of the following holds:
>
>   (i) $f(1) = 2; f(2) = 1$; and, for $k = 3, 4, \ldots, n, f(k) = k$.
>   (ii) There exists an integer m, $1 < m < n$, such that $f(m) = m + 1$; $f(m + 1) = m$; and, for $k = 1, 2, \ldots, m$ but $k \neq m$ and $k \neq m + 1, f(k) = k$.
>   (iii) $f(n) = n - 1$; $f(n - 1) = n$; and, for $k = 1, 2, \ldots, n - 2$, $f(k) = k$.

Clearly any permutation is the result of successive composites of permutations by inversion of a pair. For example, $(3, 1, 2)$ is the permutation of $(1, 2, 3)$ which results from the successive inversions of pairs $(1, 2, 3)$, $(1, 3, 2)$, $(3, 1, 2)$.

> **Definition A-6.** A permutation of $(1, 2, \ldots, n)$ is *even* if it is the result of an even number of successive inversions of pairs and *odd* if it is the result of an odd number of successive inversions of pairs.

In this way the triple $(1, 2, 3)$ has six permutations: the even permutations $(1, 2, 3)$, $(3, 1, 2)$, and $(2, 3, 1)$ and the odd permutations $(1, 3, 2)$, $(3, 2, 1)$, and $(2, 1, 3)$.

Definition A-7. If $A = (a_{i,j})$ is an n by n matrix, the *determinant of A*, det A, is the number

$$\sum (-1)^{S(j_1,j_2,\ldots,j_n)} a_{1,j_1} a_{2,j_2} a_{3,j_3} \cdots a_{n,j_n}$$

where the summation is taken over all possible permutations $(j_1, j_2, \ldots, j_n)$ of $(1, 2, \ldots, n)$ and

$$S(j_1, \ldots, j_n) = \begin{cases} 0 & \text{if } (j_1, \ldots, j_n) \text{ is an even permutation} \\ 1 & \text{if } (j_1, \ldots, j_n) \text{ is an odd permutation} \end{cases}$$

EXAMPLE. For $n = 3$,

$$\det \begin{bmatrix} a_{1,1} & a_{1,2} & a_{1,3} \\ a_{2,1} & a_{2,2} & a_{2,3} \\ a_{3,1} & a_{3,2} & a_{3,3} \end{bmatrix} = \begin{aligned} & a_{1,1}a_{2,2}a_{3,3} + a_{1,3}a_{2,1}a_{3,2} \\ & + a_{1,2}a_{2,3}a_{3,1} - a_{1,1}a_{2,3}a_{3,2} \\ & - a_{1,3}a_{2,2}a_{3,1} - a_{1,2}a_{2,1}a_{3,3} \end{aligned}$$

Definition A-8. If A is an m by n matrix, B *is a submatrix of* A means that B is the matrix which results from eliminating from A one or more horizontal rows or one or more vertical columns.

EXAMPLE. The matrix

$$\begin{bmatrix} 2 & 1 & 3 \\ 5 & 0 & 4 \end{bmatrix}$$

has submatrices

$$\begin{bmatrix} 2 & 1 \\ 5 & 0 \end{bmatrix}, \quad \begin{bmatrix} 2 & 3 \\ 5 & 4 \end{bmatrix}, \quad \begin{bmatrix} 1 & 3 \\ 0 & 4 \end{bmatrix}, \quad (2, 1, 3), \quad (5, 0, 4),$$

$$\begin{bmatrix} 2 \\ 5 \end{bmatrix}, \quad \begin{bmatrix} 1 \\ 0 \end{bmatrix}, \quad (2), \quad (1), \quad (3), \quad (5), \quad (0), \quad \text{and} \quad (4)$$

Definition A-9. The *rank* of an m by n matrix A is the integer k, $0 \le k \le \min(m, n)$ such that there exists a k by k submatrix of A with nonzero determinant and every larger square submatrix of A has zero determinant.

EXAMPLE. The rank of

$$\begin{bmatrix} 2 & 1 & 3 \\ 5 & 0 & 4 \end{bmatrix}$$

is 2 since the submatrix

$$\begin{bmatrix} 2 & 1 \\ 5 & 0 \end{bmatrix}$$

has determinant -5 and there are no square submatrices of size greater than 2 by 2.

We state without proof the following result:

Theorem A-7. If, for the n by n matrix A, $\det A \neq 0$, then there exists a unique n by n matrix A^{-1} such that $AA^{-1} = A^{-1}A = (\delta_{i,j})$, where

$$\delta_{i,j} = \begin{cases} 1 & \text{if } i = j \\ 0 & \text{if } i \neq j \end{cases}$$

And we conclude with the theorem we have used in our treatment of Jacobians:

Theorem A-8. If A is an n by n matrix for which $\det A \neq 0$ and $\mathbf{k}$ is a 1 by n matrix (i.e., a vector of $\mathbf{V_n}$), then

$$[A^{-1}(A\mathbf{k}^*)]^* = \mathbf{k}$$

Proof. Let $A = (a_{ij})$ and $A^{-1} = (b_{ij})$. Then

$$A^{-1}A = \sum_{s=1}^{n} b_{is}a_{sj} = \delta_{ij}$$

For $\mathbf{k} = (k_1, k_2, \ldots, k_n)$,

$$[A\mathbf{k}^*]^* = \left(\sum_{r=1}^{n} a_{1r}k_r, \sum_{r=1}^{n} a_{2r}k_r, \ldots, \sum_{r=1}^{n} a_{nr}k_r \right)$$

$$[A^{-1}(A\mathbf{k}^*)]^* = \left(\sum_{s=1}^{n} b_{1s} \sum_{r=1}^{n} a_{sr}k_r, \sum_{s=1}^{n} b_{2s} \sum_{r=1}^{n} a_{sr}k_r, \ldots, \sum_{s=1}^{n} b_{ns} \sum_{r=1}^{n} a_{sr}k_r \right)$$

$$= \left(\sum_{r=1}^{n} \left[\sum_{s=1}^{n} b_{1s}a_{sr} \right] k_r, \sum_{r=1}^{n} \left[\sum_{s=1}^{n} b_{2s}a_{sr} \right] k_r, \ldots, \sum_{r=1}^{n} \left[\sum_{s=1}^{n} b_{ns}a_{sr} \right] k_r \right)$$

$$= \left(\sum_{r=1}^{n} \delta_{1r}k_r, \sum_{r=1}^{n} \delta_{2r}k_r, \ldots, \sum_{r=1}^{n} \delta_{nr}k_r \right)$$

$$= (k_1, k_2, \ldots, k_n)$$

$$= \mathbf{k} \qquad \blacksquare$$

EXERCISES

1. Prove Theorem A-5.

2. Prove Theorem A-6.

3. Find, separately, all the odd and even permutations of $(1, 2, 3, 4)$.

4. Find the sum giving the determinant of a 2 by 2 matrix.

5. Find the sum giving the determinant of a 4 by 4 matrix.

6. Construct a 4 by 3 matrix of rank 2.

B SERIES SOLUTIONS OF DIFFERENTIAL EQUATIONS

B-1 Ordinary Points of Linear Differential Equations

Throughout this appendix we will consider the linear differential equation of order n:

$$(*) \qquad p_n(x)y^{(n)} + p_{n-1}(x)y^{(n-1)} + \cdots + p_0(x)y = 0$$

where $p_0, p_1, \ldots, p_n$ are polynomials. We begin with

> **Definition B-1-1.** The real number a is an *ordinary point* of the equation $(*)$ provided that $p_n(a) \neq 0$. If $p_n(a) = 0$, then a is a *singular point* of $(*)$.

We are trying to find a "general solution" of $(*)$ in the form of a function represented by a power series centered at a. We will leave untouched the question of what conditions on the coefficient polynomials $p_0, p_1, \ldots, p_n$ will suffice to insure the existence of such a solution. What we do instead is begin with the assumption that a power series solution does indeed exist and then—using the term-by-term differentiation of a power series—determine what the coefficients of this power series must be. The power series thus constructed will represent a function whose domain is the interval of convergence and such a function will then necessarily be a solution of the differential equation.

A "general" solution of an nth order differential equation is an arbitrary linear combination of n linearly independent functions, each of which is a solution. Since we are dealing with power series, we will have attained such a solution when we have a power series in which n of the coefficients are arbitrary and all the remaining coefficients are determined by these arbitrary ones.

Because of the length of the computations involved for $n > 2$, we will content ourselves with the case $n = 2$.

EXAMPLE. We find a general solution of

$$2y'' + 3xy' + y = 0$$

There are no singular points of this differential equation. If we assume the existence of a solution which can be represented by a power series centered at 0, of the form

$$\sum_{n=0}^{\infty} c_n x^n$$

then we have

$$\sum_{n=0}^{\infty} 2n(n-1)c_n x^{n-2} + \sum_{n=0}^{\infty} 3nc_n x^n + \sum_{n=0}^{\infty} c_n x^n = 0$$

$$\sum_{n=0}^{\infty} [2(n+2)(n+1)c_{n+2} + (3n+1)c_n]x^n = 0$$

Thus, for $n = 0, 1, 2, \ldots$,

$$c_{n+2} = -\frac{3n+1}{2(n+1)(n+2)} c_n$$

For the coefficients of even order,

$$c_2 = -\frac{1}{2(1)(2)} c_0$$

$$c_4 = -\frac{7}{2(3)(4)} c_2$$

$$c_6 = -\frac{13}{2(5)(6)} c_4$$

$$\cdot$$
$$\cdot$$
$$\cdot$$

$$c_{2k} = -\frac{6k-5}{2(2k-1)(2k)} c_{2k-2}$$

This means that, for $k = 1, 2, 3, \ldots$,

$$c_{2k} = (-1)^k \frac{7(13)(19) \cdots (6k-5)}{2^k \, (2k)!} c_0$$

For the coefficients of odd order,

$$c_3 = -\frac{4}{2(2)(3)} c_1$$

$$c_5 = -\frac{10}{2(4)(5)} c_3$$

$$c_7 = -\frac{16}{2(6)(7)} c_5$$

$$\cdot$$
$$\cdot$$
$$\cdot$$

$$c_{2k+1} = -\frac{(3k-1)}{2(2k)(2k+1)} c_{2k-1}$$

Thus, for $k = 1, 2, 3, \ldots,$

$$c_{2k+1} = (-1)^k \frac{2(5)(8) \cdots (3k-1)}{2^k(2k+1)!} c_1$$

If there is to be a power series solution of the given differential equation, it then must have the form

$$c_0\left[1 + \sum_{n=1}^{\infty} \frac{(-1)^n 7(13)(19) \cdots (6n-5)}{2^n(2n)!} x^{2n}\right]$$

$$+ c_1\left[1 + \sum_{n=1}^{\infty} \frac{(-1)^n 2(5)(8) \cdots (3n-1)}{(2n+1)!} x^{2n+1}\right]$$

Since each of the power series in this sum has infinite radius of convergence, the function so determined is a solution of the differential equation; and since the coefficients c_0 and c_1 are arbitrary, we do have a general solution.

EXERCISES

Find a general power series solution, centered at 0, for each of the following differential equations. Then determine the interval of convergence for the resulting series.

1. $3y'' + xy' + 4y = 0$
2. $(2 + x^2)y'' - 6y = 0$
3. $(1 + x^2)y'' - 4xy' + 6y = 0$
4. $(1 + x^2)y'' + 10xy' + 20y = 0$
5. $(1 - 4x^2)y'' + 6xy' - 4y = 0$

B-2   Singular Points: The Indicial Equation

We now turn to consideration of a possible power series solution of a linear differential equation in the case that the power series is centered at a singular point of the equation. Some singular points are more pleasant than others, and we draw a distinction in

Definition B-2-1. If the real number a is a singular point of the differential equation

$$p_n(x)y^{(n)} + p_{n-1}(x)y^{(n-1)} + \cdots + p_0(x)y = 0$$

then a is said to be a *regular singular point* provided that, for $k = 1, 2, \ldots, n,$

$$\lim_{x \to a}\left[(x-a)^k \frac{p_{n-k}(x)}{p_n(x)}\right]$$

exists.

In the case of a second-order equation, the real number a will be a regular singular point if the coefficients can be expressed by

and

$$\frac{p_1(x)}{p_2(x)} = \frac{a_{-1}}{x - a} + \sum_{n=0}^{\infty} a_n(x - a)^n$$

$$\frac{p_0(x)}{p_2(x)} = \frac{b_{-2}}{(x - a)^2} + \frac{b_{-1}}{x - a} + \sum_{n=0}^{\infty} b_n(x - a)^n$$

EXAMPLE. The number 0 is a regular singular point of

$$4xy'' + 3y' - 3y = 0$$

We will now attempt to find a power series solution, centered at 0, for this differential equation. If the function given by $\sum_{n=0}^{\infty} c_n x^n$ is to satisfy

$$4xy'' + 3y' - 3y = 0$$

we must have

$$\sum_{n=0}^{\infty} 4n(n - 1)c_n x^{n-1} + \sum_{n=0}^{\infty} 3nc_n x^{n-1} + \sum_{n=0}^{\infty} (-3)c_n x^n = 0$$

or

$$\sum_{n=0}^{\infty} [4(n + 1)nc_{n+1} + 3(n + 1)c_{n+1} - 3c_n]x^n = 0$$

Thus, for $n = 0, 1, 2, \ldots$,

$$c_{n+1} = \frac{3}{(n + 1)(4n + 3)} c_n$$

For $n = 1, 2, \ldots$, we then have

$$c_1 = \frac{3}{1(3)} c_0$$

$$c_2 = \frac{3}{2(7)} c_1$$

$$c_3 = \frac{3}{3(11)} c_2$$

$$\vdots$$

$$c_n = \frac{3}{n(4n - 1)} c_{n-1}$$

$$c_n = \frac{3^n}{n! \, 3(7)(11) \cdots (4n - 1)} c_0$$

The series

$$1 + \sum_{n=1}^{\infty} c_n x^n$$

which converges on $]-\infty, +\infty[$ is thus a solution of the given differential equation. But we need another solution, linearly independent of this one, in order to have a general solution of the equation. The device used to determine two solutions involves assuming the existence of a solution of the form

$$x^{\lambda} \sum_{n=0}^{\infty} c_n x^n = \sum_{n=0}^{\infty} c_n x^{n+\lambda}$$

where the exponent λ is left undetermined. If the given equation is to have such a solution, then we have

$$\sum_{n=0}^{\infty} 4(n+\lambda)(n+\lambda-1)c_n x^{n+\lambda-1} + \sum_{n=0}^{\infty} 3(n+\lambda)c_n x^{n+\lambda-1} + \sum_{n=0}^{\infty} (-3)c_n x^{n+\lambda} = 0$$

or

$$[4\lambda(\lambda-1) + 3\lambda]c_0 x^{\lambda-1}$$
$$+ \sum_{n=0}^{\infty} [4(n+\lambda+1)(n+\lambda)c_{n+1} + 3(n+\lambda+1)c_{n+1} - 3c_n]x^{n+\lambda} = 0$$

From the coefficient of the first power shown, we have the equation

$$4\lambda(\lambda-1) + 3\lambda = 0$$

which is called the *indicial equation* of the differential equation $4xy'' + 3y' - 3y = 0$. This particular equation has 0 and $\frac{1}{4}$ as solutions. If we choose $\lambda = 0$, we find precisely the relation between coefficients obtained above and find that

$$1 + \sum_{n=1}^{\infty} \frac{3^n}{n!\, 3(7)(11) \cdots (4n-1)} x^n$$

is a solution.

On the other hand, if we choose $\lambda = \frac{1}{4}$, then we have, for $n = 0, 1, 2, \ldots$,

$$[4(n+\tfrac{1}{4}+1)(n+\tfrac{1}{4}) + 3(n+\tfrac{1}{4}+1)]c_{n+1} - 3c_n = 0$$

$$c_{n+1} = \frac{3}{(n+1)(4n+5)} c_n$$

Thus, for $n = 1, 2, \ldots$,

$$c_1 = \frac{3}{1(5)} c_0$$

$$c_2 = \frac{3}{2(9)} c_1$$

$$c_3 = \frac{3}{3(13)} c_2$$

$$\cdot$$
$$\cdot$$
$$\cdot$$

$$c_n = \frac{3}{n(4n+1)} c_{n-1}$$

$$c_n = \frac{3^n}{n!\, 5(9)(13) \cdots (4n+1)} c_0$$

The general solution of $4xy'' - 3y' - 3y = 0$ is thus

$$A\left[1 + \sum_{n=1}^{\infty} \frac{3^n}{n!\, 3(7) \cdots (4n-1)} x^n\right] + B \sum_{n=0}^{\infty} \frac{3^n}{n!\, 5(9) \cdots (4n+1)} x^n \quad \blacksquare$$

In general, for $n = 2$, if the real number a is a regular singular point of the differential equation

$$p_2(x)y'' + p_1(x)y' + p_0(x)y = 0$$

then there are numbers $a_{-1}, a_0, a_1, a_2, \ldots$ such that

$$\frac{p_1(x)}{p_2(x)} = \frac{a_{-1}}{x-a} + \sum_{n=0}^{\infty} a_n(x-a)^n$$

and numbers $b_{-2}, b_{-1}, b_0, b_1, b_2, \ldots$ such that

$$\frac{p_0(x)}{p_2(x)} = \frac{b_{-2}}{(x-a)^2} + \frac{b_{-1}}{x-a} + \sum_{n=0}^{\infty} b_n(x-a)^n$$

In the series expansion for

$$y'' + \frac{p_1(x)}{p_2(x)} y' + \frac{p_0(x)}{p_2(x)} y$$

under the substitution

$$y = \sum_{n=0}^{\infty} c_n(x-a)^{n+\lambda}$$

the coefficient of the first term becomes

$$[\lambda(\lambda-1) + a_{-1}\lambda + b_{-2}]c_0$$

and the equation

$$\lambda(\lambda-1) + a_{-1}\lambda + b_{-2} = 0$$

is the *indicial equation*. When there are two distinct solutions to this algebraic equation and when those solutions do not differ by an integer, each one can be used to form a series solution to the given differential equation.

EXERCISES

Find series solutions, centered at 0, for the following:

1. $2xy'' + 5(1 + 2x)y' + 5y = 0$

2. $3xy'' + (1 + x)y' - 2y = 0$

3. $4xy'' + (3 + x)y' + 2y = 0$

4. $3xy'' + (4 - x)y' + 3y = 0$

5. $7xy'' + (5 + 2x)y' - 3y = 0$

B-3   Indicial Equation with Equal Roots

We examine a second-order differential equation for which the indicial equation has one double root:

$$xy'' + y' + xy = 0$$

If we consider the function given by

$$f(x, \lambda) = \sum_{n=0}^{\infty} c_n x^{n+\lambda}$$

we have

$$xf_{11}(x, \lambda) + f_1(x, \lambda) + xf(x, \lambda) = \sum_{n=0}^{\infty} (n + \lambda)(n + \lambda - 1)c_n x^{n+\lambda-1}$$

$$+ \sum_{n=0}^{\infty} (n + \lambda)c_n x^{n+\lambda-1} + \sum_{n=0}^{\infty} c_n x^{n+\lambda+1}$$

$$= \lambda^2 c_0 x^{\lambda-1} + c_1 x^{\lambda}$$

$$+ \sum_{n=1}^{\infty} [(n + \lambda + 1)(n + \lambda)c_{n+1}$$

$$+ (n + \lambda + 1)c_{n+1} + c_{n-1}]x^{n+\lambda}$$

The function given by $f(x, \lambda)$ will satisfy the differential equation $xy'' + y' + xy = 0$ provided we have $\lambda = 0$ and

$$c_0 = 1$$
$$c_1 = 0$$

and, for $n = 1, 2, \ldots,$

$$c_{n+1} = \frac{-1}{(n + \lambda + 1)^2} c_{n-1}$$

This will mean that, for $k = 0, 1, 2, \ldots,$

$$c_{2k+1} = 0$$

and, for $n = 1, 2, \ldots,$

$$c_2 = \frac{-1}{(\lambda + 2)^2} c_0$$

$$\vdots$$

$$c_{2n} = \frac{-1}{(\lambda + 2n)^2} c_{2n-2}$$

$$c_{2n} = \frac{(-1)^n}{(\lambda + 2)^2(\lambda + 4)^2 \cdots (\lambda + 2n)^2} c_0$$

Collecting these results, we have

$$f(x, \lambda) = x^\lambda + \sum_{n=1}^{\infty} \frac{(-1)^n}{(\lambda + 2)^2(\lambda + 4)^2 \cdots (\lambda + 2n)^2} x^{2n+\lambda}$$

with the property that

$$xf_{11}(x, \lambda) + f_1(x, \lambda) + xf(x, \lambda) = \lambda^2 x^{\lambda-1}$$

Clearly $f(x, 0)$ is a solution of $xy'' + y' + xy = 0$. But we also have

$$xf_{211}(x, \lambda) + f_{21}(x, \lambda) + xf_2(x, \lambda) = 2\lambda x^{\lambda-1} + \lambda^2 x^{\lambda-1} \log x$$

so that the function $f_2(x, 0)$ is also a solution of this differential equation. Denoting f by

$$f(x, \lambda) = x^\lambda + \sum_{n=1}^{\infty} c_n(\lambda)x^{2n+\lambda}$$

we will have

$$f_2(x, \lambda) = x^\lambda \log x + (\log x)\sum_{n=1}^{\infty} c_n(\lambda)x^{2n+\lambda} + \sum_{n=1}^{\infty} c_n'(\lambda)x^{2n+\lambda}$$

$$= f(x, \lambda) \log x + \sum_{n=1}^{\infty} c_n'(\lambda)x^{2n+\lambda}$$

In this particular case, logarithmic differentiation yields

$$c_n'(\lambda) = 2c_n(\lambda)\left(\frac{1}{\lambda + 2} + \frac{1}{\lambda + 4} + \cdots + \frac{1}{\lambda + 2n}\right)$$

We finally have

$$f(x, 0) = \sum_{n=0}^{\infty} \frac{(-1)^n x^{2n}}{2^{2n}(n!)^2}$$

and

$$f_2(x, 0) = f(x, 0) \log x + \sum_{n=1}^{\infty} \frac{(-1)^n}{2^{2n}(n!)^2} H_n x^{2n}$$

where H_n is the nth partial sum of the harmonic series.

In the general case when the indicial equation has equal roots, the procedure consists of carrying through an unspecified λ to find the general form of $c_n(\lambda)$, picking $c_0(\lambda) = 1$ and then using the derivatives $c_n'(\lambda)$ to form the function $f_2(x, \lambda)$. Then $f(x, \lambda_0)$ and $f_2(x, \lambda_0)$ will give two linearly independent solutions of the given differential equation.

EXERCISES

Find two linearly independent solutions in the form of a series, centered at 0, for

1. $x^2 y'' + 3xy' + (1 - 2x)y = 0$
2. $x(x - 4)y'' + (x - 1)y' - y = 0$

3. $x^2y'' + x(x + 7)y' + 9y = 0$

4. $xy'' + (1 - x)y' - y = 0$

B-4   Difference of Roots a Nonzero Integer: Nonlogarithmic Case

When the indicial equation has two distinct roots which differ by an integer, say r and $r + p$, where p is a positive integer, we would expect series solutions of the form

$$\sum_{n=0}^{\infty} c_n x^{n+r} \quad \text{and} \quad \sum_{n=0}^{\infty} c_n x^{n+r+p}$$

It is certainly possible that these ostensibly different series are in fact the same since the second involves exponents which are all included in the first. We examine first the more pleasant situation in which we do have different series; in fact, the first "series" is a polynomial with fewer than p terms.

EXAMPLE. We consider the differential equation

$$xy'' - (x + 3)y' + 2y = 0$$

Assuming a solution of the form

$$\sum_{n=0}^{\infty} c_n x^{n+\lambda}$$

yields, for the left side,

$$\sum_{n=0}^{\infty} (n + \lambda)(n + \lambda - 1)c_n x^{n+\lambda-1} + \sum_{n=0}^{\infty} [-(n + \lambda)]c_n x^{n+\lambda}$$

$$+ \sum_{n=0}^{\infty} (-3)(n + \lambda)c_n x^{n+\lambda-1} + \sum_{n=0}^{\infty} 2c_n x^{n+\lambda}$$

$$= [\lambda(\lambda - 1) - 3\lambda]c_0 x^{\lambda-1} + \sum_{n=0}^{\infty} \{[(n + \lambda + 1)(n + \lambda) - 3(n + \lambda + 1)]c_{n+1}$$

$$+ [-(n + \lambda) + 2]c_n\}x^{n+\lambda}$$

$$= (\lambda^2 - 4\lambda)c_0 x^{\lambda-1} + \sum_{n=0}^{\infty} [(n + \lambda + 1)(n + \lambda - 3)c_{n+1} - (n + \lambda - 2)c_n]x^{n+\lambda}$$

The roots of the indicial equation are thus 0 and 4. For $\lambda = 0$ we have, for $n = 0, 1, 2, \ldots$,

$$(n + 1)(n - 3)c_{n+1} = (n - 2)c_n$$

Considering this recurrence relation from right to left tells us that, for $n = 3, 4, \ldots, c_n = 0$. In addition, we have

$$-3c_1 = -2c_0$$

$$-4c_2 = -c_1$$

$$c_1 = \tfrac{2}{3}c_0, \qquad c_2 = \tfrac{1}{6}c_0$$

Thus a solution to the given differential equation is

$$1 + \tfrac{2}{3}x + \tfrac{1}{6}x^2$$

On the other hand, for $\lambda = 4$ we have, for $n = 0, 1, 2, \ldots$,

$$c_{n+1} = \frac{n + 2}{(n + 5)(n + 1)} c_n$$

and, for $n = 1, 2, \ldots$,

$$c_1 = \frac{2}{5(1)} c_0$$

$$c_2 = \frac{3}{6(2)} c_1$$

$$\vdots$$

$$c_n = \frac{n + 1}{n(n + 4)} c_{n-1}$$

$$c_n = \frac{(n + 1)! \, 24}{n! \, (n + 4)!} = \frac{24(n + 1)}{(n + 4)!}$$

Thus a second solution to the given differential equation is

$$\sum_{n=0}^{\infty} \frac{24(n + 1)}{(n + 4)!} x^{n+4}$$

EXERCISES

Find two linearly independent solutions in the form of series centered at 0 for

1. $x^2 y'' + x(x - 3)y' + (x - 5)y = 0$
2. $x^2 y'' + 2x(x - 2)y' - 4xy = 0$
3. $4x^2 y'' + 8x(x - 1)y' - (12x + 7)y = 0$
4. $xy'' + 3(x - 1)y' - 6y = 0$
5. $xy'' + (x - 7)y' - 5y = 0$

B-5 Difference of Roots an Integer: Logarithmic Case

We now turn to the attempt to find two linearly independent solutions of a second-order differential equation in the case in which the indicial equation has two distinct roots, where these roots differ by an integer and an attempt to use the smaller of the roots does not yield a simple polynomial solution.

EXAMPLE. For $x(1 - x)y'' + 2(1 - x)y' + 2y = 0$, application of the left side to $\sum\limits_{n=0}^{\infty} c_n x^{n+\lambda}$ yields

$$[\lambda(\lambda - 1) + 2\lambda]c_0 x^{\lambda-1}$$
$$+ \sum_{n=0}^{\infty} [(n + \lambda + 1)(n + \lambda + 2)c_{n+1} - (n + \lambda + 2)(n + \lambda - 1)]c_n x^{n+\lambda}$$

The indicial equation is

$$\lambda^2 + \lambda = 0$$

whose solutions are -1 and 0. An attempt to use -1 gives a recurrence relation in which $c_0 = 0$ and so produces only a trivial solution. We adopt a procedure similar to that used when the indicial equation had a single repeated root and defer the substitution of -1 for λ. We then have, for $n = 0, 1, 2, \ldots$,

$$c_{n+1} = \frac{(n + \lambda + 2)(n + \lambda - 1)}{(n + \lambda + 2)(n + \lambda + 1)} c_n$$
$$= \frac{n + \lambda - 1}{n + \lambda + 1} c_n$$

Thus, for $n = 1, 2, \ldots$,

$$c_1 = \frac{\lambda - 1}{\lambda + 1} c_0$$

$$c_2 = \frac{\lambda}{\lambda + 2} c_1$$

$$\cdot$$
$$\cdot$$
$$\cdot$$

$$c_n = \frac{\lambda + n - 2}{\lambda + n} c_{n-1}$$

$$c_n = \frac{(\lambda - 1)\lambda(\lambda + 1) \cdots (\lambda + n - 2)}{(\lambda + 1)(\lambda + 2) \cdots (\lambda + n)} c_0$$

Since we hope eventually to substitute -1 for λ, it would be helpful to avoid any problems of an attempted division by zero. We do this by choosing

$$c_0 = \lambda + 1$$

We then are considering

$$f(x, \lambda) = (\lambda + 1)x^{\lambda} + \sum_{n=1}^{\infty} \frac{(\lambda - 1)\lambda(\lambda + 1) \cdots (\lambda + n - 2)}{(\lambda + 2)(\lambda + 3) \cdots (\lambda + n)} x^{n+\lambda}$$

Applying the left side of the given differential equation yields

$$x(1 - x)f_{11}(x, \lambda) + 2(1 - x)f_1(x, \lambda) + 2f(x, \lambda) = \lambda(\lambda + 1)^2 x^{\lambda-1}$$

We then also have

$$x(1 - x)f_{211}(x, \lambda) + 2(1 - x)f_{21}(x, \lambda) + 2f_2(x, \lambda)$$
$$= (\lambda + 1)^2 x^{\lambda-1} + 2\lambda(\lambda + 1)x^{\lambda-1} + \lambda(\lambda + 1)^2 x^{\lambda-1}(\lambda - 1)\log x$$

Thus both $f(x, -1)$ and $f_2(x, -1)$ satisfy the given differential equation.
Denoting the coefficients of the series in $f(x, \lambda)$ by $c_n(\lambda)$, we see that

$$f_2(x, -1) = f(x, -1) \log x + \sum_{n=1}^{\infty} c_n'(-1)x^{n-1}$$

But

$$c_n'(\lambda) = c_n(\lambda)\left[\frac{1}{\lambda - 1} + \frac{1}{\lambda} + \frac{1}{\lambda + 1} - \frac{1}{\lambda + n - 1} + \frac{1}{\lambda + n}\right]$$

Carrying through the appropriate cancellations and substituting -1 yields, for $n = 3, 4, \ldots$,

$$c_n'(-1) = \frac{2(n-3)!}{(n-1)!} = \frac{2}{(n-1)(n-2)}$$

For the first three terms we have

$$c_1(\lambda) = \lambda - 1$$

$$c_2(\lambda) = \frac{\lambda}{\lambda + 2}$$

$$c_3(\lambda) = \frac{\lambda + 1}{\lambda + 3} c_2(\lambda)$$

Thus

$$c_1'(\lambda) = 1$$

$$c_2'(\lambda) = 1 - \frac{3}{(\lambda + 2)^2}$$

Substitution of -1 for λ throughout gives

$$f(x, -1) = -2 + 2x$$

$$f_2(x, -1) = (-2 + 2x) \log x + 1 - 2x + \sum_{n=3}^{\infty} \frac{2}{(n-1)(n-2)} x^{n-1}$$

In general we find

$$f(x, \lambda) = c_0(\lambda)x + \sum_{n=1}^{\infty} c_n(\lambda)x^{n+\lambda}$$

determining the $c_n(\lambda)$ from the recurrence relation. With an indicial equation of the form

$$(\lambda - r_1)(\lambda - r_2) = 0$$

with $r_1 < r_2$, we choose

$$c_0(\lambda) = \lambda - r_1$$

so that application of the left side of the differential equation to $f(x, \lambda)$ yields

$$(\lambda - r_1)^2(\lambda - r_2)x^{\lambda-1}$$

Then $f(x, r_1)$ and $f_2(x, r_1)$ will both be solutions of the given differential equation.

EXERCISES

1. $xy'' + 2(x - 1)y' + 4y = 0$

2. $9x^2y'' - 15xy' + 7(1 - x)y = 0$

3. $x^2y'' + xy' + (x^2 - 1)y = 0$

4. $xy'' + (3 + 2x)y' + 8y = 0$

PARTIAL C
DIFFERENTIAL
EQUATIONS

We give here a very brief glance at one particular aspect of the theory of partial differential equations: separable equations. A partial differential equation of the form

$$F(u, u_1, u_2, u_{11}, u_{12}, u_{22}) = 0$$

is called *separable* if there exists a solution in the form

$$u(x, y) = f(x)g(y)$$

where f and g are functions on sets of real numbers, and if there are two functions G and H such that

$$F(u, u_1, u_2, u_{11}, u_{12}, u_{22}) = G(x, f'(x), f''(x))g(y) - H(y, g'(y), g''(y))f(x)$$

Under these conditions we must have

$$\frac{G(x, f'(x), f''(x))}{f(x)} = \frac{H(y, g'(y), g''(y))}{g(y)}$$

true for all values of x in the domain of f and all values of y in the domain of g. For any fixed value of y, the left side of this last equation must then be a constant. Further, for any fixed value of x, the right side of this equation must be the same constant. We then have two ordinary differential equations to solve.

EXAMPLE. For $a > 0$, we consider the partial differential equation

$$a^2 u_{11} - u_{22} = 0$$

For a solution to be given by

$$u(x, y) = f(x)g(y)$$

we must have

$$a^2 f''(x)g(y) - f(x)g''(y) = 0$$

There is then a constant k such that

$$\frac{a^2 f''(x)}{f(x)} = \frac{g''(y)}{g(y)} = k$$

We are now faced with the two ordinary differential equations

$$a^2 f''(x) - kf(x) = 0 \quad \text{and} \quad g''(y) - kg(y) = 0$$

For $k > 0$, we have

$$f(x) = a_1 e^{\sqrt{k/a}\,x} + a_2 e^{-\sqrt{k/a}\,x}$$

$$g(y) = b_1 e^{\sqrt{k}\,y} + b_2 e^{\sqrt{k}\,y}$$

For $k = 0$, we have

$$f(x) = a_1 x + a_2$$

$$g(y) = b_1 y + b_2$$

and, for $k < 0$, we have

$$f(x) = a_1 \cos \sqrt{\frac{-k}{a}}\, x + a_2 \sin \sqrt{\frac{-k}{a}}\, x$$

$$g(y) = b_1 \cos \sqrt{-k}\, y + b_2 \sin \sqrt{-k}\, y$$

If, in addition to the differential equation, we have further conditions to be satisfied, then we can use these to determine the appropriate character of the constant k and also to determine the proper values of the constants a_1, a_2, b_1, and b_2.

We consider a typical "boundary value problem." We begin with a function h on $[0, a]$ into the real numbers and we are looking for a function u on $[0, +\infty[\times [0, a]$ into the real numbers such that

   (i) For a fixed $k > 0$, $u_2 = k^2 u_{11}$.

   (ii) For each $x \in [0, a]$, $\lim_{y \to 0+} u(x, y) = h(x)$.

   (iii) For each $y > 0$, $\lim_{x \to 0+} u(x, y) = \lim_{x \to a-} u(x, y) = 0$.

Assuming a solution of the differential equation in (i) of the form $u(x, y) = f(x)g(y)$ gives

$$f(x)g'(y) = k^2 f''(x)g(y)$$

$$\frac{f''(x)}{f(x)} = \frac{g'(y)}{k^2 g(y)} = \lambda$$

where λ is to be determined.

Then f is a solution of

$$z'' - \lambda z = 0$$

and g is a solution of

$$z' - k^2 \lambda z = 0$$

We then have

$$f(x) = \begin{cases} A \cos \sqrt{-\lambda}\, x + B \sin \sqrt{-\lambda}\, x & \text{for} \quad \lambda < 0 \\ Ax + B & \text{for} \quad \lambda = 0 \\ Ae^{\sqrt{\lambda}\,x} + Be^{-\sqrt{\lambda}\,x} & \text{for} \quad \lambda > 0 \end{cases}$$

and

$$g(y) = Ce^{k^2\lambda y}$$

The requirement that $\lim\limits_{x\to 0+} u(x, y) = 0$ will be met if we choose $\lambda < 0$ so that

$$\lim_{x\to 0+} u(x, y) = g(y)\lim_{x\to 0+}(A\cos\sqrt{-\lambda}\,x + B\sin\sqrt{-\lambda}\,x)$$
$$= Ag(y) = 0$$

This can be done by the choice $A = 0$ and we can have a nontrivial solution by making sure $B \neq 0$.

For $\lambda < 0$, we now have

$$u(x, y) = g(y)B\sin\sqrt{-\lambda}\,x$$

Then

$$\lim_{x\to a-} u(x, y) = g(y)B\sin\sqrt{-\lambda}\,a$$

The second requirement of (iii) will then be met by choosing λ so that $\sqrt{-\lambda}\,a$ is an integer multiple of π.

If, for $n = 1, 2, \ldots, \sqrt{-\lambda}\,a = n\pi$, then

$$\lambda = -\frac{n^2\pi^2}{a^2}$$

and we have for any constant b_n

$$u_n(x, y) = b_n\exp\left(-\frac{n^2\pi^2}{a^2}y\right)\sin\frac{n\pi x}{a}$$

satisfying conditions (i) and (iii).

Assuming uniform convergence, the functions given by

$$u(x, y) = \sum_{n=1}^{\infty} b_n\exp\left(-\frac{n^2\pi^2}{a^2}y\right)\sin\frac{n\pi x}{a}$$

will also satisfy conditions (i) and (iii). For this function

$$\lim_{y\to 0+} u(x, y) = \sum_{n=1}^{\infty} b_n\sin\frac{n\pi x}{a}$$

If we now extend the given function h to $[-a, a]$ by $h(-x) = -h(x)$ and call this extension H, then the Fourier series of H on $[-a, a]$ will have no cosine terms and, provided h is a pleasant enough function, the Fourier series of H on $[0, a]$ will converge uniformly to h. We can then satisfy condition (ii) by choosing the constants $b_1, b_2, \ldots$ to be precisely the coefficients in the "Fourier sine series" of h on $[0, a]$.

EXERCISES

Find general solutions to the following partial differential equations:

1. $u_{11} + u_{22} = 0$

2. $u_{11} + 2bu_1 - c^2 u_{22} = 0$

3. $u_{11}(x, y) + 4xu_1(x, y) + u_{22}(x, y) = 0$

4. $u_1(x, y) - xu_2(x, y) = 0$

5. $xu_1(x, y) - yu_2(x, y) - u(x, y) = 0$

6. Find a solution to the boundary value problem $u_{22} = 9u_{11}$, for all $x \in [0, 1]$,

$$\lim_{y \to 0+} u(x, y) = x$$

and, for all $y > 0$,

$$\lim_{x \to 0+} u(x, y) = \lim_{x \to 1-} u(x, y) = 0$$

ANSWERS TO SELECTED EXERCISES

1-1 Vector Spaces

1. $A = B$.

3. V-1 follows directly from the definition.

V-2. $(a, b, c) + (p, q, r) = (a + p, b + q, c + r) = (p + a, q + b, r + c)$
$= (p, q, r) + (a, b, c)$.

V-3. $(a, b, c) + [(p, q, r) + (x, y, z)]$

$= (a, b, c) + (p + x, q + y, r + z)$
$= (a + [p + x], b + [q + y], c + [r + z])$
$= ([a + p] + x, [b + q] + y, [c + r] + z)$
$= (a + p, b + q, c + r) + (x, y, z)$
$= [(a, b, c) + (p, q, r)] + (x, y, z)$.

V-4. Let $\mathbf{0} = (0, 0)$. Then $(a, b, c) + \mathbf{0} = (a, b, c) + (0, 0, 0) = (a + 0, b + 0, c + 0) = (a, b, c)$.

V-5. Let $-(a, b, c) = (-a, -b, -c)$. Then $(a, b, c) + [-(a, b, c)] = (a, b, c) + (-a, -b, -c) = (a + (-a), b + (-b), c + (-c)) = (0, 0, 0) = \mathbf{0}$.

S-1. $(1)(a, b, c) = ((1)a, (1)b, (1)c) = (a, b, c)$.

$(0)(a, b, c) = ((0)a, (0)b, (0)c) = (0, 0, 0) = \mathbf{0}$.

S-2. $a[(p, q, r) + (x, y, z)] = a(p + x, q + y, r + z)$

$= (a[p + x], a[q + y], a[r + z]) = (ap + ax, aq + ay, ar + az)$
$= (ap, aq, ar) + (ax, ay, az) = a(p, q, r) + a(x, y, z)$.

S-3. $(a + b)(p, q, r) = ([a + b]p, [a + b]q, [a + b]r)$

$= (ap + bp, aq + bq, ar + br) = (ap, aq, ar) + (bp, bq, br)$
$= a(p, q, r) + b(p, q, r)$.

5. $f + g = \{(x, f(x) + g(x)) \mid x$ is in the domain of f and in the domain of $g\}$.

7. Pick $(a, b) \in g$. Then $a \in A$ and $b = g(a)$. But $g(a) = f(a)$, so that $b = f(a)$. Consequently $(a, b) \in f$ and $g \subseteq f$.

1-2 Norms in a Vector Space

1. (i) $\sqrt{a^2 + b^2} \geq 0$.

(ii) $\sqrt{a^2 + b^2} = 0$ if and only if $a^2 + b^2 = 0$ if and only if $a = b = 0$.

(iii) $\dfrac{ap + bq}{\sqrt{a^2 + b^2}\,\sqrt{p^2 + q^2}} = \cos\theta$, where θ is the angle between the lines which pass through $(0, 0)$ and (a, b) and through $(0, 0)$ and (p, q).

(iv) Let O, A, B, and C be the points with coordinates $(0, 0)$, (a, b), (p, q), and $(a + p, b + q)$, respectively. Then $\|(a, b)\|$ is the length of AO, $\|(p, q)\|$ is the length of OB, and $\|(a, b) + (p, q)\|$ is the length of OC.

3. (i) $|a| + |b| \geq 0$.

(ii) $|a| + |b| = 0$ if and only if $a = b = 0$.

(iii) $\|(a, b) + (p, q)\| = \|(a + b, b + q)\| = |a + p| + |b + q|$
$\leq |a| + |p| + |b| + |q| = (|a| + |b|) + (|p| + |q|)$
$= \|(a, b)\| + \|(p, q)\|$.

5. Let $f(x) = 1$ for $0 \leq x \leq 1$ and $g(x) = 0$ for $0 < x \leq 1$ but $g(0) = 1$. Then $\|f\| = \|g\| = 1$ but $f \neq g$. Thus the norm of $f - g$ is 0, but $f \neq g$.

$$\|f\| = \int_0^1 |f| \text{ does give a norm.}$$

7. Let $\delta_g = \delta_F$.

9. Let $\delta_\varphi = \delta_g$.

1-3 Geometric Aspects

5. $\mathbf{a} + \mathbf{b} = (-1, 6)$; $\mathbf{a} - \mathbf{b} = (3, -2)$; $\mathbf{a} + \mathbf{b} + \mathbf{c} = (-4, 7)$; $(\mathbf{a} + \mathbf{b}) - (\mathbf{c} + \mathbf{d}) = (-1, 13)$.

7. Exactly the same statement as for $\mathbf{V_2}$.

9. If no three of the points P, Q, R, and S are on one line and the four points do not lie in one plane, if PQ represents $\mathbf{a}$, PR represents $\mathbf{b}$, and PS represents $\mathbf{c}$, then for any vector $\mathbf{v} \in \mathbf{V_3}$ there exists unique real numbers x, y, and z, such that $\mathbf{v} = x\mathbf{a} + y\mathbf{b} + z\mathbf{c}$.

1-4 Linear Independence and Dependence

1. If $c_1 f_1 + c_2 f_2 + c_3 f_3 = 0$, then for $0 \leq t \leq 1$, $c_1 + c_2 t + c_2 t^2 = 0$. In particular, for $t = 0$, $c_1 = 0$ and for $t = 1$, $c_2 + c_3 = 0$. Differentiating yields, for $0 < t < 1$, $c_2 + 2c_3 t = 0$. Differentiating again yields $2c_3 = 0$. Thus $c_1 = c_2 = c_3 = 0$.

If $c_1 f_1 + c_2 f_2 + c_4 f_4 = 0$, then for $0 \leq t \leq 1$, $c_1 + c_2 t + c_4(4t^2 - 3t - 5) = 0$. For $t = 0$, $c_1 = 5c_4$ and for $t = 1$, $c_1 + c_2 - 4c_4 = 0$. As above, $c_2 - 3c_4 + 4c_4 t = 0$ and $8c_4 = 0$. Thus $c_1 = c_2 = c_4 = 0$.

Since $5f_1 + (-3)f_2 + 4f_3 + (-1)f_4 = 0$, $\{f_1, f_2, f_3, f_4\}$ is a linearly dependent set.

3. Linearly independent.

5. Linearly independent.

7. Linearly independent.

9. See exercise 9 of Section 1-3.

11. Any set of $n + 1$ nonzero vectors will be linearly dependent.

1-5 Inner Products and Orthogonality

1. $\mathbf{i} \cdot \mathbf{j} = (1, 0, 0) \cdot (0, 1, 0) = 0 + 0 + 0 = 0$; $\mathbf{j} \cdot \mathbf{k} = 0$; $\mathbf{k} \cdot \mathbf{i} = 0$.

3. 13.

5. $|a \cdot b| = $ length of OP.

7. (i) $(a, b, c) \cdot (p, q, r) = ap + bq + cr = pa + qb + rc$

$$= (p, q, r) \cdot (a, b, c).$$

(ii) $(a, b, c) \cdot [(p, q, r) + (x, y, z)] = (a, b, c) \cdot (p + x, q + y, z + r)$

$= a(p + x) + b(q + y) + c(z + r) = ap + ax + bq + by + cz + ca$

$= ap + bq + cr + ax + by + cz = (a, b, c) \cdot (p, q, r) + (a, b, c) \cdot (x, y, z)$.

(iii) $(p, q, r)[c \cdot (x, y, z)] = (p, q, r) \cdot (cx, cy, cz) = pcx + qcy + rcz$

$= c(px + qy + rz) = c[(p, q, r) \cdot (x, y, z)]$; also $pcx + qcy + rcz$

$= (cp, cq, cr) \cdot (x, y, z) = [c(p, q, r)] \cdot (x, y, z)$.

(iv) $(a, b, c) \cdot (a, b, c) = a^2 + b^2 + c^2 = \|(a, b, c)\|^2$.

9. If the line passes through (a, b, c) and (p, q, r) and the plane contains the point (α, β, γ), then an equation will be

$$[(x, y, z) - (\alpha, \beta, \gamma)] \cdot [(p, q, r) - (a, b, c)] = 0.$$

11. $\mathbf{v}_i \cdot [c_1 \mathbf{v}_1 + \cdots + c_{i-1} \mathbf{v}_{i-1} + c_i \mathbf{v}_i + c_{i+1} \mathbf{v}_{i-1} + \cdots + c_k \mathbf{v}_k]$

$= \mathbf{v}_i \cdot (c_1 \mathbf{v}_1) + \cdots + \mathbf{v}_i \cdot (c_{i-1} \mathbf{v}_{i-1}) + \mathbf{v}_i \cdot (c_i \mathbf{v}_i) + \mathbf{v}_i \cdot (c_{i+1} \mathbf{v}_{i+1}) + \cdots + \mathbf{v}_i \cdot (c_k \mathbf{v}_k)$

$= c_1(\mathbf{v}_i \cdot \mathbf{v}_1) + \cdots + c_{i-1}(\mathbf{v}_i \cdot \mathbf{v}_{i-1}) + c_i(\mathbf{v}_i \cdot \mathbf{v}_i) + c_{i+1}(\mathbf{v}_i \cdot \mathbf{v}_{i+1}) + \cdots + c_k(\mathbf{v}_i \cdot \mathbf{v}_i)$

$= 0 + \cdots + 0 + c_i(\mathbf{v}_i \cdot \mathbf{v}_i) + 0 + \cdots + 0 = c \|\mathbf{v}_i\|^2 = c(1) = c$.

13. $\left(\sum\limits_{i=1}^{n+1} a_i^2\right)\left(\sum\limits_{i=1}^{n+1} b_i^2\right) - \left(\sum\limits_{i=1}^{n+1} a_i b_i\right)^2$

$= \left(\sum\limits_{i=1}^{n} a_i^2 + a_{n+1}^2\right)\left(\sum\limits_{i=1}^{n} b_i^2 + b_{n+1}^2\right) - \left(\sum\limits_{i=1}^{n} a_i b_i + a_{n+1} b_{n+1}\right)^2$

$= \left(\sum\limits_{i=1}^{n} a_i^2\right)\left(\sum\limits_{i=1}^{n} b_i^2\right) - \left(\sum\limits_{i=1}^{n} a_i b_i\right)^2 + a_{n+1}^2 \sum\limits_{i=1}^{n} b_i^2 + b_{n+1}^2 \sum\limits_{i=1}^{n} a_i^2$

$\quad - 2 a_{n+1} b_{n+1} \sum\limits_{i=1}^{n} a_i b_i$

$\geq a_{n+1}^2 \sum\limits_{i=1}^{n} b_i^2 + b_{n+1}^2 \sum\limits_{i=1}^{n} a_i^2 - 2 |a_{n+1}||b_{n+1}| \left| \sum\limits_{i=1}^{n} a_i b_i \right|$

$\geq |a_{n+1}|^2 \left[\left(\sum\limits_{i=1}^{n} b_i^2\right)^{1/2}\right] + |b_{n+1}|^2 \left[\left(\sum\limits_{i=1}^{n} a_i^2\right)^{1/2}\right]$

$\quad - 2 |a_{n+1}||b_{n+1}| \left(\sum\limits_{i=1}^{n} a_i^2\right)^{1/2} \left(\sum\limits_{i=1}^{n} b_i^2\right)^{1/2} \geq 0.$

1-6 The Cross Product in V_3

1. $(a, a, a) \times c(b, b, b) = (a, a, a) \times (cb, cb, cb)$
$\quad = (ca\,b - ca\,b,\, ca\,b - ca\,b,\, ca\,b - ca\,b) = c[(a, a, a) \times (b, b, b)]$
$\quad = [c(a, a, a)] \times (b, b, b).$

3. $\mathbf{a} \times \mathbf{b} = (3, 0, 3)$; $\mathbf{b} \times \mathbf{c} = (-3, 0, -2)$; $\mathbf{a} \cdot (\mathbf{b} \times \mathbf{c}) = \mathbf{b} \cdot (\mathbf{c} \times \mathbf{a}) = \mathbf{c} \cdot (\mathbf{a} \times \mathbf{b}) = 9.$

5. If $\mathbf{b} \cdot \mathbf{a} \neq 0$, there is no such vector. If $\mathbf{b} \cdot \mathbf{a} = 0$, we need $\|\mathbf{a}\| \|\mathbf{r}\| \sin \theta = \|\mathbf{b}\|$ and $\mathbf{r} \cdot \mathbf{a} = \|\mathbf{r}\| \|\mathbf{a}\| \cos \theta$. There will be two solutions.

7. $5x + y + 5z = 8.$

9. $V = [\mathbf{a} \cdot (\mathbf{b} \times \mathbf{c})]/6.$

11. $(\mathbf{a} \times \mathbf{b}) \times (\mathbf{c} \times \mathbf{d}) = ([\mathbf{a} \times \mathbf{b}] \cdot \mathbf{d})\mathbf{c} - ([\mathbf{a} \times \mathbf{b}] \cdot \mathbf{c})\mathbf{d}$
$\quad = (\mathbf{d} \cdot [\mathbf{a} \times \mathbf{b}])\mathbf{c} - (\mathbf{c} \cdot [\mathbf{a} \times \mathbf{b}])\mathbf{d} = (\mathbf{a} \cdot [\mathbf{b} \times \mathbf{d}])\mathbf{c} - (\mathbf{a} \cdot [\mathbf{b} \times \mathbf{c}])\mathbf{d}.$

13. A circle in the x-y plane with center at $(0, 0, 0)$ and radius 1.

15. $\mathbf{r}''(t) = (-\cos t, -\sin t, 0)$; Representations are directed toward the center.

1-7 Applications to Geometry

1. Let AB be parallel to DC and AD be parallel to BC. Let $\overrightarrow{AB}$ represent $2\mathbf{a}$ and $\overrightarrow{AD}$ represent $2\mathbf{b}$. Let P be the midpoint of AC. Then $\overrightarrow{BC}$ represents $2\mathbf{b}$, $\overrightarrow{AC}$

represents $2\mathbf{a} + 2\mathbf{b}$, $\overrightarrow{AP}$ and $\overrightarrow{PC}$ represent $\mathbf{a} + \mathbf{b}$. $\overrightarrow{BP}$ then represents (via the path BAP) $-2\mathbf{a} + (\mathbf{a} + \mathbf{b}) = \mathbf{b} - \mathbf{a}$, and $\overrightarrow{PD}$ represents (via the path PAD) $-(\mathbf{a} + \mathbf{b}) + 2\mathbf{b} = \mathbf{b} - \mathbf{a}$. Thus P is the midpoint of BD.

3. Let P, Q, and R be the midpoints of AB, BC, and AC, respectively. Let $\overrightarrow{AB}$ represent $2\mathbf{a}$ and $\overrightarrow{AC}$ represent $2\mathbf{b}$. Let T be the intersection of the line through R, perpendicular to AC, and the line through P, perpendicular to AB. Let $\overrightarrow{TP}$ represent $\mathbf{v}$. Then show that TQ is perpendicular to BC.

5. Let P be the intersection of the line through C, perpendicular to AB, and the line through A, perpendicular to BC. Let $\overrightarrow{AB}$ represent $\mathbf{a}$, $\overrightarrow{AC}$ represent $\mathbf{b}$, and $\overrightarrow{AP}$ represent $\mathbf{v}$. Show that PB is perpendicular to AC.

7. $\frac{1}{14}\sqrt{14}$.

9. $\frac{5}{37}\sqrt{74}$.

11. $\frac{7}{61}\sqrt{61}$.

2-1 Continuous Functions

1. Pick $\mathbf{a}$ and $\mathbf{b}$ in D. Since D is connected, there exists a curve, $\mathbf{r}: [0, 1] \to D$, such that $\mathbf{r}(0) = \mathbf{a}$ and $\mathbf{r}(1) = \mathbf{b}$. But $\mathbf{F} \circ \mathbf{r}$ is a curve, $\{\mathbf{F} \circ \mathbf{r}\}(0) = \mathbf{F}(\mathbf{a})$, $\{\mathbf{F} \circ \mathbf{r}\}(1) = \mathbf{F}(\mathbf{b})$, and the range of $\mathbf{F} \circ \mathbf{r}$ lies entirely in the range of $\mathbf{F}$. Thus the range of $\mathbf{F}$ is connected.

4. $\mathbf{r}(t) = (2 - 2t, t, 1 + 2t); 0 \le t \le 1$ or

$$\mathbf{v}(s) = (2s, 1 - s, 3 - 2s); 0 \le s \le 1.$$

6. $\mathbf{r}(u, v) = (u, v, c); 0 \le u \le a, 0 \le v \le b$ (where $a > 0$ and $b > 0$).

8. $\mathbf{r}(u, v) = (\sin v \cos u, \sin v \sin u, \cos v); 0 \le u < 2\pi, 0 \le v \le \pi$.

11. One needs to find a continuous function whose domain is a rectangle and whose range is the domain of the given surface.

2-2 Differential Curves

1. For every $\epsilon > 0$ there exists $\delta > 0$ such that if $0 < |t - c| < \delta$ then $\|\mathbf{u}(t) - \mathbf{L}\| < \epsilon$.

3. Pick $(p, q) \in \mathbf{u}' \times \mathbf{v} + \mathbf{u} \times \mathbf{v}'$. $\mathbf{q} = \{\mathbf{u}' \times \mathbf{v} + \mathbf{u} \times \mathbf{v}'\}(a)$. $\mathbf{q} = \{\mathbf{u}' \times \mathbf{v}\}(p) + \{\mathbf{u} \times \mathbf{v}'\}(p)$. $\mathbf{q} = [\mathbf{u}'(p)] \times [\mathbf{v}(p)] \times [\mathbf{u}(p)] \times [\mathbf{v}'(p)]$. $\mathbf{v}$ is continuous at p. $\lim_{h \to 0} \mathbf{v}(p + h) = \mathbf{v}(p)$.

$$\lim_{h \to 0} \frac{1}{h} [\mathbf{u}(p + h) - \mathbf{u}(p)] = \mathbf{u}'(p).$$

$$\lim_{h \to 0} \left\{ \frac{1}{h} [\mathbf{u}(p + h) - \mathbf{u}(p)] \right\} \times [\mathbf{v}(p + h)] = [\mathbf{u}'(p)] \times [\mathbf{v}(p)].$$

$$\lim_{h \to 0} \frac{1}{h} [\mathbf{v}(p + h) - \mathbf{v}(p)] = \mathbf{v}'(p).$$

$$\lim_{h \to 0} [\mathbf{u}(p)] \times \left\{ \frac{1}{h} [\mathbf{v}(p + h) - \mathbf{v}(p)] \right\} = [\mathbf{u}(p)] \times [\mathbf{v}(p)].$$

$$\lim_{h \to 0} \left(\left\{ \frac{1}{h} [\mathbf{u}(p + h) - \mathbf{u}(p)] \times [\mathbf{v}(p + h)] \right\} + \left\{ [\mathbf{u}(p)] \times \frac{1}{h} [\mathbf{v}(p + h) - \mathbf{v}(p)] \right\} \right)$$

$$= [\mathbf{u}'(p)] \times [\mathbf{v}(p)] + [\mathbf{u}(p)] \times [\mathbf{v}'(p)].$$

$$\lim_{h \to 0} \frac{1}{h} \{ [\mathbf{u}(p + h)] \times [\mathbf{v}(p + h)] - [\mathbf{u}(p)] \times [\mathbf{v}(p)] \}$$

$$= [\mathbf{u}'(p)] \times [\mathbf{v}(p)] + [\mathbf{u}(p)] \times [\mathbf{v}'(p)].$$

$$\lim_{h \to 0} \frac{1}{h} [\{ \mathbf{u} \times \mathbf{v} \}(p + h) - \{ \mathbf{u} \times \mathbf{v} \}(p)] = \{ \mathbf{u}' \times \mathbf{v} + \mathbf{u} \times \mathbf{v}' \}(p).$$

$$\{ \mathbf{u} \times \mathbf{v} \}'(p) = \mathbf{q}. \quad (p, \mathbf{q}) \in \{ \mathbf{u} \times \mathbf{v} \}'.$$

5. $\mathbf{u}''(t) = \frac{1}{6}t^3 \mathbf{a} + \frac{1}{2}t^2 \mathbf{b} + t\mathbf{k}_1 + \mathbf{k}_2.$

7. $\dfrac{1}{[(x')^2 + (y')^2]^2} \{ [2(x')^2 x'' + (y')^2 x'' + x'y'y'']^2 + [x'y'x'' + 2(y')^2 y'' + (x')^2 y'']^2 \}^{1/2}$

9. Since the trace of $\mathbf{r}$ lies entirely in the x-y plane, $\mathbf{B}$ must be either the constant function given by $\mathbf{k}$ or by $-\mathbf{k}$. Since $\mathbf{B}' = -\tau\mathbf{N}$, and $\mathbf{N}$ is not the $\mathbf{0}$ function, then τ must be the 0 function.

11. The theorem applies to $\mathbf{V}_n$ as it is stated.

2-3 Differentiability

1. From the definition of differentiability,

$$f(\mathbf{a} + \mathbf{h}) - f(\mathbf{a}) = \mathbf{A} \cdot \mathbf{h} + \|\mathbf{h}\| \eta(\mathbf{h}).$$

Thus

$$\frac{1}{h} [f(a_1, \ldots, a_{k-1}, a_k + h_k, a_{k+1}, \ldots, a_n) - f(\mathbf{a})]$$

$$= A_k + \frac{|h_k|}{h_k} \eta(0, \ldots, 0, h_k, 0, \ldots, 0).$$

Since $\left| \dfrac{|h_k|}{h_k} \right| = 1$ and $\lim\limits_{\mathbf{h} \to 0} \eta(\mathbf{h}) = 0$, we conclude that $f_k(\mathbf{a})$ exists and is A_k.

3. $f_1(x, y) = f_2(x, y) = (x + y)^{-1}; f_{11}(x, y) = f_{12}(x, y) = f_{22}(x, y) = -(x + y)^{-2}.$

5. $\dfrac{1}{h} [\varphi(t + h) - \varphi(t)] = \dfrac{1}{h} [f(a + tp + hp, b + tq + hq) - f(a + tp, b + tq)]$

$$= \frac{1}{h} [(f_1, f_2)(a + tp, b + tq) \cdot (hp, hq) + |h| \sqrt{p^2 + q^2}\ \eta(hp, hq)$$

$$= pf_1(a + tp, b + tq) + qf_2(a + tp, b + tq) + \frac{|h|}{h} \sqrt{p^2 + q^2}\ \eta(hp, hq)$$

7. $p^2 f_{11} + 2pq f_{12} + q^2 f_{22} = f_{11}\left(p^2 + 2q\dfrac{f_{12}}{f_{11}} p + \dfrac{f_{12}^2}{f_{11}^2} q^2 \right) + q^2 f_{22} - \dfrac{f_{12}^2}{f_{11}} q^2$

$$= f_{11}\left(p + \frac{f_{12}}{f_{11}} q \right)^2 + q^2 \frac{f_{11}f_{22} - f_{12}^2}{f_{11}}.$$

9. $\varphi'(0) = 0$ and $\varphi''(0) < 0.$

11. $f(0, 0) = 0$ is a relative minimum.

13. No relative extreme values.

2-4 Differentiable Surfaces

1. $\mathbf{n} = \mathbf{r}.$

3. $\mathbf{n}(u, v) = \left(\dfrac{u}{\sqrt{u^2 + v^2}},\ \dfrac{v}{\sqrt{u^2 + v^2}},\ -1 \right).$

5.
$$\mathbf{r}(u, v) = \begin{cases} (0, vb, -uc); & -1 \le u \le 0, & 0 \le v \le 1 \\ (ua, vb, 0); & 0 \le u \le 1, & 0 \le v \le 1 \\ (ua, 0, -vc); & 0 \le u \le 1, & -1 \le v \le 0 \\ (ua, b, [v - 1]c); & 0 \le u \le 1, & 1 \le v \le 2 \\ (a, vb, [u - 1]c); & 1 \le u \le 2, & 0 \le v \le 1 \\ ([3 - u]a, vb, c); & 2 \le u \le 3, & 0 \le v \le 1 \end{cases}$$

7. $A(\mathbf{r}) = \displaystyle\iint_D \|\mathbf{r}_1 \times \mathbf{r}_2\| = \iint_D \|\mathbf{r}_1\|\, \|\mathbf{r}_2\| \sin \theta$

$$= \iint_D \sqrt{\|\mathbf{r}_1\|^2 \|\mathbf{r}_2\|^2 (1 - \cos^2 \theta)} = \iint_D \sqrt{\|\mathbf{r}_1\|^2 \|\mathbf{r}_2\|^2 - (\|\mathbf{r}_1\|\, \|\mathbf{r}_2\| \cos \theta)^2}$$

$$= \iint_D \sqrt{\|\mathbf{r}_1\|^2 \|\mathbf{r}_2\|^2 - (\mathbf{r}_1 \cdot \mathbf{r}_2)^2}.$$

9. $16(10)^6 \frac{7}{180}\pi(\sin 49° - \sin 45°) = 93{,}600$ sq mi.

11. n $= \dfrac{1}{\sqrt{(F_1)^2 + (F_2)^2 + (F_3)^2}} (F_1, F_2, F_3)(x, y, z).$

3-1   Surface Integrals

1. $3abc.$

3. $0.$

5. $\{\mathbf{r_1} \times \mathbf{r_2}\}(x, y) = (-f_1, -f_2, 1)(x, y).$

7. $\displaystyle\iint_D [L - Mh_1 - Nh_2].$

9. $\displaystyle\iint_D [(-g_1, 1, -g_2)(x, y)] \times [(L, M, N)(x, g(x, z), z)].$

11. $\mathbf{0}.$

13. $\mathbf{0}.$

15. The determinant is $L(\mathbf{r})[g_1 h_2 - g_2 h_1] - M(\mathbf{r})[f_1 h_2 - f_2 h_1] + N(\mathbf{r})[f_1 g_2 - f_2 g_1]$
$= [(L, M, N)(\mathbf{r})](\mathbf{r_1} \times \mathbf{r_2}).$

3-2   The Gradient

1. $(yz, xz, xy).$

3. $\dfrac{1}{\sqrt{x^2 + y^2 + z^2}} (x, y, z).$

5. $\text{grad}\,(fg) = ([fg]_1, [fg]_2, [fg]_3) \supseteq (fg_1 + f_1 g, fg_2 + f_2 g, fg_3 + f_3 g)$
$= (fg_1, fg_2, fg_3) + (f_1 g, f_2 g, f_3 g) = f(g_1, g_2, g_3) + g(f_1, f_2, f_3)$
$= f[\text{grad}\,g] + g[\text{grad}\,f].$

7. $F(\mathbf{r}): D \to \{0\}.$

9. For all $(u, v) \in D$, $F(\mathbf{r})(u, v) = 0$. Thus, for $i = 1, 2$, $\{F_1(\mathbf{r})r_i^{(1)} + F_2(\mathbf{r})r_i^{(2)} + F_3(\mathbf{r})r_i^{(3)}\}(u, v) = 0$. That is, $\{[\{\text{grad}\,F\}(\mathbf{r})] \cdot \mathbf{r}_i(u, v)\} = 0$. Hence representations of $\{\text{grad}\,F\}(P)$ with initial point P are perpendicular to the tangent plane at P.

11. $3x + 4y - 5z = 0.$

13. $2\sqrt{2}\,x + (\sqrt{2} - 1)y = 3\sqrt{2} - 1.$

3-3 Divergence and Curl

1. $\{\text{div } \mathbf{v}\}(x, y, z) = 3$; $\{\text{curl } \mathbf{v}\}(x, y, z) = \mathbf{0}$.

3. $\{\text{div } \mathbf{v}\}(x, y, z) = 2(x^2 + y^2 + z^2)^{-1/2}$.

5. $\nabla(\nabla \cdot \mathbf{v}) - (\nabla \cdot \nabla)\mathbf{v}$.

6. $(\nabla \times \mathbf{u})\mathbf{v} - (\nabla \times \mathbf{v})\mathbf{u}$.

3-4 Line Integrals

1. The path of the original curve is retraced in the opposite direction.

3. $\frac{11}{28}$.

5. $\frac{5}{4}$.

7. Use the result of exercise 1.

4-1 The Fundamental Theorem of Calculus

1. $\delta_{\epsilon,x} \leq \epsilon/2$.

3. $2x + h + 3$.

5. $t^2 + 3t - 4$.

7. $\delta_{\epsilon,x} \leq \sqrt{x^2 + \epsilon} - x$.

9. $3x^2 + 3xh + h^2$.

11. $(t^3 - 1)/3$.

13. The graph consists of the line segment joining $(0, 0)$ to $(1, 1)$—excluding $(1, 1)$, the line segment joining $(1, 3)$ to $(2, 5)$—excluding $(2, 5)$, and the line segment joining $(2, 8)$ to $(3, 11)$.

15.
$$G(t) = \begin{cases} \frac{1}{2}t^2 - \frac{1}{2} & \text{for } 0 \leq t \leq 1 \\ t^2 + t - 2 & \text{for } 1 < t \leq 2 \\ \frac{3}{4}t^2 + 2t - 6 & \text{for } 2 < t \leq 3. \end{cases}$$

17. The graph consists of those points on the line segment $(0, 1)$ to $(1, 1)$ and on the line segment $(2, 1)$ to $(3, 1)$ which have rational x coordinates; those points on the line segment $(0, 2)$ to $(1, 2)$ and on the line segment $(2, 2)$ to $(3, 2)$ which have irrational x coordinates; and the portion of the parabola which is the graph of $y = x^2$ joining the points $(1, 1)$ and $(2, 4)$.

19. $G(t) = \frac{1}{3}t^3 - \frac{1}{3}$, $\quad 1 \leq t \leq 2$.

21.
$$H(t) = \begin{cases} 2(t-1), & 0 \le t \le 1 \\ \frac{1}{3}t^3 - \frac{1}{3}, & 1 \le t \le 2 \\ 2t - \frac{5}{3}, & 2 \le t \le 3. \end{cases}$$

23. $\{D_-H\}(1) = 2$; $\{D_+H\}(1) = 1 = f(1)$; $\{D_-H\}(2) = 4 = f(2)$; $\{D_+H\}(2) = 2$.

4-2   The Classical Divergence Theorem

1.
$$\iiint\limits_{W} \operatorname{div} \mathbf{v} = \int_0^c \int_0^b \int_0^a L_1(x, y, z)\, dx\, dy\, dz + \int_0^a \int_0^c \int_0^b M_2(x, y, z)\, dy\, dz\, dx$$

$$+ \int_0^b \int_0^a \int_0^c N_3(x, y, z)\, dz\, dx\, dy$$

$$= \int_0^c \int_0^b [L(a, y, z) - L(0, y, z)]\, dy\, dz + \int_0^a \int_0^c [M(x, b, z) - M(x, 0, z)]\, dz\, dx$$

$$+ \int_0^b \int_0^a [N(x, y, c) - N(x, y, 0)]\, dx\, dy$$

$$= \int_0^c \int_0^b \{\mathbf{v} \cdot \mathbf{i}\}(a, y, z)\, dy\, dz + \int_0^c \int_0^b \{\mathbf{v} \cdot (-\mathbf{i})\}(0, y, z)\, dy\, dz$$

$$+ \int_0^a \int_0^c \{\mathbf{v} \cdot \mathbf{j}\}(x, b, z)\, dz\, dx + \int_0^a \int_0^c \{\mathbf{v} \cdot (-\mathbf{j})\}(x, 0, z)\, dz\, dx$$

$$+ \int_0^b \int_0^a \{\mathbf{v} \cdot \mathbf{k}\}(x, y, c)\, dx\, dy + \int_0^b \int_0^a \{\mathbf{v} \cdot (-\mathbf{k})\}(x, y, 0)\, dx\, dy$$

$$= \iint\limits_{S} \mathbf{v} \cdot \mathbf{n}.$$

3. Let $O = (0, 0, 0)$, $A = (4, 2, 2)$, $B = (6, 6, 4)$, and $C = (2, 4\ 6)$. The face OAB projects onto the triangle with vertices $(0, 0)$, $(4, 2)$, and $(6, 6)$; the sides of this triangle have equations $x - y = 0$, $x - 2y = 0$, and $2x - y = 0$. OAC projects onto the triangle with vertices $(0, 0)$, $(4, 2)$, $(2, 4)$; the sides of this triangle have equations $x - 2y = 0$, $x + y = 6$, and $2x - y = 0$. OBC projects onto the triangle with vertices $(0, 0)$, $(6, 6)$, $(2, 4)$; the sides of this triangle have equations $x - y = 0$, $x - 2y = -6$, and $2x - y = 0$.

5. $f_{BR}(y) = \begin{cases} 2y, & 0 \le y \le 2 \\ 6 - y, & 2 \le y \le 6 \end{cases}$; $\quad f_{BF}(y) = \begin{cases} \frac{1}{2}y, & 0 \le y \le 4 \\ 2y - 6, & 4 \le y \le 6 \end{cases}$.

7.

$$\varphi_B(x, y) = \begin{cases} (-5x + 7y)/3; \; x \leq y \leq 2x, \, 0 \leq x \leq 2; \, x \leq y \leq \tfrac{1}{2}x + 2, \\ \qquad\qquad\qquad\qquad\qquad\qquad\qquad\qquad 2 \leq x \leq 6 \\ (x + y)/3; \; \tfrac{1}{2}x \leq y \leq x, \, 0 \leq x \leq 4; \, 6 - x \leq y \leq x, \, 4 \leq x \leq 6. \end{cases}$$

$$\varphi_T(x, y) = \begin{cases} (-x + 5y)/3; \; \tfrac{1}{2}x \leq y \leq 2x, \, 0 \leq x \leq 2; \, \tfrac{1}{2}x \leq y \leq 6 - x, \\ \qquad\qquad\qquad\qquad\qquad\qquad\qquad\qquad 2 \leq x \leq 4 \\ -x + y + 4; \; 6 - x \leq y \leq \tfrac{1}{2}x + 3, \, 2 \leq x \leq 4; \, 2x - 6 \leq y \leq \\ \qquad\qquad\qquad\qquad\qquad\qquad\qquad \tfrac{1}{2}x + 3, \, 4 \leq x \leq 6. \end{cases}$$

9. Let $\mathbf{v} = (L, M, N)$. Then $\displaystyle\iint_S \mathbf{v} \cdot \mathbf{n}$

$$= \left[\left\{ \int_0^2 \int_x^{2x} + \int_2^6 \int_x^{\frac{1}{2}x+3} \right\} \{ \tfrac{5}{3}L - \tfrac{7}{3}M + N \}(x, y, -\tfrac{5}{3}x + \tfrac{7}{3}) \right.$$

$$+ \left\{ \int_0^4 \int_{\frac{1}{2}x}^{x} + \int_4^6 \int_{6-x}^{x} \right\} \{ -\tfrac{1}{3}L - \tfrac{1}{3}M + N \}(x, y, \tfrac{1}{3}x + \tfrac{1}{3}y)$$

$$+ \left\{ \int_0^2 \int_{\frac{1}{2}x}^{2x} + \int_2^4 \int_{\frac{1}{2}x}^{6-x} \right\} \{ -\tfrac{1}{3}L + \tfrac{5}{3}M - N \}(x, y, -\tfrac{1}{3}x + \tfrac{5}{3}y)$$

$$+ \left. \left\{ \int_2^4 \int_{6-x}^{\frac{1}{2}x+3} + \int_4^6 \int_{2x-6}^{\frac{1}{2}x+3} \right\} \{ -L + M - N \}(x, y, -x + y + 4) \right] dy \, dx.$$

11. Observe the cancellation of components.

5-1 Quadrable Sets

1. Either $R_1 = [a, b] \times [c, d]$ and $R_2 = [a, b] \times [d, p]$ or $R_1 = [a, b] \times [c, d]$ and $R_2 = [b, r] \times [c, d]$.

3. $(kc/n, b + mkc/n)$ for $k = 1, 2, \ldots, n - 1$.

5. $\dfrac{mc^2}{2}\left(1 + \dfrac{1}{2n}\right)$.

7. Eliminate rectangular portions of the given rectangle which lie outside the given triangle.

9. Further subdivide each rectangle by vertical lines so that the width of the resulting rectangles is c/p, where p is the least common multiple of the denominators of the given rational number multiples of c. Then discard the unneeded rectangle portions.

11. Since $V_{2,e}(m)$ is the infimum of numbers of the form $V_{C,2,e}(M)$ and for any covering C there exists a covering of the form C_n with a smaller (or equal) approximation to outer area, then $\lim_n V_{C_n,2,e}$ will be the infimum.

13. $\dfrac{mc^2}{2}\left(1 - \dfrac{1}{2n}\right).$

5-2 Integration on Quadrable Sets

3. $\displaystyle\underline{\int}_A f = V_{n,i}(A); \qquad \overline{\int}_A f = V_{n,e}(A).$

5. $\inf f(R_{i,j}) = \dfrac{j-1}{n}$; $\sup f(R_{i,j}) = \dfrac{j}{n}$.

7. 2.

11. 9.

13. $\displaystyle\underline{\int}_D f = 1; \qquad \overline{\int}_D f = 3.$

5-3 Integrable Functions

1. $\dfrac{3B}{4\epsilon}$.

3. $\delta = \dfrac{\epsilon\sqrt{2}}{2B}$.

5. $N_4 = \dfrac{B\sqrt{2}}{\epsilon}$.

7. $N_6 = \dfrac{B}{\epsilon}$.

9. Because of uniform continuity.

11. 1 or any larger number.

13. $N_7 \geq N_6$ and $N_7 \geq N_5$.

15. $V_2(\{(0, y) \mid 0 \leq y \leq 1\}) = 0.$

5-4 Iterated Integrals

1. $\psi(x + h) - \psi(x)$

$$= [\varphi_B(x) - \varphi_B(x + h)]f(x + h, \varphi_B(x + h) + \theta_1[\varphi_B(x) - \varphi_B(x + h)])$$
$$+ [\varphi_T(x + h) - \varphi_T(x)]f(x + h, \varphi_T(x) + \theta_2[\varphi_T(x + h) - \varphi_T(x)])$$
$$+ [\varphi_T(x) - \varphi_B(x)][f(x + h, y + \theta_2[\varphi_T(x) - \varphi_B(x)])$$
$$- f(x, y + \theta_3[\varphi_T(x) - \varphi_B(x)])].$$

5. $\displaystyle\int_{-1}^{1} \int_{-2\sqrt{1-x^2}}^{2\sqrt{1-x^2}} \int_{-\frac{3}{2}\sqrt{4-4x^2-y^2}}^{\frac{3}{2}\sqrt{4-4x^2-y^2}} f(x, y, z)\, dz\, dy\, dx$

$$= \int_{-2}^{2} \int_{-\frac{1}{2}\sqrt{4-y^2}}^{\frac{1}{2}\sqrt{4-y^2}} \int_{-\frac{3}{2}\sqrt{4-4x^2-y^2}}^{\frac{3}{2}\sqrt{4-4x^2-y^2}} f(x, y, z)\, dz\, dx\, dy$$

$$= \int_{-1}^{1} \int_{-3\sqrt{1-x^2}}^{3\sqrt{1-x^2}} \int_{-\frac{2}{3}\sqrt{9-9x^2-z^2}}^{\frac{2}{3}\sqrt{9-9x^2-z^2}} f(x, y, z)\, dy\, dz\, dx$$

$$= \int_{-3}^{3} \int_{-\frac{1}{3}\sqrt{9-z^2}}^{\frac{1}{3}\sqrt{9-z^2}} \int_{-\frac{2}{3}\sqrt{9-9x^2-z^2}}^{\frac{2}{3}\sqrt{9-9x^2-z^2}} f(x, y, z)\, dy\, dx\, dz$$

$$= \int_{-3}^{3} \int_{-\frac{2}{3}\sqrt{9-z^2}}^{\frac{2}{3}\sqrt{9-z^2}} \int_{-\frac{1}{6}\sqrt{36-9y^2-4z^2}}^{\frac{1}{6}\sqrt{36-9y^2-4z^2}} f(x, y, z)\, dx\, dy\, dz$$

$$= \int_{-2}^{2} \int_{-\frac{3}{2}\sqrt{4-y^2}}^{\frac{3}{2}\sqrt{4-y^2}} \int_{-\frac{1}{6}\sqrt{36-9y^2-4z^2}}^{\frac{1}{6}\sqrt{36-9y^2-4z^2}} f(x, y, z)\, dx\, dz\, dy.$$

7. $\displaystyle\int_{-r}^{r} \int_{-\sqrt{r^2-x^2}}^{\sqrt{r^2-x^2}} f(x, y)\, dy\, dx = \int_{-r}^{r} \int_{-\sqrt{r^2-y^2}}^{\sqrt{r^2-y^2}} f(x, y)\, dx\, dy.$

9. $\displaystyle\int_{0}^{4} \int_{\sqrt{y}}^{6-y} f(x, y)\, dx\, dy = \left\{ \int_{0}^{2} \int_{0}^{x^2} + \int_{2}^{6} \int_{0}^{6-x} \right\} f(x, y)\, dy\, dx.$

11. $\left\{\int_{-1}^{1}\int_{-|x|}^{|x|}\int_{-\sqrt{1-x^2}}^{\sqrt{1-x^2}} + \int_{-1}^{1}\left[\int_{-1}^{-|x|} + \int_{|x|}^{1}\right]\int_{-\sqrt{1-y^2}}^{\sqrt{1-y^2}}\right\}f(x, y, z)\, dz\, dy\, dx$

$= \left\{\int_{-1}^{1}\left[\int_{-1}^{-|y|} + \int_{|y|}^{1}\right]\int_{-\sqrt{1-x^2}}^{\sqrt{1-x^2}} + \int_{-1}^{1}\int_{-|y|}^{|y|}\int_{-\sqrt{1-y^2}}^{\sqrt{1-y^2}}\right\}f(x, y, z)\, dz\, dx\, dy$

$= \int_{-1}^{1}\int_{-\sqrt{1-y^2}}^{\sqrt{1-y^2}}\int_{-\sqrt{1-xz^2}}^{\sqrt{1-xz^2}} f(x, y, z)\, dx\, dz\, dy$

$= \int_{-1}^{1}\int_{-\sqrt{1-z^2}}^{\sqrt{1-z^2}}\int_{-\sqrt{1-xz^2}}^{\sqrt{1-xz^2}} f(x, y, z)\, dx\, dy\, dz$

$= \int_{-1}^{1}\int_{-\sqrt{1-x^2}}^{\sqrt{1-x^2}}\int_{-\sqrt{1-z^2}}^{\sqrt{1-z^2}} f(x, y, z)\, dy\, dz\, dx$

$= \int_{-1}^{1}\int_{-\sqrt{1-z^2}}^{\sqrt{1-z^2}}\int_{-\sqrt{1-z^2}}^{\sqrt{1-z^2}} f(x, y, z)\, dy\, dx\, dz$

5-5 Changes in the Order of Integration

1. $A_{xy} = \left\{(x, y) \mid 0 \le y \le b\left(1 - \dfrac{x}{a}\right), \quad 0 \le x \le a\right\}$

$= \left\{(x, y) \mid 0 \le x \le a\left(1 - \dfrac{y}{b}\right), \quad 0 \le y \le b\right\}.$

$A_{xz} = \left\{(x, z) \mid 0 \le z \le c\left(1 - \dfrac{x}{a}\right), \quad 0 \le x \le a\right\}$

$= \left\{(x, z) \mid 0 \le x \le a\left(1 - \dfrac{z}{c}\right), \quad 0 \le z \le c\right\}.$

$A_{yz} = \left\{(y, z) \mid 0 \le y \le b\left(1 - \dfrac{z}{c}\right), \quad 0 \le z \le c\right\}$

$= \left\{(y, z) \mid 0 \le z \le c\left(1 - \dfrac{y}{b}\right), \quad 0 \le y \le b\right\}.$

5. $\displaystyle\int_0^a \int_0^{b(1-x/a)} \int_0^{(1-x/a-y/b)} f(x, y, z)\, dz\, dy\, dx$

$\displaystyle= \int_0^b \int_0^{a(1-y/b)} \int_0^{c(1-x/a-y/b)} f(x, y, z)\, dz\, dx\, dy$

$\displaystyle= \int_0^c \int_0^{a(1-z/c)} \int_0^{b(1-x/a-z/c)} f(x, y, z)\, dy\, dx\, dz$

$\displaystyle= \int_0^a \int_0^{c(1-x/a)} \int_0^{b(1-x/a-z/c)} f(x, y, z)\, dy\, dz\, dx$

$\displaystyle= \int_0^c \int_0^{b(1-z/c)} \int_0^{a(1-y/b-z/c)} f(x, y, z)\, dx\, dy\, dz$

$\displaystyle= \int_0^b \int_0^{c(1-y/b)} \int_0^{a(1-y/b-z/c)} f(x, y, z)\, dx\, dz\, dy.$

7. $\displaystyle\left\{ \int_0^1 \int_0^{\sqrt{x}} + \int_1^{3/2} \int_0^{(3-x)/2} \right\} f(x, y)\, dy\, dx.$

9. $\pi r^2 h.$

11. $(4\pi r^3)/3.$

13. If one face is the graph of $Ax + By + Cz + D = 0$ and the vertex not on that face has coordinates (p, q, r), then the area is $\dfrac{1}{6} \dfrac{|Ap + Bq + Cr + D|}{\sqrt{A^2 + B^2 + C^2}} S$ where S is the area of the first (triangular) face.

5-6 Nonrectangular Coordinate Systems

2. $\displaystyle\int_\alpha^\beta \int_{\Phi_{zi}(\theta)}^{\Phi_{z0}(\theta)} \int_{\Phi_B(r,\theta)}^{\Phi_T(r,\theta)} rf(r, \theta, z)\, dz\, dr\, d\theta$

$\displaystyle= \int_p^q \int_{\Phi_{zb}(r)}^{\Phi_{ze}(r)} \int_{\Phi_B(r,\theta)}^{\Phi_T(r,\theta)} rf(r, \theta, z)\, dz\, d\theta\, dr$

$\displaystyle= \int_c^d \int_{\Phi_{\theta i}(z)}^{\Phi_{\theta 0}(z)} \int_{\Phi_b(r,z)}^{\Phi_e(r,z)} rf(r, \theta, z)\, d\theta\, dr\, dz$

$\displaystyle= \int_p^q \int_{\Phi_{\theta B}(r)}^{\Phi_{\theta T}(r)} \int_{\Phi_b(r,z)}^{\Phi_e(r,z)} rf(r, \theta, z)\, d\theta\, dz\, dr$

$\displaystyle= \int_c^d \int_{\Phi_{rb}(z)}^{\Phi_{re}(z)} \int_{\Phi_i(\theta,z)}^{\Phi_0(\theta,z)} rf(r, \theta, z)\, dr\, d\theta\, dz$

$\displaystyle= \int_\alpha^\beta \int_{\Phi_{rB}(\theta)}^{\Phi_{rT}(\theta)} \int_{\Phi_i(\theta,z)}^{\Phi_0(\theta,z)} rf(r, \theta, z)\, dr\, dz\, d\theta.$

4. $\displaystyle\int_{\alpha}^{\beta}\int_{\Phi_{rn}(\theta)}^{\Phi_{rs}(\theta)}\int_{\Phi_{i}(\theta,\varphi)}^{\Phi_{0}(\theta,\varphi)} r^2 f(r,\,\theta,\,\varphi)\,dr\sin\varphi\,d\varphi\,d\theta$

$\displaystyle= \int_{\alpha}^{\beta}\int_{\Phi_{\varphi i}(\theta)}^{\Phi_{\varphi 0}(\theta)}\int_{\Phi_{n}(r,\theta)}^{\Phi_{s}(r,\theta)} f(r,\,\theta,\,\varphi)\sin\varphi\,d\varphi\,r^2\,dr\,d\theta$

$\displaystyle= \int_{p}^{q}\int_{\Phi_{\varphi e}(r)}^{\Phi_{\varphi w}(r)}\int_{\Phi_{n}(r,\theta)}^{\Phi_{s}(r,\theta)} f(r,\,\theta,\,\varphi)\sin\varphi\,d\varphi\,d\theta\,r^2\,dr$

$\displaystyle= \int_{\gamma}^{\delta}\int_{\Phi_{\theta i}(\varphi)}^{\Phi_{\theta 0}(\varphi)}\int_{\Phi_{e}(r,\varphi)}^{\Phi_{w}(r,\varphi)} f(r,\,\theta,\,\varphi)\,d\theta\,r^2\,dr\sin\varphi\,d\varphi$

$\displaystyle= \int_{p}^{q}\int_{\Phi_{\theta n}(r)}^{\Phi_{\theta s}(r)}\int_{\Phi_{e}(r,\theta,\varphi)}^{\Phi_{w}(r,\varphi)} f(r,\,\theta,\,\varphi)\,d\theta\sin\varphi\,d\varphi\,r^2\,dr.$

7. $\displaystyle\int_{0}^{1}\int_{0}^{2\pi}\int_{0}^{1} f(r,\,\theta,\,z)\,r\,dr\,d\theta\,dz.$

9. $\pi r^2 h.$

11. If, on the unit sphere, the plane with rectangular coordinate $z = k$ $(0 < k < 1)$ slices off a section of the sphere, this plane has the spherical coordinate equation $r\cos\varphi = k$. The volume of the portion of the sphere below this plane is

$$\int_{\cos^{-1}\frac{1}{k}}^{\pi}\int_{0}^{2\pi}\int_{0}^{k\sec\varphi} r^2\sin\varphi\,dr\,d\theta\,d\varphi = \frac{2\pi}{3}k^3(1+k).$$

6-2   Continuity

2. $\delta_{c,\epsilon} \le \min\{\epsilon/2,\, c,\, 1-c\}.$

4. For c rational, $c \ne \frac{1}{2}$, $f(c) = c$. Let $\epsilon_c = |c - \frac{1}{2}|$. Given $\delta > 0$, pick x_δ such that x_δ is irrational, $|c - x| < \delta$. Then $f(x_\delta) = 1 - x_\delta$. But $|f(x_\delta) - f(c)| > |c - \frac{1}{2}|$ since the points (c, c) and $(x_\delta, 1 - x_\delta)$ are on opposite sides of the horizontal line with equation $y = \frac{1}{2}$. For c irrational, reverse this procedure.

5. For $b \le 0$, $f^{-1}(]a, b[) = \varnothing$. For $a \le 0$ and $b < 2$, $f^{-1}(]a, b[) =]0, b/2[$. For $a > 0$ and $b < 2$, $f^{-1}(]a, b[) =]a/2, b/2[$. For $0 < a < 2$ and $b \le 2$, $f^{-1}(]a, b[) =]a/2, 1[$. For $a \ge 2$, $f^{-1}(]a, b[) = \varnothing$. Let Ra be the set of all rational numbers and S be the set of all irrational numbers. For $b \le 0$, $g^{-1}(]a, b[) = \varnothing$. For $a \le 0$ and $b \le \frac{1}{2}$, $g^{-1}(]a, b[) = (]0, b[\cap Ra) \cup (]1 - b, 1[\cap S)$. For $a > 0$ and $b \le \frac{1}{2}$, $g^{-1}(]a, b[) = (]a, b[\cap Ra) \cup (]1 - b, 1 - a[\cap S)$. For $a \le 0$ and $\frac{1}{2} < b < 1$, $g^{-1}(]a, b[) = (]0,\, 1 - b[\cap Ra) \cup\,]1 - b,\, b[\cup (]b, 1[\cap S)$. For $0 < a \le \frac{1}{2}$, $\frac{1}{2} < b < 1$, and $a < 1 - b$, $g^{-1}(]a,\, b[) = (]a,\, 1 - b[\cap Ra) \cup\,]1 - b,\, b[\cup (]b,\, 1 - a[\cap S)$. For $0 < a < \frac{1}{2}$, $\frac{1}{2} < b < 1$, and $a \ge 1 - b$,

$g^{-1}(]a, b[) = (]1 - b, a[\cap Ra) \cup]a, 1 - a[\cup (]1 - a, b[\cap S)$. For $0 <$
$a \le \frac{1}{2}$ and $b \ge 1, g^{-1}(]a, b[) = (]0, a[\cap Ra) \cup]a, 1 - a[\cup (]1 - a, 1[\cap S)$.
For $a \ge \frac{1}{2}$ and $b < 1$, $g^{-1}(]a, b[) = (]1 - b, 1 - a[\cap Ra) \cup (]a, b[\cap S)$.
For $\frac{1}{2} \le a < 1$ and $b \ge 1$, $g^{-1}(]a, b[) = (]0, 1 - a[\cap Ra) \cup (]a, 1[\cap S)$.
For $a \ge 1, g^{-1}(]a, b[) = \varnothing$.

7. For $f: R \to R, f$ a constant function, when G is open $f^{-1}(G)$ is either R or $\varnothing$.

9. For G open, $f^{-1}(G) = \{x \mid x$ is an integer and $x^2 \in G\}$. Then $f^{-1}(g) =$
$\left(\bigcup_{x \in f^{-1}(g)}]x - \frac{1}{3}, x + \frac{1}{3}[\right) \cap Z$, where Z is the set of all integers, and this
union is an open set.

11. $\delta_{\epsilon,x} = \min \{\sqrt{x^2 + \epsilon} - x, x, 1 - x\}$.

13. Since $|x^2 - c^2| = |x + c||x - c| \le (|x| + |c|)|x - c| \le 2|x - c|$, we may
take $\delta = \epsilon/2$.

6-3 Uniform Continuity

3. $\dfrac{1}{n^2}$.

5. By exercise 4 there exists an ϵ_0 with the property that for $n = 1, 2, \dots,$
$|f(r_n) - f(s_n)| \ge \epsilon_0$. Given $\delta > 0$, there exists an integer n such that $\dfrac{1}{n} < \delta$.
Thus we have r_n and s_n such that $|r_n - s_n| < \delta$ but $|f(r_n) - f(s_n)| \ge \epsilon_0$. This
is in direct contradiction to the definition of uniform continuity.

7. For $b \le 0, f^{-1}(]a, b[) = \varnothing$. For $a \le 0$ and $0 < b < 1, f^{-1}(]a, b[) =]0, \sqrt{b}[$.
For $a \le 0$ and $b \ge 1, f^{-1}(]a, b[) =]0, 1[$. For $a > 0$ and $b \le 1, f^{-1}(]a, b[) =$
$]\sqrt{a}, \sqrt{b}[$. For $0 < a < 1$ and $b \ge 1$, $f^{-1}(]a, b[) =]\sqrt{a}, 1[$. For $a \ge 1$,
$f^{-1}(]a, b[) = \varnothing$. Thus the inverse image of every open set is open.

9. $\delta_{\epsilon,a,h} \le \min \{\sqrt{a^2 + \epsilon} - a, a, 1 - a\}$.

10. No.

11. Yes.

12. Yes.

6-4 Heine-Borel Theorems and Uniform Continuity

3. inf $= p$, sup $= q$.

5. inf $= 0$, no supremum.

7. inf $= 0$, sup $=$ max $= 2$.

9. $c_\epsilon = \min\{(p + \epsilon)/2, (p + q)/2\}$; $b_\epsilon = \max\{(q - \epsilon)/2, (p + q)/2\}$.

11. $c_\epsilon = \frac{1}{2}\epsilon$.

13. $c_\epsilon = \dfrac{1}{\left(\dfrac{1}{\epsilon}\right) + 1}$, $\qquad b_\epsilon = 1$.

15. $c_\epsilon = \dfrac{1}{2\left(\dfrac{1}{\epsilon}\right) + 1} + \dfrac{1}{2\left(\dfrac{1}{\epsilon}\right) + 1}$; $\qquad b_\epsilon = 2$.

17. If $A \subseteq B$, then inf $A \leq$ inf B.

19. $\delta_x = \epsilon/e^x$.

6-5 Uniform Convergence

1. $\delta_{\epsilon,x} = \dfrac{\epsilon}{4\,|x|}$.

2. $\min\{\delta_{\epsilon,x} \mid 1 \leq x \leq 2\} = \epsilon/8$.

7. $\delta_{\epsilon,x} = \epsilon/2$.

12. $\left| \dfrac{1}{1 - x} - \displaystyle\sum_{k=0}^{n} x^k \right| = \dfrac{|x|^{n+1}}{1 - x}$. For this to be $< \epsilon$ we need

$$n + 1 > \frac{\log(1 - x) + \log \epsilon}{\log|x|} .$$

13. No.

6-6 Sequences

1. $\lim a_n = 0$; $\qquad N = \dfrac{1}{\epsilon} + 1$.

3. $\lim a_n = 3$, $\qquad N = \dfrac{1}{\sqrt{\epsilon}} + 1$.

5. $\frac{1}{2}\sqrt{3}$.

7. $-\frac{1}{2}\sqrt{3}$.

9. 0.

11. 0.

7-1 The Derivative

1. If $(a, b) \in 2ff'$, then $b = \{2ff'\}(a) = 2f(a)f'(a)$. To find $\{f^2\}'$, we need to examine

$$\frac{1}{h}[\{f^2\}(a + h) - \{f^2\}(a)] = \frac{1}{h}\{[f(a + h)]^2 - [f(a)]^2\}$$

$$= \frac{1}{h}[f(a + h) - f(a)][f(a + h) + f(a)].$$

Since $f'(a)$ exists, f is differentiable at a and thus continuous at a. Thus $\lim_{h \to 0} f(a + h) = f(a)$ and $\lim_{h \to 0} [f(a + h) + f(a)] = 2f(a)$. Thus $\{f^2\}'(a)$ exists and is $2f(a)f'(a) = b$, or $(a, b) \in \{f^2\}'$.

3. $\left(\frac{1}{f}\right)(a + h) - \left(\frac{1}{f}\right)(a) = \frac{f(a) - f(a + h)}{f(a)f(a + h)}$.

5. Let $\epsilon_1 = \frac{1}{3}$. Given $\delta = 0$ chose x_δ a rational number such that $|x_\delta - a| < \delta$. Thus $f(x_\delta) = 0$ and $|f(x_\delta) - 1| = 1 > \frac{1}{3}$.

7. Exercise 5 shows that $\lim_a f \neq 1$. Exercise 6 shows that for $b \neq 1$, $\lim_a f \neq b$. Thus $\lim_a f$ does not exist.

9. The range of g is $\{0\}$. Given any open set G, $g^{-1}(G)$ is either $\varnothing$ or the set of all rational numbers. The empty set $\varnothing$ is open and the set of all real numbers R is open. Thus $g^{-1}(G)$ is the intersection of an open set with the domain of g.

10. The function h is continuous only at 0, but it is not differentiable at 0.

11. $f' = \{(x, -1) \mid x < 0\} \cup \{(x, 1) \mid x > 0\}$.

13. $f' = \{(x, \frac{1}{2}\sqrt{x}) \mid x > 0\}$.

7-2 The Chain Rule

3. The Mean Value Theorem has been applied to g.

5. The Mean Value Theorem has been applied to f.

7. By hypothesis, g' is continuous at a.

9. By hypothesis, f' is continuous at $g(a)$.

11. If g' is continuous at a and f' is continuous at $g(a)$, then $f(g)$ is differentiable at a and $\{f(g)\}'(a) = g'(a)f'(g(a))$.

7-3 Differentiability in General

1. For $i = 1, 2, \ldots, m, f^{(i)}$ is differentiable at $\mathbf{a}$.

3. $\{\mathbf{f} \cdot \mathbf{g}\}(\mathbf{a} + \mathbf{h}) - \{\mathbf{f} \cdot \mathbf{g}\}(\mathbf{a})$

$\qquad = \{\mathbf{f}(\mathbf{a}) + [\mathbf{f}(\mathbf{a} + \mathbf{h}) - \mathbf{f}(\mathbf{a})]\} \cdot [\mathbf{g}(\mathbf{a} + \mathbf{h}) - \mathbf{g}(\mathbf{a})]$

$\qquad + [\mathbf{f}(\mathbf{a} + \mathbf{h}) - \mathbf{f}(\mathbf{a})] \cdot [\mathbf{g}(\mathbf{a})]$

$\qquad = \{\mathbf{f}(\mathbf{a}) + [\mathbf{f}'(\mathbf{a})\mathbf{h}*]* + \|\mathbf{h}\|\eta_{\mathbf{f}}(\mathbf{h})\} \cdot \{[\mathbf{g}'(\mathbf{a})\mathbf{h}*]* + \|\mathbf{h}\|\eta_{\mathbf{g}}(\mathbf{h})\}$

$\qquad + \{[\mathbf{f}'(\mathbf{a})\mathbf{h}*]* + \|\mathbf{h}\| \eta_{\mathbf{f}}(\mathbf{h})\} \cdot [\mathbf{g}(\mathbf{a})]$

$\qquad = [\mathbf{f}(\mathbf{a})] \cdot [\mathbf{g}'(\mathbf{a})\mathbf{h}*]* = [\mathbf{f}'(\mathbf{a})\mathbf{h}*]* \cdot [\mathbf{g}(\mathbf{a})] + \|\mathbf{h}\|\eta_{\mathbf{f}\cdot\mathbf{g}}(\mathbf{h})$

$\qquad = [\{\mathbf{f} \cdot \mathbf{g}\}'(\mathbf{a})] \cdot \mathbf{h} + \|\mathbf{h}\|\eta_{\mathbf{f}\cdot\mathbf{g}}(\mathbf{h}).$

5. If $(a, b) \in f' + g'$, then $b = \{f' + g'\}(h) = f'(a) + g'(a) = \{f + g\}'(a)$ so that $(a, b) \in \{f + g\}'$.

7-4 Differentiability of Composites

1. $\mathbf{A}_1 = (0, 2).$ $\qquad \eta_{g^{(1)}}(h, k) = \dfrac{h^2}{\sqrt{h^2 + k^2}}.$

$$|\eta_{g^{(1)}}(h, k)| = \frac{|h|}{\sqrt{h^2 + k^2}} \, |h| \le |h|.$$

3. $\mathbf{A}_3 = (3, 0).$ $\qquad \eta_{g^{(3)}}(h, k) = \dfrac{-k^2}{\sqrt{h^2 + k^2}}.$ $\qquad |\eta_{g^{(3)}}(h, k)| = \dfrac{|k|}{\sqrt{h^2 + k^2}} \, |k| \le |k|.$

5. $\{f(g)\}(u, v) = 2u^2 + 4v - u^2v^2 + 3u - v^2.$

9. $f'(x, y, z) = (2, -2y, 1);$

$$g'(u, v) = \begin{pmatrix} 2u & 2 \\ v & u \\ 3 & -2v \end{pmatrix}$$

$\{f'(g)\}(u, v) = (2, -2uv, 1)$

$\{f(g)\}'(u, v) = (4u - 2uv + 3, 4 - 2uv - 2v).$

$$(2, -2uv, 1)\begin{pmatrix} 2u & 2 \\ v & u \\ 3 & -2v \end{pmatrix} = (4u - 2uv^2 + 3, 4 - 2u^2v - 2v).$$

7-5 Differentiation by the Chain Rule

1. $h(u, v) = 9u - 11v.$ $(h_1, h_2)(u, v) = (9, -1).$

$(f_1, f_2, f_3)(x, y, z) = (3, -2; -1).$

$\{f_1(g)g_1^{(1)} + f_2(g)g_1^{(2)} + f_3(g)g_1^{(3)}\}(u, v) = (3)(4) + (-2)(2) + (1)(1) = 9.$

$\{f_1(g)g_2^{(1)} + f_2(g)g_2^{(2)} + f_3(g)g_2^{(3)}\}(u, v) = (3)(-1) + (-2)(3) + (1)(-2) = -11.$

3. Subsets of the plane with equation $2x + 3y - z = 6$ have as images the set $\{6\}$.
$f(x, y) = 2x + 3y - 6.$ $(f_1, f_2)(x, y) = (2, 3).$

5. $h(y, z) = 3 - \frac{3}{2}y + \frac{1}{2}z.$ $(h_1, h_2)(y, z) = (-\frac{3}{2}, \frac{1}{2}).$

7. A neighborhood of $(1, \frac{7}{3}, 3).$

9. $\{(x, y, z) \mid 0 \leq x \leq 1, 1 \leq y \leq 2, -3 \leq z \leq 1\}.$

11. $\{(x, y, z) \mid \frac{1}{2} \leq x \leq 3, 1 \leq y \leq 2, 2 \leq z \leq 3\}.$

13. Under g a neighborhood of $(1, 1)$ has as an image some neighborhood of 1 and (ξ, g, η) gives a neighborhood of $(1, 1, 1)$. $F(\xi, g, \eta)$ gives as image the set $\{1\}$.

15. $f_1(1, 1) = -3,$ $f_2(1, 1) = -2,$ $g_1(u, y) = 2;$ $g_2(u, y) = 3.$ The composite $F(\xi, \eta, f, g)$ is the constant function given by $(4, 10)$. This function transforms a neighborhood of $(1, 1)$ into a neighborhood of $(1, 1, 1, 1).$

7-6 Implicit and Inverse Functions

1. $\mathbf{f}^{-1}(u, v) = (u, \frac{1}{3}v - \frac{2}{3}u).$

3. $\mathbf{f}^{-1}(u, v) = (u, \frac{1}{3}v - \frac{1}{3}u^2 - \frac{2}{3}u).$

5. $\{\mathbf{J_f}\}(x, y) = \begin{pmatrix} \varphi'(x) & 0 \\ 0 & \psi'(y) \end{pmatrix}.$ $\{\det \mathbf{J_f}\}(x, y) = \Phi'(x)\psi'(y).$

7. $\{\mathbf{J_f}\}(x, y) = \begin{pmatrix} \cos y & -x \sin y \\ \sin y & x \cos y \end{pmatrix}.$ $\{\det \mathbf{J_f}\}(x, y) = x.$

9. $\{\mathbf{J_f}\}(x, y) = \begin{pmatrix} \sin y \cos z & x \cos y \cos z & -x \sin y \sin z \\ \sin y \sin z & x \cos y \sin z & x \sin y \cos z \\ \cos z & 0 & -x \sin z \end{pmatrix}$

$\{\det \mathbf{J_f}\}(x, y) = -x^2 \sin z.$

11. $\{J_f\}(u, v) = \begin{pmatrix} A & 0 \\ 0 & B \end{pmatrix} = \{J_f(g)\}(x, y).$ $\{J_g\}(x, y) = \begin{pmatrix} C & 0 \\ 0 & D \end{pmatrix}.$

$\{J_f(g)J_g\}(x, y) = \begin{pmatrix} AC & 0 \\ 0 & BD \end{pmatrix}.$ $\{f(g)\}(x, y) = (AC\,x,\ BD\,y).$

$\{J_{f(g)}\}(x, y) = \begin{pmatrix} AC & 0 \\ 0 & BD \end{pmatrix}.$

13. $\{J_f\}(u, v) = \begin{pmatrix} 2u & -2v \\ 2v & 2u \end{pmatrix}.$ $\{J_f(g)\}(x, y) = \begin{pmatrix} 2x\cos y & -2x\sin y \\ 2x\sin y & 2x\cos y \end{pmatrix}.$

$\{J_g\}(x, y) = \begin{pmatrix} \cos y & -x\sin y \\ \sin y & x\cos y \end{pmatrix}.$

$\{J_f(g)J_g\}(x, y) = \begin{pmatrix} 2x\cos 2y & -2x\sin 2y \\ 2x\sin 2y & 2x\cos 2y \end{pmatrix}.$

$\{f(g)\}(x, y) = (x^2\cos 2y,\ x^2\sin 2y).$

$\{J_{f(g)}\}(x, y) = \begin{pmatrix} 2x\cos 2y & -2x\sin 2y \\ 2x\sin 2y & 2x\cos 2y \end{pmatrix}.$

15. $g(x) = (x, -3x, -7x).$

7-7   Inverse and Implicit Function Theorems

3. $g(x) = -\frac{2}{3}x.$ $g'(x) = -\frac{2}{3} = \left\{-\dfrac{F_1}{F_2}\right\}(x, y).$

5. $g'(x) = \left\{-\dfrac{F_1}{F_2}\right\}(x) = -\dfrac{x}{g(x)}.$

7. $\{J_f\}(x, y, z) = \begin{pmatrix} 1 & 0 & F_1 \\ 0 & 1 & F_2 \\ 0 & 0 & F_3 \end{pmatrix}(x, y, z).$

If $F_3(a, b, c) \neq 0$, then there exists g, whose domian is a neighborhood of (a, b) and for which $g(a, b) = c$ such that for (x, y) in this neighborhood of (a, b), $F(x, y, g(x, y)) = 0$.

9. $g(x, y) = \dfrac{-1}{C}(Ax + By).$

11. $g(x, y) = -\sqrt[3]{x + y^2}.$

7-8 The Jacobians and Their Fight for Independence

1. $\{J_f\}(x, y, z) = \begin{pmatrix} 1 & 2 & -1 \\ 3 & -1 & 1 \\ 5 & 3 & -1 \end{pmatrix}.$ $\{\det J_f\}(x, y, z) = 0.$

3. $\{J_F\}(x, y, z) = \begin{pmatrix} 1 & 2 & -1 \\ 3 & -1 & 1 \\ 0 & 0 & 1 \end{pmatrix}.$ $\{\det J_F\}(x, y, z) = -7.$

5. $h(u, v, w) = 0.$

15. $\{J_f\}(w, x, y, z) = \begin{pmatrix} 1 & 1 & 1 & -1 \\ 0 & 2 & 0 & -1 \\ 1 & -1 & 1 & 2 \\ 2 & 0 & 2 & 3 \end{pmatrix}.$

17. $\{J_F\}(w, x, y, z) = \begin{pmatrix} 1 & 1 & 1 & -1 \\ 0 & 2 & 0 & -1 \\ 0 & 0 & 1 & 0 \\ 0 & 0 & 0 & 0 \end{pmatrix}.$ $\{\det J_F\}(w, x, y, z) = 2.$

8-1 Improper Integrals

1. Let P be a partition of $[a, b]$ for which $\underline{S}(f; P)$ is near $\int_a^b f^*$. Discarding the interval $[a, x_1]$ leaves a partition P' of $[x_1, b]$. P may also be chosen so that $\underline{S}(f; P)$ is near $\int_{x_1}^b f$. For $x_1 - a$ small, $\int_{x_1}^b f$ is near $\lim_{\epsilon \to 0+} \int_{a+\epsilon}^b f.$

3. $\int_{-\infty}^a f$ is convergent to I provided that $\lim_{B \to +\infty} \int_{-B}^a f$ exists and is I. $\int_{-\infty}^\infty f$ is convergent to I provided that $\lim_{A \to +\infty} \int_{-A}^c f$ exists and is I_1, $\lim_{B \to +\infty} \int_c^B f$ exists and is I_2, and $I = I_1 + I_2.$

5. For $0 < p < 1$, $\displaystyle\int_{-a}^{-\epsilon} t^{-p}\, dt = \frac{1}{1-p}\,[(-\epsilon)^{1-p} - (-a)^{1-p}]$. $\displaystyle\lim_{\epsilon \to 0+} (-\epsilon)^{1-p} = 0$.

Thus $\displaystyle\int_{-a}^{0} t^{-p}\, dt$ converges to $-(-a)^{1-p}/(1-p)$. For $p = 1$, $\displaystyle\int_{-a}^{-\epsilon} t^{-1}\, dt =$

$\log \epsilon - \log a$. $\displaystyle\lim_{\epsilon \to 0+} \log \epsilon = -\infty$. Thus $\displaystyle\int_{-a}^{0} t^{-1}\, dt$ is divergent. For $p > 1$,

$\displaystyle\lim_{\epsilon \to 0+} \epsilon^{1-p} = +\infty$ so that $\displaystyle\int_{-a}^{0} t^{-p}\, dt$ is divergent.

7. For $p > 1$, $\displaystyle\int_{-B}^{-a} t^{-p}\, dt = \frac{1}{1-p}\,[(-a)^{1-p} - (-B)^{1-p}]$. $\displaystyle\lim_{B \to +\infty} (-B)^{1-p} = 0$.

Thus $\displaystyle\int_{-\infty}^{-a} t^{-p}\, dt$ is convergent to $(-a)^{1-p}/(1-p)$. For $p = 1$, $\displaystyle\int_{-B}^{-a} t^{-1}\, dt =$

$\log a - \log B$. $\displaystyle\lim_{B \to +\infty} \log B = +\infty$. Thus $\displaystyle\int_{-\infty}^{-a} t^{-1}\, dt$ is divergent.

For $p < 1$, $\displaystyle\lim_{B \to +\infty} B^{1-p} = +\infty$ and $\displaystyle\int_{-\infty}^{-a} t^{-p}\, dt$ is divergent.

9. $\dfrac{a^{1-p}}{p-1}$.

11. Let $f(x) = x^{-2}$ for x not an integer, and for n any positive integer $f(n) = 1$.
Then $\displaystyle\varlimsup_{x \to +\infty} f(x) = 1$ and $\displaystyle\varliminf_{x \to +\infty} f(x) = 0$.

8-2 Convergence Tests

1. $\displaystyle\int_{a}^{r} g - \int_{a}^{r} f$.

3. Convergent to $\pi/2$.

5. Divergent. $(x - x^3/3 < \sin x < x$ for $0 < x < 1)$.

7. Divergent.

9. Convergent for $p > 1$, divergent for $0 < p \le 1$.

11. Convergent to $\dfrac{1}{\sqrt{2}}\left(\dfrac{\pi}{2} - \arctan \dfrac{1}{\sqrt{2}}\right)$.

8-3 Improper Integrals in the *n*-dimensional Case

3. Convergent.

5. Divergent.

7. Convergent for $p < 4$, divergent for $p \ge 4$.

9. Convergent.

11. Convergent for $p < 3$, divergent for $p \geq 3$.

13. Convergent for $p < 5$, divergent for $p \geq 5$.

8-4 Extension to Functions with Negative Values

1. 0.

3. Convergent for $p < 3$, divergent for $p \geq 3$.

6. $|f| = f_+ - f_-$.

7. $|f| \leq |g|$ implies that $f_+ \leq g_+$ and $g_- \leq f_-$.

9. 0.

8-5 The Divergence Theorem with Improper Integrals

3. $\{\text{div } \mathbf{v}\}(x, y, z) = (2 - p)(x^2 + y^2 + z^2)^{-p/2}$.

4. $p > 2$.

7. $p < 2$.

8. $p < 2$.

8-6 Stokes' Theorem with Improper Integrals

5. $\{\text{curl } \mathbf{v}\}(x, y, z) = (x + y + z)^{-(p/2)-1}(z + y, x - z, y - x)$.

7. $S^+ = S \cap \{(x, y, z) \mid x < y\}$. $S^- = S \cap \{(x, y, z) \mid x < y\}$.

9. $p > 2$.

9-1 Series

2. $\sin x = x - \dfrac{x^3}{6} + \dfrac{x^4}{24} \sin t;$ $|R| \leq x^4/24$.

3. $\cos x = 1 - \dfrac{x^2}{2} + \dfrac{x^4}{24} \cos t;$ $|R| \leq \frac{1}{24}$.

4. $\log x = (x - 1) + \frac{1}{2}(x - 1)^2 + \frac{1}{3}(x - 1)^3 + \frac{1}{4}(x - 1)^4 + \frac{1}{5}(x - 1)^5 t^{-5};$
$$|R| \leq \tfrac{32}{5}|x - 1|^5.$$

7. $\sin (x + y) = x + y + \frac{1}{6}(x + y)^3 + \frac{1}{24} \sin (\theta x + \theta y)$.

11. 0.75.

9-2 Sequence of Real Numbers

5. Limit points are -1 and 1. $\overline{\lim} = 1$. $\underline{\lim} = -1$.

6. Limit points are 0, $\frac{1}{2}\sqrt{3}$, and $-\frac{1}{2}\sqrt{3}$. $\overline{\lim} = \frac{1}{2}\sqrt{3}$. $\underline{\lim} = -\frac{1}{2}\sqrt{3}$.

10. Limit points are 0, $\pm\sin \pi/5$, $\pm\sin 2\pi/5$. $\overline{\lim} = \sin 2\pi/5$. $\underline{\lim} = -\sin 2\pi/5$.

11. The only finite limit point is 0. $\overline{\lim} = +\infty$. $\underline{\lim} = -\infty$.

9-3 Series

3. Divergent.

5. Convergent.

7. Divergent.

9. Convergent.

11. Convergent.

13. Convergent.

15. Divergent.

9-4 Operations with Series

3. $2^p = (1 + 1)^p = \sum_{k=0}^{p}\binom{p}{k}$; $0 = (1 - 1)^p = \sum_{k=0}^{p}(-1)^k\binom{p}{k}$.

5. If $f(x) = \lim_{n}\sum_{k=1}^{n} x^k = \dfrac{1}{1 - x}$,   then $\dfrac{1}{(x - 1)^2} = f'(x)$

$= \lim_{n}\sum_{k=1}^{n} kx^{k-1} = \lim_{n}\sum_{k=0}^{n-1}(k + 1)x^k.$

6. $(-1)^p \sum_{n=0}^{\infty}\binom{-p}{n}x^n$ or $(-1)^p \sum_{n=0}^{\infty}\dfrac{(-1)^n p(p + 1)\cdots(p + n - 1)}{n!}\,x^m.$

9-5 Estimates of Error

1. 1.081.

3. 0.574.

5. 2.718.

7. 1.291.

9. 100 terms are needed.

11. The error is $\dfrac{r^{n+1}}{1-r}$.

9-6 Series of Functions

4. $[-1, 1]$.

6. $]-2, 2[$.

8. R.

10. R.

12. $M_n = \dfrac{1}{2^n}$.

9-7 End Points and Applications

1. $[-1, 1]$.

3. $\left[-\dfrac{1}{e}, \dfrac{1}{e}\right]$.

5. $b_n = \displaystyle\sum_{k=n+1}^{2n} \dfrac{1}{k} + \log 2$.

13. $\dfrac{d}{dx} \displaystyle\sum_{n=0}^{\infty} \dfrac{x^n}{n!} = \sum_{n=1}^{\infty} \dfrac{nx^{n-1}}{n!} = \sum_{n=1}^{\infty} \dfrac{x^{n-1}}{(n-1)!} = \sum_{k=0}^{\infty} \dfrac{x^k}{k!}$.

14. $2xe^{-x} - x^2e^{-x} = \dfrac{d}{dx}(x^2 e^{-x}) = \dfrac{d}{dx} \displaystyle\sum_{n=0}^{\infty} \dfrac{(-1)^n}{n!} x^{n+2} = \sum_{n=0}^{\infty} \dfrac{(-1)^n(n+2)}{n!} x^{n+1}$.

For $x = 2$, $0 = -\displaystyle\sum_{n=0}^{\infty} \dfrac{n+2}{n!}(-2)^{n+1} = 4 - \sum_{n=1}^{\infty} \dfrac{n+2}{n!}(-2)^{n+1}$.

10-1 Representations of Functions

1. P is its own Maclaurin series.

3. $\displaystyle\sum_{n=0}^{\infty} \dfrac{(2p+1)(2p+3)\cdots(2p+2n-1)}{n!} x^n$.

7. $\displaystyle\sum_{n=0}^{\infty} \frac{(-1)^n x^{n+1}}{n+1}$.

9. $\displaystyle\sum_{n=0}^{\infty} \frac{x^n}{n!}$.

11. $\displaystyle c_1 \sum_{n=0}^{\infty} \frac{(-1)^n x^n}{n!} + c_2 \sum_{n=0}^{\infty} \frac{3^n x^n}{n!}$.

10-2   Representations by Integrals

1. $f'(x) = x^n$.

3. $f'(x) = 2x \log (1 + x^2)$.

5. $f'(x) = 0$.

7. $(1 + e^{3x})e^x - (1 + \sin^3 x) \cos x$.

9. $f^{(m)}(x) = (n + m + 1)(n + m) \ldots (n + 2) \left[\displaystyle\sum_{k=0}^{m} \binom{m}{k} \frac{(-1)^k}{n + k + 1} \right] x^{n+1}$

$f(x) = \left[\displaystyle\sum_{k=0}^{m} \binom{m}{n} \frac{(-1)^k}{n + k + 1} \right] x^{m+n+1}$.

10-3   Representation by Improper Integrals

4. For $x \geq 1$, $e^{-xt^2} \leq e^{-t^2} < e^{-t}$.

6. $|\cos tx| \leq 1$ and $|\sin tx| \leq 1$.

9. $F(x) = \dfrac{1}{2} \sqrt{\dfrac{\pi}{1 + x^2}}$.

10-4   The Laplace Transform and the Gamma Function

6. $\dfrac{1}{x - k}$,   for $x > k$.

10-5   Representation by Fourier Series

3. $\dfrac{4}{\pi} \displaystyle\sum_{n=1}^{\infty} \frac{1}{n} \sin nx$.

5. $\dfrac{\pi^2}{2} + 2 \displaystyle\sum_{n=1}^{\infty} \dfrac{(-1)^n}{n^2} \cos nx.$

7. Let $x = \dfrac{\pi}{2}$.

9. Let $x = \dfrac{\pi}{2}$.

A-1 Matrices and Determinants

4. $a_{11}a_{22} - a_{12}a_{21}.$

5. $a_{11}a_{22}a_{33}a_{44} + a_{11}a_{23}a_{34}a_{42} + a_{11}a_{24}a_{32}a_{43} + a_{12}a_{21}a_{34}a_{43} + a_{12}a_{23}a_{31}a_{44}$

$\quad + a_{12}a_{24}a_{33}a_{41} + a_{13}a_{22}a_{34}a_{41} + a_{13}a_{21}a_{32}a_{44} + a_{13}a_{24}a_{31}a_{42} + a_{14}a_{21}a_{33}a_{42}$

$\quad + a_{14}a_{22}a_{31}a_{43} + a_{14}a_{23}a_{32}a_{41} - a_{11}a_{22}a_{34}a_{43} - a_{11}a_{23}a_{32}a_{44} - a_{11}a_{24}a_{33}a_{42}$

$\quad - a_{12}a_{21}a_{33}a_{44} - a_{12}a_{23}a_{34}a_{41} - a_{12}a_{24}a_{31}a_{43} - a_{13}a_{22}a_{31}a_{44} - a_{13}a_{21}a_{34}a_{42}$

$\quad - a_{13}a_{24}a_{32}a_{41} - a_{14}a_{21}a_{32}a_{43} - a_{14}a_{22}a_{33}a_{41} - a_{14}a_{23}a_{31}a_{42}.$

B-1 Ordinary Points of Linear Differential Equations

1. $\displaystyle\sum_{k=0}^{\infty} \dfrac{(-1)^k 2^k (k+1)!}{3^k (2k)!} x^{2k};\qquad \displaystyle\sum_{k=0}^{\infty} (-1)^k \dfrac{(5)(7)(9) \cdots (2k+3)}{3^k (2k+1)!} x^{2k+1}.$

3. $1 - 3x^2;\qquad x - \tfrac{1}{3}x^3.$

5. $1 + 2x^2;\qquad 1 + \displaystyle\sum_{k=1}^{\infty} (-3) \dfrac{2^{k-1}(5)(9) \cdots (4k-3)(3)(5) \cdots (2k-1)}{(2k+1)!} x^{k+4}.$

B-2 Singular Points. The Indicial Equation

2. $1 + 2x + \tfrac{1}{4}x^2;\qquad \displaystyle\sum_{n=0}^{\infty} \dfrac{8}{3^n n! \,(3n-4)(3n-1)(3n+2)} x^{n+(2/3)}.$

4. $1 - \tfrac{3}{4}x + \tfrac{3}{28}x^2 - \tfrac{1}{280}x^3;\qquad \displaystyle\sum_{n=0}^{\infty} \dfrac{280}{(3n-10)(3n-7)(3n-4)(3n-1)3^n n!} x^{n-(1/3)}.$

B-3 Indicial Equation with Equal Roots

1. $\displaystyle\sum_{n=0}^{\infty} \dfrac{2^n}{(n!)^2} x^{n-1};\qquad \log x \displaystyle\sum_{n=0}^{\infty} \dfrac{2^n}{(n!)^2} x^{n-1} - \displaystyle\sum_{n=0}^{\infty} \dfrac{2^{n+1}}{(n!)^2} H_n x^{n-1}.$

2. $x^{-3} + 3x^{-2} + \frac{3}{2}x^{-1} + \frac{1}{6}$; $(x^{-3} + 3x^{-2} + \frac{3}{2}x^{-1} + \frac{1}{6}) \log x + x^{-3} - 7x^{-2}$

$$- \frac{23}{4}x^{-1} - \frac{11}{12}.$$

B-4   Difference of Roots a Nonzero Integer: Nonlogarithmic Case

2. $1 + 4x + 8x^2$; $\displaystyle\sum_{n=0}^{\infty} \frac{(-1)^n 2^n}{(n+5)(n+4)(n+3)} x^{n+5}.$

4. $1 - 6x$; $x^2.$

INDEX